# Chronicle of a
# WORKING LIFE

# Chronicle of a WORKING LIFE

## ONE PAIR OF HANDS

## ONE PAIR OF FEET

## MY TURN TO MAKE THE TEA

# MONICA DICKENS

### FOREWORD BY
# LIBBY PURVES

SUTTON PUBLISHING

CHRONICLE OF A WORKING LIFE
*One Pair of Hands* first published by Michael Joseph, 1939
*One Pair of Feet* first published by Michael Joseph, 1942
*My Turn to Make the Tea* first published by Michael Joseph, 1951

This edition first published in 2004 by
Sutton Publishing Limited · Phoenix Mill
Thrupp · Stroud · Gloucestershire · GL5 2BU

British Library Cataloguing in Publication Data
A catalogue record for this book is available from the British Library.

ISBN 0 7509 3784 X

Printed and bound in Great Britain by
J.H. Haynes & Co. Ltd, Sparkford.

# Contents

# Foreword
## by Libby Purves

I met Monica Dickens once, in mid-1980s a few years before her death. It was a long-held ambition, but when we sat down together – appropriately enough in a canteen – I did not want to talk about the children's books she was latterly best known for: the *Follyfoot* series. Nor did I much want to discuss her novels, nor even her distinguished ancestry (she was Charles Dickens' great-granddaughter). I just wanted to thank her for the books which to me will always be her masterworks: these three light-hearted memoirs, written respectively in 1939, 1942 and 1951.

In them she relates – with well-judged exaggeration and fictional flourishes – her youthful jobs. Bored by the pointless idleness imposed on gently-bred unmarried girls, she had successively enrolled as a domestic skivvy, a nurse, and a local newspaper reporter. She did not, she always stressed, do these things with a crafty journalistic purpose but in a genuine spirit of independence, starting out as a maid in the first place simply for something to do and for the pleasure of earning her own money instead of hanging around waiting for a husband. Then she wrote about them in the same spirit of gung-ho, girlish optimism and amusement and the books became small classics, loved and recognised by women like me, half a century her junior, and by our children in turn.

The key word there is 'recognised'. On one level these stories are glimpses of another world, beautiful little sketches of their various periods. When Monica enrolled as a 'cook-general' in a series of determinedly refined middle-class households, domestic service in Britain was on its last legs. After the war such people could only dream of the days when everyone of their class had a maid, even in the most cramped suburban houses. Then when she was nursing, it was in wartime; the wards and the matrons she depicts are a microcosm of a hardy, hierarchial Britain which has also vanished. And as for the local newspaper she paints – small, privately owned, eccentric and dusty – that too is part of a lost Atlantis. Certainly social historians of the mid-twentieth century could do worse than study Monica Dickens' portraits of Pooterish domesticity, wartime austerity on the wards and louche boarding-house life in provincial England in the forties. She is no Orwell: she makes no complaint or analysis. But she paints it for us vividly and truthfully.

But why, then, did I feel in my own twenties – a full generation later – such a pang of absolute recognition whenever I re-read these books? Why are they perennials and not period curiosities? The answer lies in the author herself: her relish for hard work and for the sense of apprenticeship, and her appreciation of something which never dates: the larky, downtrodden comradeship, the cunning Sergeant Bilko shortcuts and the irreplaceable workplace humour of almost anyone's first few jobs. What teenage waitress will not smile and nod at the ghastliness of some of her Madams in *One Pair of Hands*? What shift-worker (I was one, for years) does not need a comforting literary companion in the bone-weary confusion of the small hours? Even modern nurses shake their heads in rueful recognition of her life in the darkened ward, the nursing station a soft-lit island in a sea of sickness. What tyro, in any field, will not cringe in happy recognition of the snubs and errors of her cub reporter? And anybody who has ever lived in cheap digs, or had flatmates, will nod in recognition at the frowsty atmospheres, small tyrannies and cosy conspiracies of *My Turn to Make the Tea*.

Monica Dickens' descriptions are clear-eyed, very funny, fearlessly sharp and always humane: therefore they are timeless. Her youthful and optimistic spirit, unwilling to take reverses too seriously, is intensely likeable. Above all, though, in these three books she wrote from the bottom of the heap, and immortalized the subversive worms'-eye view that we each experience in early working life. Salute her.

# ONE PAIR OF HANDS

# Chapter One

I WAS fed up. As I lay awake in the grey small hours of an autumn morning, I reviewed my life. Three a.m. is not the most propitious time for meditation, as everyone knows, and a deep depression was settling over me.

I had just returned from New York, where the crazy cyclone of gaiety in which people seem to survive over there had caught me up, whirled me blissfully round, and dropped me into a London which seemed flat and dull. I felt restless, dissatisfied, and abominably bad-tempered.

'Surely,' I thought, 'there's something more to life than just going out to parties that one doesn't enjoy, with people one doesn't even like? What a pointless existence it is – drifting about in the hope that something may happen to relieve the monotony. Something has got to be done to get me out of this rut.'

In a flash it came to me:

'I'll have a job!'

I said it out loud and it sounded pretty good to me, though my dog didn't seem to be deeply moved. The more I thought about it, the better I liked the idea, especially from the point of view of making some money.

My mind sped away for a moment, after the fashion of all minds in bed, and showed me visions of big money – furs – a new car – but I brought it back to earth with an effort to wonder for what sort of a job I could possibly qualify. I reviewed the possibilities.

Since leaving school I had trained rather half-heartedly for various things. I had an idea, as everyone does at that age, that I should be a roaring success on the stage. When I came back from being 'finished' in Paris, I had begged to be allowed to have dramatic training.

'Try anything once,' said my parents, so off I went, full of hope and ambition, to a London dramatic school. I hadn't been there more than two weeks before I and everybody else in the place discovered that I couldn't act, and, probably, never would be able to. This was discouraging, but I ploughed on, getting a greater inferiority complex every day. Part of the policy of this school is to 'knock the corners off the girls' (not the men, they are too rare and precious). It is only the tough, really ambitious girls who weather the storm of biting sarcasm and offensive personal remarks that fall on their cowed heads. This is a good thing, really, as it means that only the ones with real talent and endurance go through with it to that even tougher life ahead. The uncertain and inept ones like myself are discouraged at the start from a career in which they could never make a success, and so are saved many heartbreaks later on.

Once having made up my mind that I had no vocation, I enjoyed my year there immensely, and walked about the stage quite happily as the maid, or somebody's sister, with hands and feet growing larger every minute. Gazing into a still pool at sunset, or registering grief, fear, and ecstasy in rapid succession, was wonderful fun, too: especially when performed in the company of fifty other girls in rather indecent black tights.

It didn't occur to me that it might be a little irritating for the authorities to have someone trailing unambitiously about in the dust raised by the star pupils. No one was more surprised than myself, therefore, when I found myself – thrown out, figuratively speaking, on my ear – standing on the pavement with my books under one arm and my black tights under the other.

The next possibility was dressmaking. I dismissed that, too, at once, because it has always seemed to me to be the resort of inefficient, but certainly decorative, society girls, who are given jobs in dress shops, in the hope that they will introduce their rich friends. After that, they stand about the place in streamlined attitudes, wearing marvellous clothes and expressions of suffering superiority.

That didn't seem quite my style, so I turned to cooking.

4

That was the thing which interested me most and about which I thought I knew quite a lot. I had had a few lessons from my 'Madame' in Paris, but my real interest was aroused by lessons I had at a wonderful school of French cookery in London.

I went there quite unable to boil so much as an egg and came out with Homard Thermidor and Crêpes Suzette at my fingertips. I was still unable to boil an egg, however, or roast a joint of beef. The simple things weren't considered worth teaching, so I had a short spell at a very drab school of English cooking, where there were a great many pupils clamouring for the attention of the two ancient spinsters who taught us. When they hadn't time to tell me what to cook next, it was: 'Get washed up, Miss Dickens,' and Miss Dickens had to clean up other people's messes at the sink, till, at last, if she was lucky she was allowed to make a rock-cake.

When I told my family that I was thinking of taking a cooking job, the roars of laughter were rather discouraging. No one believed that I could cook at all, as I had never had a chance to practise at home. Our cook, aged sixty-five and slightly touched, had ruled in the kitchen for thirty years and had an irritating tendency to regard the saucepans, stove, and indeed all the kitchen fittings as her own property.

I once crept down there when I thought she was asleep in her room to try out an omelette. Noiselessly I removed a frying-pan from its hook and the eggs from their cupboard. It was the pop of the gas that woke her, I think, for I was just breaking the first egg when a pair of slippered feet shuffled round the door and a shriek of horror caused me to break the egg on the floor. This disaster, together with the fact that I was using her one very special beloved and delicately nurtured frying-pan, upset cook so much that she locked herself in the larder with all the food and we had to make our Sunday dinner off bananas.

If the family weren't going to be helpful I would look for a job all by myself and not tell them about it till I'd got one. I had no idea of exactly what job I should apply for, so I decided to go to an agency. I had seen one advertised in a local paper, so as soon as there was no one about to say, 'Where are you going?' I clapped on my mildest hat, and rushed out of the house in search of it. I was wildly excited, and as nervous as if I were going to a stage audition. Finding the place quite easily, I tore up three flights of stairs, and swung breathlessly through a door which said, 'Enter without knocking, if you please.'

The dingy, bottle-green atmosphere of the office sobered me, and I sat meekly down on the edge of a chair and could see my nose shining out of the corner of my eye. I thought perhaps it was a good thing, it might look more earnest. The woman at the desk opposite scrutinized me for a while through rimless pince-nez, and I became absorbed in the question of whether or not she wore a wig. I had just decided that it was too undesirably shabby to be anything but her own hair, when I realized that she was murmuring questions at me. I answered in a hoarse whisper because it seemed to be the thing, and because all of a sudden I started to feel rather pathetic. She hinted in a delicate way that she wondered why I was looking for this sort of job, so I felt impelled to give her a glimpse of a widowed mother and a desperate struggle against poverty. I almost made myself believe in the pathos of it, and we had to cough and change the subject. I felt even more pathetic when she told me that it would be difficult to get a job without experience or references. She rustled about among her papers for a bit and I wondered whether I ought to leave, when the telephone on her desk rang. While she was conducting a cryptic conversation she kept looking at me. Then I heard her say:

'As a matter of fact, I've got someone in the office at this very moment who might suit.' She wrote down a number, and my spirits soared as I took the slip of paper she held out to me, saying: 'Ring up this lady. She wants a cook immediately. In fact, you would have to start tomorrow by cooking a dinner for ten people. Could you manage that, I wonder?'

'Oh, yes,' said I – never having cooked for more than

6

four in my life. I thanked her profusely, paid a shilling, and dashed out to the nearest telephone box. I collected my wits, powdered my nose, took a deep breath, and dialled the number. A piping voice at the other end informed me that I was speaking to Miss Cattermole. I assured her, with all the bluff at my command, that I was just what she was looking for.

'Are you sure?' she kept saying. 'Are you *sure*? It's a celebration for my brother – just home from B.A., you know.' I expressed suitable awe, though for all I knew B.A. might have been anything from an outpost of Empire to a long spell of Penal Servitude, and she decided to engage me for the dinner-party, anyway, and as a permanency if I fulfilled the promise of my self-praise. I asked her what tomorrow's menu was to be.

'Just a small, simple dinner: lobster cocktails, soup, turbot Mornay, pheasants with vegetables, fruit salad, and a savoury.' In rather a shaken voice, I promised to turn up in good time, and rang off.

I spent the intervening hours feverishly reading cookery books, and wishing that I hadn't let myself in for something about which I knew so little. My family were still highly amused at the idea of my attempting it, which didn't increase my confidence. I told my mother she was a widow and she took it quite well.

Miss Cattermole lived in Dulwich in one of the most depressing houses ever seen. It had a great many grimy turrets and smatterings of stained glass, and though quite small, was approached by a semi-circular drive round an unhealthy tangle of laurels. I rang at the back door and the depression of the house closed round me as I was admitted by a weary-looking maid. She was so thin that her dress and apron drooped on her, and even her cap fell over her eyes as if the whole lot wanted to slide despairingly to the ground. I followed her through a sort of stone rabbit-warren to where an ancient brooding figure sat hunched in a chair in the sitting-room. She was introduced to me on a note of reverent horror, as: 'Nannie' – evidently a family pensioner who had transferred her awesome sway from the nursery to the basement. It was quite obvious why Miss Cattermole had difficulty in keeping a cook. The maid was called away by a bell and Nannie condescended to show me the kitchen, though I could see that she hated me at sight.

As I started to prepare the dinner I began to share her gloomy view of myself, as it dawned on me more and more that high-class cooking lessons are all very well, but a little practical experience is necessary, too, in order to cope with the vicissitudes that crop up in the kitchen.

I made the fruit salad first. That was quite easy, as all I had to do was cut up fruit and mess it together in a bowl. After a bit, I got tired of scraping the pith off oranges, and I also caught sight of the time, so I pushed the rest, all stringy, to the bottom of the dish, and rushed the pheasants into the oven. Then I washed the vegetables sketchily, and put them on to cook. Feverishly I opened the tins of lobster. When I came to from the agonized delirium of a torn thumb, I was confronted by the problem of how on earth one made a lobster cocktail. I started to make them into a sticky mess with some tomato, thinned down with a little of my life-blood. At this critical point the mistress of the house careered into the kitchen in full feather.

The first impression one got of Miss Cattermole was like looking into one of those kaleidoscopes, in which coloured beads whirl about in a dazzle of changing patterns. When your eyes got used to her, she resolved into a mass of multi-coloured scarves, sewn haphazardly together, so that loose ends waved gaily from unlikely places to the answering flutter of straggling orange-wool hair. Out of this profusion, a pair of beady eyes darted a piercing glance of horror at my poor lobster.

'Oh, dear!' she shrilled. 'Is that the way you make lobster cocktails? It looks funny to me; oh, dear, I do hope everything's going to be all right. Are you *sure* – ' I saw the eyes jump round to where the turbot lay keeping warm. I had cooked it too early and it was getting harder and drier every minute while it waited for its sauce to cover it.

There was a desperate sinking feeling inside me, and I had to call to my aid all the bluff I knew.

I threw a careless shake of red pepper over the prawns, and, with the air of one who knows so much that it's almost boring, I drawled:

'Well, actually, I was talking to a famous chef the other day, and he gave me a special recipe – they use it at the Savoy, too. I thought you might like to have it, but, of course, if you prefer the ordinary –' I shrugged my shoulders, watching her closely from under scornfully-drooped eyelids. Would she buy it? She did. I had luckily hit upon a good line, for that gaudy exterior cloaked a drab little snobbish soul. She retired under my supercilious gaze and I returned frantically to my lobster. Dinner was at eight and it was already a quarter past seven. I discovered some cream and poured that on; the lobster began to look more appetizing; I wanted more cream and there was none, but I discovered three milk bottles in the larder, so I opened them all and used the top part. The lobster looked all right now, so I started to put them into their sherry glasses. I broke one, of course, and had to creep into the pantry when the sad thin maid wasn't looking to find another. I rushed back to the kitchen to sweep up the broken bits, as I could see a pair of silver slippers descending the stairs. I only just had time to kick the glass under the stove and pour more water on to the potatoes, which had boiled dry and were starting to burn, before taking up my stance, negligently stirring the soup. She smelled the potatoes, of course, so I opened the oven door and took her mind off them with a fine smell of roasting as I basted the pheasants.

'It just came into my mind that some tomatoes and mushrooms would be rather tasty lying round the dish,' she said; 'there should be some in the larder.' My silent curses followed her as she withdrew. I would never be ready in time! I put the tomatoes into the soup to loosen their skins and one of them burst and I had to strain the soup. Thank goodness I had been taught at the French school that mushrooms taste better unpeeled. I put them on to cook, and the next ten minutes were a mad turmoil as everything decided to finish cooking itself at once. I rushed about, snatching things away here and there as they were about to burn. I turned the oven down, and put everything inside to keep warm, and stood back wiping the sweat off my brow and feeling rather pleased with myself. Even the savoury was ready – it would be pretty dried up by the time it appeared, but it was a load off my mind.

I only just got this done before the hired waitresses came in with trays and said that the guests were there and they wanted to serve dinner. I got it away all right as far as the fish, forgetting to put the sherry in the soup, but I was past bothering about trifles like that. I was carefully carving the pheasants, calculating that it would take them a little time to drink their soup and toy with their fish while conversing elegantly of this and that. However, they evidently had nothing to say to each other and were concentrating on quick eating, because the waitresses came back for the pheasants long before they were ready. In a frenzy, I tore the wretched birds limb from limb with my bare hands, and scattered mushrooms over the ragged pieces as best I could. Nannie had arrived in the kitchen at this point and was observing my distress with the utmost satisfaction. She kept either sniffing or clicking her teeth, whichever it was it was maddening, and I said:

'Would you mind taking the vegetables out of the oven?'

She shuffled off to get a cloth, and took care not to return till I'd done it myself. Black despair settled on me and I could have cried with exhaustion and hatred of everybody in this horrible house. I remembered to make the coffee. Luckily Nannie didn't see it boil up all over the stove. Things were a little calmer now, except that dirty dishes kept on arriving in astonishing numbers and being piled up wherever there was an inch of space. The sad maid – her name was Addie – I discovered, and the two waitresses were behaving like people acting in a play. They would sweep into the kitchen as if coming off the stage into the wings, with trays held high and a tense expression of

10

hauteur still on their faces, relax for a moment in the frenzy of getting the new dishes loaded, and glide off again with faces prepared to make their next entrance. The nurse and I were left like stage hands among the debris, as if having seen a glimpse of another world; we almost listened for the applause of the unseen audience.

The washing up took an age. I began to regret the days when a huge dish was put on the middle of the table and everyone helped themselves with their fingers. It was finished at last, and we all sat down in the sitting-room round the unappetizing remains of the feast, 'hotted up' by me. I was too tired to do more than drink a cup of tea. They regarded me with pity, and Nannie said, 'Slimmin', I suppose – mad I call it,' as she packed potato away behind her well-filled black alpaca. Addie ate rapaciously and I wondered at her thinness. I was enlightened, however, when her apology for passing her plate for a third helping was: 'It's me little strangers, there's no satisfyin' 'em, it seems.'

This led to other interesting topics. Nannie's feet, it appeared, were inclined to 'draw' in the damp, and Violet, one of the waitresses, had some information on the subject of varicose veins. The other waitress, whose name sounded like Mrs Haddock, had a daughter who had just had a bad time with her first, so, not to be outdone, I told them about my dropped arches. This went down well, and I went up a bit in their estimation. Cigarettes were lit, and we settled down to a cosy discussion of the people upstairs.

'Some people', said Addie in her rather moaning voice, 'have got a nerve. That Mrs Bewmont, I mean to say, asked for a second sponge finger, straight she did. "Well," I said to myself, "what cheek, eh?"'

'Well I never. *She* never took one.'

'Didn't she then? Too busy talking to his Lordship, I dessay. "Go it, my lady," I says to myself, "we seen you without your party manners."'

'What about Miss May? She got married, didn't she? Isn't she going to have a baby yet?'

'No, dear – she can't, I've heard. It's '*is* fault, they say, but of course – '

I was beginning to feel a trifle uncomfortable, and was relieved when, at this point, the drawing-room bell broke into Addie's revelations.

'Oh, bells, bells, bells, they'd drive you mad,' said Violet calmly as she rose without haste to answer the summons. I thought it was about time I was going, so I went and put my coat on. I wanted to know what time I had to come the next day, and nothing had as yet been settled about my wages.

Violet came downstairs again and said: '*She* wants to see you before you go.'

'She' was in the hall, her plumage drooping a little from the strain of sociability. 'Ah, Miss Dickens!' I could see she was trying to carry something off, as her voice was higher than ever, and falsely bright. 'I really don't think I can settle anything permanent just now, so please don't bother to come tomorrow. Thank you *so* much. *Good* night!' She pressed some coins into my hand and vanished into the drawing-room. When the door had shut behind her on the swell of voices, I opened my hand on two half-crowns and a shilling.

'Well,' I said to myself, as I banged out into the Dulwich night and nearly fell into the laurels, 'what a cheek, eh?'

# *Chapter Two*

I THINK Miss Cattermole must have refrained from telling the agency what she thought of me, for they rang me up a few days later and offered me another job. This time it was a Mrs Robertson, who wanted someone twice a week to do washing and ironing and odd jobs. As I had already assured the agency that I was thoroughly domesticated in every way, I didn't feel like admitting that I was the world's worst ironer.

They gave me the address, and I went along there in a clean starched apron which I hoped made me look crisp and efficient. The porter of the flats let me in, as Mrs Robertson was out, but she had left a note for me, and a pile of washing on the bathroom floor. I sorted it out, and it was not attractive. It consisted mainly of several grubby and rather ragged pairs of corsets and a great many small pairs of men's socks and stockings in a horrid condition of stickiness.

I made a huge bowl of soapsuds, and dropped the more nauseating articles in with my eyes shut. I washed and rinsed and squeezed for about an hour and a half. There was no one but me to answer the telephone, which always rang when I was covered in soap to the elbow. I accepted a bridge party for the owner of the corsets, and a day's golfing for the wearer of the socks, but did not feel in a position to give an opinion on the state of cousin Mary's health.

I had just finished hanging out the clothes, and had wandered into the drawing-room to see what sort of books they had, when I heard a latch key in the door. I flew back to the bathroom, and was discovered diligently tweaking out the fingers of gloves when Mrs Robertson walked in. It had occurred to me that she must be a very trusting person to allow a complete stranger the run of her flat, and I now realized that it was probably because she was the soul of honesty herself, that she expected everyone else to be the same. Her large blue eyes gazed candidly on the world, from a face that shone with integrity. She gave me a hearty smile and a handshake, and looked round to inspect my labours. If she expected everyone to be honest, she also expected them to be as efficient as herself. She was horrified to see that I had not hung the stockings up by the heels, and told me so with a charming frankness. However, she still wanted me to come back the next day to iron the things I had washed, so my heart warmed towards her, and I offered to make her a cup of tea. Mr Robertson arrived just as I was going out, and we collided at the front door. He threw me a terrific glance upwards, for he was a fiery man, and scuttled for safety into his dressing-room.

I returned the next day, still crisp and efficient, and scorched Mrs Robertson's best *crêpe de Chine* camisole. She was more than frank in her annoyance over this trifling mishap and it made me nervous. The climax came when I dropped the electric iron on the floor and it gave off a terrific burst of blue sparks. I supposed it had fused, and Mrs Robertson came hurrying in at the sound of the crash, and she knew it had. It was all very awkward, and I felt very small indeed under her candid remarks. It ended by her paying me at the rate of a shilling an hour for the time I had put in, and a tacit agreement being formed between us that I should never appear again. I just caught a glimpse of Mr Robertson flitting into a doorway as I came into the hall. I was sorry not to have known him better, we could have been friends, I think – except for the sticky socks.

\*

Well, so far I didn't seem to have been much of a success as a working girl. I wasn't exactly piling up money in large quantities either, and the rate of pay didn't come anywhere near compensating for the mental agonies that I had undergone. I was still undaunted, however, and told myself that there are so many people in the world that it doesn't matter if one doesn't hit it off with one or two of them. I pinned my faith in the whispering woman in the agency, and went and had a heart-to-heart talk with her.

'What I want is something where I'll really get a chance to get some practical experience,' I told her.

'Well, we have one or two people asking for cook-generals,' she said. 'You might go and see this Miss Faulkener, at Chelsea. She wants someone to do the work of a very small flat, and cook dinner at night, and sometimes lunch. You ought to be able to manage that, I think.' She gazed at me thoughtfully, but without much confidence. 'Well, anyway, there's no harm in having an interview. Here's the address.'

I rang up Miss Faulkener, and she told me to come and see her that afternoon. The burning question of what to wear exercised me very much. Should I dress the part in two slashing shades of green and Woolworth ear-rings?

No, I would keep up the pretence of tragic gentility – plain, but clean and honest. A black coat and an uncompromising black felt hat would meet the case. Mourning, perhaps, for 'the Dad'. I might be a soldier's daughter, and he had told me with his last breath to 'Take care of your mother, the gallant little woman.'

I added a pair of cotton gloves to the outfit and went off, full of hope and very excited, to Miss Faulkener's flat off the King's Road. A sharp-featured maid opened the door and looked me over suspiciously.

'You come after the job?'

'Yes,' I whispered humbly.

'Got an appointment?'

'Yes.' I gave her my name, and she let me in reluctantly. I stood shifting my feet in the narrow hall, while she disappeared through a door, presumably to give a report on me to someone inside. Eventually she came out and told me I could go in. I found myself in one of those long rooms that have an archway in the middle and velvet curtains to divide it into drawing-room and dining-room. I was in the drawing-room end. On a sofa in front of a coal fire, groomed to the last eyebrow, sat my prospective employer. Though quite young, she had a self-confident poise beyond her years. Undeniably attractive, there was yet a hard, almost inhuman quality about the faultlessness of her appearance. She didn't look the sort of girl who could be persuaded to buy a dud article like myself, unless she wanted to of her own free will.

She told me to sit down, and scrutinized me pretty closely while we talked. It was a funny feeling to think that I was in her power to be accepted or rejected with contumely, and I had a strong schoolgirl desire to giggle.

'What experience have you had, and have you references?' I knew this was bound to come, but nevertheless it was still a disturbing question. I had thought of an answer, though, and got it out fast, stumbling a little in my desire to appear eager and worthy.

'Well, you see, I haven't actually had a job quite like this before, but I've kept house for my mother for quite a time, and also, I've done quite a lot of cooking for dinner parties at various houses.' (Oh, Miss Cattermole, how art thou magnified!)

Then I gave her exaggerated accounts of my training in cookery, and sat back to let her think it over.

'Well, yes,' she said thoughtfully, 'I must say I'd rather you had more actual experience, but I'm in a hurry to get someone as my Mrs Baker, who let you in, wants to go tomorrow. Her father's ill. I don't want to be left without anybody. You really think you could manage the work all right?'

Trying to hit on a nice mixture of pride and deprecation, I assured her that I could. I hadn't the slightest idea how much money I ought to ask for.

She said: 'How about twenty-five shillings a week? Sunday afternoon and evening off, and one half-day a week.'

It sounded quite a lot to me, for something that I thought I was rather going to enjoy. She looked an amusing woman, and it would be marvellous to have the run of a kitchen to mess in to my heart's content. It was all fixed up; I was to start the next day. It seemed too good to be true to think

16

that I'd really landed the job. In my enthusiasm, even the idea of getting up early seemed quite rosy. I asked her what time I had to be there in the mornings.

'I have my breakfast in bed at a quarter past nine, so if you get here in time to get that ready, and lay this fire, that'll be all right. You can get this room done after that, as I don't get up very early.'

I could picture her, lying in bed, holding long telephone conversations, wearing something rather pink and lacy. I was sure she had lovely night-dresses.

She indicated that the interview was at an end, and told me to go and find Mrs Baker, who would show me where everything was. I found her in the kitchen. She was much pleasanter now that I was an accepted member of the household and not a suspicious intruder, and quite un-burdened her soul to me over a pot of strong black tea. I heard all about her father's illness. The details were terrifying; it seemed to me about time someone went and looked after him.

'It's a long time now since I lived at 'ome,' she said. 'Dad and Mr Baker, they never could get on together, so we went out Streatham way and set up on our own. Then when Mr B was called above, with pneumonia, poor soul, six years ago, that was, I went into service. Been with Miss Faulkener nearly a year now. Ever such a nice young lady she is, but particular. Oh, my, yes. Some folks seem to 'ave nothin' better to do all day than to run their fingers along the shelves, lookin' for dirt. Not that I'd say anything against her, mind, she's always been very nice to me, I'm sure. Her parents are divorced. I expect you won't mind that.'

She said this last with such emphasis, and looked at me so severely that it was obvious that she didn't approve her-self and would be shocked but not suprised if I did.

I said airily: 'Ah well, of course, Mrs Baker, in these days, you know, one has to make allowances; after all, it's happen-ing every day.'

'Those whom God hath joined together – ' she replied

sternly. That's the one remark to which there is never any answer, so I suggested that she might show me round a bit. It was a dear little kitchen and beautifully clean. I looked forward to having it to myself, though I was afraid it wouldn't look quite so spotless after I'd been in occupation for a bit.

The flat consisted of Miss Faulkener's bedroom, a tasteful chamber of the peach satin and white woolly rug order, a spare room, bathroom, and the drawing-cum-dining-room which I had already seen. There didn't look a great lot to do – not that I'd had any experience of housework, but Mrs Baker took care to point out that all the floors were parquet.

'You'd be surprised at the amount of polishing they take.'

I pursed my lips knowingly and nodded, trying to look as though I'd been polishing floors all my life.

She then told me a lot of things about the routine of the establishment. I didn't take in all of them, but I was pleased to hear that Miss Faulkener took an interest in food and 'liked things done appetizing'. It would give me plenty of scope for practising.

I suddenly remembered that I must go and buy a uniform before the shops shut, so Mrs Baker and I went out of each other's life and I made tracks for an Oxford Street store where I could get something on my mother's account.

They had a huge variety of really quite decorative uniforms. 'There's no need to look drab even if I am only a general,' I thought to myself. I bought a plain blue dress and some very tricky little frilled aprons with cuffs and collars to match. I tried on a few caps, but decided I looked too like a waitress, and anyway it was rather the modern idea for maids to revolt against wearing caps. I finished off my trousseau by getting some bright-coloured overalls to ward off depression in the early morning and a very attractive peasant apron for cooking.

I rushed home to try on my uniform, and was so fascinated by it that I had to keep it on the entire evening. I was to get sick of the sight of it only too soon, when it began to wilt a little under the stress of work!

I went to bed early, with the cook's alarm clock at my side, but in spite of that I didn't sleep well. I kept dozing off and then waking with a start, thinking that the alarm had gone wrong and I had overslept. Its strident note eventually broke into a confused dream about floor polishing and terrified me right out of bed into the damp chill of a November morning. I rigged myself out in my uniform, which was cold with the unfriendliness of all new garments and only put on just enough make-up to establish my self-respect. My breakfast arrived at this point, and I bolted down some coffee and rushed off, clutching my overalls and aprons, feeling distinctly queasy about the stomach, and, arriving in good time, let myself in, feeling like an old hand. I had a look over her letters, but there was nothing that looked exciting, so I took myself off to the kitchen. It was looking rather inhumanly neat, and was distinctly cold. There was no boiler as it was a flat, and a small refrigerator stood in one corner. I hung my coat behind the door, put on an overall, and, rolling up my sleeves, prepared to attack the drawing-room fire. I found the wood and coal, but I couldn't see what Mrs Baker had used to collect the ash in. However, I found a wooden box which I thought would do, and took the coal along the passage in that. I hadn't laid a fire since my girl-guide days, but it seemed quite simple, and I took the ashes out to the dustbin, leaving a little trail of cinders behind me from a broken corner of the box. The trouble about housework is that whatever you do seems to lead to another job to do or a mess to clear up. I put my hand against the wall while I was bending down to sweep up the cinders and made a huge grubby mark on the beautiful cream-coloured paint. I rubbed at it gingerly with a soapy cloth and the dirt came off all right, but an even larger stain remained, paler than the rest of the paint, and with a hard, grimy outline. I didn't dare wash it any more, and debated moving the grandfather clock over to hide it. However, it was now a quarter past nine, so I had to leave it to its fate and pray that Miss Faulkener wouldn't notice, as it was time to get her breakfast ready. She only wanted coffee and toast and grape-fruit, which didn't take long. I tried to make some butter balls, but though I rotated the pats in the approved style something was wrong somewhere, because the butter just stuck to them in a shapeless mess. I had to give it up as it was half past nine, so I combed my hair and powdered my nose in an effort to look like 'the fresh-faced maid', who draws people's curtains in novels, 'letting in the full radiance of the morning sun'. I needn't have bothered, for she was buried under the peach eiderdown and remained there while I put down the tray and drew the curtains on the beginnings of a fog. I turned on the gas-fire and wondered whether I ought to wake her up, so I coughed. The eiderdown heaved and I went out.

I had dusted the living-room, swept all the dirt down the passage and into the kitchen, and gone through the usual tedious business of chasing it about, trying to get it into the dustpan before her bell and back-door bell rang at the same moment. People don't realize when they put their finger on a button what a chaotic effect it has on the maid's nerves. I stood quivering in the middle of the kitchen, recovering from the shock while I tried to decide which to answer first. The back door was the nearest, so I opened it on a man in a bowler hat and bicycling clips who tapped a paper pad and said 'Grosher.'

'Do you mean orders?'

'Yesh, mish.'

'Well, I don't really know yet –'

'O.K., Mish, I'll do the other flats firsht and call back.'

'All right.'

He went on up the outside stairs whistling, and I rushed to the bedroom, wiping my hands on my overall before going in.

'Good morning, Monica, I hope you're getting on all right.'

Just as I thought, very expensive-looking pink satin and lace –

'Yes, thank you – madam.' I'd been practising this at home, but it still sounded a little self-conscious. After much deliberation I'd chosen it in preference to ma'am or 'm, or even ma*darm*, which is popular in some basement circles.

'I just want to talk about food. Have you got a pencil and paper?' I went back to the kitchen for it, and there was the milkman jangling outside the door. I had to rush back to the bedroom, ask 'How much milk?' rush back to the kitchen, receive a bottle, look for the little book to check it in, and then rush back to the bedroom to take up the threads. By the time I'd got there a man wanted to be let in to read the meter.

This incessant conflict between the summonses of upper and lower regions is one of the most annoying things about domestic service. One gets used to it in time, but it is always a bit of a strain on the nerves.

Eventually we got down to the food question. 'I shall be out to lunch,' she said, 'but there's a gentleman coming to dinner. Perhaps you could suggest something nice?' All cooks' minds are a hopeless blank when confronted with this question, and mine was no exception. She laughed, realizing this, and I liked her. She looked very gay when she laughed, and much more friendly.

I daringly suggested a mushroom *soufflé* to start with. It was a bit of a risk as I'd only made one once at the cookery school, but she was delighted. Evidently Mrs Baker's cooking hadn't run to much more than plain things, which was a help, as it meant less chance of unfavourable comparison between us. We fixed the other courses, and I rushed back to the kitchen as I could hear that the 'Grosher' was back again. I polished him off, and after that dealt in rapid succession with various butchers, fishmongers, greengrocers, etc., not to mention a small boy with a huge hat-box. A few original and pungent remarks about the weather had to be exchanged with each.

I'd never realized what a sociable lot of back-door traffic there is, especially in a house where the mistress doesn't order the things at the shops herself. It adds a great deal of amusement to life, but it is a little harrying when one is trying to do thousands of other things at the same time.

The telephone rang while Miss Faulkener was in the bath, so I had to go into the bedroom and answer it. When I picked it up and said, 'Hullo!' a voice at the other end surprised me with:

'Good morning, darling sweet.'

'This is Miss Faulkener's maid,' I said reprovingly.

'Oh, Lord! That's not Mrs Baker, surely?'

'No sir, Mrs Baker left and I have taken her place.'

'Well, I hope your cooking's as nice as your voice.'

'I beg your pardon?' I thought him a trifle impertinent, but I must remember my place.

'Well, it couldn't be worse than Mrs B's.'

At this point my mistress drifted in from the bathroom in a cloud of perfume and a pink satin dressing-gown, and wondered what I was conversing about.

'Someone for me?'

'Yes, madam. Here is Miss Faulkener to speak to you now, sir.'

I put down the receiver, and went out of the room as she picked it up with a 'Really, darling, must you always ring up when I'm in the bath?'

Her 'best boy' evidently, as we say below stairs. I wondered if it was he who was coming to dinner.

I had to do the bathroom now, and was delighted to see that she was not one of those people who leave the place in a sickening mess – with cigarette ends and hairs all over everything.

She had lots of scented things to put in the bath, and I approved of her toothpaste. Her sponge was not greasy and sticky from long use, and I liked her even more – I crashed around among the bottles and things with a cloth and wiped the bath.

I kept my eyes severely turned away from one piece of furniture lest it should remind me that it was my duty to clean it or something. I struck at that.

Miss Faulkener went out soon, looking smart in black,

with a lovely fur coat, so I made her bed, and spent an intriguing ten minutes among her personal effects. The Voice on the Telephone stood on the dressing-table seen from two aspects, in one of those double-folding frames. I studied him carefully and found him rather attractive in a military-looking way, though I should have liked him a bit younger. I wasn't sure about the moustache, it was a little too long and looked as if he curled it while he talked. However, the egg without salt, perhaps.

Her clothes were lovely and plentiful, and her dressing-table held a comprehensive selection of the make-up of one of the expensive firms. By the time I'd done her room and opened the door to one or two errand boys I was beginning to feel hungry, and saw with surprise that it was nearly one o'clock. I was amazed at the speed with which time goes when you're working. I thought of the many mornings that I'd spent doing things just to pass the time until lunch, and felt incredibly diligent.

In the afternoon I had to polish the parquet.

I took up all the rugs and moved the furniture back – putting the wax polish on the floor was rather wearing on the knees and stockings, and I began to see that I should have to abandon my principles and wear lisle thread. After that I walked about a mile pushing a broom with a duster tied round it, and it really was most pleasant to see how it polished. I had to keep kneeling down and looking sideways along the floor to see how the sheen was coming up. There was a large area of parquet and it was four o'clock before I'd finished, so I put back the furniture, changed my filthy overalls to a fancy little apron, and made myself a cup of Mrs Baker's black brew.

I was glad to see that Miss Faulkener took the one daily paper that is read in nearly every kitchen all over England. I was able to 'take the weight off me feet' for quite ten minutes, while engrossed in the amusement both intentional and unconscious that it provides, before my mistress arrived demanding tea. I was glad when she revealed some China tea in a tin, because I didn't think the rank black weeds that I had been drinking would suit my constitution for long.

She lit the fire in the drawing-room and I had to persuade her that it was the peculiar direction of the wind and not my inexpert laying that made it belch forth smoke instead of crackling flames. It started to go out altogether, though I knelt in front of it for some time, despairingly holding up a sheet of newspaper with no effect. However, while she was in her bedroom I took the opportunity of getting some methylated spirits from the kitchen and pouring it liberally over the coals. Bravely I threw on a match, and by the time she came back it was crackling away beautifully. She regarded the blue flames a bit suspiciously but said nothing, so I went back to the kitchen to start cooking the dinner. I wasn't going to have a repetition of the Cattermole episode, so I started in good time and tried to figure things out into some sort of order. It was quite a simple dinner, anyway, and she had told me not to put the *soufflé* in till 'Major Nixon' (yes, that sounded like the moustached one) arrived. They would drink their sherry while it was cooking. I appreciated the fact that she realized that a *soufflé* must be waited for and not kept waiting. Miss Faulkener put on a long pale green dinner dress and seemed to be excited. She walked about from room to room, putting on fresh dabs of scent, patting her hair, and puffing up the cushions on the sofa.

As the place was small, the kitchen was not hidden away from the goings-on in the rest of the fiat, and I got quite infected with her excitement and felt a thrill myself when the front bell rang.

I took off my cooking apron, and had a look in the glass before flinging open the front door in my best parlour-maid manner.

Yes, it was Moustaches all right, and not bad at that, though his scrutiny of me as I took his hat and coat was a little too intimate. I didn't quite know how to behave. It is rather difficult to be dignified when clad in a short skirt and frilly collar and apron, so I rather hustled him into the drawing-room. His back view was marred by the glimmerings of a bald patch. My *soufflé* was much more fascinating anyway, so I hurried back to the kitchen, and my prayers went with it into the oven. Then I laid the table, lit four green candles, and turned out the lights. The air was pregnant with romance.

Much to my surprise the *soufflé* rose like a bird. When it was nearly cooked I went along to the drawing-room and hung about outside for a bit, saying, 'Dinner is served! Dinner is ready!' to myself to see which sounded best. I finally decided that 'Dinner is served!' can only be done justice to by butlers and the sort of parlour-maids who are called by their surnames.

I said my piece in the intimate manner demanded by the *tête-à-tête* occasion, wrapped a napkin round my *soufflé*, and it was still standing up when I thrust it proudly under Miss Faulkener's nose. I watched anxiously to see how it looked inside, bravely suffering agonies on the hands, as it hadn't occurred to me to put a plate under the dish. She delved delicately in, and revealed it to be miraculously light. Little did she know that it was luck and not judgement that made it so, and she was thrilled, thinking that she had found a really good cook.

The rest of the dinner seemed to go off all right too, though after a time, with wine flowing pretty freely, they were so delighted with each other that anything would have tasted ambrosial.

They were sitting quite close together at the oval table and there was some funny business going on, because I got a hack on the ankle as I came between them to hand him the savoury. I gave them coffee on the sofa in the other half of the room, and, leaving the moustache fairly bristling with anticipation, returned to the disheartening wreckage of the kitchen.

It didn't occur to me in those days to wash up as I went along, not that I would have had time, as cooking took me quite twice as long as it should. I kept doing things wrong and having to rush to cookery books for help, and everything I wanted at a moment's notice had always disappeared. I had hunted round for ages for a wooden spoon, to find it eventually balanced on top of the clock, where I had put it in a moment of abstraction due to a minor crisis. Two minutes later it had gone again, and this time it didn't turn up till the porter of the flats was emptying the dustbin a week later, and asked me if I meant to throw away a perfectly good spoon.

Every saucepan in the place was dirty; the sink was piled high with them. On the floor lay the plates and dishes that couldn't be squeezed on to the table or dresser, already cluttered up with peelings, pudding basins, and dirty little bits of butter.

I didn't feel like eating anything; tasting and picking at oddments as I went along had made me feel rather sick, so I had some coffee, trod on a plate, and started listlessly on the washing-up. The rush and excitement of cooking the dinner, serving it, and watching the progress of *l'amour* had kept me keyed up and energetic. Now that I was alone with the sordid aftermath I suddenly realized how tired I was and that, in the words of the Cattermole cook, 'Me feet were drawing.'

At eleven o'clock I was still at it and my back and head were aching in unison. The washing-up was finished, but the stove was in a hideous mess, and I had got to that stage when one's tired nerves make one feel almost superstitious about anything left undone. I felt I should be run over on the way home or something if I left it dirty till the morning.

Miss Faulkener came in to get some glasses as I was plying the Vim tin and was horrified to see me still there. 'Goodness, Monica, I thought you'd gone hours ago. Run off now, anyway; you can leave that till tomorrow.'

'Thank you, madam, but I think I'd rather get it done now.'

'Well, just as you like, of course, but if it was me –'

She wafted back to the drawing-room and I thought: 'If it was you, you'd be thinking of how depressing it will be tomorrow morning to arrive at crack of dawn and find things filthy. People may think that by telling you to leave a thing till the next day it will get done magically, all by itself over-night. But no, that is not so, in fact quite the reverse, in all probability it will become a mess of an even greater magnitude.' Exhaustion was making my brain think pedantically. It formed momentous beautifully rounded phrases that meant nothing, as I slaved away automatically. At last I had finished, and, resolutely turning my back on a large spot of grease on the floor, I was washing my hands preparatory to leaving when the pair of them arrived in the kitchen to speed me on my way. Was it my fancy, or did I detect a distinct impatience to be rid of me and have the flat to themselves?

It was, undoubtedly, just normal solicitude for my welfare that made them fairly hustle me out of the front door. I fell into the lift and out again, and propped myself against a lamp-post till my bus arrived. I arrived home in a sort of coma, and if the family were expecting to be regaled with anecdotes of my first day's work they were disappointed. My mother helped me to undress and brought me hot milk, and as I burrowed into the yielding familiarity of my own dear bed, my last thought was thankfulness that I was a 'Daily' and not a 'Liver in'.

# Chapter Three

AFTER a week or two at Miss Faulkener's I was beginning to get a bit more efficient, and, therefore, less tired. I was still pretty exhausted by the end of the evening, and it sent me into such an immediate and deep slumber that I felt quite fresh again by the time the alarm clock lifted its voice. I liked the familiarity of my little kitchen and the cooking gave me enormous pleasure. I wasn't so keen on the house-work part – though I liked polishing the parquet. I devoted most of my time to it, and it shone with a rare blue gleam. Unfortunately it didn't take Miss Faulkener's attention off other things. Mrs Baker had been right about the finger along the shelves. Life was a wordless and unacknowledged battle of wits between us, with her keeping a sharp look-out for signs of dirt and neglect, and me trying to disguise my slovenliness by subterfuge.

I became an adept at sweeping dust under the bed, and always used the same few pieces of silver, so that I didn't have to keep polishing the rest. Sometimes, if she was in the room while I was making the bed, she would say:

'How about turning the mattress?' She didn't seem to get suspicious of my always answering: 'I turned it only yesterday madam,' so somehow I don't think the thing was turned all the time I was there. It was much too heavy, anyway.

If she was in the mood she would chat to me very amus-ingly. My conversation, naturally, was limited, as it had to be discreetly deferential, and I couldn't start talking unless she did, or stay in a room after she had finished what she wanted to say.

A maid makes a good defenceless listener for people who want to talk about themselves and not be answered back.

Any repression this may have caused me to feel was fully made up for by the social whirl of the back door. I was getting to know all the tradesmen so well that I felt as if I had been in the place for years. The milkman, who suspected his wife of carrying on with a travelling salesman, often dropped in for a cup of tea and a bit of advice on how to treat women, but my real pal was the 'Grosher'. He was a pools maniac, and he got me so infected with his enthusiasm that, with his assistance, I took it up.

His was the first finger every morning to give me the nerve storm still produced by that dreadful bell. I would give him the orders first, before I forgot, and then we would get down to the more important business of selection, interrupted here and there by reminiscences of his pools experiences.

'When I won shixteen poundsh by a lucky shot with me four awaysh' was an anecdote I never got tired of hearing, or he of telling. Despite the fact that it was two years ago, and he hadn't won a penny since, we were not disheartened. Thursday mornings, when he helped me to fill in my form, were grim and earnest affairs, involving much heavy breathing and licking of a short stump of pencil.

'Arshenal, Mish? Never touch 'em meshelf. Chelshea neither, for that matter – too variable. Put a cross in 'ere – *sho*, heresh away win – *sho*,' as we put in the last mystic sign. 'That ought to bring us home thish week. Gawd shave us if that new centre forward isn't worth his prysh money.'

Monday morning found us slightly damped but not discouraged, and we would discuss with undaunted optimism the new week's chances. Dear 'Grosher'! I wonder whether he has ever repeated his historic success. I gave up the pools when I went elsewhere, as I couldn't do them without him. Whenever football is mentioned I think of bicycling clips; it keeps his memory green.

Miss Faulkener seemed to have a great many friends, and she often went to lunch and cocktail parties. Her evenings were mostly dedicated to Major Nixon. When he didn't come to dinner at the flat they would go out together – she very gay with orchids and glamorously scented.

I was becoming such a familiar piece of furniture about the place by this time that they didn't always bother to address their remarks in French when I was in the room.

One day, while I was handing them some rather choice grilled kidneys, she said: 'Darling, I think we ought to give a cocktail party.'

'Why, my sweet, we don't want a whole lot of frightful people all over the place.'

'No, but I think we ought. I owe a lot of people, and it would be rather fun. Monica could make us some attractive things to eat, couldn't you, Monica?'

'Certainly, madam.'

'Let's fix a date.'

'Must we, darling? I tell you I don't like the idea of people barging around our dear little flat – I like to have you to myself here.'

He laid a tender hand on her arm.

'*Pas devant la bonne, chérie.*'

I didn't always slide tactfully out of the room when they said that. I wasn't going to let on that I knew French, because they sometimes said entertaining things which they thought I didn't understand.

The party date was fixed and I was given piles of half-penny stamped envelopes to post on my way home. It was going to be rather a crush, if everyone accepted, even with most of the furniture turned out of the double room.

Looking through the names, I discovered to my horror that she had invited a couple I knew. Even if I warned them beforehand, they were a most indiscreet pair and would be sure to embarrass me horribly.

I had to search through the letters on her desk every day when she wasn't looking to see if they had accepted. I was greatly relieved when I discovered a letter saying that they were away and would be unable to come. I just got the letter back in time to be dusting busily as she came into the room. Pool discussions were postponed while I ordered a large supply of drink and various cocktail accessories from the 'grosher'.

I spent nearly all the day of the party making cheese straws, sausage rolls, sandwiches, and other oddments, and thought it a good excuse not to do any more housework than the bare essentials. Moustaches arrived at tea-time, and the pair of them came into the kitchen to make the cocktails. We were all very merry, and they had their tea sitting on the kitchen table, feeling as if they were doing a bit of slumming. I regaled them with imaginary anecdotes of other employers, and they did a lot of tasting the cocktails; by the time they had finished they were so mellow that they gave me one.

They went off, giggling like a couple of schoolchildren. I think they thought I would get drunk on it.

She went to get dressed, and I spread out the food and drink in tasteful array, while Major Nixon was out getting cigarettes. I didn't much care for the idea of being alone in a room with him. I had a new apron for the occasion and a coy ribbon in the hair. The guests would probably be too taken up with the impression they were going to create to notice me when I opened the door, but still, one has one's pride.

The hostess, suitably enough, wore what is known as a 'Hostess Gown'. A lovely clinging dress of cherry red which made her look almost frighteningly sophisticated. The host wore a red carnation and his most debonair manner. The porter of the flats was 'obliging' in a smart white coat. He was to hand the drinks, and I had to open the door, take coats and hats, offer the ladies the bedroom, and announce the names. This was quite a business as, after the first trickle of people, everybody seemed to arrive at once, and I went back and forth like a shuttle between the front door and the drawing-room. Some of the guests had the most extraordinary sounding names, or else I didn't hear properly – people do mumble so, and you can't very well ask them to repeat themselves more than once. I had a shot at them all, but some of them sounded even more extraordinary when announced by me in loud but refined accents.

The party seemed to be going very well. Major Nixon helped the porter with handing the drinks and I must say the pair of them were very efficient. Everyone got all they wanted and more, and the noise rose to great height. Miss

Faulkener did her stuff well, too, willowing from one person to another, introducing people, and having a word here and there with everyone. 'My dear, how *lovely* to see you again. How *are* you? And John too?

'I *adore* your hat, Alice – Paris? It looks like it – Basil, you simply *must* meet a most attractive girl I've asked specially for you.' And so on, after the same manner of all cocktail parties. Once I looked in from the hall, and she was talking to someone rather abstractedly, and shooting irritable glances to where the moustache was being at its most fascinating in conversation with a glamorous red-head. When people started to go I got a bit muddled up with the coats and tried to palm off hats on them that were much too small, but they didn't seem to mind, so it didn't really matter. One woman was a bit annoyed because I had put her gloves in the wrong coat pocket, and someone else had gone off with them, but luckily her husband got tired of waiting while she made a fuss and hustled her off.

At last even the hangers-on had been almost pushed out by the hostess, who was looking forward to the *tête-à-tête* celebration at a restaurant that she and Major Nixon had planned. He was rather loath to let the red-head go, but Miss Faulkener manoeuvred her safely away. When everybody had gone she vented a slight irritation on him by cursing him for keeping her waiting when she was ready to go, thanked the porter and me, and swept out with the moustache escorting her sulkily, several yards in the rear.

The porter had a quick swig of some cocktail that was left and descended to his *True Story Magazine* on the chair by the main door. I rushed to the telephone as I had arranged with a friend of mine that I would ring her up as soon as everyone had gone and she would come and help me clear up the mess. She was waiting at a house quite near by, and didn't take long to come round. Our hearts quailed before the amount of debris, so we decided to fortify ourselves first. Isobel went round the room collecting all the drink left in shakers and glasses while I made a choice selection of food, and we had a very good party all to ourselves in the kitchen.

After a bit we felt in much too good form to apply ourselves to washing up, but it had to be done, so we turned on the wireless and accompanied our labours with song. We didn't break much, but it's a curious fact that good glass cracks at a touch, while cheap stuff can be hurled about with perfect safety. We were only about half finished, and luckily were singing a *pianissimo* phrase when I heard a key in the lock. There was no time to turn off the wireless, but I was just able to push Isobel out on to the back staircase before Miss Faulkener walked in with a face like thunder. 'Not done yet?' she said as I appeared from the kitchen wearing an expression of innocent inquiry.

'I'm getting on, thank you, madam.'

'Well, be as quick as you can, and turn off the wireless – I've got a splitting head.' She banged into her bedroom before I could apologize about the wireless, so I switched it off and quietly let Isobel in again. She appeared still clutching a dishcloth and a plate, and we finished the work sketchily and could only speculate in whispers as to what they had quarrelled about.

Moustaches would get hell for it tomorrow anyway, for she was a woman who could be quite charming when she chose, but perfectly intolerable when roused.

Luckily for him, he did the right thing by sending a huge box of roses in the morning and arriving at half past six in a white tie with orchids and theatre tickets and a table booked at the Savoy.

She had been to bed early the night before, so her liver was in good order, and she evidently forgave him, for she went and dressed, and they went off together most amicably.

After this the days rolled on uneventfully for some time, marked only by such high spots as pay-day, and discovering how to make Welsh Rarebit. There were a few contretemps, of course, such as the day when I decided to clean the stove and took it all to bits and couldn't put it together again. We had to have the gas man in before Miss Faulkener could have so much as a cup of tea. He also solved the mystery for me of why the ice in the refrigerator was always melting. He roared with uncouth laughter when he realized that I didn't know that one had to keep the door shut.

Apart from such slight matters as these kitchen life went smoothly, and so did life 'above stairs', but it was not to last.

One evening Major Nixon arrived to fetch Miss Faulkener, distinctly the worse for alcohol. She was in her bedroom so she didn't hear him greet me with 'Hullo, Sweetheart!' when I let him in. I ignored it and stalked away to go on with what I was doing. He came into the kitchen while I was mixing some dough at the table with my back to the door. A beery breath whistled over my shoulder as he implanted the merest suspicion of a kiss on the back of my neck. I thought it would be more dignified to pretend I hadn't noticed, so I went on mixing.

'Have we got any gin?' he asked, going over to the cupboard. I indicated the bottle, and when he turned round with it in his hand I saw that he was wearing the repulsive leer that some men keep for women of a lower order.

'I didn't really come here for gin, my dear,' he said, advancing on me, and before I had time to take my hands out of the dough he clutched me to him in a very unrefined embrace.

A voice of icy calm spoke from the doorway: 'I am ready to go, John, whenever you are.'

It was true to the best novelette standards. He released me hurriedly and trailed out after Miss Faulkener. Not a word was spoken, and I heard the front door bang as I went on with my mixing.

I was scared stiff of meeting my mistress the next morning. She was awake and sitting up in bed when I took in her breakfast.

She was courtesy itself as she explained to me that she was suddenly obliged to go away and would therefore no longer require my services.

'I shall be going at once, so I will give you a week's wages in lieu of notice and you can go today.'

'Yes, madam, thank you,' I whispered. I felt terribly crushed and guilty. I hadn't expected quite such drastic retribution for something that was really not my fault. She went out early (to look for another maid I suppose), and, though I could see she was livid inside, she was well bred to the last, and we parted with a chilly but civilized handshake.

*

It took me the best part of the day to clear up the flat, and leave things tidy, which I felt was the least I could do. I arrived home in the middle of a dinner party and had a great success with the story of my disgrace, which I exaggerated a bit so as not to make it too ignominious.

Expulsion of any sort always seems to tickle the sense of humour. It had been just the same when I was thrown out of the Dramatic School, and before that when my school authorities told me that I could not attend any more if I persisted in my refusal to wear the school hat. Staying in bed the next morning was lovely, but, much to my surprise, I began to feel restive about lunch-time and itching for a bit of work. I had not yet had my fill of manual labour, so I trailed off again to the agency in my special job-hunting hat.

I gave the agency a fundamentally true but prejudiced story of my dismissal, vindicating my honour completely, and the woman took it well. She thought it a pity that I had not got a reference, but was sure that she could fix me up again at once. It seemed that one need never be unemployed, as the demand for cook-generals greatly exceeded the supply. She gave me three numbers to ring up, and I went out very excited at the thought of starting on a new and possibly exciting phase of my career. One of the numbers was that of the London editor of an American paper. I dialled that first as I thought it might be fun to see a bit of life among the journalists.

'*American Post* speaking – Mr Feldbaum's secretary,' said a brisk voice, American in its efficiency but Tooting in its accent.

'I wish to inquire about the post as cook-general in Mr Feldbaum's flat.'

'What experience and qualifications have you, please?'

35

Drawing largely on my imagination, I gave her the works, and she told me that I could go round to the office and see Mr Feldbaum at once.

I had got myself a shillingsworth of pennies, so I thought I might as well ring up the other numbers while I was in the box. The next shot was a Miss Jones-Haweson of West Kensington.

I said: 'With reference to the post of cook-general – '

She said: 'Thank you, I am already suited.'

I said, 'Oh,' and we rang off.

Short and to the point, but a waste of twopence. The third name that the agency had given me was Martin Parrish, Esq., of a Campden Hill address. The name seemed vaguely familiar, but I couldn't think in what connexion. A petulant voice answered the telephone, but he sounded quite hopeful, so I arranged to go and see him after I had been up to the city to see Mr Feldbaum.

The London headquarters of the *American Post* seethed with activity, but they were not imposing. One enormous room, with as many desks as possible crammed in jig-saw fashion, comprised the whole outfit.

The editor's office was a minute square in one corner, divided from the commotion by two thin pieces of match-boarding which didn't even reach to the ceiling. It was possibly due to the fact that one had to shout to be heard above the rattling typewriters that Mr Feldbaum's conversation was monosyllabic. He was completely bald. He looked very surprised when I was shown in, and raised the place where his eyebrows should have been. I sat down on the edge of a hard, narrow chair, and we gazed at one another in silence for a bit.

'Mm,' he said at last, 'very young.'

'Oh, but this isn't my first place, sir. Were you wanting someone a little older?'

'Mm – much older woman – I'm a bachelor. People will talk.'

It was my turn to look surprised. I thought I looked drab enough 'in me Blacks' to stop any gossip. I didn't know what to say, so I just sat while he pondered over me, and the typewriters filled the silence between us with their clicking. Eventually he said:

'What can you do?' So I embarked on my usual recital of self-praise, but it didn't seem to make much impression. He had already made up his mind. 'So sorry,' he said. 'Pity.' Though not eloquent, he was very polite and I was sorry too. However, I had another string to my bow, so took myself off quite jauntily. I had a little difficulty in finding Martin Parrish's house. It was in one of those ex-slum streets that have been converted into dear little bijou residences with window-boxes and red front doors. I roamed round the neighbourhood of Notting Hill Gate for quite a time, and when at last I found it, I was quite thankful to sit down on the chair that Martin Parrish offered me. Though I didn't much care for the looks of him – he was short and pink-faced with soft yellow hair and a little snapdragon mouth – he seemed quite pleased to see me. In my innocence, I thought this was a good sign, so when he offered me thirty shillings a week I jumped at it. Heaving his plump body out of an armchair, he showed me over the house. I began to think I quite liked him. He was affably polite, and very anxious that I should like everything, and at first sight it seemed a pleasant enough job. The house was tiny, with the drawing-room and bathroom on the top floor, dining-room and bedroom below, and kitchen in the basement at the bottom of a steep narrow flight of stairs. I had no time for more than a cursory glance over things, as Mr Parrish suddenly caught sight of a clock and gave a yelp.

'Good heavens – I'd no idea it was so late. I'm supposed to be miles away from here in ten minutes' time. I must fly.' He explained about his breakfast, and one or two minor whims, and the whole thing seemed fairly simple. I was glad that the misgivings of Mr Feldbaum didn't seem to have crossed his mind. The only snag to an otherwise pleasant prospect was that although he didn't want his breakfast early, he wanted me to get there at eight o'clock in the morning.

'Mimi wakes at eight, and likes to be let out, poor darling, You haven't met Mimi, have you? I do so hope you're fond of Pekes.'

'Yes, sir, I adore them,' I said, crossing my thumbs to eradicate the lie.

'Well, then, that's settled. Now I must rush; and you'll be sure to come in good time tomorrow – splendid.' We parted, and I went home and early to bed, setting my alarm clock at an even more ungodly hour than before.

I was dying to find out in what connexion I had heard the name of Martin Parrish, so the first thing I did when I arrived next morning was to rummage among the papers in the streamlined desk which stood in one corner of the drawing-room. It didn't take long to discover that he was a dress designer and writer of fashion articles for various magazines. Of course! Now I recalled how I had heard of him: 'Martin Parrish designs a glamorously Edwardian ball dress for our readers.' '"Stripes and ultra-smart and entrancingly gay," says Martin Parrish.' 'Martin Parrish shows you how to add sophistication to the "little black dress".' I was startled out of my investigations by a bell even shriller than the one at Miss Faulkener's, and rushing to look at the indicator in the kitchen, found a little red arrow agitating madly in the space marked 'bedroom'.

The first thing that struck me (literally) as I entered my master's room was the atmosphere. It practically knocked me down, but I recovered, reeling, and saw that he had gone to sleep with the window shut and the electric fire on. He was sitting up in bed, unappetizingly tousled.

'Mimi's been asking to go out for hours – she woke me up,' he grumbled. 'You're pretty late. Still – as it's your first morning – ' There was a heaving under the bedclothes, and a dirty brown ball of fur scrambled up and took off from Martin's chest to land on mine with yelps of joy or hatred.

'There! She likes you, that's splendid. Take the darling down and let her out.' He thumped down under the bedclothes and pulled the sheets over his head, and I slung the darling into the street, praying that she might never return, and went back to the kitchen. Now that I had time for a proper inspection, I began to see that, although the rest of the house had been done up in a modern fashion, the kitchen had been rather skimped – the stove was evidently an old one from another house and was encrusted with the grease and spillings of years. The dresser was only half made; there were no doors to the cupboards underneath it; there was no plate-rack, and no grooves in the draining board.

My eye observed these things with misgiving, for by such little details is kitchen life governed. I opened a few drawers and saw that there was also a distinct shortage of utensils. I wondered if my predecessor had cooked, like the Maltese, entirely with the aid of her hands. However, the walls and woodwork were freshly painted and the red tiled floor was nice. I decided that if the dress designer would let me have, perhaps, a bit of stuff left over from Lady Whatsit's trousseau for curtains, this room, the hub and focus of my existence, might not be so bad. Better still, if I could get rid of the various broken jugs, vases, cardboard boxes, and other junk which were piled on the mantelpiece and the top of the cupboard and dresser. Mr Parrish had evidently mistaken the kitchen for a lumber room.

He didn't want his breakfast till about ten o'clock, so I had plenty of time to lay the drawing-room fire and do a little dusting. The carpet was a new one, and when in a fit of enthusiasm I started to brush it the pile came off in great furry lumps and made more mess than before. If that was what was going to happen when I expended a little extra zeal, I wasn't going to waste my energy, so I left it to its fate and went downstairs to start burning toast and over-boiling eggs for Martin's breakfast.

When I took it up he had gone to sleep again, so I took the opportunity to open the window surreptitiously, glancing at the bed to see whether the blessed little breath of air would upset him. All I could see was a few matted hairs sticking out of the top of the round hump under the bed-clothes. There was no sign of life, so I was just going quietly out when the telephone rang. I went back to the bed and answered it. He woke and heaved himself up to mumble into it in a doped sort of way when I handed it to him, then an unfamiliar presence smote his consciousness.

'For God's sake, shut that damned window,' he moaned to me. 'No, not you, Norman,' into the telephone, 'I'm in the most frightful draught, that's all.' I gave a bitter laugh inside myself and swept from the room.

Shortly afterwards I had to brave the gas-chamber again, to ask whether there was any food to be ordered.

He was still in bed, and I took up my stand by the window while he consulted a messy note-book, so loose-leaved that pages kept fluttering out and had to be retrieved from under the bed.

'My secretary will be here to lunch, so we shall be two; three tonight, as a lady and gentleman are coming.' He lay back against the pillows and deliberated, and I felt it might be a good thing to make an impression by rattling off suggestions in a proficient way. This was a mistake as it gave him *illusions de grandeur,* and he chose an elaborate dinner that was going to be quite a strain to cope with.

I was glad to hear that the tradesmen called, though I thought it wouldn't have done his figure any harm to trot round the shops.

'Order what you need. There may be one or two things you like to have in stock. We've only just moved in, so I'm afraid the kitchen isn't quite fully equipped.'

I took advantage of this understatement to clarify the need for a few essentials such as sieves, spoons, saucepans, etc.

'Well, you'd better get those yourself. I'll give you some money and you can pop round to Woolworth's some time – you can get out every afternoon between lunch and tea; by the way, I think people ought to get all the fresh air they can.' I refrained from saying: 'Then why sleep with your window shut?' and left the room, as I could hear faint cries of 'Milko!' from the street. The milkman wasn't nearly as nice as the one with the unfaithful wife. I went out to give his pony some sugar and discovered that they were both bad tempered. One cursed me for not putting out the empties and the other bit me.

There was no sign of Martin getting up, so I couldn't contemplate doing his room yet. Anyhow, I could hear the faint strains of the bell from below, and I ran downstairs to find the arrow bouncing at 'Back door'. I began to see why people have to move into flats because they can't get maids for their houses. However, running up and down stairs may be death to the arches of the feet, but it is very good for the figure.

The greengrocer was a perfect Adonis, but not talkative. I gave him a string of orders and an allusion to the weather, and his sole contribution to the conversation was 'Ah'.

'Beautiful but dumb,' I thought as he sped off on his bicycle like a Greek charioteer. 'Still, you can't have everything.' Looking through the store cupboard, I found it contained practically nothing but salt and pepper and a few old tins of cocoa, permanently sealed with rust and age. I had been told to order what I needed, so I made out a long list for the grocer, and was in the middle of dictating it to him when the bell rang from upstairs. I thrust the list into his trembling hands – he was an ancient grocer of the high collar era – and panted up to the top floor.

Mr Parrish was out of bed and wrapped in another of the flowery garments that he favoured – a sort of kimono this time.

'Please light the drawing-room fire so that the room can warm up before I go down,' he said. After I had done that I heard sounds of him going to his bath, so I thought I might as well make his bed. The pillow was smeary with grease and the sheets were covered with Mimi's dirty hairs. The bell rang while I was fighting down the nausea that this aroused in me, and after having toiled all the way down to the basement, only to find that it was the front bell this time, I opened the door on a very nice young man indeed.

'Whom did you wish to see?' I said.

'I am Mr Parrish's secretary,' he said with a shy smile, tapping the brief case under his arm. He went into the drawing-room to wait for his employer. Something about his gentle boyishness appealed to my maternal affection, so I poked up the fire for him and said there was a nip in the air, before returning to my bed-making. I thought Mr Parrish was still in the bath, so I walked into the bedroom without knocking and surprised the gentleman in long woollen pants.

'Monica,' he said, in a controlled but cutting voice, 'it is not considered manners to enter a bedroom without knocking. Please remember this.'

I didn't think it was worth while explaining, so I retired with dignity. When eventually he was out of his room it was time to start the lunch, so I left the bed, meaning to do it in the intervals of cooking, but, somehow, what with one thing and another there were no intervals. Bells rang, sauces boiled over, the spinach took hours to wash and prepare, and as there were so few saucepans I had to keep washing them.

The first opportunity I had to get upstairs was when I had handed round the first course and shut the door on the sounds of eating. I raced up, and just had time to do the bed before the dining-room bell sent me flying down again. Mr Parrish wanted a second helping it seemed. This was surprising in view of the fact that he had done nothing in the short time since eating a hearty breakfast, except lie in bed or recline on a sofa dictating a few letters.

I just had time while they were on the next course to go back again and flick around with a duster, removing cigarette ash and talcum powder, to make the rooms at least look as if I'd done them. I had made the mistake of doing the bathroom before Martin Parrish was up, and he had turned the place into a dripping shambles, so my good work had gone for naught. A shambles it remained, for 'they' were screaming for coffee and my stomach was screaming for food.

It was half past two before I eventually relaxed over the

dried-up remains of the lunch that had been keeping warm in the oven.

I had only shovelled down one or two mouthfuls in the unladylike manner that one employs when tired, hungry, and alone, when the red arrow started to do the rumba under 'Drawing-room'. I went upstairs chewing, and discovered that they wanted more coffee, and I wondered when they were going to get down to a little serious designing – they certainly did not look like it at the moment.

When I had finished my lunch I lit a cigarette, and putting my feet upon the table as there was only one chair, I 'took time off', resolutely shutting my mind to dishes that wanted washing. Let bells ring themselves hoarse all round me, I was on strike for five minutes.

# Chapter Four

Now that I had time to reflect at leisure on my new situation I came to a great many conclusions. The chief one was that now that Mr Parrish had got a maid safely installed he was a changed man. He was still quite friendly, but that affable solicitude for my happiness had rather worn off. I realized that there was more than enough work for one person to do in this house, and that I would have to bring all my labour-saving ingenuity into play to cope with it. He had said that I could go out every afternoon if I liked, so after I had washed up the lunch things I thought I might make a little trek to Woolworth's to buy what I needed. I was just climbing out of my uniform when the drawing-room bell rang and I had to climb back into it and run upstairs. The secretary was typing in a dilettante way, while the designer sat on the sofa with a large board on his knee – presumably designing.

Holding up the top of my apron with one hand, as I hadn't had time to find a pin, I inquired what they wanted. The creative genius was suspended for a moment while he said: 'A lady is coming to tea at half past four. Could you make us some scones and little cakes, or something?'

'With pleasure, sir.'

'Thank you *so* much.' He threw me a fascinating smile, as if he knew that I would not now have time to go out and was trying to placate me. When he was once more safely immersed in his drawing I responded with an ironical leer and returned below.

Making cakes is not my strong point, especially with very few materials at hand and no cake-tins. However, I managed to throw together some fairly passable rock cakes and short-bread, and made a few surprisingly successful scones with a tin of Ideal milk. I thought I might as well make enough to keep them quiet for a few days so that I could be sure of getting out one afternoon in the near future. It was getting quite dark by half past four, always a cosy time of day, and the kitchen, which was beautifully warm and smelt pleasantly of baking, would have been quite snug if I had had some curtains to draw.

Feeling quite happy, I went upstairs to answer the front door bell, and admitted a competent-looking girl, fashionably dressed, though a trifle spotty about the face, carrying a large brown paper parcel. When I took in the tea the drawing-room was draped in lengths of material of all colours, and the three of them were flinging themselves among it, holding up a piece here and there and exclaiming ecstatically. I put the tea-tray down on a vacant stool and was just going out when Martin Parrish rushed at me with a bit of gold *lamé*, and, commanding me to stand still, draped it swiftly and skilfully round my form. He stepped back with clasped hands, surveying with his head on one side, and I stood there feeling like one of those improbable-looking effigies in shop windows.

'Look!' he cried, calling upon the other two to admire. 'Quite perfect for that blonde type – the whole effect in gold could be *too* marvellous. Take a note, Kenneth; what's the number of the stuff? Oh, yes. Here – avoid any contrasts with BX 17 – accessories, etc., unbroken line important to carry on colour effect. Oh, wait – how about this?' Very excited, he wound something dark red round my middle, only to tear it off again impatiently – pushing me about dispassionately as if I really were canvas and sawdust.

'Ah, delicious!' they all cried when the desired effect had been obtained. I wanted to go and put the joint in the oven and started to edge towards the door when the *lamé* was unpinned.

'No, don't go away, I haven't finished,' said my employer irritably as he advanced on me with a length of black taffeta which he bunched round me, crying: 'The classic contrast! You can't get away from it!' I began to think I might soon ask for a rise. He was quite carried away by his art and had evidently forgotten that I was only the cook and had better things to do than stand around all day being draped. I wished I had a union which would forbid me to act as a model during working hours. Eventually he became absorbed in a discussion with Kenneth, the secretary; and, having also discovered the cakes, they were quite happy waving them about in the air and talking with their mouths full. I seized the opportunity, while I was temporarily forgotten, to escape to the kitchen and start preparing the dinner.

I took a great deal of trouble over it as I wanted to make an impression on my first day. I got along quite well, in spite of being interrupted by summonses from above – the first time to clear the tea. I saw my employer looking at me meditatively while he fingered a piece of blue chiffon, so I fairly skipped out of the room with the tray before he could pounce. The next time it was to help the spotty girl fold up the stuff, and yet again when she and Kenneth had gone, to make up the fire and bring sherry.

The guests were a little late, luckily, otherwise the dinner would not have been ready. They were Americans, she rather loud-voiced and voluble and he a little quiet man with a sad smile, and a glance for me round the corner of his pince-nez. I tried out 'Dinner is served' on them in a vain attempt to better myself, but the effect was rather spoiled by the door-knob coming off in my hand as I said it. Evidently the kitchen wasn't the only room in the house that was lacking in efficient construction, and Mr Parrish said 'tch, tch,' and glared at me as if it was my fault. I replaced the handle apologetically and took the tattered remnants of my dignity downstairs. They followed close on my heels, and I handed round the soup, justly proud of its creamy smoothness. 'He' had asked for *potage bonne femme*, so I had made it in its most superior form, sparing neither cream nor eggs. The American woman was smoking so I placed an ash-tray beside her, but to my horror she did not put out her cigarette but held it in her left hand, taking puffs in between almost every mouthful of soup. I was terribly upset and moved the ash-tray a little nearer as I passed, but she was talking and didn't notice.

The next course was *œufs mornay*. One of the eggs was rather overcooked and shrivelled, so I put it at the end, and handed her the dish so that she would be pretty sure to take that one. She did so, waving a freshly-lighted cigarette over the other eggs and ate it abstractedly, so that I was tempted to give her boot polish instead of anchovy for the savoury, to see if she would notice. Having learnt my lesson at Miss Faulkener's, I washed up as much as I could as I went along, but it was an unequal struggle. Some of the things had to be cooked while they were eating the course before, and the end of dinner found me exhausted and surrounded by almost every plate we had in stock, all dirty. I took up the coffee and tried to send a telepathic hate wave to the American woman, which can't have reached her, for her hand never faltered as she lit a fresh cigarette from the stub of her last. I ploughed through the washing-up, fury lending speed if not deftness to my hands, and stacked the dishes in the doorless cupboards where they would rapidly collect the dust again. Then I slung a few odd bits of broken china into the huge inverted electric light bowl which did duty as a rubbish bin, and left the premises by my private route – the area steps – not forgetting to put out the milk bottles.

The next morning Mr Parrish's first words to me were:

'You must not rush off like that without letting me know; we might want something before you go. Last night I had some letters I wanted you to post.'

The morning followed much the same course as the day before, except that about eleven o'clock I answered the front door to a small brisk man with a neat moustache who wanted to sell me a vacuum cleaner. I thought this was a very good idea; it would save me a lot of work and give me endless amusement. He gave me a card which said: 'E. L. Robbins, representative "Sucka" vacuum cleaners,' so I·left him in the hall and went upstairs to give my employer a short résumé of his sales talk. It went down quite well, and I managed half to convince him that no house could possibly be kept properly without a vacuum cleaner and that it saved expense in the long run.

'I'm wasted as a servant – a commercial traveller's what I ought to have been,' I thought as I went downstairs to tell the man that Mr Parrish would see him in the drawing-room. He had gone in there already, which I thought was rather presumptuous, and I gave a hasty glance round to see whether he'd pinched any cigarette-boxes or anything. Not that I really cared whether the dress designer was robbed of his trinkets, but they might suspect me.

He was quite a long time coming, and as I couldn't see anything missing I unbent towards E. L. Robbins and we had quite a cosy little chat.

He told me all about the vagaries of door-to-door life. 'Ever so nice, some are,' he said, fingering his Old (high) School tie. 'Talk away for hours, as pleasant as you please – even give you a cup of tea.' If this was a hint I ignored it. 'Then at the end they break it to you that a vacuum cleaner is the last thing in the world they'd think of buying, and there you are. A morning wasted, and what to show for it? Nothing. No, reely I'd rather they'd slam the door in your face at once like some do – ever so rude. Time is money *I* say.'

'Well, I hope you'll be able to persuade him to buy one of your thingammies here,' I said. 'It'll be a great help to me – there's so much to do, and he expects me to be a human dynamo.'

'No, reely? What a crying shame.'

'Yes, honestly – do you know – '

Here we launched off, with one eye on the door, into a wonderful gossip, he registering suitable horror and sympathy as I unfolded an exaggerated account of my hardships.

'Put upon you are, my dear – that's what *I* say.' At this point I suddenly recollected that perhaps there is such a thing as loyalty to one's employer, and I didn't much care for the 'my dear' or the too sympathetic gleam in his bulging eye. Anyway, I could hear the flop-flop of bedroom slippers descending the stairs, so I took myself off as Martin Parrish entered in a black dressing-gown with a gold dragon on the back. I left them to it, and the result was that Mr Parrish consented to see a demonstration. I was summoned from the kitchen to attend, and Kenneth arrived while the parts were being fitted together, so Mr Robbins had quite an audience as he trotted briskly about with his machine, sucking up quantities of dust from the most astonishing places.

It was a great success. He fairly brought down the house by blowing a current of air under the carpet to 'freshen away the damp', which made it bulge and billow like a gentle sea. Mr Parrish and Kenneth conferred together while the machine was being dismantled, and the upshot of it was that they decided to buy a small one on the hire-purchase system, which, expounded by E. L. Robbins, sounded almost too reasonable. When he had gone I went down to answer the back door to my dream greengrocer, who was much chattier this morning and actually delivered himself of the information that lettuces were fourpence each.

I felt in quite good spirits today. My employer had been roused out of his morning torpor by the vacuum cleaner, so I was actually able to do the bedroom and bathroom after lunch. I didn't waste much time on them; I thought the dirt could wait till tomorrow, when it could be sucked neatly away. They were going to have cold meat and salad for lunch, and were going out to dinner, so I got down to a bit of cleaning in the kitchen. The floor was filthy, so I went on my hands and knees and scrubbed it. I started by the door. so as to be able to get fresh water from the sink without treading on the clean part, but this turned out to be not such a good plan. The back door bell kept ringing and I had to raise myself creaking and groaning and paddle over a morass to answer it. I was distinctly short with the trades-men – they seemed to be doing it on purpose, and the milkman gave me back as good as he got.

'Keep yer bleedin' 'air on, if you call it 'air,' was his brilliant parting shot.

'The only way I can tell you and your horse apart is the horse is better looking,' I shouted after him up the area steps. Not scintillating, but good enough by dairy standards.

So, quite satisfied, I waded back to where I had left off scrubbing. When I had finished my arms were streaked with grey to above the elbows, and as I had taken the precaution of removing my stockings, my legs were in the same state. I thought I had better wash before handing round the lunch, so I shut myself in the bathroom and scrubbed with the best scented soap. I didn't hear Martin trying the door as the tap was running, and when I came out he was hovering about irritably and intimated to me that the kitchen sink was the proper place in which to clean my vile body. I swelled with class consciousness, but said nothing and retired below, leaving a trail of 'Ashes of Roses' in my wake.

After lunch I got myself dirty all over again cleaning the stove, so as a protest I didn't bother to wash before taking up the tea. Mr Parrish stared very hard at a large smudge on my cheek and the black borders of my finger-nails, but decided not to waste his breath on me. I was able to go soon after that as he was going out. I laid the breakfast tray all ready so as to save time in the morning. I was pleased with the results of my field day in the kitchen. It was looking very trim, and I discovered a gloomy insect-ridden hole under the stairs where I stacked all the old vases and rubbish. Needless to say, I had no sooner done this than Mr Parrish came clattering down the stairs looking for 'that iridescent glass bowl that I put on top of the dresser'.

He exclaimed at the unaccustomed tidiness and was pleased, I think, but he said: 'Oh, dear, what have you done with all that stuff I put in here to be out of the way? Not thrown it away, I hope?'

'Oh, no, sir, I put it in a cupboard. It did catch the dust so. I'll soon get it for you.'

I unearthed it while he fiddled around on a tour of inspection in the kitchen.

'Didn't you know that you mustn't keep marmalade in an open bowl? It ought to be kept in the pot and just turned into the bowl when it's wanted. Oh! and you oughtn't to squeeze the orange juice overnight, even if you do put it in the frig. It loses its vitamins, you see. What became of that tin of milk that was in the cupboard?'

'I used it to make scones, sir.'

'Oh, dear, I was keeping it for Mimi. She does so love it. *Ought* you to have used it for scones? Were they all right? I always think it gives things a tinny flavour when cooked.'

All this was said in quite a tolerant if patronizing way. He really meant to educate me quite kindly, and he may have known more about things than I did – certainly no one could have known less, but I began to understand how our old cook at home felt when she guarded 'her' kitchen in that proprietary way. Anyway, a man shouldn't interfere with domestic details.

'In fact, a cook's what you're turning into, mentally and physically,' I thought as I pulled my gloves over my work-soiled hands and flapped off to Woolworth's on my dropped arches.

I arrived the next morning with my arms full of brown paper bags containing all I needed to make kitchen life happy. I had only spent about six shillings, but it had cleared me out, as it was a long time since pay-day, so when I went up for my master to order the food, I mentioned quite casually in the course of conversation what I had spent.

'You rather let yourself go, didn't you?'

'Well, sir, they were really all things I had to have.' I enumerated them, and though he tut-tutted a bit he couldn't dispute it.

'I don't seem to have any change. Well, never mind. I'll give it you another time. Now about lunch. I shall be alone as my secretary doesn't come today. I shall be out for tea. I have a gentleman coming to dinner. I thought perhaps we might have a chicken, some soup to start with, and perhaps a sweet omelette, plenty of jam. I like that. Oh, heavens! don't tell me that's Mimi!'

A terrible yelping was coming from outside accompanied by shrill barks. Mr Parrish shot out of bed, and we both rushed to the window. Mr Parrish nearly fainted with

51

horror. Mimi was standing on the top step, snarling and yapping, and looking even more objectionable than usual, while in the street a small terrier was jumping up and down, barking with frenzied rage at the Peke.

'Oh, run down at once and get poor Mimi!' wailed Martin, so down I had to go and pick up the crazy thing, at great peril to my own skin, and take it indoors, holding it tightly round the middle.

'All right, all right, I sympathize with you,' I said to the terrier who was jumping up my legs, and shutting the front door in his enraged face. I took Mimi upstairs to her anguished father. The climax was reached when we discovered a drop of blood on her chest, and even when, after an exhaustive search, we discovered it must have been the other dog's blood, he was still not appeased.

'I'd no idea you just put her out in the street and left her all on her own. You ought to stay and watch her till she's had her little run and then bring her in. You never know *what* may happen in London.'

'No, really,' I thought, 'this is too much – a model, perhaps, but *not* a Peke's nursemaid.'

Aloud I said: 'I'm very sorry, sir, but I'm afraid I really wouldn't have time in the mornings to stop after that.'

'Well then you must *make* time.' This remark was so ridiculous that I couldn't even bother to answer it, so I put Mimi down on the bed and left the room in a sullen silence.

Soon after that E. L. Robbins arrived with his vacuum cleaner, and while he was initiating me into its mysteries I poured out my grievances as one does into the first ear that comes along. He was all sympathy, and we got very matey over a cup of tea. We had just got to the stage when he was begging me to call him Ernest when Mr Parrish rang down for more breakfast. I rushed round, throwing eggs and bacon into a pan, and roping Ernest in to watch the toast.

'Two breakfasts, upon my word!' he said, scraping the black part off a bit he had burnt.

'Here, put this milk in that little saucepan and heat it up,' I said. 'This wretched egg's gone and broken, but it'll have to do.' It was soon ready, and I clattered off upstairs with the tray, leaving Ernest washing saucepans quite happily in the sink wearing one of my aprons.

My employer was talking on the telephone as I forced my way through the thickness of the atmosphere to his bedside. 'Just going to have some breakfast – is it really eleven o'clock? Yes, I'm still in bed. Isn't it *monstrous*? I know, but I did a lot of work yesterday, and I don't think I feel in the mood to do any more for a bit. All right about tonight? About a quarter to eight, then? Delightful. Good-bye, Simon.' He rang off and said to me:

'You might bring me my letters up here as my secretary isn't coming today. I'll read them in bed.'

I was afraid he might have the idea of using me as a secretary, so I flung them at him and ran downstairs before he could think of it. Ernest had finished the saucepans and was making himself quite at home with the paper and a cigarette. But I had a lot of work to do, so I told him that he'd have to go.

'Anyway,' I said, 'why aren't you doing your own trade? Is there a slump in the vacuum cleaner trade?'

'There's not a lot doing today, as a matter of fact,' replied Ernest, picking up his bowler hat and little attaché-case. 'When can I see you again, my dear? I always love a chat. In any case I ought to bring another screw for that handle sometime.'

I had thought of asking Isobel to come to tea as my employer would be out, so I told him he could come along too, if he wanted to meet an attractive girl. He jumped at it.

'I say, I am a lucky fellow – two ladies all to myself.' I hustled him off down the passage, and he was just going out of the back door, still chattering about 'charming ladies' and 'the cup that cheers', when we suddenly realized that my employer had not signed the agreement which he had brought with him. I took it up to the bedroom, with a pen and ink, but Mr Parrish was lying back on the pillows,

53

looking rather wan, and he waved me away with a limp hand.

'No, no, I can't possibly sign anything today; my head's terrible. Even to see the printed word – take it away.' I raised my eyebrows and removed myself with the breakfast tray, which showed every sign of having been attacked with hearty appetite.

I explained the situation to Ernest and we did a bit of shoulder shrugging and exchanging of 'Well I nevers', and at last I got rid of him and returned to my housework. I lugged the 'Sucka' up to the dining-room, plugged it in, and had been having a happy time with it for about ten minutes when a fat figure appeared in the doorway, propping itself up with one hand and holding its head with the other.

'For God's sake stop that filthy row,' he wailed. 'I've been shouting for ages and my head's splitting.'

'I'm so sorry, sir. Very thoughtless of me.' Perhaps he really had got a headache after all. 'Shall I make you a nice cup of tea?'

'God, no!' He retired and I went down, trailing the tube of the vacuum cleaner bumpety-bump down the stairs behind me. It got caught round the post of the banisters when I turned the corner at the bottom and brought me up with a jerk. When I disentangled it I discovered that a rather vital-looking part had been broken off. More work for E. L. Robbins. The edges of the stairs were looking a little dirty so I decided to 'take a brush to them' as I couldn't use the 'Sucka'. There is quite soothing rhythm about brushing stairs, crawling methodically from one to the next, and my brain was lulled into vacancy by the mechanical strokes of my right arm, so that I didn't notice the 'knock, knock, crash, crash' that accompanied the cleaning of each stair. I was soon shocked out of my coma, however, for when I was about half-way Martin shot out of his bedroom with an agonized roar. I gave up. I had done half the stairs anyway. Or, no, I hadn't even achieved that – I had made the elementary mistake of starting at the bottom instead of the top, and had been carefully brushing the dirt down on to the clean stair below.

Martin revived about lunch time and actually managed to stagger as far as the dining-room, where he sat staring moodily into space while I handed him his lunch. I had not reckoned on him being able to eat half a pound of steak and two apple dumplings, so there was not much left for me to eat. I counted up the eggs in the larder, and leaving enough for the omelette for dinner, I could spare myself a couple for lunch.

I put them in the oven to bake while I was serving my employer and, forgetting about them, recollected them just in time to remove them before they should be spoiled. I hurriedly seized a too thin cloth, and, plucking the pots out of the oven, burnt my hands so badly that I dropped them upside down on to the floor. I could have cried with rage and frustrated hunger. Mr Parrish, hearing the crash on his way upstairs from the dining-room, poked his head round the door and said, 'What's broken?'

I hastily put my body between him and the wreckage and said:

'Oh, nothing at all, sir, I just dropped one of the oven shelves.'

I found Mimi in the dining-room, so I hauled her into the kitchen to lick up the eggs. I myself made a pathetic and inadequate meal of bread and cooking cheese. I didn't dare eat any of the fruit in the dining-room, as Mr Parrish sometimes 'fancied' an apple or an orange last thing at night, and, if he ate fruit at dinner, there might not be any left.

He went out quite soon, and I washed up and tidied the kitchen for my tea party. Isobel fell down the area steps and broke a milk bottle, and not knowing that the house was empty was scared that my employer would come out and find her, so I found her hiding in the coal cellar till the danger was past.

Ernest Robbins arrived soon after and I hit on the brilliant idea of making them help me clean the silver.

When it was done, we had tea with masses of hot buttered toast and the best raspberry jam, which Isobel had delved into before I could stop her. I would have to think up a good excuse for its disappearance.

We had great difficulty in getting rid of Ernest. He was one of those people who can never find their way out. I wanted to show Isobel over the house before they came back, but we didn't fancy having him trailing us about through the bedrooms.

It turned out that he had forgotten the screw, anyway, so he would have to come back the next day. Could he be doing it on purpose? I eventually turned him out, saying that I was going to scrub the kitchen floor, and he left us with a:

'Good night all. Thanks for ever such an enjoyable time.'

We toured the house after that, and Isobel was suitably repulsed by the personal habits of my employer. We saw Mr Parrish from the window paddling down the street in a green pork-pie hat, so we had time to rush back to the kitchen before he got in. He came down to get a flower vase. I hastily put away the raspberry jam pot, but didn't bother about Isobel. I didn't think it would matter having a friend in, but it was a bit awkward to know whether or not to introduce them. Mr Parrish evidently didn't expect it, because he stopped on the threshold, said, 'I *beg* your pardon' rather coldly and retreated. I shot out and got his vase out of the cupboard for him, saying, for form's sake:

'I hope you don't mind my having a friend in the kitchen, sir?'

'No, but don't overdo it – and *not* men. No followers.'

Isobel made an apt but rather coarse remark as he retired to his bedroom to change. When she had gone I started to cook the dinner. While I was getting the eggs from the larder they 'slipped out of me 'and' and all but two were broken. That wouldn't be enough for the omelette, so, cursing, I had to put on my coat and run out into the rain to the little dairy down the road. When I got back the red arrow was dancing madly in all the spaces at once.

'Wherever have you been?' said Mr Parrish when I rushed upstairs. 'I've been ringing all the bells for ages, I thought perhaps they didn't work.' I had to explain about the broken eggs, and he made no offer to refund me, but I suppose that was really quite fair. 'Will you put out the sherry and tell Mr Nichols to wait in here if he comes before I'm ready? I'm going out now; you might take Mimi for a little run some time.'

'Very well, sir.' (I don't think!) Simon Nichols arrived while I was in the middle of a delicate operation with a sauce, which rather prejudiced me against him. However, he seemed quite a little gentleman, and he and Martin Parrish had a cosy dinner by candlelight, and if I was a little surprised by some of the conversation which I heard when I listened outside the dining-room door I thought no more of it when they had retired to the pink-shaded light of the drawing-room. Tomorrow was pay-day, anyway, so I flung myself with heart and soul at the uninspiring array of greasy plates and other sordid articles that make up the background of a kitchen life.

# Chapter Five

WHEN I had been with Mr Parrish about ten days I began to think it was time I got some pay. I had not liked to ask for my six shillings again, and he seemed to have forgotten about it. I hoped he wasn't going to forget my wages too. I was wondering how I could tactfully jog his memory when he gave me the opportunity himself.

He rang for me one morning, when I was very busy making cakes, to say:

'Will you pay the laundry when they come, for last week, and let me know how much it is?'

I saw my chance to drop a hint. 'I'm so sorry, sir, but I'm afraid I haven't enough money on me. I'm rather short as it's the end of the week.'

'Good Lord, is it? I must give you your wages. I don't owe you anything else, do I?'

'Well, sir, there *was* that money I spent at Woolworth's.'

'What was that? Oh, yes, I remember. Five shillings, wasn't it? Didn't I give it to you?'

'Not yet, sir – it – er, was six shillings.'

'Well, I'll give you ten shillings extra – you can take it out of that when you've paid the laundry.'

He handed me two pound notes, and I went back to take the by now very rock-like cakes out of the oven.

When the laundry man came he was in rather a bad temper as it was raining, and he felt cold and wet and wanted his tea. He looked even blacker when I offered him a pound, and muttered: 'Haven't got any change.' I didn't know what to do, but luckily just at that moment I saw Ernest Robbins' boots descending the area steps. I never thought I should be so pleased to see him. It was evidently his pay day too, for he was able to supply all the silver we needed. I was sorry to see that the laundry bill came to six and sixpence, so I should have to launch a fresh attack on Mr Parrish's pocket, which always seemed so short of change. I offered the laundry man a cup of tea to cheer him up, but he refused with a mumbled:

'Thanks – no time,' and drove off through the rain.

Ernest said he had come to fit a screw to the handle of the 'Sucka', and I had to give him a cup of tea and some of my burned cakes. I got rid of him quite early by telling him that I 'wasn't allowed followers', in the kitchen.

'Well, it's the last thing in the world I want, my dear, to get you into trouble,' he said, and paddled off quite tractably; I hoped the soles of his boots weren't too thin.

Soon after Mr Parrish and I 'had words'. He came down to the kitchen with the grocer's book in his hand and a look of dismay on his pink face. I didn't hear him descending the stairs as he was wearing slippers, and he very nearly caught me having a quick swig of the cooking wine which I was using to make a sauce. Trusting that he might attribute my guilty flush to the heat of the stove, I listened in silence while he ranted at me.

'Monica, this is a terrible grocer's bill! I'd no idea you were ordering such strings of things. I really can't have you running up such bills as this, it's absolutely scandalous. Two bottles of salad oil in one week, and all this butter. It's absurd. Either you're very extravagant or they're swindling us. Let me see the invoices. I suppose you've kept them?' This was rather a ghastly moment as, of course, I had never bothered to keep those grubby little lists which bore such mystic signs as 2 Dem and ½ Dig. Bisc. My stomach sank with the cold sick feeling that I hadn't felt since my school days, when one thought the world had come to an end if one was caught talking in the cloak-room.

I hung my head and mumbled.

'Well, really,' said my master, outraged, 'you are impossible – you must do better than that.' I suddenly saw red and all my Bolshie instincts rose and bade me stand up for myself.

'I'm sorry about the invoices, but as to the amount of things on the bill, I ordered what was necessary for the dishes that you asked me to do. I can't cook with air, and the store cupboard was practically empty when I came. Perhaps you would find it more satisfactory to go out and order the things yourself.'

'That will do, Monica. There is no need to speak in that impertinent way. I will think about it, though it is a pity that I should be bothered with household details when I'm so busy.'

I managed to change my involuntary snort of derision into a cough, and Mr Parrish removed himself sulkily.

His aunt came to dinner that night, so I listened outside the door in order to make sure of entering in the middle of a conversation about me, so that I could have the pleasure of hearing them break off suddenly as I went in.

Mr Parrish's French wasn't very good, but he achieved the general idea with:

'*Pas avant le Qweeseenyayer*' as I took in the sweet course.

When I had gone out again, I stamped my feet with a *diminuendo* effect so as to sound as if I was returning to the kitchen, while I really waited outside the door, balancing the tray of meat plates and vegetable dishes on my hip.

The aunt was quite a nice old thing and I'm sure was bored, as everyone is, by the discussion of other people's domestic worries. However, I heard her say politely: 'But she really seems quite a good cook; the dinner is very nice, I'm sure.' (It had been one of my flash-in-the-pan successful evenings.)

'Oh, she occasionally produces things that are quite eatable,' said Martin Parrish in a tired voice, 'but she's a rotten servant really. No experience at all I should think, and a bit of a slut.' There was a pause while knives and forks clattered a little. Then the aunt said: 'I thought she seemed rather a nice-looking girl – quite pretty in a common way.'

'Oh, d'you think so?' said her nephew. '*I* don't.'

Crash! You would not have thought that one gravy tureen lid, sliding to the floor under stress of emotion, could have made so much noise. I went quickly to the kitchen and

60

exchanged my tray for the dessert plates which I took in at once, so that when Mr Parrish said: 'What was that? Something broken?' I was able to say:

'No, sir, one of the fruit plates just slipped out of my hand as I was bringing them in.'

I did not dare add to my unpopularity by admitting the breakage, so my life after this was an incessant struggle to conceal the fact that one of the tureens was minus a lid. Luckily it belonged to a set still in stock at a big store, so I ordered another, but they were very slow in sending it. I had to steer him away from the idea of ordering dishes that needed both sauce and gravy, or else suggest a cold sauce, that would not arouse comment if brought in uncovered.

He told me what he had decided about the bills.

'I don't like to run up these big bills. You are to pay the grocer and greengrocer at the door every day when they come for orders, for what we have had the day before. Be sure to keep the invoices and check them when the things are delivered. Then you can ask me for the money for what we have had before the man comes.'

I thought this was a ghastly idea, and one calculated to give the greatest possible amount of trouble to myself, but perhaps that was the intention.

It turned out to be even worse in practice. I have always been very incompetent about money, and hate having to deal with other people's. What with invoices finding their way into the dustbin, or arriving on a rainy day, an illegible blur, I got into distressing muddles, and was consequently often out of pocket, through having to make good the results of my inefficiency. The question of change was very tedious, too. Mr Parrish never had any, and would give me a ten-shilling note the evening before to pay the grocer, who, after much fumbling in an ancient red leather purse concealed beneath several layers of coats and aprons, would produce one paltry sixpence. I had to toil upstairs to see whether perhaps he had some change this morning, which was rare. I generally had to pay out of my own money in the hope of refunding myself when, if ever, I got change for the note.

One gets used to anything in time, however; even money worries become part of the routine of the day, and I began to settle down like a fairly contented vegetable into my Campden Hill life.

The thing that was really the greatest bore was E. L. Robbins' pertinacity. The vacuum cleaner was always giving trouble. It would work marvellously for a little, to make me realize what an indispensable joy it was, and would then suddenly develop some extraordinary disease. One terrifying day it started to give off blue smoke and sparks, and other times it would just go sullen and refuse to travel over the carpet in that effortless glide described in the advertisements. I had, therefore, to send for Ernest, and I firmly believe that, although he mended the immediate damage, he nobbled it in some mysterious way so that he would have to be called in to repair it again.

He was quite useful at doing odd jobs in the kitchen, but it was a bit of a bore to be incessantly making tea, and fobbing him off when he said:

'What do you do on your evenings out?' I wouldn't have minded 'sixpenn'rth of Dark' with the greengrocer, but Ernest did not appeal.

In any case my evenings out were generally devoted to sleeping. Sometimes, when Mr Parrish went out to dinner, I got off quite early, but he was a lazy brute, and generally preferred to dine *chez lui*, often in the company of Simon Nichols.

Christmas time approached and I wondered if he was going to have parties and be very gay at the expense of the poor cook-general. Great was my relief when he announced that he was going to spend it in the country, with Simon and his mother. I heard them discussing it at lunch one day. Kenneth sat silently crumbling bits of bread or poking his food round the plate with a fork. He wasn't going away. I wondered if he had a nice home, perhaps his mother was a callous sort of woman who didn't understand his sensitive little nature. However, I couldn't make out how anyone could be less than overjoyed by the idea of London being rid of Martin for a few days; I myself was almost skipping round the table with the spinach at the thought.

It was one of the spotty girl's days to arrive with her paper parcel, and, still imbued with the Spirit of Xmas Cheer, I submitted quite happily to being told to walk with a piece of satin wound tightly round my nether limbs to test the practicability of the hobble skirt. As I detached myself from the clutch of Kenneth, into whose arms I had fallen after tripping over a footstool, I saw his expression change from a gentle concern to bitter resentment. Turning to follow his gaze, I saw that Mr Parrish had evidently answered the door to Simon while we were pre-occupied, and he was now entering the room in a beautiful smooth grey suit. Work was abandoned while he and Martin fell to discussing Christmas plans, and when I took up the tea, spotty face had gone, and Kenneth too. Mr Parrish was going away directly after lunch on Christmas Eve. I was telling Isobel this one afternoon when she was visiting me below stairs, and we were suddenly struck with the most perfect idea.

'Let's give a cocktail party on Christmas Eve, here in the kitchen!'

'Marvellous! It'll be frightfully original – I should think we could cram in at least twenty people, wouldn't you?'

We got down to plans and fixed it all up. Unfortunately, it happened to be one of the days when Ernest Robbins was sitting in a corner of the kitchen, doing something mysterious to the internals of my vacuum cleaner, so, as he had heard all the plan-making, we had to ask him to come. I was glad we did, because he was so frightfully pleased and excited. We told him to come about an hour later than we were going to ask the others, as he was sure to turn up much too early.

About this time, the tradesmen began to get very obliging, in the hope, I suppose, that the master of the house would give Christmas boxes accordingly.

'Some hope – ' I thought, but he did actually ask me

which ones I thought ought to have tips, so I put in a good word for my special friends. I had discovered a latent charm in the baker, who, at first sight, had seemed uninteresting and stodgy as his dough. This must have been shyness, because, after we had met every day for quite a long time, he quite thawed, and we were soon telling each other our life histories with true back-door lack of reticence. It appeared that he had a daughter – 'Just about your age, our Violet would be. Proper little piece she is, and no mistake. And smart! Keeps the boys guessing all right. She's got a regular now though, lovely steady boy he is – got a good job in the gent's hose at Gamidges. He give our Vi a ring too, straight he did – though of course they'll be walking out for a couple years or so yet.'

I managed to see that he got something, and also the greengrocer, and the decrepit old grocer. I got my own back on the milkman by telling Mr Parrish that the Milkmen's Union didn't allow Christmas boxes. I hated that man, he looked capable of watering the milk with the tears of little children.

The day before Christmas Eve there arose the important and exciting question of whether my employer was going to romp out with any sort of a present for me. Like the tradesmen, I became almost maddeningly obliging all day, and kept offering nice cups of tea. I even did most of his packing for him, and made doubly sure of not being overlooked, by arriving next morning with a box of chocolates bearing a label saying 'A Merry Xmas from Monica'. He came up to scratch nobly, I must say, and presented me with ten shillings. I was surprised into a last-minute affection for him, as he drove off in his little cream-coloured coupé, with Mimi in her basket on the back seat. Kenneth and I waved from the front door like a couple of old family retainers. He had to stay for a little to write a few letters, but I thought he would be gone by the time I started preparing for my party. I had made most of the food, and was just going to go out to a shop nearby to get the drink, when it occurred to me that I hadn't heard him leave. I looked into the drawing-room, and there he sat by the dying fire, with a writing-pad on his lap and a pen idle in his hand, staring into space. I went up to him, and saw that his eyes were filled with tears, and when I asked him what the matter was, he could hardly speak.

'I'm a fool, I know,' he gulped, 'but it's the ingratitude of it that I can't bear, the awful ingratitude – ' To my dismay he suddenly burst into floods of tears, and, though I hadn't the least idea what he was talking about, it was all so tragic that I started to cry myself, and we sobbed on each other's shoulder for fully five minutes. It was a lovely cry, just as good as seeing a pathetic film at the cinema, and when we had finished I think he felt better.

I thought it might cheer him up to tell him about the cocktail party. I made him swear not to tell Parrish and asked him if he'd like to come. He was quite delighted at the idea, like a child, and we went off together to buy the drink. When we got back, Isobel was already sitting on the area steps waiting to be let in. I explained away Kenneth to her when he was upstairs getting something, and then he came down and helped us make the cocktails. He must have had a very weak head, poor darling, for, even after only doing a little tasting, he got wildly excited and started to enjoy himself very much. We explained to him that the party hadn't begun yet, and he calmed down a little, but I thought he was going to become rather a handful before long. Needless to say, E. L. Robbins arrived much too early in spite of our precautions. If we had told him the right time, I believe he would have come before tea. He came in shuffling his feet and holding his hands behind his back, and eventually, giggling coyly, he said: 'Please don't think me a presumptuous chap, but I would like to present the two charming ladies with a little token of seasonable good wishes.'

Thereupon he produced from behind his back two of the most ghastly brooches ever seen on the counter of any multiple store, and, thanking him gushingly, we simply had to wear them.

People were now starting to arrive. We had said 'area steps' on the invitation, and it was funny to see them being amused by what was my daily trek to and from duty. We got Ernest off with an accommodating girl, and the party really went marvellously – that kitchen has never known such a cheerful atmosphere before or since. I had put away most of the crockery, but half-way through the party, Kenneth suddenly fell to the ground like a dead thing, and lay fast asleep with his head pillowed on the remnants of a vegetable dish that he had broken in his fall. We left him there, and he looked so happy and peaceful.

\*

I felt more than disinclined to go back to work on the day after Boxing Day, when I had to go and prepare the house for my employer's return. He was due to arrive at about seven o'clock, so I trailed along as late as possible, and then had a terrific rush to get things tidied up in time. I hadn't felt like clearing up after the cocktail party, and the kitchen looked a wreck. More things had been broken than I had thought, and the electric light bowl was soon pretty well crammed with pieces of china and glass, as well as the cigarette ends and odd bits of food that had been strewn everywhere in drab confusion.

I made a list of the things I would have to replace, and was thankful that I had been given some money at Christmas, though it seemed rather a pathetic way to spend it.

Suddenly remembering that I had not yet lit the drawing-room fire, I rushed upstairs, cleared the grate and laid it in a haphazard way, and did my usual incendiary trick with the methylated spirits. I shook up the cushions a bit to make the room look a little less neglected, and went down to finish the washing up.

I forgot all about the fire, though I had meant to go up and put more coal on it as it burned through, and when I eventually did remember, it was practically out. There was no more methylated, so I resorted feverishly to all the dodges I had ever read of in the *Home Magazine* – lumps of sugar, candle-ends, etc., but all to no purpose. I held a large sheet of newspaper in front of it for ages, and was rewarded at last by a faint crackling. There was more smoke than fire, however, and Martin Parrish had to choose this inconvenient moment to arrive, tired and cross from a long cold drive. He walked into the room where I was still kneeling, and was greeted by clouds of belching black smoke. Coughing and wiping my eyes, I apologized, but he took himself off in high dudgeon to huddle over his electric fire upstairs. When the fire had exhausted itself by smoking, it quietly died. The only thing to be done was to start all over again from rock-bottom, which I did, very harassed by the fact that Mr Parrish called down that he would like to have supper as soon as possible.

When the fire was at last beginning to burn, I hastily laid the table with what was left of the crockery and glass, and heated up a stew of rather dubious age, which had been congealing in the larder over Christmas. I put in a lot of herbs and seasoning, to disguise any possible rank taste, and he ate it all right, but gloomily.

I wasn't going to offer to unpack, in case he accepted, and he luckily didn't think of asking me, so I finished up downstairs quickly, and left him crouched over the struggling fire.

The next high spot was New Year's Eve, and, to my intense disgust, Martin Parrish started to talk about giving a party. He and I made out an approximate list of the food and drink that would be needed, and he took it away to count up the cost. Evidently he found the total too vast, for the next thing I heard was that his ideas had descended with a rush from having twenty people and giving them champagne, to three couples and Simon and giving them bridge and fruit punch. The dinner was to be on quite a large scale, however, and I took the first opportunity of rushing out when I should have been polishing the silver, to replace the breakages of my party.

Mr Parrish was nosing around in the kitchen when I got back, so I had to hide my parcels in the coal cellar until he had gone. 'Where have you been?' he inquired, as I entered humming innocently. He had evidently forgotten that he had told me I could go out any afternoon I liked, I suppose because I hardly ever did, as there was always too much to do.

'Just popped out to get some eggs, sir.'

'Eggs, what for? They're dear just now, aren't they?'

'Well, sir, I – er – thought I might make the trifle today for tomorrow's dinner.'

'Oh, I see, well, I suppose that's all right. We seem to be rather short of glasses. You didn't tell me you'd broken any – '

'Oh, I haven't, sir, I just put some in another cupboard, that's all.'

My prayers that he wouldn't ask 'which cupboard?' were answered, for Mimi started yapping upstairs, so he had to hurry away. The next day was a terrible one for me. I started preparing the dinner quite early, so as not to have such a panic in the evening, and Martin chose that day to have a migraine. He stayed in bed till six o'clock and kept his finger almost permanently on the bell-push all day – I wonder the red arrow didn't drop off. First his breakfast egg was too hard and he must have another, then he wanted some cigarettes, then orange juice, and once it was for me to go into the street and send away a barrel organ. I didn't like to do this without giving the man any money, and as none was forthcoming from the Parrish purse, and I had none, I had to borrow it from Ernest Robbins, who needless to say was in the kitchen again, getting underfoot and altogether being a nuisance.

When Kenneth arrived, he was very annoyed in his gentle way that he hadn't been told he would not be wanted. He had to go up to his employer's bedroom to ask him to sign something, though even that would probably be too great a strain for Martin. I was giving the dining-room a quick flick-over, and I heard a great deal of complaining talk going on – I couldn't hear what they were saying, even when I stood outside the door and polished the knob, till Martin's voice suddenly rose to a scream:

'Damn it all, I pay you, don't I? What else do you want, you jealous little – !' I recoiled and Kenneth staggered out, white and shaking and, before I could try to comfort him, ran unsteadily downstairs and banged out of the front door.

I didn't give Martin much of a lunch, I was too busy doing things for the dinner, but he polished off what I took him quite happily, and then settled down to a well-earned sleep.

As the evening drew on, I was involved in a frenzy of cooking, and getting more exhausted and harassed every minute as I kept remembering things that still had to be done. Mr Parrish did not help my confusion by strolling languidly down to the kitchen with a book on how to make punch, with which he wanted me to help him. I said:

'I can't spare you a minute, sir.'

He was very affronted, and I had to scare him away by nearly spilling some egg on his sleeve as he pored over the book on the table which I wanted to use. I couldn't help it if he was annoyed; he'd be much more so if the dinner wasn't ready, and I did not see why he shouldn't do a little work for his silly party. He shuffled away into the dining-room and spent a sulky half-hour throwing fruit peel, spices, and the contents of various bottles into a huge china bowl.

I got hotter and hotter as I basted meat and stirred sauces like mad, trying at the same time to fry potatoes in a deep pan of fat, which spat viciously at me whenever I went near it. When the door bell rang I was in too much of a turmoil to tidy myself or even take off my apron. My one idea was to rush upstairs and down again to my cooking as quickly as possible. I thought the couple that I admitted looked at me a little queerly, so when I returned below I took a look in the pathetic little square of spotted mirror that hung behind the kitchen door. I certainly was rather a terrifying sight. The steam and heat had turned my hair from a mass of fascinating curls to a sort of hayrick of lank straight locks; spots of brown grease were spattered all over my face, and there was egg in one eyebrow. It was not surprising that the guests had seemed a little taken aback; I looked as if I had some sort of plague. There was no time for repairs now, as a piece of paper, which was covering something on the stove, suddenly caught fire, and dropped black ash into the Hollandaise Sauce. I skimmed and strained it feverishly, but it was useless to try to remove all the little black specks, and equally useless to start it again, as there simply wasn't time. I was in a panic, but I suddenly had a brainwave and turned the sauce into Béarnaise by adding some chopped herbs and gerkins which effectively mingled with the black specks and camouflaged them.

I had barely time to do this before the bell rang again. I hastily did something about my plague-ridden face, broke a comb on my hair, and tied it back with a bit of ribbon. I tore off my apron as I ran upstairs, flinging it into the gent's toilet as I passed. The rest of the party had all arrived together, and I announced them in my most up-stage manner, hoping that the first couple would think that there were two maids, and not connect me with the apparition who had let them in. Dinner was rather a sticky affair, the punch didn't seem to imbue any of them with a wild party spirit. My *bête noire*, the chain-smoking American woman, sat on the host's right and blew cigarette smoke into his face in a half-hearted attempt at fascination. He was still sulking, I'm afraid, and sat hunched over the end of the table, throwing out an occasional moaning word or two by way of conversation. A fat gentleman told long and pointless stories which made nobody laugh except himself, and that only a spasmodic wheezing.

However, I could not pay much attention to the social aspect of the party. Serving up and handing a four-course dinner to six people all by oneself is a distinct strain, and I got pretty hectic. It was difficult to preserve an air of calm efficiency in the dining-room, while my nose told me that all was not well in the kitchen. The necessity for concealing the fact that my hands were filthy was troublesome too. When I cook and dish up in a hurry, it is rather a messy process, what with tasting and all, and of course there was no time to wash before taking the food in. I had to slide my hands carefully under the dishes; it's not easy to get the second hand under, and involves clutching the dish to the bosom, but it's better than shoving a grubby unappetizing thumb under the noses of the guests. When they finally went upstairs to play bridge, I felt as if I had been through a battle, and had to 'take five minutes off' before washing up. When I was in the thick of it, they rang for me to take up drinks, which meant taking off my overall and decking myself out once more in my frills.

One of the tables was holding a rather acrimonious postmortem, and voices were getting shrill. I withdrew thankfully to my kitchen, whose peace was only broken by the occasional gluggle glug of the Frigidaire. It was half past eleven before I had finished, and I was just going to go when they rang for me again. Martin Parrish came out into the hall and told me to make some more punch for them to drink the New Year in. He offered me the book of words, but I thought I would probably make a better one than he without its aid. I put in all the drink I could lay hands on, which wasn't much as Parrish never kept a proper supply of anything, but I poured in the dregs of any bottles I could see, including the cooking brandy. After adding the fruit, I heated the whole thing to boiling-point, poured a big glass out for myself, and took it upstairs for the still slightly querulous company. It was rather a beastly party really – I was glad to be an accessory and not a member of it. When midnight struck, and grating sounds of 'Auld Lang Syne' floated down the staircase, I drank myself a toast in the poisonous Punch: 'A kick in the Pants for all employers.'

New Year's Eve marked the beginning of a down-grade in my spirits. Work and dirt seem to pile up every day, and I got more and more tired. I was always getting desperate

71

and leaving things to be done the next day, and, in spite of the frequent assistance of Ernest, I never seemed to catch up on myself.

Exhaustion made me miserable, and many were the times when the plates in the sink were washed with my tears of self-pity.

One evening as I was sobbing brokenly over a soup tureen, I felt a trembling hand placed round my shoulders. The back door had evidently been left open and Ernest had walked in all unbeknownest. He was very sympathetic and said: 'Come, come, don't take on so,' and 'dry your tears, little woman.' I soon recovered, if only to make him remove his arm, and we had a long chat about Life and its Injustices which ended by his saying:

'Give notice, dear, that's what *I* say. Face it out, now come on, do.'

Really, when I thought about it, it seemed a good idea. As I felt sure of getting another job, I saw no reason why I shouldn't decamp before I got into a complete rut.

I promised Ernest that I would give Mr Parrish a week's notice the next day, but, by the time I arrived the next morning, I was so taken with the idea of leaving that I felt I couldn't even bear to stay a week. Once I had made up my mind to go, I felt I must go at once or bust, and so, nerving myself for the ordeal, I delivered the bombshell to my master. 'Sir,' I said, depositing the breakfast tray on his chest, 'I wish to hand in my notice.'

He shot bolt upright and spilt some coffee on the grubby sheet.

'Well, really, this is a bit thick! Perhaps you will tell me why you don't wish to stay?'

Common civility prevented me from giving several reasons, so I just said:

'I'm afraid I find the work too tiring, there is really too much for one person to do.'

'What rubbish. Anyone with any method would find this a very easy job, with all the consideration I have given you. However, if you're not capable of managing, there is no use in your staying. I thought from the first that your lack of experience would lead to inefficiency.' As I was going anyway, I thought I might as well let him have it, so I raved, in the most ill-bred and childish way for quite five minutes.

'All I can say is,' I finished, 'that you'll never get anyone to do the amount I've been doing. Your ingratitude amazes me – I shall go at once.'

'No, you can't do that,' he said, regarding me with cold and withering distaste. 'You will have to stay a week or at least until I get someone else – that's the legal position.' I flounced out of the room; as I passed the dining-room I savagely wrenched the handle of the door – it had never been mended – and hurled it out of the window. It gave me the utmost satisfaction.

I bided my time, and maintained a brooding silence all day. Mr Parrish thought he had won, so did not mention the matter again, but gave himself some sadistic pleasure by summoning me upstairs countless times when he knew I was busy, and sending back his omelette at lunch, demanding another one less leathery.

At six o'clock he went out to a sherry party, and with a whoop of joy I let out the emotion that had been bubbling in me all day. I had realized that, if I left my last week's wages behind, I was quite within my rights if I walked out. Thinking to heap coals of fire, I left the kitchen tidy, with the breakfast tray laid ready. When I had removed the things that I had had to buy with my own money, the kitchen equipment was greatly depleted. I had a pang of pity for my successor, so I salved my conscience by leaving behind a rather beautiful green egg whisk. Upstairs, I celebrated my Independence Day by drinking a great deal of inferior Parrish sherry, and, thus inspired, I'm ashamed to say I wrote a very rude limerick indeed, and pinned it, with my thirty shillings wages, to Martin Parrish's pillow.

# Chapter Six

AFTER my débâcle *chez* Parrish, I did not look for another job at once. A slight rest seemed to be indicated, and I spent quite a contented few days lying in bed late in the mornings and massaging my hands with cold cream, in a despairing effort to get them back to normal. Also, the family were planning a motor trip in Alsace-Lorraine in the near future, partly to see the country and partly to eat the local food. I wasn't going to miss that for anything, and I thought I might learn a great deal about my Art.

The only regret I had about leaving Martin was that I had never said good-bye to E. L. Robbins. I felt really bad about that. He had stood by me through thick and thin, and it was on his advice that I had eventually given notice, and now I had gone and left him flat without a word. I thought the least I could do was to write a letter of thanks and farewell, which was sent to him c/o The 'Sucka' Company. In a few days I got his reply.

MISS MONICA DICKENS
DEAR FRIEND,

Perhaps you will allow me to pen a few words of thanks for yours. I cannot tell you how I shall miss my delightful visits to your kitchen, and to see yourself and the other charming member of the fair sex. Nevertheless, for your sake, I am delighted that you are no longer subjected to the *inconsiderateness* and may I say *unkindness* of the person whose name I will not mention. In conclusion may I take the liberty of wishing you success in the future, and hoping that you will accept these lines in the spirit of sincere kindliness with which I offer them.

> *I remain*
> *Yours faithfully*
> ERNEST L. ROBBINS

By the same post as this touching epistle came a letter from the agency asking me if I would consider taking a job in the country for three weeks, to help out a man who had a sick wife and three children on his hands and no cook. The call of the kitchen was strong, and the family sounded so nice that I rang up the agency there and then and said that I would just have time to fit it in before going away.

They gave me the address – a Major Hampden, living at Yew Green, a village near Wallingford in Berkshire. I had passed through this county and always been attracted by it and wanted to get to know it better. I pictured myself roaming over the Chilterns in the afternoons when I was off duty, not realizing that I would be much too busy washing up the lunch and making cakes for a nursery tea to even poke my nose out of doors. When I rang up Major Hampden, he was so delighted at the idea of getting somebody that he fairly stuttered and stumbled over his words.

'When would you like me to come?' I asked.

'Oh, at once, at once, if you would be so good. We've been at our wits' end with no one to look after the children – my wife's an invalid – and no one to cook. We've been living on s-sausages and rice pudding, which are the only things I can do. We have an old body who comes in every morning – she'll help you with the housework. Oh, dear, it *will* be a relief to have you here – I can't tell you how p-pleased I am.'

It seemed as if I should have my hands full, what with being a nursemaid, cook-general, and housekeeper all at once, but he sounded so perfectly sweet that I promised to go down the next day.

\*

YEW GREEN GROVE
YEW GREEN
NR WALLINGFORD
BERKS
*Wednesday*

DARLING MUMMY,

Well, here I am, safely installed *chez* Hampden, after an

75

uneventful journey. The old boy met me at the station in an ancient car tied up with string, and drove me here through lovely country. It's quite a primitive village, sitting at the bottom of the Chilterns, and surrounded by vast ploughed fields, with clumps of elms stuck about here and there. The house is what's known as 'rambling', you hit your head in unlikely places, and a draught whistles at you round every corner. But I like it here, I've decided already.

First of all, let me tell you that, much to my surprise, I am not a servant – I am 'one of the family', and they treat me real nice. It was very amusing trying to find out exactly what my status was. I arrived, all humble, like a tweeny with her wicker basket, to be greeted like a most welcome guest, sat down at the table where they were lunching off Bully Beef and oranges, and addressed throughout as 'Miss Dickens'. Gone are the days when I clear one end of the kitchen table to crouch pathetically over the scraps off the dining-room plates.

Old man Hampden is a perfect darling, and behaves as if I were here as a favour instead of in return for wages. He has mild blue eyes, and wears a fawn cardigan, riddled with holes, and short, tight plus fours. I don't know what's wrong with Mrs H. She lives in bed in a sort of summer-house in the garden; it must be freezing. What is it you have that makes you have to be in the open air? R.S.V.P. The children are adorable and consist of one boy of nine and one of six, and a minute thing of three called Jane. They are very independent, which is a good thing, as I've got to look after them, and the two eldest are at school nearly all day. I didn't tell Mr Hampden that I had never looked after children, and didn't know the first thing about them. The children soon discovered it, and were highly amused each time I slipped up in the ritual of bathing them. However, I didn't drown them. Jane is a little touchy about details, and cried for five minutes because I took off her left shoe before the right. I had to run the bath water, so that the fond parents shouldn't hear.

I begged them not to call me 'Miss Dickens', it sounds so

fearfully governessy and flat-chested, so I now answer universally to 'Monty'.

Mrs H. comes in for supper, which we have all cosy and homey by the drawing-room fire. She retires quite early into the Arctic night, so I have come up to my room, which is also Arctic. A bit of my window seems to be missing. I shall go to bed when I've finished this, as I have to get up at seven to dress the children, do a bit of dusting and cook the breakfast. Oh, the delights of a simple country life! But definitely like heaven after the Parrish *ménage*.

All my love to everybody,

From your cookie<br>MONTY

P.S. – Please send my trousers and any thick sweaters you can find. It doesn't seem to matter what I wear, and it's *so* cold. I wish I hadn't bothered to bring my uniform.

*

YEW GREEN GROVE<br>YEW GREEN<br>WALLINGFORD<br>*Friday*

DARLING,

Still here and still the most popular, seem to be the Most Popular girl in the School. Their last cook apparently was half drunkard and half-witted, and the one before that had religious melancholia and cried all the time. Major Hampden says he thinks that was why her gravy was always so watery – ha, ha. So, as I have most of my faculties, I am quite a change, and they don't seem to mind even when I do make a mess of things. After all, how was I to know how to make suet pudding? I've always tried to forget that such things existed. Jane was sick in the hall after eating it, and I had to clear it up.

I am supposed to keep the boiler stoked up – the old gardener lights it – but of course I forgot yesterday and it went out, so nobody could have a bath. I expected to be ticked off, but no. Mrs Hampden just said:

'Oh, well, it's the sort of thing anyone might do,' and her husband giggled and said, 'Well, no one must mind if I stay dirty then.' I've quite changed my mind about humanity – the so-called servant problem wouldn't exist if everyone was as nice as these people. Mrs Johns, the woman who comes in the morning to 'do', is a perfect scream. She comes from Devonshire, and something in her inside has slipped, I don't know what, or where to, but the doctors say it's a very interesting case. Her husband has Anaemia and has to sit in the kitchen with his feet up. Why? you ask. I'll tell you. I had it all this morning over our elevenses. A year ago, Mr Johns was: 'real nasty with this Anaemia; wastin' 'e was, Lovey, and "Nellie," 'e says, "I'm goin' to get to me bed and stay there." "Not if I knows it," I says, "if you go up they stairs, you woan't come down again, till you come feet first."' I didn't know what that meant, but apparently it's the way you arrive at your own funeral! All among the sherry and seed cake. So Mrs Johns had a marvellous idea. She remembered something that her sister-in-law's cousin had once told her at a whist drive as an infallible cure for Anaemia. You sit with your feet higher than your head, so that all your blood rushes to your head and keeps you going. It doesn't seem to matter if your feet wither and drop off – Mr Johns' haven't, anyway, and he's been like that for six months. His wife says to him: 'if you bring down they feet, Lovey, you woan't last till Spring.' It seems a depressing sort of existence for him.

I have stuffed the broken bit of my window up with paper, but it's terribly cold getting up at crack of dawn. I just leap into about six jerseys and an overall and rush down to the kitchen, which is a bit warmer. This morning I overslept and there was a fearful panic to get the children up and the breakfast cooked in time for them to bus to school. I dressed them in the kitchen so that I could do everything at the same time, but the water for the poached eggs simply wouldn't boil, and Peter started to scream because he thought his favourite mistress would give him a bad mark if he was late. Really, it is a bit of a strain coping with it all before breakfast, children ought not to be so lively at such uncivilized times of day. Breakfast is fearfully hearty – you wouldn't know me – I have to sing 'The Teddy Bears' Picnic' and have my hair pulled, answer riddles, and wipe egg off chins, while still feeling half asleep and rather sick.

You might write. You haven't answered my question about Mrs Hampden and her summer-house. She is so nice, but she looks awfully sad, and sometimes cries, I think.

Love and kisses from<br>
MONTY

*

YEW GREEN GROVE<br>
YEW GREEN<br>
WALLINGFORD<br>
Monday

DARLING,

How absolutely *ghastly*. I wonder if you're right.

Love<br>
M.

*

YEW GREEN GROVE<br>
YEW GREEN<br>
WALLINGFORD<br>
Wednesday

DARLING MUMMY,

Major Hampden had to go out to dinner tonight, so Mrs H. and I took down our back hair over our cocoa, and told each other our life history. You were right about her – it's awful. She said, quite jokingly: 'The ridiculous doctors have given me six months, isn't it absurd?' No wonder she cries.

Today the children's Uncle Conrad came to tea with their grandmother. She is quite a nice old lady in a black sort of way, except that she would call me Miss Dixon, but I'm afraid Uncle Conrad is not at all normal. Mrs Johns had told me beforehand that he was 'not quite the thing', so I was not unduly surprised when he broke into a thin scream on being told to eat up his chocolate biscuit. The children love him, and see nothing peculiar; it was a sweet sight to see Jane and him playing on the floor with dolls.

I have had to discover how to make all sorts of revolting things, like Sago, Spotted Dick, Blancmange, and Prune Mould, but I suppose it's all part of one's education.

No more now, as I must go and wash some wee woolly garments. I mended Major Hampden's cardigan one day, but I don't think he really liked it; he is very conservative and missed the old aerated feeling. I have hardly been out of the house yet, except to the pillar box – so much for my ideas of rustic rambles.

Love to all,

MONTY

\*

YEW GREEN GROVE

ETC

*Monday*

DARLING,

Sorry I haven't written for such ages. but I've been most fearfully busy, as Mrs Johns has got flu – I have to do all the housework alone – not that there's much dirt in the country compared to London. She arrived the other day with a streaming cold, and went about the house saying: 'Oh dear, what it is to be a laaady.' Whether she meant that she was one, or envied those who were, I don't know. I don't know either how Mr Johns will manage to nurse her and keep his feet up at the same time. What a life these people have.

Jane has been with me in the kitchen all day, as her mother is not so well. Her idea of help is to cut all the pictures out of Mrs Beeton and put them into the saucepans. I didn't know she had, until I found a highly-coloured Charlotte Russe in my soup tonight. It's funny, but I hardly break anything here, where it wouldn't matter much if I did. Innumerable were the various things that slipped through my nerveless fingers in the Parrish basement.

Major H. says the church roof needs repair, and they must have a bazaar – not here, I hope.

Lots of love<br>
MONTY

*

YEW GREEN GROVE<br>
ETC<br>
*Thursday*

DARLING,

I've been here over two weeks now, and it seems more like two days. I shall be awfully sorry to leave them all. Today I said to Jane at lunch: 'Empty your mouth before you speak,' and believe it or not, she calmly spat everything out all over the table. Logical, I suppose, but messy. The vicar's wife called this morning to discuss the bazaar and laughed at me. She is a very hearty woman with wild red hair. I suppose a pair of trousers worn with a cooking apron and bedroom slippers does look a little odd, but no odder than her hat.

I have told the children all about you, and they are very struck by the idea, and even mention you in their prayers: 'Make Mrs Dickens a good girl.' Do you feel any better yet?

Your loving<br>
MONTY

*

YEW GREEN GROVE<br>
ETC<br>
*Tuesday*

DARLING,

Well, I shall be home tomorrow. The train gets in about six, I think. The Austrian Jewess who is replacing me has arrived, and is very pleasant, so they are fixed up all right.

The church bazaar is off, as my poor old Major Hampden can't think of anything at the moment but his wife. Mummy, I can't write about the awful things that may happen to this dear little family – I'll tell you everything tomorrow. Till then –

Your loving<br>
MONTY

# Chapter Seven

I came home from the tour in Alsace more than ever convinced that I knew less than nothing about cooking, but after visiting the kitchens of almost every inn and hotel, I was fired with an enthusiasm to try out some of the marvellous things we had tasted over there. I determined to look for a job before the flat after-holiday feeling descended upon me.

I was rather put off going to the agency, because while I was away they had sprung a horrid shock on me.

They had never asked me for more than the initial shilling that I had paid to be enrolled on their books, and I, with an imbecile simplicity, had imagined that it was the employers only who paid a fee when they engaged a servant, and had never thought of inquiring what they were going to charge me. Judge, therefore, of my horror when a bill followed me out to Alsace, saying: 'To suiting Miss Dickens, on such and such dates,' or words to that effect. The total came to over £2 and I was furious. I reckoned up that in my various positions, I had earned about £20, and here they were asking for more than 10 per cent of it, as well as taking goodness knows how much from my employers. They could take millions from Martin if they liked, but I grudged them anything out of the earnings of my sweated labour. I went about for a bit muttering, 'Dual commission, it's illegal,' but I had to pay it. Anyway, they had been very nice to me and got me jobs for which I really was not qualified. I decided that this time I would chance my luck with advertisement, so after much thought I concocted something very conceited and sent it to a 'situations wanted' column where it looked most imposing:

'Working cook-housekeeper seeks daily post, capable, honest, and refined – excellent English and French cooking. Write Box —'

I got several answers almost at once, but nearly all of them only went to illustrate the fact that some people never read anything properly, or if they do, they ignore what they see. Some wanted a living-in-maid, and a dear old lady wanted me as a sort of nurse-companion – heating up her milk at night was all the cooking I should get there probably – but the third was quite hopeful.

'In reply to your advertisement in the *Daily* —' (it ran) 'I am looking for a temporary cook-general to do the cooking and housework of a very small house. There are just two of us, and it would only be for about a month, as I have engaged somebody else who is not able to come to me till then – if you are not yet suited, please call at the above address any morning before eleven o'clock.

Yours truly,
(MRS) BARBARA RANDALL

I liked the idea of another temporary job – it doesn't give time for the novelty to wear off, and for one to get sick of it, so I fished out the dowdy hat, which was looking even more battered after quite a long sojourn in an ottoman. I arrived at the address in South Kensington to find a builder's board hanging on the area railings, and a sound of hammering in the air. I looked again at the address on the letter, because it didn't look the sort of house that anyone was living in, but this was it all right, so I knocked, as there was only a hole where the bell ought to be. The door was opened by a very pretty and quite young girl, in an overall with her hair tied up in a handkerchief.

'Mrs Randall?' I said, astutely observing the wedding ring on her left hand.

'Yes – that's me.'

'I've come about the post as cook-general.'

'Oh, are you the advertisement in the *Daily* —, I mean, the one who put it in? *Do* come in, I'm afraid the place is in an awful mess, the men promised to have finished yesterday, but of course they're not nearly done, goodness knows when they'll be out of the place.' She led the way, prattling gaily, to what I presumed was going to be the dining-room in the fullness of time, as there was a round mahogany table in the middle of the room. The rest of the space was cluttered up with toppling piles of books – vases, lamps, and even a dirty clothes basket. Sweeping one or two volumes of the Encyclopedia from a chair to the floor, she told me to sit down, and hunted about among the confusion on the table for a cigarette for herself. When she had lit it up, she leant against the mantelpiece and giggled.

'I've never engaged a maid before, you know,' she said with endearing candour, 'so I don't know all the things to say. I do so badly want to move in as soon as we've got things just a tiny bit straight. The workmen are only in the basement – they're doing something mysterious to the foundations, and building a maid's bedroom – that's why I can't have anyone to sleep in yet, you see. I'm sure you'll do marvellously, if you don't mind a bit of a muddle.'

This was swift work, and my professional instincts told me that it was all wrong that I should have been engaged without having a chance to tell her how marvellous I was – Mrs Hampden had given me a reference, saying I was willing, obliging, and a good worker, which sounded more like a cart horse than a cook, but I produced it now and handed it to Mrs Randall. She barely glanced at it, and she seemed to have made up her mind. I believe she would have engaged anybody, one-legged, armless, or deaf and dumb, provided they'd been the first to apply for the job. She was so pleased at the idea of getting someone, and being able to settle down in her little love-nest – she was obviously very newly married, and I thought she was sweet, and would be delightful to work for. She was small, with curly brown hair and huge wide-open eyes that looked at you innocently out of her pretty round face. She didn't look more than twenty, but I thought it preferable to be bossed by someone younger than myself, rather than by an old trout in a flowered kimono.

After showing me the rest of the house, which consisted only of a drawing-room and dining-room on the ground floor, a double bedroom and spare room upstairs, and a bathroom half-way, we descended to the kitchen, stepping over planks and heaps of cement on the way – the kitchen, however, was more or less ready for use, as far as one could see from the litter of shavings, crockery, and pots and pans that was strewn about.

It was done up quite pleasantly in blue and white, with check curtains, there was a clean-looking new sink and gas stove, but, oh horrors! What was this? The old-fashioned range had evidently been removed, and in its place under the mantelpiece, charged with sinister menace, stood – a boiler. Mrs Randall followed my gaze, which was riveted on it in awful fascination, and said cheerfully:

'You won't mind lighting the boiler in the mornings, will you? Actually – I believe it's quite a simple one. My husband will be able to explain all about it to you, anyway.'

I thought it would have to be a pretty intensive explanation to make me understand it. It has always been my contention that no woman ought to have to look after a boiler. They're simply not made that way – it's like over-arm bowling.

However, it would be their lookout if the bath-water wasn't hot through my getting confused with dampers, drawers, and what not.

We arranged that I was to come quite early the next day and between us we would try to get the house straightened up so that they could sleep there that night.

'Oh,' said Mrs Randall suddenly, as I was just going out of the front door, 'we haven't settled anything about wages. Would £1 do?'

'Well, er, hm –' I was going to say that it was less than my usual wage, but it occurred to me that they were probably very hard up and had only just been able to afford to marry. Everyone likes to help young love along, so I said: 'Yes, thank you, that's quite all right.' She looked relieved, and I left her, thinking that the small pay would anyway give me an excuse for being even less thorough than usual. I arrived before her the next day, but the workmen had got the back door open – so I went in that way, and was nearly brained by a small plank that came hurtling from the roof into the area. I looked up, furious, and a face with a walrus moustache looked over the parapet and said, 'Wotcha, Blondie!' I flounced into the house, to be treated to a few desultory tooth-suckings as I passed the future servant's bedroom – where four or five men were sitting on the floor drinking tea out of enamel mugs.

'Never speak to strange men' is evidently not a maxim that applies below stairs, for they were very offended when I ignored them, and yelled out, 'Can't yer say "Good morning"?' So I had to yell back from the kitchen, 'Good morning!' to which they replied, 'Oi-oi' on various notes like a male chorus. However, this wasn't the B.B.C., so I vouchsafed no more, and, putting on an overall, attacked the kitchen with morning zest. After I had put all the rubbish into the dustbin, and arranged the plates and dishes on the dresser, it began to look more presentable. All the crockery was dirty, of course, and would have to be washed, but as I couldn't find any soap flakes or powder, I left it for the time being. I decided to hang up some saucepans. Most of the workmen seemed to have disappeared by now. They had gone either on the roof or on strike, but there was a sad, pale youth of about sixteen sitting in the area, chipping stones, so I bearded him and said, 'Could you oblige me with a hammer and some nails?'

'Yes, miss,' he said, getting up and hunting round in a vague way till he found what I wanted. He handed them to me with an ''Ere y'are,' and returned sadly to his stones.

I had great fun knocking in nails at every possible point – I love to see saucepans and ladles and things hanging round a kitchen, it gives it a cosy olde worlde look, and Mrs Randall had lovely new matching sets of everything, which it would have been a pity to hide. The noise of my hammering drowned her arrival and she entered with a shriek as she saw me miss the last nail and hit my thumb. I hopped round the room in agony for a bit, and she trotted after in a distressed way, begging to be allowed to have a look. When I eventually uncovered the injury, there was nothing to see at all, which is often the case, but is always disappointing, so we went upstairs, after she had admired my efforts in the kitchen. A van had deposited several more things in the hall since yesterday. They seemed to have had a lot of wedding presents.

I spent the rest of the morning carrying endless loads of books and knick-knacks up to the drawing-room where she arranged them, prattling all the time. Even when I went out of the room, she raised her voice to follow me downstairs, but nevertheless I missed some of her remarks, and she would say 'D'you think so?' as I arrived back, hidden under a pile of books on a sofa cushion.

'Yes, madam,' I panted, or, if that didn't seem to be the right answer, 'I mean, no, madam.'

Eventually, we couldn't get anything more into the drawing-room, which was already beginning to look rather early Victorian, so we stacked a lot of things in the spare room.

'It's rather a pity,' said Mrs Randall, 'because I shan't be able to have my mother to stay till I get rid of some of this rubbish. Really, why *do* some people have such ghastly taste? Look at this vase, just like a dustbin!'

I thought there was an excuse for it, if it was going to help in preventing a mother-in-law from staying with a newly-married couple, but refrained from comment and descended for a fresh load.

At lunch time she sent me out to buy some sausages, which I cooked, and we both ate them at the kitchen table, washed down with huge cups of coffee and more chatter.

I asked her if she was going to arrange with any of the tradesmen to call for orders.

'Oh, goodness,' she said, 'yes, I suppose I ought. There seem to be quite a lot of grocers and things round here. Mother says it's a good thing to change your tradesmen quite often, as they're more likely to try and please you if you're a new customer, but I shan't tell the first lot that, of course.'

She went upstairs proudly, to get her coat, and I started in on the crockery washing, as I had bought some soap flakes when I got the sausages. She came down in her trousseau fur coat. 'I say, are you washing all the plates and things? That's *marvellous*. I wonder if you could possibly give us dinner here tonight? Just a chop or something? Could you really – oh, that'll be lovely – what shall I get?' I gave her a list of things; and she trotted out, saying, 'Now don't go and do too much and get tired on your first day.'

What a change from Parrish! I prayed that she might never get like that, but a few years of coping with rather frightful domestics like myself might easily sour that sweet good-nature. Who knows, perhaps ever Mr Parrish had been a sunny soul at that age, and had treated his cooks as if they were human, but, somehow, I couldn't imagine it. At tea-time the Walrus Moustache came tramping in a very dirty pair of boots into the kitchen which I had just swept.

'Be a love and put the kettle on, so's we can have our tea.' When it was boiling I yelled out to them, and was answered by the usual chorus of 'Oi-oi,' and Walrus came along with a grubby-looking billycan. I pointedly spread sheets of newspaper on the floor between him and the stove, and he advanced over them like Queen Elizabeth, saying, 'Pardon me, Duchess.' I wanted to laugh at him, because he really was very funny, but I didn't dare let him see I thought so. I controlled myself while he poured water on to the black tea leaves in the can, and stirred the whole lot round with a screwdriver – which he carried in his breast-pocket in place of a fountain pen. He picked his way delicately back over the newspaper crying, 'Dinnah is served!' turning at the door to give me a very familiar wink. He seemed to be the leading light of the party next door, because I could hear his voice leading the conversation, interrupted occasionally by the sucking noise of tea being drawn through his moustache. The others expressed themselves chiefly in guffaws.

They packed up soon after this, having evidently come to the conclusion that they had drunk enough tea for one day. The idea of knocking off seemed rather to go to their heads, and I heard a lot of ragging and shuffling in the passage, and eventually a very fat man was propelled violently into the kitchen and landed on his back on the floor.

'He's just come to say good night, miss,' said a grinning face appearing in the doorway. I was beginning to understand how school teachers feel when their pupils persecute them, but I said 'Good night' quite politely to the figure on the floor, who, however, thought the whole thing so screamingly funny that he could do nothing but giggle. He scrambled to his feet with a large red hand over his mouth and tottered out, shaking like a jelly.

I was thankful when the last hobnail boot clattered away up the area steps and I was left in peace. I had been thinking how lovely it was that there were no electric bells in the house yet, but I wasn't sure that the workmen were not even more unnerving.

I was looking forward to seeing the second half of the Randalls, and I knew he was due to arrive soon, when I went up to light the drawing-room fire and found her in a different dress with her hair and face carefully done.

When he arrived she took him all over the house to admire her handiwork, and brought him down to the kitchen to be introduced to me. He was rather embarrassed, as most men are when they have to talk to a domestic about anything that doesn't concern household matters, but managed a shy 'How d'you do?' and a handshake. He was tall, with a good-looking if not intelligent face, and together they really looked the sort of couple that makes old family nurses say, 'Don't they make a lovely pair?'

They seemed blissfully happy and enraptured with everything, even the rather dull dinner I gave them, and when I went up to say good night they were sitting hand in hand on the drawing-room sofa – a charming picture.

'Oh, but my husband must explain about the boiler to you before you go,' said Mrs Randall, jumping up and pulling him towards the door. 'You see,' she said as we all went down to the kitchen, 'it's very important for the water to be hot by half past eight for his bath, otherwise it makes him late for work.'

He seemed to know a lot about the boiler in theory, anyway, and I listened to all the talk about opening dampers, and when to make it draw, and when not to, but I didn't take it all in – it seemed so complicated. Surely in these enlightened and lazy days they could be made a bit more foolproof. Though not at all reassured myself, I assured them that I understood perfectly and left them, praying that all might go smoothly in the morning.

My misgivings were more than justified the next day, when the boiler gave me a taste of the vice in its soul. I made a great effort and, getting up early, arrived at the South Kensington house by half past seven. Much to my relief, the chain gang had not yet arrived, so I took the front off the boiler and carefully filled it with paper and wood. It blazed up beautifully, and I thought I would let it burn for a bit before I put on any coke, so I went upstairs to dust the dining-room. When I got back to the kitchen the boiler stared coldly at me and the ashes of the wood and paper lay dead inside.

I started grimly all over again, and added some coke on top before going up to sweep the carpet. I only stayed away a few minutes this time, but even more depressing results awaited me. Nothing had been burnt except the paper, and the carefully stacked wood and coke had just collapsed, and most of it had fallen out on the floor as, of course, I had forgotten to put the front on.

The kitchen clock told me it was getting quite late, and as I was on my knees, feverishly making another effort at laying the boiler, I was startled by shouts of '*Good* morning!' from the doorway. I was much too rattled to answer, so I just waved them away without turning round.

'Hoity-toity!' said a voice which sounded like the Walrus Moustaches's, and though he said no more I could feel from the way my spine prickled that he stayed in the doorway watching me pityingly. Eventually he departed roofwards with a snort and never saw the blaze-up that suddenly happened for no reason at all and nearly took off my eyebrows. This time I stayed by the boiler, and fed it, like an invalid, with one lump of coke at a time, only leaving it for a minute to take up the early morning tea. I was absorbed for quite a long time, dropping bits in through the top, and was trying to persuade myself that it was only my imagination that made the small red glow inside seem to be getting even less, when my employer came rushing into the kitchen in his dressing-gown with a blue unshaven chin.

'I say, what's happened? The water's stone cold.'

'I'm terrible sorry, sir. I've had such trouble with this thing.'

'Oh, Lord, let me look. Here, surely you ought to have this little door open, not this one. Look – I haven't got time now – I'll skip my bath this morning. You might heat me some shaving water.' I put the kettle on and abandoned the boiler, which in any case had now definitely given up the ghost, as it was time to start cooking the breakfast.

When I took up the eggs and bacon they had started on their grapefruit and coffee, and she was reading him extracts from her letters while he was trying to get a hasty glance through *The Times*.

'Mother wants to come to dinner tonight, darling. I'm longing for her to see the house now we're actually in it.'

A mumble came from behind the paper: 'Oh, Lord, what a day, everything at once. First the boiler, and then your mother – '

'*What* did you say, Peter?'

'Oh, nothing, darling, nothing, nothing, nothing. I say – poor old Cummins is dead! Stroke on the golf course – who'd have thought it!'

I went out of the room, leaving her still brooding a little. As she kissed him good-bye in the hall I heard her say: 'Darling, you do *want* to have mother to dinner, don't you?'

'Of course, my sweet, if you want her. Good-bye, darling – take care of yourself,' he called as he rushed off in a great hurry. I wondered what his work was that made him behave like a little boy who is afraid of getting a bad mark if he's late for school.

When Mrs Randall had ordered the meals, which consisted chiefly of her sucking a pencil and saying, 'Um – ' and me sucking my teeth and saying nothing, she said:

'It was a pity about the boiler. I wonder if you could light it now – why don't you get one of the workmen to help you? They're sure to know all about it.'

This had already occurred to me and, though I didn't much like the idea, I saw that I should have to resort to it in the end.

The boiler had got to be lit some time, so I screwed up my courage and when the Walrus came padding in to make the first of those frequent brews of tea I said:

'Could you *possibly* help me to light this boiler? I've tried and tried but it's no good and I must get it lit.'

I sat down, as he was not very tall, and I wanted to be able to throw him an appealing upward glance. He regarded me with the confident mockery of a man who has women in his power and tosses them aside like broken dolls.

'I will ask the second footman to attend to it, your ladyship,' he said, and minced off over the newspaper. A few moments later the pale youth popped his head round the door and said:

'Fred says I've got to light yer biler.' I welcomed him with open arms, and he took the lid off the thing and peered gloomily inside.

'Cor, what you bin at?'

'I know, isn't it awful? Can you possibly get it to light, d'you think?'

'Gimme a knob or two of coal, miss, and I'll soon get her going.'

I rushed out to the coal cellar and returned with my arms full, blacking my face and clean overall in my excitement. He stacked the boiler up methodically with paper and wood, and twiddled a few knobs, and when it was filled with a magical crackling he put on the coke.

'Must have a touch of coal to start it off like,' he said, 'then you can put on the coke when she's glowing, see?' I got him to show me what to do with the wretched little doors, once it was going properly, and thanked him warmly. He had missed his tea through it, so I offered him a cup in the kitchen, which he accepted. 'Got a horrible pain,' he confided to me as he sat down, holding his pale face in his hands, 'it's me teeth. Spent ten pounds on 'em last year, but they don't seem to fit yet. Ma says they always play you up for the first five years. Ten pounds I spent, and they're lovely, too; I think they look ever so nice.' He bared them at me in a false and gleaming grin. I thought it terrible that he should have false teeth at his age; but it seemed more a matter of pride than regret with him. 'Ah well,' he said at length, getting wearily up, 'this won't buy the baby new clothes.' He gave the fire a last poke, and shutting everything down on the cheering glow inside, shuffled back to his stone chipping.

Mrs Randall went out quite early, saying she would not be back till after tea, so I prepared to do a little intensive cleaning. Carpenters and packers had left their traces of dust and shavings all over the house, and I thought that I had better do something before the eye of Mrs Randall's mother, which I suspected would be a carping one, descended on it. I attended to all the more obvious things, such as the stairs and linoleum in the hall, and after sweating much and grief to the knees I got the place to look fairly presentable. I was in the bedroom making the bed when I heard a sound that made my blood run cold – it was the tramp of boots descending the stairs, and, before I could stop him, Fred had galloped along the hall and out of the front door. I was sure he had done it on purpose.

There was a heap of rubble on the top landing where he had descended through the trap-door from the roof. A dirty footmark adorned every stair, and my beautifully polished linoleum was a tragedy.

I was furious and told him so the next time I saw him, but that man had no shame, he just giggled and said, 'Aw, come off it, Chloë.' He insisted on calling me that – it seemed to be his idea of a stuck-up name. I was washing some saucepans at the time and, still assured of his irresistible charm,

93

he offered to help me, a suggestion which I didn't think even worthy of an answer. Lunch-time came with its usual tea-brewing nuisance, and I thought I might try to snatch a little peace to eat an egg or two, and read my morning paper, the dear little Servant's Delight. Fred, however, had other ideas – the kitchen window looked out on to a tiny strip of garden at the back of the house, and this was where he had taken up his stand, with the walrus moustache spread out against the window-pane. I moved my chair to the other side of the table so that my back was towards him, but it was impossible to ignore the melancholy strains of 'You're a sweet'eart *hif* there ever was one, it's yew', which banished all hope of peace and quiet.

After lunch I started to prepare one or two things for dinner. Fred had given up on 'You're a sweetheart', and was working in the next room to the accompaniment of 'Ain't she sweet?'; but I was getting used to it, so it didn't bother me so much.

I was feeling quite pleased with life in general, and had made a mayonnaise without curdling it, but a bitter blow was in store for me. I went to the sink to rinse something out and ice-cold water came out of the hot tap. There sat the boiler grinning smugly with the bars of its front door, and saying, 'I told you so.' I gave it a sharp clout with a rolling-pin, but it wasn't really its fault for going out when I had forgotten to make it up all day. I went to look for the young boy, but he was nowhere to be found.

'Gone home wiv toothache,' said Fred with great satisfaction. 'Something I can do for you, Chloë?'

'Well, all right, blast you,' I said. I felt it was rather a climb down, and I had to stay in the kitchen while he relaid and lit the boiler in case his distorted sense of humour led him astray.

'You got a boy, Chloë?' he said when he had finished, getting up from his knees and dusting his hands. 'Yes, thank you,' I replied. 'He's a heavyweight boxer.'

'O.K., dearie, you win,' replied Fred, retreating with a

wave of his hand. I recollected my manners and called out, 'Thanks awfully for lighting the boiler!'

'Think nothing of it, Chloë.' I thought I had heard the last of him for that day as it was time for them to knock off, but while I was rolling out some pastry I realized that a little scene was being staged outside the kitchen door for my benefit.

'Je-ames,' I heard in accents of falsetto refinement, 'would you maynd brushing off my coat? Hit's a trayfle creased. Her ladyship is sure to pass a remark about it.'

'Ho, certainly, may lord. What a beautiful fit, if ay may say so!'

They peeped round the door before they left to see the effect on me. I pretended not to have noticed anything, and rolled away like mad, ruining the pastry, as it turned out afterwards, by pressing heavily on it in my efforts to keep from laughing.

I wished I didn't have to be haughty with them, but I saw no other way of coping with their peculiar brand of teasing. I really felt quite shy of them; they were quite a different proposition from some of the tradesmen with whom I had made friends.

Mrs Greene, my mistress's mother, arrived very early, considering she was only supposed to be coming to dinner, before either of the young couple had returned. She was a small stout widow of about fifty, ambitiously but unsuccessfully dressed in a black satin suit, whose short skirt displayed a great deal of plump leg in shiny orange stockings. A too frisky hat was perched at the wrong angle over her busy little black eyes, which swept over me as I let her in, darted all round the hall, and finally returned to me.

'Yes, yes,' she said, tottering into the hall in her tight court shoes. 'You're Monica, I expect, that's right. I've heard all about you.' I wondered how she knew so much already, but I soon discovered that she made it her business in life to know all about everything. She roamed all over the house, peering everywhere in the most inquisitive way, giving vent to an occasional 'Dear, dear!' or 'Well, I don't know,' as she trotted briskly from room to room. When I was laying the table in the dining-room I could hear her rummaging about, opening drawers and cupboards in the bedroom next door. Mrs Randall arrived at this point and they greeted each other fondly. Mrs Greene said: 'I think the house looks sweet, darling. There are just one or two suggestions – but that can wait. I think you ought to try to get Peter to be more careful of his clothes. This suit will have to go to the cleaners; look here, there's a terrible stain on the coat, and the trousers want pressing.'

'Yes, mother. Would you like to come upstairs and have some sherry? I'll ring for Monica to bring some up.'

'Don't ring, dear, she's just in the dining-room, I think. I'll ask her. You look tired, my darling. I hope you haven't been doing too much. Come and put your feet up on the sofa, I'll make you comfy.'

'No, really, mother, I –'

'Come along, dear. Goodness, you get thinner every day. I hope you're eating properly.'

When I took up the sherry Mrs Randall was reclining obediently on the sofa, while her mother pottered about the room, moving ashtrays and ornaments. She seemed to devitalize her daughter and sap her of her usual bubbling personality. But the effect on her son-in-law was even more noticeable. He started off dinner making a great effort at a rather hearty politeness, rubbing his hands and laughing at nothing. Mrs Greene's incessant flow of remarks soon wore him down, however, and he sank into a depressed and glum silence. After dinner Mrs Greene actually had the sauce to come down to the kitchen to see what sort of a hash I was making of things. She arrived just as I was going to have some food, which infuriated me. She was one of those women who don't realize that servants do anything so human or normal as eating, and my supper stood congealing on the table while she talked to me and poked around in the cupboard.

'My daughter doesn't know much about housekeeping yet, you know. I've taught her a lot, of course. I've run a

house now for thirty years with no fuss. Do a lot of the cooking myself, too. My daughter always says I give her better
food than anybody.' I murmured false sounds of approba-
tion, but could not bring myself to answer when she said:
'I'm surprised to see you using self-raising flour; it's so much
better, you know, to use the plain and add baking powder.
Still, you're young. You've plenty of time to learn.' Taking
my silence for agreement, she left me, to my intense relief,
and went away to see what other improvements she could
make in the world upstairs.

# Chapter Eight

THE next morning was catastrophic. I made no attempt to light the boiler when I got there, thinking that I would get False Teeth to do it when he came. The rest of the workmen arrived, and I waited and waited for him, until finally it was getting so late that I had to accost Fred.

'Bert ain't coming 'smorning,' he said. 'What a disappointment, eh, Chloë?'

'You light it,' I said decisively, and remembering the heavyweight boxer, he did. It was too late though, and I was treated to the same vision of Mr Randall in his dressing-gown, saying that the water was an improvement on yesterday, but how the hell was he to have a bath and shave in tepid water? I quailed; he was really angry, probably still the aftermath of the evening before, and he sat down to breakfast, ready to fly off the handle at a moment's notice. His poor tactless little wife remarked brightly from behind the coffee-pot:

'Mother says your brown suit ought to go to the cleaners, darling –'

'Does she, indeed?' He lowered *The Times* and glared at her. 'And what the hell business is it of hers, anyway? If that old witch puts her nose into our affairs any more – I'll kick her out of the front door.'

'Peter!' Mrs Randall clutched the arms of her chair, aghast. 'Darling, how *can* you talk like that about mother? I thought you liked her – you were all over her before we were married.'

'She was all over *me* before she found out I hadn't any money.'

'What a beastly thing to say – after all the trouble she takes, the things she's done for us.' She was on the verge of tears.

'Well, it's her or me. I warn you, Ba, if she comes messing

around here much more – I shall walk out, and you can go back and live with her – you're always telling me how *mar*vellous it was!'

'You beast! I shall, I shall,' she sobbed as he strode out of the room, nearly knocking me down, clapped on his hat, and banged out of the door. I had, of course, been listening in the hall. I wasn't going to miss a good row for anything, though it did distress me to hear two people who really loved each other saying things they didn't mean in the heat of the moment.

I thought I'd better look in and see if she was all right, and she looked so pathetic, weeping brokenly, that I forgot I was only the cook and took her in my arms to try and comfort her; she was much younger than me, anyway. It seemed to be my fate to have people crying all over me. I wondered who it would be next, probably the Walrus. I felt it wasn't exactly what I had been engaged for. 'It's not my work,' I said to myself, patting and making soothing noises automatically. Eventually she came to, and, hiccupping madly, told me All. 'I haven't told him yet, you see,' she said, 'and now I don't see how I can.'

'Well, you are a silly ass,' I said, forgetting my place completely. 'Why on earth didn't you say anything before? You tell him the minute he comes home, whatever you do. You'll be able to have your mother here every day, or anything else you like.'

She cheered up and became more normal, and I remembered that she was my mistress, and apologizing for my loss of respect, I withdrew.

She evidently took my advice for, after this, there were no more rows for a bit, and Mr Randall cherished his wife with an even greater affection than before. She, on her side, continued to only have her mother about the place during the daytime.

However, they were evidently both the sort of people to whom life without an occasional quarrel is a slightly dull and monotonous thing. After three or four evenings of amicable and often amorous conversation at the dinner table she started to goad him, over the steak-and-kidney pie, about one of his friends. They had been talking about giving a house-warming dinner party, and were discussing whom to ask. He said:

'Well, we must have old Godfrey – he's so amusing – make any party go.'

'Oo, darling, you *know* I can't bear him, he's so common and – and *uncouth*.'

'Since when have you been so particular? What about that shocking boy-friend you used to have? Ronald – Donald – Harold, whatever his ghastly name was.'

'That was quite different. He was a gentleman, which is more than you can say for Godfrey. Anyway, I was very fond of Ronnie.'

'My dear Ba, you know you couldn't stand the sight of him. You only took me in order to get away from him.' This was an effort to be conciliatory, but she wasn't having any.

'I wouldn't have done that if I'd known what your friends were like. What you can see in that conceited great ape I simply can't imagine.'

'Shut up, Ba,' said her husband, now beginning to lose his temper. 'I put up with your mother, and you're jolly well going to be agreeable to my friends.' I should have left the room long ago, but, as usual, I was much too intrigued and remained, fiddling with things on the dresser as an excuse for staying, though they didn't really notice I was there.

'Well, I'm going to have mother to the dinner party, anyway.'

'My God, you're not! No, darling, it's no good your throwing your "condition" in my face, because this time it makes no difference. That woman'll bitch up the whole show.'

'Don't call me "Darling", it doesn't ring true. You're the most selfish, inconsiderate, ungrateful beast of a husband I've ever met. I wish you – I wish I never –' Unable to control her tears any longer, she pushed back her chair and rushed into the bedroom with her napkin to her eyes.

'Oh, Lord, these hysterical women,' said her husband, half to himself and half to my back view as I withdrew disapprovingly. We females must stick together, and whether I thought so or not I wanted to convey that he was in the wrong, not that they either of them noticed me when they were heated up about something. It was a curious casual attitude they had towards me, and the world in general for that matter. They were perfectly friendly, so friendly in fact that they behaved with an almost detached lack of reticence, and certainly no feeling of self-consciousness. I suppose it's a sign of these modern times, this breaking of every rule and pretence observed by our grandparents and their forbears in order to keep servants 'in their place'.

This quarrel, of course, was made up as rapidly as it had started, and there were one or two others of the same calibre before there dawned the day of the First Dinner Party. I was amused to hear that both Godfrey and Mrs Greene were to be among those present, so neither side had achieved anything by the arguments, except a waste of time which they might have spent being happy together.

One other married couple made up the rest of the party, which I did want to be a success for my mistress's sake, and also to show the Greene monstrosity that other people in the world besides her could arrange and cook a dinner.

I took a lot of trouble over it, and spent a very busy day. Fred was even more annoying than usual and did his best to put me off by popping into the kitchen with such questions as, 'Do you know Monica? Monica who?' and rolling round the room convulsed with laughter at the rather rude answer.

I was going to give them a *soufflé* to start with, hoping to time it right, as I had done with my first one at Miss Faulkener's. Mrs Greene arrived first, needless to say, and noticed that the umbrella stand had been moved from one side of the hall to the other. The other couple, a very pretty dark girl with a nondescript husband, arrived soon after, and, when I announced them, I saw her watching them and taking in every detail. I hoped, for their sakes, that their clothes were new or fresh from the cleaners.

I had put the *soufflé* into the oven when Mrs Greene arrived, and I was beginning to get more and more nervous as the minutes passed and Godfrey had not come. It was nearly cooked and, if he didn't come soon, would be completely spoiled. There came the moment when it had just risen to its full height with a billowing brown top and should have been served at once. I turned down the heat, but had to leave it there as there was still no sign of the wretched man, and I began to sympathize with Mrs Randall in her dislike, when a cascade of knocks thundered on the front door and I rushed upstairs. Godfrey was a large panting man with protuberant eyes and teeth, and a distinct tendency to pinch servants' behinds. I whisked mine quickly out of the way, and announced him and dinner at the same time.

I opened the oven door with trepidation and saw that the *soufflé* was rather flat but still fairly presentable. By the time I had carried it upstairs, however, it was flatter than ever, and looked what it was – a failure. I was very upset as I knew my mistress was very nervous and desperately wanted everything to go off well. She would not realize that the *soufflé* was spoiled through waiting and would think I had let her down. There was no hope of her mother not noticing its appearance, as I had to hand it to her first. It was one of the most ghastly moments of my life. Everyone was watching as I produced my poor wizened offering, and I would have given a fortune to have been able to turn it upside down on the closely marcelled head of Mrs Greene, whose gloating smile of superiority as she took the smallest possible helping was the last straw. Mrs Randall looked like a child who has been promised a treat and then disappointed; she opened her eyes very wide at me in mute inquiry. Only Godfrey seemed to take the affair in his stride; he took a large helping without looking at it and proceeded to tuck in, talking with his mouth full to the dark-haired beauty on his right. He was very taken with her, and from her expression of faint loathing and his of suggestive glee he seemed

102

to be saying some pretty impossible things. Her husband was staring glumly across the table and paying hardly any attention to Mrs Greene, who was apparently telling him her life history. My brain took in all this automatically, it was so used to spying on other people's affairs, but I was really too shaken by the catastrophe of the first course to pay much attention to the party. I just got a general impression of ghastliness from Godfrey, which grew as the dinner progressed, and he became more frightful than ever. The only good thing about him was that he prevented Mrs Greene from leading the general conversation. For some inexplicable reason the host found him extremely amusing and roared with laughter at his stories, encouraging him to still further futilities. It was not that his jokes were vulgar, perhaps there would have been more point to them if they had been, but it was a sort of tap-room humour, interlarded with cries of 'Ha-ha-ha! What?' from Godfrey as he invited everybody to join in the fun.

The rest of the food held its own fairly well, though it was not impressive enough to make up for the *soufflé*. The fried potatoes had gone flabby, and I had forgotten to put any jam in the trifle, and little things like that, and I saw Mrs Greene noting every slip. I felt embittered, and thought sourly that they wouldn't have me long, anyway, but Mrs Randall completely disarmed me by running down to the kitchen after the ladies withdrew and saying:

'It was a *lovely* dinner, Monica! Thank you so much for doing it so nicely. I'm sure everyone thought it was marvellous.'

'I'm afraid the *soufflé*, madam – '

'Oh, that didn't matter, it was perfectly all right, really. Mother said you'd timed it wrong, but I suppose it was the fault of that ghastly Godfrey creature. Oh dear, I shouldn't say that, I suppose. Well, good night! Go home as early as you can, you must be tired.' Bless her heart. I really got quite fond of her before my month was up and, in spite of the quarrels, was quite sorry to leave them.

The workmen finished at last, a few days before the new

maid was due to come and occupy the bedroom they had constructed for her. I had got so used to being baited that I was even quite sorry to see them go. There was a touching scene when they all filed into the kitchen, outwardly solemn but inwardly giggling at their own drollery, and I said good-bye to each. It was rather like Snow White and the Seven Dwarfs. Like Dopey, Fred came back for more after they had gone and lingered for a few words.

'Y'know, Chloë,' he said, shaking his head, 'you bin a great disappointment to me. Maids is my speciality – when the wife's not around.' I was surprised; I had somehow not imagined him as a married man. I apologized for my lack of response to his charms, and he patted me on the shoulder and went out, saying patronizingly:

'Ah, well, we can't all be hot stuff. I expect you're not ripe for romance, dear, that's what it is.' He gave me another of his winks, well satisfied with his parting shot.

'Why, you – ' I cried, picking up the rolling-pin, but he was gone, whistling away down the passage and out of my life. The Randalls and I parted affectionately. He came down to the kitchen before going off to work and, fearfully embarrassed, pressed a pound note into my hand. 'No, really – ' I said, deeply touched, but pocketing it before he could take it back. 'I've so enjoyed working for you, sir, you've been ever so good to me.'

More embarrassed than ever, he mumbled his way out of the kitchen door and ran up the stairs, vastly relieved to have got it over. I was more than ever convinced by this time that there are only two types of men in the world – those who are shy of maids and those who are not shy enough. Before we parted I asked Mrs Randall to give me a reference, and she didn't know what to put, so I offered to help her, and between us we concocted the following flight of fancy:

'This is to say that M. Dickens has worked for me for several weeks in the capacity of working cook-housekeeper. I found her sober, honest, and most refined, a very well-spoken girl. Her cooking, both plain and fancy, is excellent;

she is scrupulously clean in her methods and her person, and has no eccentricities of religion.'

I had really enjoyed being at the Randalls and thought it would probably be difficult to get anywhere else as pleasant. Not wanting to risk a repetition of the Parrish episode, I turned over in my mind the idea of taking something quite different – perhaps going to the country as a living-in cook and seeing a bit of Servant's Hall life. Though up till now I had thought it preferable to be on my own in the kitchen, it always meant doing housework, and the idea of escaping that particular form of drudgery appealed to me enormously.

I scanned the situations vacant columns to see if there was anything attractive before inserting an advertisement of my own. There seemed to be even more demand for living-in cooks than for 'dailies', and one notice in particular caught my eye. 'First-class Cook wanted immediately for country. Staff 8. Kitchen-maid kept. Own bedroom. 30s. a week. Apply – Housekeeper, Chilford House, Birching, Devon.' Thirty shillings sounded like big money, considering that I would have no opportunity of spending it, so I wrote to the address given and generously offered the housekeeper that paragon of skill and efficiency – myself.

She answered quite soon, telling me to call on a certain day at – (Here followed the address of a flat in a fashionable block.)

I tortured the black hat into an even more uncompromising no-nonsense shape, then added a great deal to my age but nothing to my charms, and set off in a coat that was too long for me and a pair of 'sensible' shoes.

Arriving at the luxurious entrance hall of the block of flats, I felt too humble and unprepossessing to use the lift, so trotted modestly up four flight of stairs and arrived panting at my destination. I was let in by a stout black body of about fifty who I guessed to be the housekeeper, and she led me to a sitting-room, half shrouded in dust-sheets. In spite of the vastness downstairs the flat was quite small, evidently a *pied-à-terre* for occasional visits to London.

We sat down on two of the unshrouded chairs and she began to ask me searching questions with a terrifying intensity of manner that made me more nervous than usual. She was all hung about with emblems of religious fervour; gold crosses on chains, and holy-looking brooches were scattered at random over her person. She jangled like an old monk and this put me off, making me unable to do myself justice, so that I was quite surprised when, after reading my references and even holding them to the light to detect any forgery, she said: 'I'll engage you. The first week shall be in the nature of a trial, you understand, giving me the opportunity to make a change if I'm not satisfied. You wish it to be a permanent job, of course?'

'Oh, yes,' I said, casting down my eyes so as not to have to lie to that penetrating stare. I knew I should not get the job unless I gave the impression that I was prepared to live and die if necessary in the service of Chilford House.

I couldn't really understand why she had engaged me at all. She was the sort of woman you can't fool, and must have sized me up at once for the incompetent and inexperienced messer that I was.

I realized afterwards that she didn't want to have anyone in the kitchen of Chilford House who might challenge her supremacy over its domestic affairs, which she guarded jealously. She didn't even tell me the name of my future employers or how large a household it was. We arranged such details as half-days, and then she intimated that the interview was at an end, saying:

'It would be convenient for you to arrive tomorrow as we are making do at the moment with a village woman, but it's *not* satisfactory.' Then she told me the time of the train, and I left her, feeling elated but rather in the dark about the immediate future.

To make myself look more like the country house cook of tradition I bought a whole lot of vast white aprons, which enveloped me starchily and gave me quite a look of ample cosiness. These I packed, with the rest of my things, into a battered suit-case and, dressed once more with a suitable but drab respectability, bade farewell to my family who were by now more than ever convinced that I was crazy.

'You must live in your part, get yourself under the skin of it' had been one of the frequent sayings of the old lady of my dramatic school, so I started in right away. At Paddington I settled myself diffidently into the corner of the carriage and read a twopenny *Home Blitherings,* my face, innocent of make-up, shining like a young moon and my unrouged lips moving with absorbed delight while I followed the lines with my finger.

At Exeter I had to change into a little local train which stopped at every station for the guard to have a gossip, before it eventually arrived at Birching. A porter directed me to a sort of lorry, which looked as if its usual function was to take pigs to market, so I threw my case into the pig part of it and climbed up beside the red-haired youth who lounged in the driver's seat.

'Good afternoon!' I said brightly. 'Turned out nice again!'

He seemed to feel that he was destined for higher things than fetching cooks from the station, for he vouchsafed no more than a mumbled 'G'arternoon' and a sniff. I was determined, however, that in this job I was going to get on with everybody and everything, so, thinking to draw him out by flattery, I asked, 'You the shovver?'

'No!' he roared with scoffing laughter. 'Gardener's boy more like!'

He was tickled to death by my remark, and though obviously disinclined for further conversation, continued to give vent to spasmodic guffaws as we rattled and bumped along the narrow Devonshire lanes, bright with the first green of spring.

Eventually we turned to the left through an open lodge gate and drove up an avenue of oak trees which ran alongside a large park. We came to some iron gates, and I just caught sight of a low grey stone house at the end of a gravel drive before we swung away uphill to the left. We passed a farm and, describing a circle, arrived via the back

107

drive and stables at the kitchen entrance of Chilford House.

'Here yew be,' said the gardener's boy. 'In yew go.'

I got out, heaving my luggage after me, and he drove away at once, leaving me standing forlornly on the gravel with a tin suit-case at my feet.

The door was open so I stepped inside and advanced apprehensively down the dim red-flagged passage to the unknown regions beyond.

# Chapter Nine

My first impressions of Chilford House were so confused that it took me one or two days to get everything sorted out, days which passed in a whirling panic of new faces, voices, and masses of food. I thought at first that I was going mad, because there seemed to be more to do than I had ever imagined possible. However, when I stopped being hysterical about the whole thing, and the mists cleared a little, I saw that by systematic concentration I might succeed in saving my reason. My work was only cooking, and though it involved coping with the nursery and kitchen meals as well as the dining-room it made it easier to apply some sort of method. I calmed down after a while and was able to take stock of my situation.

Chilford House was divided into two parts by the green baize swing-door which separated the kitchen regions from the abode of the Gentry. My life, of course, was centred on the inferior side of that door, and indeed I hardly went through it all the time I was there. Although I had nothing to do with 'them' on the other side, they were the subject of so many intimate and derogatory comments in the servants' hall that there was not much I didn't know about them.

My mistress, Lady W—, was a semi-invalid lady of nearly eighty, who had long handed over the reins of government to Mrs Lewis, the housekeeper. She was the mob cap and shawl type of old lady, and spent most of her time sitting in a basket-chair with a high hood back to it, like a Punch and Judy show. I only encountered her after I had been there a week, when I fell off the under-housemaid's bicycle right under the nose of her Daimler as it turned out of the drive on its way to evening church. She had not the slightest idea who I was, but smiled graciously, and, lowering the window, hoped I wasn't hurt. Little did she know that it was I who was responsible for those creamed sweetbreads that she loved, or for that matter one or two little errors such as overdone beef, lumpy sauces, and burnt porridge, about which Mrs Lewis had been instructed to 'speak to me'.

Sir Harold W— was slightly younger than his wife and still quite hale. He ambled about in a tweed jacket with leather patches all over it and a sloppy, slobbering spaniel at his heels. He did himself extremely well, and after the third glass of vintage port had turned him a rare old mulberry colour there would be talk of apoplexy in the servants' hall.

The house at the moment was filled with their children and grandchildren whom I never got properly sorted out. Their son and two daughters, all married, were staying over Easter with their young in various stages of childhood, pimply adolescence, or maturity. I caught an occasional glimpse of a young man in a racing car, or a buxom girl pounding up the back drive on a huge grey horse with enormous feet. Various children buzzed into the kitchen at odd times during my first few days and said: 'Where's Mrs Munny? Who d'you think *you* are?' grabbed a cake or anything handy and rushed out again before I could introduce myself.

Much more fascinating than the family was the staff, who were gradually sorting themselves out from a rather terrifying mass of humanity into individuals. Mrs Lewis lived a life apart, suspended as it were permanently in space between the upper and lower regions in a bedroom and sitting-room of her own. She even had her meals carried there on a tray by Nellie, the under-housemaid, and only descended to the kitchen to order the meals and quiz into the larders and store cupboards.

The rest of her life which was not occupied with letter writing and linen cupboards was spent, apparently, in prayer.

'Locks herself in,' Nellie was saying one day as we all sat at the table in the servants' hall over a huge lunch of pork – 'praying away like nobody's business – praying to the devil, I should think – the old cow.'

110

'Now then, my girl,' this from Dawkes, the butler, 'mind your tongue.'

'You mind your own business,' retorted Nellie, who had no respect at all for the conventions. Besides Dawkes and Lady W—'s personal maid, Miss Biggs, there were two parlour-maids and a head housemaid who all came above her on the social scale. I wasn't quite sure where I came in. For some mysterious reason all cooks, whether married or not, like to be addressed as 'Mrs', and I was universally known as 'Mrs Dixon', which, though it made me feel rather illicit, gave me quite a standing. Dawkes ignored Nellie and offered Miss Biggs another slice of pork. She was a withered old thing, who had grown so grey and wizened in Lady W—'s service that her corsets didn't fit her as well as they used to and made her high-necked dress of lavender silk stick out like a shelf before and behind. Her two penchants were for platitudes and food, and she now attacked a tempting piece of crackling with zest, but it proved too much for her ancient teeth and had to be spat genteelly out behind her hand.

There was certainly no stint of food in this house, and I wondered what Lady W— would say if she had any idea of the waste that went on and the innumerable little newspaper parcels that found their way to village homes under the coats of chars, pantry-maids, and even telegraph boys. Almost every day I cooked a big joint for the kitchen alone, and Dawkes sat at the head of the table and carved it as if he was cutting up bodies.

He had one of those hungry-looking death's-head sort of faces with deep-set eyes, and was a complete dual personality.

On the farther side of the baize door he was apparently the perfect stage butler, and in spite of his rather criminal appearance was highly prized by his employers for his efficiency and loyalty to the family. In the servants' hall, however, though he occasionally, for form's sake, rebuked 'the girls' for an indiscretion, he was a perfect sink of slanderous gossip about the entire family, and anyone else who came to the house. He was a good actor, that man, he even had a special voice which he used when he was being a seneschal – I could hear it sometimes floating through from the dining-room. When he was relating a juicy piece of scandal to us, pop-eyed with eager appreciation, his accents would become the lowest of the low, and his expressions not always suitable for the youthful ear of Polly, the kitchen-maid, who, however, was so simple that she didn't really take it all in. It made me feel very superior to have someone to boss, even such a half-witted creature as she was. She was not much practical use as she would get into a panic if spoken to sharply.

I, being myself in a frenzy to get things done in time, yelled: 'Hurry up with shelling those peas, for heaven's sake!' She would drop everything and rush about wildly with her apron over her head.

'Lor!' she would scream, running round the kitchen in small circles. 'Oh! whatever shall I do? Oh, Mrs Dixon, don't hustle me, I feel ever so queer!'

I wondered why such a mad creature was kept on, but apparently a kitchen-maid's life is such hell that no normal girl will take it on.

She cherished a dog-like passion for the chauffeur, whose name, appropriately enough, was Jim Driver. He had a room over the garage, but being a bachelor took his meals with us, and Polly could hardly eat a thing for staring at him. He was a young man of about thirty whose slight tendency to boils on the back of the neck was counteracted by bright blue eyes and a tinge of Irish in his speech. Apart from the embarrassing Polly, whom he ignored, he distributed his favours impartially among the girls, treating me at first with the deference due to my married name and recent arrival. He had no rival as Dawkes was definitely out of the market. He took no interest in women as such, though he was reputed to have at least two wives secreted in different parts of England.

I think it will give a clearer idea of my life in this intriguing household if I run through the events of one particular day, picking one at random from those that stand out in my memory and starting at the chill bleak hour of seven o'clock when the alarm cut shrilly into my dreams.

I had been at Chilford House about a week, and no longer spent a minute or two of semi-consciousness wondering where I was. My little room, with its sloping attic ceiling that stunned you if you sat upright in bed, was by now quite familiar, but this morning as I travelled my eye round the room from where I lay I reflected that it could never really be made a home from home. I had stuck a lot of photographs about, and even stolen some flowers from the garden after dark, but nothing could disguise the blackness of the iron bed or the yellowness of the chest of drawers and vaguely indecent-looking washstand. Old-fashioned, cheap wooden furniture has a peculiar smell, a sort of indefinable mixture of acid and old boots, and I had to sprinkle a great deal of lavender water about. In spite of this I got such a mania about the chest of drawers that I thought it was infecting my clothes, so I kept most of them in the tin suitcase under the bed. Its lock now took a piece of skin off my ankle as I put my feet on to the tatty little red mat, and I hopped painfully over the bare boards to take a look at the day. The view from my window was the chief attraction of my Royal suite. I looked out over a long lawn, cut in three terraces, with a lily pond in the middle, and ending in a ha-ha wall which dropped into the park. I could see a few deer grazing among the scattered oaks, which were the only things that broke my vista of green, until the park ended with a jumble of roofs and a steeple that was the village. 'Very sharp for the time of year,' I said to myself, shivering, in spite of the sun which was picking out the dew with a dancing sparkle. It was too cold to do more than wash my face before putting on one of my vast aprons over a layer of very unglamorous woollen underwear that was a relic of the Yew Green days. After my usual battle with the mirror – it would swing forwards all the time and present me with its back view – I got my hair and face done – and hurtled down the back stairs to my kitchen. It was warm there, because the huge fire in the range was never allowed to go out; it heated the water and did all the cooking that wasn't done on the gas stove.

Polly was before me and working away like mad. It was her job to clean the kitchen before breakfast. Nellie, who rose early to lay fires, used to see that she got up, and would chivvy her down to the kitchen. Once started off, she could work like a clockwork train, unless somebody threw a spanner into the works by shouting at her and making her panic.

'Hullo, Mrs Dixon,' she said, looking up from her pail and scrubbing-brush on the floor. 'I'd a lovely dream last night.'

'Did you, now?' I said, hurling coal on to the glowing remains of last night's banked-up fire. 'What about?'

'About him – Mr Driver, I mean. 'E come right up to me and kiss me, ever so gentle, and what do you think he says?'

'Go on, Poll, tell us.'

'"Polly," he says, "you are my dream girl, I love you," he says, just like that – then I come all over faint and sorter melt in his arms. Cor, it was lovely.'

'Then what happened?'

'Well, I wake up then and take a look at me dream book, and it says, "To dream of a kiss from the beloved one is a sign of impending stomach disorder." Still, it was a *lovely* dream.'

She returned to her scrubbing, still wrapped in a reminiscent ecstasy, and I put an enormous kettle on the stove and started to cut bread and butter for the innumerable trays of early morning tea that had to start going upstairs from seven-thirty onwards.

Nellie and Rose, the head housemaid, were responsible for this, and they had a slate which hung in the pantry where the little trays lived on which they wrote down what time everybody had to be called. Rose, who was an unimaginative but conscientious girl with a suet-pudding face, would write the names and times in a laborious script, giving full titles where necessary: 'Major-General Sir Robert W—, Bart, D.S.O., 8.15. The Right Reverend

Bishop of Bradshaw, 8.30 – brown bread and butter,' were current entries. The flippant Nellie would add comments underneath, such as 'Sour puss', 'Bald as a coot', or 'Pot-belly'. She said it helped her to remember who was who.

All I had to do was to fill the teapots from the kettle and plank two or three slices of bread and butter on each tray as they brought it in.

Soon after this I started one of my frenzies. Nursery breakfast was at eight-thirty and the dining-room started at a quarter to nine, not to mention a coddled egg and melba toast for Lady W—, which Miss Biggs would come creaking into the kitchen to collect when the panic was at its height. This morning was worse than usual. I generally tried to give the nursery something that I was going to cook for the dining-room so that I could do it all together, but today Mrs Lewis had ordered kidneys and mushrooms, which the nurses didn't fancy for the children, and scrambled eggs which couldn't be cooked before they were wanted. I decided to give them sausages and bacon, so I hoisted Polly from the floor to cut off bacon rinds and discovered that the big frying-pan that I wanted to fry the sausages in had not been washed, and bore traces of yesterday's smelts. I didn't dare tick her off in case it should send her queer, and I had no time to clean it myself, so I threw the sausages into the fishy fat and hoped for the best.

Nellie came in with one of her trays and said cheerfully: 'What a stink,' but I had no time to talk to anyone as I was trying to core kidneys, grill toast, heat porridge, make coffee, and watch the sausages and bacon all at the same time, as well as keep an eye on Polly, who was now peeling mushrooms with a dangerously sharp knife.

The least pleasant of the children, a smug little beast called Leonora, came prancing in at this point with her round face shining between tight sticking-out pigtails.

'Good morning, cook,' she remarked patronizingly. 'Nanny says she would like you to do some fried tomatoes for breakfast.'

'Oh, tell Nanny to go to the devil,' I said, and immediately regretted it, for the brat gave vent to a delighted 'Ooh!' and rushed off to repeat the naughty word. An infuriated nurse soon came bustling in, crackling with starch and indignation, saying: 'I don't wish to make trouble, cook, and if Leonora was not such a truthful child I could only hope that she had invented what she told me you said to her. I really must ask you to be more careful – such rudeness – a shocking example for children.' I hastily changed the subject. Banging a loaf of bread about and flourishing the bread-knife to put her off her stroke I said:

'I can't do you tomatoes, Nurse, because I haven't got any. William hasn't brought them in yet.'

'Oh, well, that's a pity I'm sure. What are you giving us? Sausages? I'm not very keen on sausages for growing children, you know.'

She was a college-trained nurse and full of theories about food values, so I got rid of her by telling her that sausages were well known to contain all four vitamins, A, B, C, and D, to which she replied, 'Tchah!' and left the room in a fury.

That uniformed body of females, 'the Nurses', were always having a feud with someone. There were actually only three of them at Chilford House, but they made up for that by being an infernal nuisance. When they were not up against their employers about some detail of child upbringing they were making our life hell by sending back food from the nursery and demanding absurd delicacies at the most inconvenient times, not to mention flying in a horrified body to Mrs Lewis at the sight of a tiny speck of dust on the nursery floor. They were also incessantly at war with the children, who conducted a well-organized and admirable campaign for their discomfiture. They would hide in the tops of thick trees and call down mocking personalities as the nurses passed below, and cryptic notes hinting at shady pasts and unbelievable vices were left lying around all over the house.

Separately, these nurses may have been perfectly charming, but as a body antagonism seemed to be a *parti pris* with them.

Miss Biggs came into the kitchen as I was piling the nursery breakfast on to a huge tray for Rose to take in, snatching the dining-room coffee off the fire with one hand, just as it was boiling over.

'Good morning, Mrs Dixon,' she said, arranging Lady W—'s breakfast on her tray with maddening deliberation and accuracy of detail. 'Quite at sixes and sevens this morning, aren't we?' Mildred and Jessie, the parlourmaids, one a pretty local girl and the other a plain but efficient machine, came in for the dining-room breakfast before it was ready, and I pointed righteously to the huge clock which showed twenty minutes to nine.

'That clock's slow, always has been,' said Jessie.

'Hurry, Mrs Dixon, lovey, us'll have Mr Dawkes after we else,' said Mildred anxiously.

Even when they had departed, weighted down by trays heaped with mountains of food and gallons of coffee – why *do* people eat so much on holiday? – my work wasn't done. It was now time for the staff to have their breakfast, and, said my stomach, high time too. A mass of sausages had been sizzling on the range, but everybody always fancied a nice bit of fried bread, so that had to be done, and there was still Mrs Lewis's tray to be sent up. I used to keep something back from the dining-room for her, she couldn't very well say that it wasn't good enough, though she was very particular and would often refuse to eat what we were having in the kitchen. At last everything was done, down to the enormous brown pot of tea, and I slid thankfully into my worn plush chair at the servants' hall table. I used to keep some coffee back for myself, for in my opinion no day is a day that doesn't start with at least two cups of it. The other servants regarded me askance over this, they felt the same way about their cup o' tea, and 'Coffee?' they said, 'never touch it. Poison to the kidneys.' But oh! the joy of those first few mouthfuls, bringing comfort to the aching void created by rising early and working feverishly on an empty stomach.

Today was Nellie's and Rose's half-day, and they were discussing what they should do. For my part, when I got time off I used to go and sleep in a hedge somewhere, rejoicing to breathe a little pure air away from the greasy vapours of the kitchen or my smelly bedroom furniture. These two, however, with the energy of town-breds, wanted a whirl of gaiety which was not to be found in sleepy little Birching.

They generally used to rush off after lunch to catch the Birching bus which stopped at the end of the avenue, and would spend the afternoon strolling round the shops arm in arm and the evening at the small and smelly local cinema. If they couldn't get their work finished in time to catch the bus they would bicycle madly into the village to gaze into the window of the one general store which sold hardly anything except sweets and matches. Anything to get away from the boredom of rural scenery.

'Mouldy hole this is,' grumbled Nellie, biting into a huge door-step of bread and butter. 'Might as well not have a 'alf-day at all. Give me Torquay, that's more my style. Why, when I was at Torquay – '

We had all heard enough about Torquay, where Nellie had had her last place, to last us a lifetime – it was one of her pet subjects. Rose cut her short by saying:

'What say we get the bus, Nell? I want to match up some ribbon, and there's a Clark Gable at the Roxy.'

'It always means coming out before the end to catch the bus back, though. Last time we had to leave before the part where they discover it was all a misunderstanding. I *was* fed up. Tell you what, I'm fed up with this hole. Don't think I'll stay much longer. I'm going to tell that old cow straight out – it's not good enough I'm going to say.'

She leaned back, stretching her arms above her head and smiling complacently with the air of one who has made an impressive and startling announcement. Nobody took any notice, however; we all went on chewing as we'd heard all this before, too.

Nellie really didn't mean it herself, but she liked to hear herself talk, and she got up soon and went off yawning, to make beds.

Mildred helped to clear the table. Washing up the kitchen crockery was yet another of poor Polly's tasks, but when I went to look for her to clamp her to the sink she was nowhere to be found. I hunted everywhere for her, even in the coal cellar, where she always hid if there was a storm getting up or electricity in the air. I eventually discovered her sitting in a sort of coma on a big stone by the side of the back drive that led to the garage and stables.

'Polly! What on earth – ?'

'Sh – go away.' She waved me aside without looking at me, and her fixed gaze became even more rapt as the big black Daimler turned out of the stable yard and swished majestically past us with her hero at the wheel.

I booted Polly back to the pantry where I left her, scraping egg off plates in an ecstatic trance. I had only time to make my bed in a slapdash way and change the water of my flowers before rushing back to the kitchen in time to be there when Mrs Lewis paid her state visit. It was a field day today for Miss Biggs, and I kept meeting her round corners or on the stairs and it gave her an opportunity to say: 'More haste less speed,' or 'All behind like the cow's tail,' each time I flashed by her.

When I got downstairs there was a strange male in a very dirty pair of grey flannels wandering about the kitchen. I thought at first that it was one of the tradesmen, but then I saw no bicycle clips and realized that it was one of the house party.

'I say,' he said, putting a handful of toast crusts into his face, 'could you possibly give me a bit of butter? I've practically burned my hand off on the exhaust pipe of my car.'

'Let's have a look,' I said, and he displayed quite a nasty place on the back of his hand. If he wanted butter on it well and good, it was not my place to suggest that he applied to

119

Mrs Lewis who was in charge of a fully equipped medicine chest. She came in as I was holding his hand in mine and dabbing it with the best Unsalted, and was deeply affronted at one of her prerogatives being usurped.

'Hullo, Lulu,' said my patient, showing dizzy lack of respect, 'just being treated for burns.'

'You come straight up to my room, Mr Teddy, and have some carron oil on it. Butter indeed! Cook should know better than to risk infection like that. Quite absurd.'

'Oh, but Lulu – ' He was dragged off, protesting, and dripping greasily over Polly's clean floor. I realized that he must be the eldest grandson. I ought to have known from his broken nose. It had been the subject of much speculation in the servants' hall. Dawkes had it on good authority that he had come by it in a brawl in an East End brothel. Jim Driver knew for certain that a car smash had caused it, but Nellie was of the opinion that Mrs Lewis had caught him a clout with the largest and heaviest crucifix one day when he tried to make love to her.

She soon came stalking back to the kitchen and vented her annoyance with me by ordering all the most troublesome dishes she could think of, such as *puréed* vegetables and *consommé*. She produced her trump card by saying that I was to make *crème brûlée* for dinner.

'I presume you know how to make it, Mrs Dixon?'

'Certainly I do, Mrs Lewis.' I wasn't going to let on that I had not even the slightest idea what *crème brûlée* was, and when she had gone I flew to my cookery books and hunted for the simplest description of how to make it. It apparently had to be left for four hours after being made, then coated with caramel and left for another four hours at least before being served. This meant that I would have to start it at once, so I had to abandon my idea of making the weekly batch of plum cakes. My first attempt was a curdled failure, and looked more like scrambled eggs than *crème brûlée*, so I put it in the dog's dinner plate and started again. Luckily there was always a huge jug of cream in the larder, sent down each day from the farm, and eggs abounded, so it didn't matter that yet another unsuccessful attempt found its way into the dog bowl before I got it right. It was now time to start doing things for lunch, and I wanted Polly to come and help me prepare vegetables, but she had disappeared again. I ran her to earth in one of the larders, busily engaged in washing the whole place down and scrubbing the shelves.

'Polly,' I said sternly, 'this is a fine time to be doing this sort of thing when I want you in the kitchen.'

'Mrs Lewis said I was to,' she said, biting her nails and looking at me with scared lunatic eyes.

I was furious with the housekeeper, but I had to control my wrath before Polly, who was on the verge of a breakdown, so I said:

'Well, never mind, you can leave it now. I'll make it all right with her. Come along now, Poll dear, and scrape a nice carrot for me. *That's* right.' I jollied her up, and had just got her going quite happily in the kitchen when we both had to knock off work as the rest of the staff came flocking in to the servants' hall to have their 'elevenses'.

It always seemed to me that breakfast was hardly over before everyone wanted to pack more tea and bread and butter inside themselves. It would not have been etiquette for me to absent myself from the gathering, however much I wanted to get on with my cooking, so I had to sit there, fretting at the waste of time. Not that I don't generally welcome any opportunity to stop work, but under the circumstances it only meant more panic afterwards trying to get things done in time.

Nellie and Rose were still talking about their plans for the afternoon and were having a rather tedious discussion as to whether Rose should wear her pink silk blouse with or without the coral beads.

Dawkes had apparently been having a very interesting morning going through the stumps of his employer's cheque books for the past year.

'That old devil's up to something,' he said. 'Two hundred

121

pounds to the Central Fur Stores. Lady W— never saw a hair of *that* partickler bit of rabbit, I'll bet.'

'Be your age, Mr Dawkes,' said Nellie, shattering his dream of scandal. 'Everybody knows that was a present he give Miss Dorothy on her twenty-first, so don't excite yerself.'

'Ah, Miss Clever, then what about "Mrs Eva Grant twenty pounds", and, farther on, "Mrs Eva Grant fifty pounds"? He never had a granddaughter by *that* name. Smells fishy to me. You mark my words, that old b— isn't above a bit of you know what, even at his age.'

Everybody drew in their breath and tut-tutted, except Polly, who was busily engaged in picking bits off the heel of her shoe. Miss Biggs always missed the implications of Dawkes' coarser remarks, so she wasn't as shocked as she should have been.

'Ah, well,' she said, rising with difficulty from a low chair, 'Live and let live. It takes all sorts to make a world, you know, Mr Dawkes.' Licking her fingers she collected a few stray crumbs that she had missed round her plate, and hobbled off saying, 'Well, I must go and get my lady dressed.' Polly and I returned to our inferno of heat and bustle. The fire in the range was blazing away and I couldn't imagine ever having felt cold. By lunch-time I was limp and dripping and couldn't find the energy to be benign to a very small child who wandered in and walked round and round the kitchen saying, 'Choccy biccy, choccy biccy,' with maddening persistence.

Nellie and Rose fairly bolted their lunch, and didn't even stay to have a second jam tart, which was all to Miss Biggs' advantage. While I was shaking the tablecloth out of the back door I caught sight of them hareing across the short cut through the park to where the bus stopped. I couldn't see whether Rose was wearing the beads or not.

I generally had a bit of time to myself after lunch to 'put me feet up' or go out and get a bit of air, before I had to start making scones for tea.

Today, however, I had to make the cakes that should

have been done in the morning, not to mention putting a caramel top on to the *crème brûlée*. This was rather fascinating, as all that had to be done was to sprinkle sugar heavily over the top, and put it under a very hot grill. It bubbled and heaved like the crater of a volcano and eventually turned a beautiful glassy brown.

'Sucks to you, Ma Lewis,' I thought, as I mixed plum cake in an enormous bowl. When I had filled the tins, I put them into the old-fashioned ovens to cook, and made up the fire well.

Polly had wandered out and I was wondering idly where she had gone, when my blood was frozen by a horrible yelling that grew louder as Polly flashed past the window and hurled herself into the kitchen, screaming: 'Fire! Fire! Oh, my Gawd! Oh, help! Fire, oh, help! Fire, fire, fire!'

'Where?' I said calmly, thinking that this was a figment of her disordered brain, but even as I spoke an ominous smell of burning drifted to my nose, and sure enough, a light rain of black ashes was falling outside the window. I rushed out and looking upwards saw that the kitchen chimney was indeed on fire and behaving like Vesuvius. Polly had followed me, still yelping, and before I could stop her, she had seized the rope that hung down outside the back door and was tolling away with desperate strength at the huge bell that was only rung for deaths and real emergencies.

The effect was dynamic. People appeared from everywhere in various conditions of excitement and horror. The old groom came galloping down the back drive on his bow legs just in time to catch Miss Biggs as she fainted stiffly away.

My friend with the burnt hand came running up with a gun that he had been cleaning, which added to the nurses' terror, and Sir Harold W— himself appeared in his braces and camel-hair slippers, having evidently been woken from his after-lunch nap. Nobody did anything; we all stood around and pointed and screamed. Someone hopefully brought out a fire extinguisher, but no one knew how to work it.

The children were enjoying themselves enormously, but the excitement didn't last long. As it gradually dawned on us that the smoke and sparks were getting less and less, and that the fire was going out of its own accord, the tension relaxed, and the annoyance which relief often brings set in. Sir Harold suddenly realized that Polly was still pealing the bell, and he sprang at her with a roar of rage.

'Who's this crazy girl? She's the cause of all this ridiculous panic. Stop it, for God's sake, d'you hear me? Get rid of her, somebody, before I go raving mad. Dawkes! Don't stand there like a fool, man, *do* something. And then ring up the sweep and tell him to come over at once and see what's happened to the damned chimney.' He disappeared into the house, muttering oaths, and somebody plucked Polly off the rope and she stopped screaming, and bursting into hiccupping sobs, flung herself to the ground.

Nurses now began to slap and shake their various charges, and the bishop was heard to speak quite sharply to a fluttering lady in green, who insisted on clinging to his arm as they wandered away with the rest of the crowd; I went back to the kitchen lugging Polly with me, and the only figure left on the scene was Sir Harold's black spaniel who was quietly throwing up the curdled *crème brûlée* on to the drive.

*

The fire was of course the chief topic at tea-time in the servants' hall. Everybody wanted to give an opinion as to the cause of it. Mrs Lewis had apparently told Dawkes that she was certain it was something that I had put on the fire, though what it could have been, short of a can of petrol, I don't know. Miss Biggs was still a little prostrated and inclined to moan: 'We shall all be burned in our beds tonight, I know it.' She would not believe that the fire was really out until the sweep himself came down from his acrobatics on the roof to take a cup of tea with us, and assured her that there was no mortal peril. He had peered down the mouth of the great chimney, and had ascertained that the fire was out, but could not tell the cause or the extent of the damage without climbing up inside it from below.

'Yew'll have to let this yere fire out in the range tonight,' he said with his mouth full of sponge cake. 'I'll pop over early tomorrow and climb up her with me ladder.'

'Oh, what a nuisance,' I said, 'must you really?'

'Well, we must know the whoiy of it, mustn't us? Might happen again else.'

'Oh, don't say that,' pleaded Miss Biggs. 'I'm afraid you'll have to put up with the slight inconvenience, Mrs Dixon. One must suffer, you know, for the cause of many.'

I saw that there was no help for it. I should just have to get up at the crack of dawn to supervise the sweep and then light the fire when he had finished so that one or two people at least should get baths before breakfast.

We had to have a clean tablecloth after the sweep had gone, as he was not at all careful with his person, and had leant sooty elbows everywhere in a free and easy way.

I had to do all the cooking for dinner myself, as Polly was definitely written off for the rest of the day. She had wandered out into the shadows after tea, probably to hang round the garage for a sight of Jim Driver who had taken Lady W— out on an all-day visit. It was a lucky thing that she had missed the Great Fire, it might have upset her health even more than Miss Biggs.

Even though I started directly after tea, I only just got everything done in time. Mercifully, I didn't have to cook a hot dinner for the staff. Our main meal was lunch, and we always had cold meat or something in the evening, and chunks of soap-like cheese, washed down with the inevitable tea. The nurses had the same, with cocoa, sitting round the nursery fire with their knitting and their magazines on mothercraft. The dining-room dinner was generally quite an extensive affair, and tonight Mrs Lewis, just to complicate things a little, fancied a mushroom omelette for herself.

Nellie and Rose came bursting into the servants' hall as we were finishing our supper, and even the phlegmatic Rose was panting to hear the news.

'Tom told us on the bus that there'd been a fire – part of the roof fell in, he said.'

'Fancy us missing it, y'know,' said Nellie, regretfully. 'Just my luck to miss the only bit of excitement we've had here since the pipes burst.'

We disillusioned them about the size of the fire, but Nellie was still upset at having missed it, as they hadn't even enjoyed the cinema. The projection was dim, and the sound part had broken down half-way through, and even Clark Gable loses glamour when mouthing silently at you out of a thick fog.

I went upstairs early as I was worn out, and also the thought of the sweep's early visit was weighing heavily on my mind. Maddeningly enough, when I did get into my high iron bed, I couldn't sleep. The more I kept thinking that I must get to sleep, the more wakeful I became, and eventually I got sick of the clanging each time I tossed, and decided it was worth the effort of going down to the kitchen to get a hot drink. While the kettle was boiling, I thought it would be a good opportunity to explore the rest of the house, which I had never really seen.

It was after one o'clock, and all was still and dark on the farther side of the swing door as I crept through in my carpet slippers. I was quite enjoying myself roaming through the rooms pretending I was the family ghost when my phantom glide was turned into the most material somersault as I tripped over a gaitered leg that was protruding unexpectedly from the depths of an easy chair.

'God bless my soul,' said the astonished bishop, waking with a start from deep slumber. 'What? Where – ?'

'Oh, I *beg* your pardon, sir, I mean your worship, your reverence, that is,' I stuttered, picking myself up and backing out of the Presence. I could hear him following me, still mumbling and exclaiming, as he tried to brush pipe ash off his apron. I fled through the swing door to the refuge of my kitchen, drank my drink, and rushed upstairs and into bed as if pursued by a bogey man instead of a bishop.

126

# Chapter Ten

AFTER Easter the house party began to break up, and by the end of the holidays everybody except a few insignificant female relations and one or two of the younger children had gone. There were always guests at the week-end, but most of the time life was delightfully slack after the turmoil of work to which I had been accustomed. We grew fat and lazy in the kitchen, though Mrs Lewis still chivvied us around to keep us up to the mark. The pretty parlourmaid Mildred went home and the pantry maid ceased to appear every day, which meant that Polly didn't have any less to do, as she had no one to help her with all the kitchen washing up. I let her off helping me with the cooking, as she really wasn't much use anyway, and either hard work or unrequited love was making her look pasty and peaky. Jim Driver had got a girl in the village and he used to rush out like a dog every evening after supper and not return till quite late. He often went courting in one of his master's cars, and if I was still awake I would hear him from my room returning to the garage. He was lucky not to be discovered. Sir Harold's window was in the front of the house, and so was Mrs Lewis's, but somehow he always got away with it.

One evening, much to my surprise, Jim came into the kitchen while I was cooking the dinner and said shyly: 'Would you care to come for a wee drive this evening, Missis?'

I was too astonished to say 'No,' though I was rather scared at the thought of the risk of being seen in the borrowed car, and also I couldn't make out what had become of Bessie, his girl. 'You won't say anything to the others now?' he asked, jerking his head in the direction of the servants' hall.

'No, of course not,' I said, rather thrilled at the prospect of this clandestine outing.. He really was quite good-looking, and as he went out I noticed that the boils on the back of his neck were almost completely cured.

After supper I made an excuse for going up early, saying I had to write letters. I changed my apron for something a little more glamorous, and crept out of the back door when no one was looking. Jim was waiting in the road just above the garage, and I got into the front seat of the Daimler beside him. I felt most opulent as we hummed along the lanes for a while in silence. Jim seemed nervous, and didn't talk much, and I didn't want to say anything until I had discovered why I had been invited. Eventually he decided that we had gone far enough, for he suddenly braked and brought the car to a standstill on the grass verge of the road.

He leant towards me, and I was just going to slap his face in the best manner when I saw it was a cigarette he was offering me, and not a passionate embrace. It was rather an anticlimax when I realized that I was not to be assaulted after all. When the cigarettes were lit, Jim leaned back in his corner and said:

'I brought you here for a wee talk. Would you mind very much giving me some advice?'

'All right by me,' I said, 'but why pick on me?'

'Well, Missis, if I was to take one of the other girls driving now, I'd be after kissing them instead of talking.'

I didn't quite know whether to take this as a compliment or a horrible slight, so I passed it over, and said:

'What d'you want my advice about? Is it Bessie?'

'It is.'

He poured out the whole story, and I must say I thought Bessie seemed rather a low character.

It appeared that although they had an understanding and were technically 'keeping company', she had ceased to dedicate all her evenings to Jim, and he was a seething mass of jealousy. Calling for her one day, he had met her just leaving the house arm-in-arm with a red-haired runt from the International Stores. Jim had made a scene, but Bessie had given him to understand that he had no proprietary rights, and had gone flouncing off with Ginger smirking at her side.

'I don't know what to do with the girl,' said Jim sadly. 'I love her, and I thought she loved me, but it's a queer way she's carrying on.'

It was a familiar story, so it didn't take me long to think of what to say.

'I think she's just going on like this for the fun of making you jealous – just to add a bit of spice to life, see? So I tell you what to do, Jim. You pay her back in her own coin. You get *her* jealous of *you*. Instead of going up there after her, you take somebody else out. She'll soon come screaming back to you if she thinks someone else is going to nab you.'

The more he thought about the idea the more he liked it. His wrath at the moment was greater than his love. 'I'll show her,' he said, 'I'll do her down. But ye'll have to help me. Will you come out with me, as a favour, somewhere where she'll see us?'

'Oh, Jim, I'd much rather not.' I didn't see why I should be involved in this romance. 'Take one of the girls out, can't you?'

'No, no, it must be you. It was your idea, anyway. How would I be explaining to them that I wasn't after walking out with them? I don't have to tell you that I wouldn't be asking you out if it wasn't for this.'

Another dubious remark, but nevertheless I realized I would have to help him, as his mind seemed to be made up. We drove back to Chilford House debating when and where to spring the shock on Bessie. Jim had a marvellous idea. There was to be a dance at the Chilford Village Hall in a few days' time, to which Bessie was sure to be going, and it coincided with my evening out. He would be able to get off, as Sir Harold and Lady W— never went out in the evening.

We put the car in the garage as quietly as possible. The groom lived in a cottage out of earshot, and if the red-haired stable boy who slept above the garage with Jim heard anything, he would never say a word, as he was a trusted ally. I sneaked down the drive and got into the house by a secret way I had discovered through the coal cellar, and arrived black but undiscovered in my bedroom, beginning already to regret what I had let myself in for.

*

Jim and I had decided that we must keep the whole thing very dark, as there would be a lot of talk if it were discovered that we were going to the dance together. Our names would be coupled in the servants' hall. The atmosphere became rather tense, therefore, when at lunch the next day Miss Biggs suddenly piped up: 'I see there's to be a dance at Chilford on Thursday. Is nobody going to trip the light fantastic?'

'You bet I am,' said Nellie. 'I'm going with me beau, and what's more I'm going to wear all me jools.' Jim and I looked at each other. It would wreck everything if Nellie was to crash in on our delicate plot. I couldn't make out whether she was joking or not.

'Are you really going, Nell?' I said, trying to sound casual.

'Course I'm not, dearie; where would I get a boy from in this dead-and-alive hole? Unless Mr Dawkes would like to take me – ?'

'Not in my line, I'm afraid,' said Dawkes, grinning. 'Kid's game, dancing, I always say.'

'And we all know Mr Driver has a date with an angel,' continued Nellie, 'so here I am on the shelf. When I think of the boys who used to take me out at Torquay – the Promised Land that was all right.'

'I can't think why you ever left your precious Torquay,' said Jessie dourly.

'Well, ducks, that's a subject over which we draw a veil,' said Nellie. 'It not being entirely to the credit of Yours Truly.'

I was glad to discover someone else besides me who had got the sack; I wasn't going to admit mine in public, but I made up my mind to have a discreet get-together with Nellie about it some time. One morning a few days later, I was lying in bed thinking about the fateful dance, when an awful thought suddenly struck me: 'My dear, I haven't a rag to wear!' Evening dress is not part of a cook's trousseau. All I had with me besides my aprons were one or two decayed-looking skirts and jerseys. I would not be busy that afternoon, so I made up my mind to go into Birching and 'look at the shops'.

When the others saw me hurrying lunch in order to catch the bus, there was a good deal of caustic comment.

'You goin' to town, Mae West?' said Nellie. 'Don't tell me you've found a young man, you lucky girl!' I couldn't help blushing guiltily, and they were all delighted. 'I do believe it's that handsome policeman at the cross-roads,' said Miss Briggs naughtily.

'How did you guess?' I said, getting up to go.

'If you can't be good, be careful!' screamed Nellie after me, as I ran up the back stairs.

I only just caught the bus and flung myself panting into a seat beside a fat farmer. I had recovered my breath by the time we got to Birching, but he was still puffing from the mere effort of being stout. Stepping down into the market square, I looked about me for a fashion salon.

There was a draper's shop on one corner, whose windows besides displaying balls of wool and innumerable lace collars, contained one or two rather depressed-looking dresses. One of them, a tasteful creation in pink sateen, had a label pinned across it saying 'à la mode', so I thought I would risk it. I opened the door and nearly knocked over a small man in pince-nez, who was waiting on the other side of it to direct customers.

'Which department, Madam?' he inquired, indicating with a wave of his hand a choice of three or four counters. 'I want to try that pink dress in the window,' I said.

'Ladies' Modes? Certainly, madam. Miss Smith, take madam to the Ladies' Modes.' A fuzzy-haired young woman with a heavy cold ushered me through a curtain into a little room at the back of the shop, containing two mirrors and an ash-tray. She brought me the dress and stood snivelling while I struggled into it. It might have been worse, even though it did make one think of 1920, when waists were somewhere round the hips. It would have to do for Chilford, though I doubted whether Bessie could possibly be jealous of Jim going out with a pink sateen dress that ended in a girlish frill about six inches from the ground.

'I'll take it,' I said, in spite of having just caught sight of my back view.

'It looks *lovely*,' said the sniffing one, sadly – 'ever so stylish.'

I smuggled it home and up to my room, and stored it carefully in the tin suitcase. I had decided that I couldn't possibly change at Chilford House without being discovered, so when the great day arrived, I borrowed Nellie's bicycle, giving them to understand that I had a heavy date with the policeman, and rode off after tea with my ball gown in a shopping bag on the handlebars. The 'Green Man' at Chilford provided me with a small dim room, in which I changed and did my face and hair as best I could. I felt far more terrified than a débutante at a state ball as I descended to the Private Bar where I was to meet Jim.

'How do I look?' I asked him, as I sipped my port and lemon.

'You look grand,' he said, chivalrously but doubtfully. He himself was looking smart and shiny in a blue serge suit, and I felt quite proud as we entered the village hall, gay with twists of coloured paper and bells left over from Christmas. 'The Four Happy Harmonists', in co-respondent shoes, were swinging it to the 'Lily of Laguna', so I took off my coat and Jim and I ventured a genteel foxtrot.

After about five minutes he suddenly pinched me, and I came to with a start from the trance that the combination of music and the smell of his hair oil was producing.

'She's here!' he breathed into my ear, and directed my gaze to the doorway. A buxom black-eyed girl was entering gaily on the arm of a small creature with red hair and a fatuous smile of pride.

'Hold me closer, Jim,' I whispered back, 'don't forget you've got to make her jealous.'

He clutched me fervently to his bosom, breathing heavily and falling over my feet in his emotion. I threw back my head with a fascinating smile of careless rapture, and had the satisfaction of seeing Bessie's jaw drop and her eyes blaze as we glided across her view. She tossed her head and danced off with Ginger, steering him deftly, as he was too small to see over her shoulder.

In the interval, I made Jim get me some fizzy lemonade, and sit by me in an attentive way, though his eyes kept swivelling round to where Bessie was chatting brightly and glancing at him covertly when she thought he wasn't looking.

My plan worked even quicker than I expected. One more passionate polka with Jim, and Bessie could contain herself no longer. At the end of the dance I skipped out of the door, and when I returned, five minutes later, the deed had been done. The pair of them were waltzing together, and if their feet were not always doing the same steps, their dreamy eyes were in perfect communion. Ginger had disappeared, presumably to drown his sorrows in the Green Man. Jim didn't even see me as he floated past ecstatically, so, having done my good deed, and feeling rather *de trop*, I decided to go home.

It was starting to rain when I got outside, and I was hanged if I was going to bicycle a mile and half in 'my Ladies' Modes'. I felt I was entitled to some reward for my evening's work, so I hopped round to the public-house yard where Jim had left the Daimler, and drove myself home in style.

After all he had Love, so I didn't see why I shouldn't have Luxury.

*

Life was almost too gay. Not long after the village dance, I began to hear talk of what was apparently an annual event at Chilford House – a Servants' Ball at Whitsun. The house was to be full again over the long week-end, and family,

133

guests, and staff would mingle with a great deal of embarrassment on all sides, and dance in the big hall to the strains of the Happy Harmonists.

There was a lot of discussion and excitement in the kitchen regions. Mildred and the pantry-maid had returned in preparation for the house party, and a stout old charlady came every day and swelled our gathering at the lunch table.

Nellie was going to wear red taffeta at the dance, and was hoping to pinch the broken-nosed Teddy from Mildred, who had had conspicuous success with him the year before.

'Did he reely kiss you behind the coats in the lobby, Mil?' she said one day when we were, as usual, discussing the topic of the hour.

'Mm,' said Mildred, blushing furiously.

'How lovely. Wait till he sees me in me red. He'll go for me in a big way, see if he don't.'

'Pride comes before a fall,' said Miss Biggs. 'Don't talk so shocking, Nellie.'

'Who else is going to be there, anyway?' Nellie asked Dawkes. 'Any guests coming except pot-bellied old geezers with flat feet?'

'One or two,' said Dawkes, who had evidently been through his employers' entire correspondence on the subject. 'Mr and Mrs Wilson-George – that dame with the fancy sparklers; the Gregorys – dirty spongers – mean as hell, no tip from them. A bloke from London – friend of Mr Teddy's, I think – '

'New Blood, eh? What's his name?'

'Let's see. Robin something or other – Brook – no Burke, Robin Burke.'

All eyes were turned on me as I choked on a fish-bone and was very nearly sick on the table. I fled from the room, thankful for an excuse to hide my horror. This was terrible! What a ghastly situation, to be cook in the house where one of the guests was to be an old flame of two years ago, and to come face to face with him at the Servants' Ball wearing pink sateen, and black strap shoes. I could not possibly go to the dance. Apart from the embarrassment of meeting him, it would lead to all sorts of complications and explanations below stairs. On the morning of the dance, I appeared at breakfast with my right foot heavily bandaged and encased in a carpet slipper. There were cries of sympathetic inquiry from all sides.

'Spilt some boiling water on it,' I explained. 'Just my rotten luck. No dancing for me.'

'Well, you are a wounded warrior!' cried Miss Biggs. 'Never mind, you shall sit with me, and we'll watch the young folk enjoying themselves.'

I was disappointed to hear that she was not going to dance. I had had visions of her doing the Rumba, clicking out the rhythm on the bones of her stays. I said: 'Not me – I'm not going to come to the rotten show if I can't dance. I shall go to bed and pray for you all.'

I really was disappointed at not being able to go; I had been looking forward to my spot of gaiety. It was just like Robin to turn up at a time like this. He had always been possessed of a charming lack of tact.

I hopped and limped about the kitchen all day, and my other leg became quite crippled under the strain. I had been very busy for the past few days making refreshments, and there was still a lot to do on the day of the dance. By five o'clock I was thankful to sink into a chair and revive myself with tea. The others looked pretty dead too, they had been hard at it all day under the eye of Mrs Lewis, and Nellie voiced the feelings of everybody when she said:

'I'm not sure that this hop isn't more trouble than it's worth. I feel more like goin' to bed and sleeping for a week than prancing round the ballroom on me poor dogs.'

'Hear, hear,' said Rose. 'I quite envy Mrs D. her scald.' Dawkes, who had gone to answer the telephone, came back at this moment, and said gleefully to Nellie:

'Got a disappointment for you, my girl. Mr Burke's just phoned to say his car's broke down and he won't be here till morning.' 'Oh, it's too much,' said Nellie, pouting. 'Just when I was all set for Romance. I shall have to make a go for that sissy curate. It's me last chance.'

I was delighted. All I had to do now was to effect a quick and plausible cure on my foot and I would be able to go after all.

I got up and went to the door, reducing my limp considerably. 'My foot's ever so much better this evening,' I said brightly. 'I think I'll just pop up and put some more ointment on it. I might be able to come after all. You never know, I might cut you out with the curate yet, Nell.'

They seemed to take this all right, so as the evening drew on I gradually got less and less lame. Each time somebody poked their head into the kitchen to say: 'How's the foot?' I gave more and more cheering bulletins, till at last I was able to announce that I was coming after all, 'if my foot doesn't turn on me.'

There was no proper dinner to cook for the dining-room; they had a cold buffet, in order to give us a chance to get cleared up and changed by nine o'clock, when the guests were due to arrive. Both servants and employers had been asked from houses in the neighbourhood; class consciousness would be thrown to the winds, and a good time enjoyed by all. After dinner Dawkes and the girls had to put out the refreshments and drinks on long tables in the dining-room, and Polly and I converted the servants' hall into a ladies cloakroom for the visiting maids.

We all went up to change and there was much giggling and shrieking and running in and out of each other's rooms to lend a hand with pins and give gasping admiration. My pink concoction had quite a success. 'Sweetly pretty' was the verdict. I had to keep away from Nellie, as it clashed horribly with her red. She had gone very festive about the hair. She had curled it tightly with the tongs and then brushed it out into a stiff frizz, into which artificial poppies were stuck at random. I thought I would like to give myself a new coiffure, so I rashly chopped some off the front with nail scissors, and, borrowing Nellie's tongs, gave myself a fringe like a pantomime juvenile. We all collected in the kitchen, pushing and nudging, and much too shy to take the plunge through the green baize door.

Polly was wearing a trailing black dress that was too big for her and hung on her skinny frame as if it would fall off at any moment. I think it must have once belonged to Lady W— for it was certainly not a dress for anyone under seventy, but Polly had added glamour to it by spilling a bottle of vile-smelling Ashes of Roses over herself. She was scared stiff and clutched me in a panic when Dawkes swished into the room, resplendent and Mephistophe-lian in white tie and tails, and said: 'Get a move on, the beauty chorus; the Bish wants to open the ball with Miss Biggs.'

He led us giggling and jostling into the hall, where the Happy Harmonists were in full swing, and a terrifying number of rather blasé-looking people in evening dress were standing about in a tired way. We clustered by the stairs like sheep, wondering what to do with our hands, and were joined by the nurses, self-conscious but fearfully genteel in lace or art crêpe, with a great many scarves and handkerchiefs trailing about. Etiquette demanded that Sir Harold should open the ball with Mrs Lewis, while Dawkes seized the eldest daughter of the house, a stout matron in black velvet, and trundled her deferentially round the room. Once these two couples were started, anyone else could dance. A few staff guests had arrived and were coming through from the back regions, pushing us forward into the room. Teddy made for Mildred, and though Nellie hypno-tized the curate with her eye, he was much too nervous to attempt anything just yet, so she accepted a sun-dried colonel from Chittagong, and bounced off with him. Would it be me for the bishop? I wondered, but then a young man with protruding teeth and no chin bore down on me and said, 'Will you tread a measure?'

'I don't mind if I do,' I said, wondering whether I had to call him 'Sir' or not. He was not a very good dancer and we fell over each other's feet rather a lot. Afterwards he got me some lemonade and obviously felt that he had done his duty by me. He stood fingering his tie for a little, but could not bring out any conversation from behind those rabbit

137

teeth, so hastily disappeared into the crowd leaving me still wearing my fixed social smile.

A footman from Birching Manor approached and whirled me efficiently into a waltz. He danced perfectly, and I thought he was probably an ex-night-club gigolo. We got on rather well together, and he called me 'Toots'. We had another dance, and then he suddenly spied a rather lovely expensive-looking woman standing by herself; so he left me hurriedly to grab her while he had the chance. After this I danced with a small boy of sixteen whose mother made him ask me, and then one or two old buffers who thought they were being very gay and devilish. A rather forced gaiety had been established, and the dance might be said to be going with a swing. Nellie had lost most of the poppies from her hair, and Polly's stockings were round her ankles. I was really quite enjoying myself, when suddenly everything turned upside down and my heart missed about twenty beats. There in the doorway, more attractive than ever, stood an all too familiar figure. He had evidently got his car mended earlier, and had just arrived, for he was not wearing evening dress.

My ancient dancing partner was asking me a question which I couldn't answer, as I was too busy feeling sick and wondering how to escape. Would Robin recognize me? I saw his eye travel over the assembly, looking for his host. I buried my face in my old man's shirt front, but I saw out of one eye that Robin was staring at me with an expression of dawning amazement.

'Excuse me,' I gasped, and releasing myself from my partner's clutch, I bolted through the crowd like a rabbit, burrowing for the safety of the baize door. I didn't care what anyone thought, my one idea was to get away. There was someone on the back stairs, and I couldn't go up there, so I shot into the kitchen and flattened myself behind the door. It was not long before I heard the clatter of running feet on the stone passage, and Robin rushed into the kitchen, and, not seeing me, went across the room and through the door that led into the pantry. He would see me if he came back the same way, so I escaped and rushed along the passage to the servants' hall. All the rooms in the kitchen quarters led into each other, they made three sides of a rectangle, with the long passage as the fourth side, and as I went in at one end of the room, Robin appeared from the pantry at the other end. 'Hi!' he shouted, as I retreated hastily, 'Hi, stop!'

I heard a crashing of chairs, as he bounded after me, and I came to a skidding stop at the end of the passage, and popped into a larder before he could see where I'd gone. I heard his feet in hot pursuit, and he opened a few doors, but I risked it and stayed where I was. Eventually he panted into my larder and I just had time to escape through the other door into the kitchen before he could grab me.

'Stop!' he shouted again, as I raced for the pantry. 'Monty! Stop! What the hell d'you think you're playing at?' Round we went again, through pantry and servants' hall, down the passage, into the kitchen, and round again, and I was getting exhausted.

Desperately I pounded down the passage on the last lap, turned a corner beyond the kitchen, and went to ground in the coal cellar.

Robin fell through the door and down the steps after me, and the rest was a confused delirium of tweed coat, gasps, and coal dust.

# Chapter Eleven

THE rest of the week-end was rather a strain on my nerves, as I had to cope with Robin, who didn't seem to take kitchen etiquette half seriously enough. I had to speak to him severely about penetrating through the green baize door, and finally beg and implore him to consider my reputation.

He came prancing in one day, when Polly was with me in the kitchen, and said: 'Good morning, Cook. I wish to lodge a complaint about the food; there was a slug in my spinach at lunch, and the horse we had for dinner last night was high.'

Polly goggled and gasped, and I did a lot of shushing and pointing, and said out of the side of my mouth: 'Shut up! She's not as crazy as all that; she thinks it all most peculiar.'

'What do you do on your evenings out?' continued Robin, unabashed. I threatened him with a carving knife, dripping blood from the corpse of a rabbit, and at that moment Mrs Lewis walked in and stopped in her tracks, scandalized. She had been unreasonably annoyed about the Teddy episode, but this made the chains and crosses on her bosom rise and sink with real fury. She had an almost feudal sense of propriety and class consciousness, and she apparently thought I was 'making free' with the Gentry, which to her was the ultimate offence. It would not have been proper for her to have ticked me off in front of one of the guests, and equally well she could not turn him out, so she held her ground, a repressed mass of rage, still heaving with a sort of 'Jingle Bells' rhythm. Robin just stood grinning sheepishly, and didn't help me out at all. It was left to me to do something to break up the petrified silence.

'The gentleman wants some lard for his fishing line,' I said wildly, inventing the first thing I could think of. It didn't sound any more plausible to Mrs Lewis than it did to me, however, and she turned to Robin with an ironical smile.

'Indeed? And how are the fish rising, Mr Burke? I didn't know Sir Harold had restocked the lake, since all the fish died last year when the drains leaked in.'

My unfortunate excuse had exhausted my inventive powers, so I winked at Robin with the side of my face farthest away from Mrs Lewis, and he suddenly came up to the scratch most unexpectedly.

'Oh, well, you know, I wasn't thinking of doing any fishing here, unless I have a try for the gold-fish in the lily pond, ha, ha, what?' he said heartily, rubbing his hands. 'I'm going up to stay on the Tay tomorrow, you see, so I just wanted to get my rod ready.'

'One of the men could easily have done that for you, sir. If you'll tell me where it is I'll get Joseph to see to it at once.' She was suspiciously anxious to see the mythical rod, and kept turning her searching gaze from me to Robin in her effort to discover whether we were deceiving her.

'Oh, no, Mrs Lewis, please don't bother,' he said hastily, 'you see, it's a very special rod, my grandfather gave it me last year, and I don't really like anyone else to handle it, thanks awfully all the same – er – yes – er – well – thanks again – ' He sidled to the door and bolted out, having done his bit, even if he did forget to take the lard. Mrs Lewis was still slightly dubious, but she left it at that and reverted to the other little bone that she had come down to the kitchen to pick with me. It was only a small matter of removing the fat from soup before sending it into the dining-room, but she elaborated it into quite a criminal offence, and left me crushed and apologetic.

The house party broke up on the evening of Whit-Monday, and I breathed a sigh of relief when I got rid of the embarrassment of Robin. He managed to drive away when Mrs Lewis wasn't about, so that she wouldn't notice the absence of the fishing rod, and I really thought that nobody suspected anything, except perhaps Polly, and she didn't count. A rude shock was in store for me, however.

One day at lunch Nellie started to talk about a book she had got out of the twopenny library. 'Ever so lovely, it is, makes me cry buckets.'

'What's it about?' asked Mrs Coombe, the charlady, who couldn't read or write her own name, but nevertheless took a deep interest in literature.

'It's all about a Dook hoo falls in love with one of his mother's maids. Her pride is her barrier, and she turns him down, but he wears her down with obstinate persistence, and they elope. Mind you, he does the right thing by her, it's that sort of book.'

'Isn't that beautiful?' said Mrs Coombe, gazing round the table with moist eyes. 'Wish I was educated like you, Nell. My Will's a rare one for books, though; he sometimes reads me the comical pieces in the papers – 'Itler and that. What do they call your tale?'

'*Flames of Desire.*'

Dawkes gave a scornful guffaw. 'Fancy you stuffing yourself with that rot. You'll get ideas above your station, my girl. No toff ever did right by a skivvy yet, in my experience. The other thing perhaps, and *not* a 'undred miles from this spot neither.'

'Why, whatever do you mean, Mr Dawkes?' said the charlady, and Nellie said, ''Ere, 'ere, 'ere, what you getting at, you nasty old man?'

'Oh, no offence, no offence,' he said, and they calmed down, thinking that this was just another of his usual incidental coarsenesses, but I suddenly realized with a shock of horror that he was having a dig at me. His narrowed eyes were fixed on me and said, as clearly as if he had spoken, 'I got something on you, my girl.'

He had evidently discovered the harmless truth of my little secret, and had characteristically inferred the worst. Why is it that one always blushes when one is innocent? Nobody else noticed my loss of composure, but Dawkes obviously thought it was an indication of guilt. The bell rang from the library, and he treated me to a slow and extremely sinister wink before rising and leaving the room.

I felt quite sick at the thought of the ideas that were churning in the slime of his filthy mind. I decided that I would tackle him and vindicate my honour at the earliest possible opportunity.

He purposely avoided seeing me alone for a day or two, until he considered that he had got me sufficiently worked up by suggestive glances and odd words thrown here and there, unnoticed by the others, but most unnerving for me.

One afternoon, however, as I was going down through the shrubbery for a moody stroll in the park, he suddenly slid out from behind a laurel bush and fell into step beside me.

'Well?' I said, walking on without turning my head.

'Well – Monty – ?' he replied insinuatingly. 'I've got a pretty tale stored up inside here,' tapping his head. 'Who am I goin' to tell it to, eh? Mrs Lewis, she might be amused, and why not Sir 'arold himself? He always appreciates my funny stories.'

'Why, you dirty, double-crossing rat!' I said, having spent my last half-day seeing a gangster film at the local cinema, 'there's not a bit of truth in your filthy insinuations, and you can't prove a thing.'

'Oho! So I suppose you and Mr Burke are total strangers, eh? Nothing between you at all?'

'More or less.'

'Well, I seen what I seen, and I'm damned if I'm going to keep it to meself. Unless – '

'Unless what?'

'You know what. You gotter make it worth my while, see?'

We had come to the gate into the park by now, and I opened it, trying to keep calm, and went through, leaving him to shut it and follow me over the long grass.

'I'm still not scared,' I said, when he had caught me up. 'I've got a perfectly clear conscience in spite of you trying to make me nervous. I'll tell you the whole truth, as I've really got nothing to hide. Mr Burke and I were friends not so very long ago, and he recognized me and wanted to talk to me. There's nothing in that. It's all perfectly normal.'

'Go on!' laughed Dawkes derisively. 'Tell that to someone else. Who's going to believe that Mr Burke had a platonic and social acquaintance with a cook? Them things don't happen outside of Nellie's books.'

'But don't you see – ?' I began, but stopped, as it was hopeless to try and explain. I was all confused, and couldn't cope with the situation. One's education doesn't provide for dealing with things like blackmail. The safest way was to be thoroughly up-stage, so I said icily: 'I refuse to discuss the matter any further,' quickened my steps to get away from him, and, tripping over a mole-hill, sat down heavily on the wet grass.

'Well, dearie,' said Dawkes, when he had recovered from his transports of mirth. 'I'll give you a little time to think it over. We'll come to terms tomorrow. Meanwhile, I got me work to do. Ta-ta! Sweet dreams!' He strode away on his long legs, looking like a man-eating spider, and I remained where I was, getting damper and damper while I grappled with a desire to yell and scream with rage.

That night I slept on it, as the saying is, and, waking early, found the solution crystal-clear in my brain. I would pack up my tin suitcase and go. Once I had given notice, it would not really be worth Dawkes' while to broadcast his bit of dirt, and even if he did, I should not be there long enough for it to affect me. I had put aside quite a tidy little nest-egg out of my wages, as the pink creation had been almost my only expenditure, and I was not going to be blackmailed into parting with it. Although I had had a highly diverting and illuminating time at Chilford House, I felt I could do with a sight of my home again; there was so much to tell everyone, and I really was getting very sick of my clothes.

When Mrs Lewis came into the kitchen that morning, I took a deep breath and said: 'I'm afraid I must give notice. We have sickness at home; my sister's been taken with Pneumonia. Double, it is.'

'Well, that *is* aggravating,' she said. 'I don't like having

144

to make changes all the time. Are you sure you must go?'

'Of course I must,' I said, as deeply affronted as if my sister really were lying at death's door and calling for me. 'People don't have Double Pneumonia every day, you know.'

'Oh, dear, it really is too trying. I suppose you'll stay until I can get someone to fill your place?'

'Oh, yes, of course, if you get someone quite soon,' I said. 'Why don't you try locally, in Exeter or somewhere? It would save a lot of time.' I marvelled at the way I was actually daring to dictate to her. Now that I was soon going to be out of her power, her domination didn't impress me at all, and when she said: 'That will do, I know my own business, thank you,' I merely laughed vulgarly as she went out of the room.

That know-all, Dawkes, knew almost as soon as I did that I had given notice, and I was careful to keep out of his way until I could get some intimation from Mrs Lewis of when I would be able to go. His face was black with rage at lunch-time and he hardly spoke a word. Once or twice he opened his mouth as if he were going to denounce me publicly, but thought better of it, and evidently decided to wait and see whether he couldn't, after all, get something out of me.

Jim Driver was told off to take Mrs Lewis into Exeter in the afternoon, so she had evidently taken my suggestion, and when she got back, I had the honour and distinction of being summoned to her room. It was rather a nuisance, as I was very involved at the moment with a Dressed Crab, about which Mrs Beeton and my French cookery book were contradicting each other. However, the opportunity of seeing the temple of prayer was not to be missed, so I sped upstairs, wiping my hands on my apron. I knocked at the door and went in, to find Mrs Lewis sitting at her desk, still wearing an unsociable black hat of shiny straw, perched high on her head. I had expected to find a mass of religious pictures, effigies, prie-dieus, and so forth, but, if Mrs Lewis prayed to any images, it must have been to the unflattering portraits of a host of fearsome relatives which covered the walls and furniture. The men were mostly whiskered, or walrus-moustached, with hair *en brosse,* and the women large, black, and forbidding. They were the sort of photographs that always give the impression that the people in them have departed this life, not so much from the age of the picture, but from the general air of the improbability of their being human; and if this lot weren't dead, they certainly ought to have been. I detached my gaze from Uncle Hugo on the mantelpiece, in the full-dress uniform of an undertaker's mute, as Mrs Lewis was addressing me.

'I am thankful to say that I have found someone in Exeter who will *more* than adequately fill your place. I have arranged for her to arrive tomorrow afternoon, and I should like you to show her the routine, such as you have followed, and where to lay her hands on everything, so please put the kitchen in order. Then you can go by the evening train. You have not had your wages yet for last week, so, as you are leaving without notice, the question of money does not arise.'

I didn't think she was being very kind to someone whose nearest and dearest was dying of Pneumonia, so I said, 'O.K.' and let her have another of my coarse laughs, which I knew grated on her gentility, and, with a smirk at Uncle Hugo, went out of the room banging the door behind me. I ran into Dawkes in the corridor, and still feeling vulgarly light-hearted, I buttonholed him. 'Well, old cock,' I said, 'I'm going tomorrow. Whatcher think of that? Puts an end to your "coming to terms", don't it?'

He stood there, biting his thumb savagely. 'I'll make your name mud before you go, you little b—,' he muttered, 'and what's more, I'll see that it don't escape your folks neither. If you *have* a respectable family, that is, which I doubt.'

'Oh, they won't mind at all,' I said, 'a spot of poison pen means nothing to them. So if you – ' At this moment the door of Sir Harold's room suddenly opened, so I fled for the back stairs, leaving Dawkes to do his worst on the spot if he chose. As a matter of fact, I don't think he ever said a word to anyone – I certainly never heard anything about it. He probably never intended from the start to carry out his threat – he thought that he would be able to scare me into transferring my pitiful little earnings from my pocket to his. He was not really cut out for blackmail, for he was too small-souled ever to carry anything through.

A gratifying concern was shown in the servants' hall when I announced at supper that I was leaving the next day. All except Dawkes, who again sat cloaked in rage, showed a deep and slightly morbid interest in the Double Pneumonia story.

'Pneumonia?' said Miss Biggs, with sad relish, 'that's bad. They do say that even if it doesn't bring you to your grave, it leaves its mark on you for life. Has she had her crisis yet, poor soul?'

'Coming at any moment, I believe,' I said, earnestly.

'It's a pity she didn't have it right at the beginning,' she went on, 'otherwise the disease takes its toll of your strength. My aunt took Pneumonia three years ago, and the crisis didn't come for quite a time, and afterwards she couldn't keep a thing down, and there are certain foods she can't hold to this day, if you'll pardon my mentioning it.'

'I'm sure we're ever so sorry for you, Mrs D.,' said Nellie. 'It's a real shame you've got to go, just when we was all getting on so well together. We shall miss you, shan't we, girls?'

The murmur of assent wasn't deafening, but it was enough, with Nellie's genuine sentiments, to make me feel rather mean to be getting their sympathy undeservedly.

I excused myself early, saying that I must go and pack, for I did not feel equal to staying for the usual gossip over the fire, to the accompaniment of a medley of clicks from Miss Biggs' knitting needles, teeth, and stay-bones. As I didn't know anything about Pneumonia, it was getting a bit difficult to discuss the symptoms of the case with that wealth of detail that seemed to be expected.

When I got upstairs, I discovered that three of my aprons were at the wash. I would ask Nellie to send them on to me, as I was not going to have the paragon from Exeter, whose name appeared to be Mrs Macbonn, swanking round the place in them. I set my alarm for an earlier hour than usual as I would have quite a lot to do tomorrow if I was to get the kitchen and larders into good enough order to save my self-respect when she arrived. The combination of Polly and me was not one calculated to make for cleanliness or tidiness. Apart from the fact that we were both messy by nature, I never seemed to have time to put anything away in its right place, and though any governess will tell you that it is just as quick to put a thing where it should go as where it should not, I have never found it so. When it means making treks down stone passages to put cheese in one larder and eggs in another, to satisfy the dictates of tradition, it becomes very unpractical.

When I woke for the last time in my little room, and inhaled its well-known smell with my first conscious breath, I felt quite a pang of regret at leaving these familiar surroundings. I felt it even more when I got up and went to the window to take a last look at the long stretch of green lawn and parkland, damp and fresh in the clean air of early morning. However, I had more important things to do than stand around in my nightdress admiring the beauties of nature. Polly was not yet about when I got downstairs, so I started in on the store cupboards in the kitchen, which were in a hopeless mess. None of the various tins, which held such things as spices and seasonings, seemed to have their lids on properly, and the paper on the shelves was encrusted with a sticky mixture of spillings from everywhere. I would have to put fresh paper down, so I took everything out, and all sorts of treasures turned up in odd corners. I discovered a lump of cheese walking about with its outside covered with a decorative green fluff, and a jar of pickles with grass growing on the top, and probably mushrooms too. All the sugars and things were in their wrong containers, and there was an old, unopened packet of Demarara hard as rock, which I had to attack with a rolling-pin. All this took time, and I only managed to get one cupboard superficially respectable, before it was time to start cooking the breakfast. Polly was on hands and knees as usual; she always cleaned floors in preference to anything else, as she seemed to prefer being on all fours – back to nature, I suppose.

Feeling a last-minute mellowness towards everyone, I hashed up a most appetizing kedgeree for the dining-room, accompanied by large, whole kidneys, whose juicy succulence was in no way impaired by the fact that I had dropped them off the grill on to the floor in my zeal. I even had a belated rush of tenderness for the nurses, and enlivened their boiled haddock with a few tomatoes. My *bonhomie* didn't extend as far as Mrs Lewis, however, as she had already made herself a nuisance by demanding an omelette, so I decided to let her wait for it until I had done all the breakfasts. Her bell began to ring before I had finished cooking our kippers, and continued to peal intermittently till Nellie went up to calm her down. She came back to the kitchen to report: '"Where's my breakfast?" she says. "It's ten minutes late!" I felt like telling her to pray for it – Manna, you know – but I daresay she can't pray on an empty stomach, so buck up, dearie, or I shall get what for, and you won't be the only one around here to get the push.'

'What do you mean?' I said, affronted. 'I didn't get the sack, I gave in me notice.'

'Only my fun, ducks, only my fun. Oh, for God's sake!' as the bell started again. 'She's at it again. Get a move on before we all go cuckoo.'

I obliged, and left the kippers, to throw an untidy-looking omelette together, and Polly clattered away with the tray. Mrs Lewis behaved exactly as if it was a day like any other when she came down to order the food. She never unbent to me at all in view of my imminent departure; I supposed I should see her to say good-bye later on. I wondered whether I would have to say good-bye or anything to Lady W— before I left, but as I had never even said hullo when I arrived, it seemed a little unnecessary.

I put Polly on to cleaning out the larders and making them

look a bit more sanitary. I myself had to tidy away everything in my bedroom, as well as do a lot of cooking, so I couldn't do any more in the kitchen, and only hoped that Mrs Macbonn wouldn't be too critical.

She arrived soon after lunch, tall, gaunt, and grim, with a hold-all grasped in each of her bony red hands and a man's felt hat skewered to her iron-grey bun by a steel hatpin. She was desperately efficient. She marched up to her room straight away to gird herself for the fray, and came down looking like an armoured car in the starchiest and most aggressive apron ever seen. I gave her several rather sickly grins of an unnatural heartiness in an effort to jolly her up, but it was no good. She tramped behind me as I took her on a tour of the kitchens, commenting only in disapproving monosyllables. She hardly glanced at the cupboard that I had turned out that morning, but fixed a steely gaze on such things as the spoon drawer, and the other store cupboard, which I hadn't had time to do. Polly had evidently got sick of cleaning out larders, for she had abandoned the last one half-way through. She had put the food on to the floor in order to scrub the shelves and there it still sat: a ham, an apple pie, three cold sausages, and a piece of Gruyère, mutely imploring Mrs Macbonn not to be too hard on it.

When we got back to the kitchen we faced each other in the middle of the floor, and I smiled deprecatingly, but she just gave me one long withering look of pity, and then, turning away, was suddenly transformed into a whirling dynamo of frenzied activity. She fell on the cupboard like a madwoman, and started to clear out its contents with raking sweeps. 'Pardon,' she said, knocking into me as I got in her way. 'Granted,' I replied, and removed myself dispiritedly to the servants' hall, where I sat kicking the table legs and listening to her hurrying back and forth among the larders and pantries on her purgative mission.

I had meant to offer to help her cook the dinner, but now I saw that I should be more of a hindrance. She had taken complete possession of my kitchen, so she could jolly

150

well stew in her own juice. When tea time came, however, I thought I had better go in and tell her about heating up the scones that I had made. It was superfluous as she had already discovered them, and though they were, admittedly, a bit moth-eaten, I was distinctly outraged when I saw that she had gone so far as to throw them away and make a fresh batch of her own. When I went in she was just taking them out of the oven, with much deft flourishing of cloths and oven trays, and I was even more infuriated to see that she had made a perfect batch, risen up to a beautiful lightness, all neat and shapely, with glazed brown tops. Swallowing my jealous resentment, I forced myself to say brightly: 'What lovely scones, Mrs Macbonn! I'm afraid you're putting me to shame.'

'Ah, well,' she said tight-lipped, 'you'll learn some day, I expect.'

'I'm afraid you found the place rather untidy,' I pursued, mortifying myself still further for the good of my soul.

She became even more righteous: 'Well, of course, it's not at *all* what I've been accustomed to, but I'll soon get things straight, I daresay. I'm afraid I never *could* do with disorder round me, but we can't all be made the same way. Where's the kitchen-maid? Surely she should be here helping me?'

'I always let her go off in the afternoon, as there really isn't much to do. She's a bit – you know – ' I tapped my forehead, 'and she likes to wander about outside. She'll be back in time for her tea.'

'Well, we'll soon alter *that*,' said Mrs Macbonn grimly. 'There are one or two things that will have to be reorganized around here, I can see that.'

I wished her joy of reorganizing Polly, who would undoubtedly go over the top at the first word; but I also felt desperately sorry for the poor girl at the mercy of this horse-faced woman.

'Oh, *please*,' I begged, '*please* be nice to Polly. She means so well, and she can't help being a bit peculiar. You'll upset her dreadfully if you say anything to her, so *please* do be kind.'

'I hope I shall treat her with the fairness which I am accustomed to show to those around me,' she said, raising the iron-grey bars of her eyebrows; 'we should all get what we deserve in this life, no more, no less. Incompetence or slovenliness is abhorrent to me.' There was not much hope for poor Poll then, so I gave it up and went into the servants' hall where the others were sitting waiting for their tea.

'What's she like?' asked Rose, making a face in the direction of the kitchen.

'Oh, divine,' I said; 'you'll love her merry little ways.'

Mrs Macbonn came in at this moment, followed by Nellie bearing the teapot. 'Where do I sit, please?' she inquired, and was given my seat beside Dawkes, while I went and sat below the salt with Polly. The atmosphere was rather strained. For one thing, Dawkes was still broody as long as I was about, and the Macbonn was unpromising material for whoopee. Stiff as a girder, she sat dispensing tea, our polite conversational remarks rebounding off her like bullets off sheet-iron. Tomorrow was Sunday, and Miss Biggs was talking about the vicar's beautiful sermons.

'Perhaps you would like to come with me to church, Mrs Mactart?' she said kindly. 'Lady W— always sends us in the Morris with Joseph. May I ask what persuasion you are?'

'Thank you,' said Mrs Macbonn, turning not only her head but her whole body round to Miss Biggs, 'but I live my religion in my life. If I wish to say my prayers I can perfectly well do so in an open field.'

The staggering vision that this conjured up definitely quenched the feeble spark of conversation, and though one or two people tried to revive it by tentative throat clearings, it was no good. I looked at the clock and was thankful to see that it was time for me to go and get my things on if I was to catch my train. When I came down again Mrs Macbonn had retired to the kitchen, so I was able to say good-bye to the others in a less restrained atmosphere. Dawkes had gone to remove the drawing-room tea, so, when no one was looking, I placed in his chair the inverted drawing-pin that I had been saving up for this purpose. Prep-school humour can sometimes be very satisfying even if one is not present at the *dénouement*.

I shook hands all round; we were suddenly very shy of one another and could only say: 'Well, good-bye – take care of yourself, good-bye – good luck, and – well – good-bye.' I popped my head round the kitchen door to wave to Mrs Macbonn, who was pounding steak with brutal thoroughness, and she favoured me with a sort of reserved fascist salute, but her face muscles wouldn't run to a smile.

Joseph was taking me to the station as Jim was out in the car. I had already said good-bye to him, and received his renewed thanks for my part in his romance, which was now going swimmingly; he had bought Bessie a ring, and she even spoke of him as 'my fiancy in the motor business'.

The tin suitcase once more found a resting-place in the piggery, and, climbing up beside Joseph, I fell back on to the seat as he let in the clutch with a jerk, and we roared up the back drive and away from Chilford House for ever.

# Chapter Twelve

WHEN I got home I found it extremely difficult to resume my normal life again. Having been surrounded for so long by the atmosphere of domestic service I felt like a fish out of water, and even to sleep in a decent bed felt peculiar. I thought I might as well go on doing a bit of work while I was in the mood for it. I didn't want to get another job through 'Jobfinders' if it meant paying commission, but it was another matter when they rang me up and offered me 'casual labour'. I inquired very sheenlly whether they wanted commission on it, and the woman at the other end evidently thought this in very bad taste, for she replied in a pinched voice, 'No, we do not,' and rang off.

She had offered me two jobs. The first was to cook and wait at a dinner for six people in a flat off Edgware Road. I got on to Mrs Drew, the prospective hostess, and she fluttered and stuttered at me through the telephone in a futile but amiable way.

'You must think it *very* stupid of me,' she said, 'but I simply don't know anything about cooking, and my maid suddenly has to go to her uncle's funeral, just on the day when I had planned this dinner. It's too late to put the guests off now, and I *do* so want it to be a tremendous success. Could you really manage the cooking and waiting by yourself?'

I said 'Yes' automatically, although I should have added, 'Not without a lot of chaos.'

'How *splendid*,' said Mrs Drew. 'I'll have everything ready for you. My maid is going to tell me what I should order before she goes. You will be sure to come in good time, won't you? What time will you get here?'

I asked her how much there would be to cook, and a lot of rustling went on at the other end, and she even dropped the telephone before she answered: 'Oh dear, I've gone and lost the list, but I think I can remember. Soup, I thought, to start with, or did I finally decide on grape-fruit? No, it was soup because I remember thinking "how warming". Grape-fruit is refreshing, of course, and rather party-like, too, don't you think? I wonder – '

'I should have grape-fruit,' I said decisively, thinking to save myself trouble.

'Do you think so? Very well then, let me just write that down. I'm afraid you'll think me very stupid, but my memory's so terrible. I simply can't remember what else I decided on. That list – '

'Well, shall I come along the day after tomorrow, at about half past four, and you can tell me then?' I said, as I was getting sick of the ravings and gaspings that were coming over the air.

'Oh, yes, that will be *splendid*. The day after tomorrow then – half past four. *Splendid* – I do hope – ' She still didn't seem able to ring off, so I said, 'Good-bye' firmly and planked down my receiver.

The other job that the agency had offered me was to be a waitress at a cocktail party, which I understood was to be in the nature of a celebration for an engaged couple. I rang up Mrs Elkington, the mother of the bride-to-be, and she put on a suspicious voice and said she must see me before she engaged me, in case I was covered with sores or something, I suppose. The party was not for a week's time, but I thought I might as well get the inspection over at once, so I arranged to go along to her house near Sloane Square that afternoon. I decided that, to make a change and to pander to the finicky sound of Mrs Elkington's voice, I would be a very superior parlour-maid, deadly refined, and expecting to be addressed by my surname. I discarded Ye Olde Blacke Hatte for once and got myself up neat, plain, and prosperous, and it all seemed to go down quite well with Mrs Elkington.

She was sitting in her large drawing-room, surrounded by patterns of stuff, lists, and catalogues and all the paraphernalia that float about when a wedding is being arranged. I sat bolt upright on a chair rising out of a sea of tissue-paper, and told her that I had practically spent my life handing round trays.

'What is your name?' she inquired at the end of the interview.

'Plover, madam,' I answered, making a bad-smell-under-the-nose face.

She seemed quite impressed by this, so my hours of hunting through the telephone book had not been wasted.

'Do you wish me to wear mai black or mai blue, madam?'

'Black, please, with a cap, of course. Well, that's all, Plover, I shall expect you here on Tuesday at five o'clock then.'

As I was going down the stairs a very pretty dark girl passed me on her way up and raised her eyebrows at me in disinterested inquiry. She had a large diamond on her engagement finger, so I supposed she was the bride-to-be. She looked a bit sulky, and not particularly happy – perhaps it was a *mariage de convenance*.

Mrs Drew was my more immediate concern, however, so I ceased to be Plover and prepared to do battle in Edgware Road. I had not worn my uniform for some time, and I had forgotten just how dirty and weatherbeaten it was. I retrieved it from where it was lying in a crimpled ball at the bottom of a drawer and ironed it and tried to sponge off some of the worst hall-marks of drudgery. I had had to cook in it when I was a 'general', covering the frills with a large gingham apron which I removed at the last minute so as to be able to transform myself from cook to parlour-maid when I had to take in the dishes.

I went along to Edgware Road in my blue as I wanted to keep the black to be Plover in. Mrs Drew was out when I arrived, but she had told the porter to let me in, and had left a long rambling note for me on the kitchen table. The menu for dinner was written out, interspersed with such remarks as: 'When the baker comes, please order one large white and one small brown or wholemeal if he has it, or currant ditto.' 'Do not use best butter. Marg. and lard in cupboard.' 'Can you stuff duck at both ends? If so, do.'

She had evidently changed her mind again about the grapefruit, for the dinner was to start with soup after all. Fried fish came next, with a shrimp sauce, and then the duck, with vegetables. 'Trifle,' said the list after that, 'with a dash of sherry, which is behind dustbin under sink.' I thought I had better make it at once if it was to get cold by dinner-time. Mrs Drew seemed to have bought the provisions more or less efficiently, though there was much too much of some things and not enough of others. Milk was rather short, so I had to make a stodgy trifle that was more sponge-cake than custard. I added quite a lot of the rather acid-smelling cooking sherry to pep it up a bit and put it into the refrigerator.

I was getting on quite nicely with the other things when Mrs Drew came to disturb my peace, staggering in under armfuls of flowers and parcels. She was an untidy little woman with wisps of hair escaping from under her hat, and only one glove.

'Dropped my other one in the shops somewhere,' she said; 'wasn't it stupid of me? I went back to look for it, but it was so difficult to remember where I'd been that, of course, I never found it. I think I've got everything now for the dinner – flowers, sweets, almonds. What's in this box, I wonder? I don't remember buying any biscuits or anything. Oh, no, of course, that must be my shoes.'

'Excuse me, madam,' I said, removing them from where she had laid them down on the fish.

'Thank you *so* much. Are you getting on all right, Miss – er? I shan't be in your way if I just arrange these flowers, shall I?'

It was not for me to say that I was in the middle of peeling vegetables in the sink, so I had to take them out and start on something else. For the next few minutes we bumped around together in the small kitchen, she chatting disjointedly about the dinner and me interjecting 'Pardon' or 'Excuse me' at intervals. After a bit I got tired of knocking into her and having to reach across or round her every time I wanted something out of the cupboard. I had heard enough to satisfy my curiosity about the people who were coming. The guests of honour, apparently, were her husband's boss and his wife, on whom Mrs Drew was desperately anxious to make an impression, and there was another married couple, a sister, thrown in to make weight. I went away to lay the table, and when I came back she had finished her flowers and was on her knees in front of the open oven, poking at the duck with a dubious finger. 'Which end did you stuff it?' she asked.

'You told me to stuff it both ends, madam,' I said righteously.

'Oh, did I? So I did. That's *splendid*. I do hope it's going to be enough for six people. What do you think?'

I didn't think it was nearly big enough myself, but there wasn't much point in adding to her anxiety by saying so, so I said, 'Ample, madam, excuse me,' and pushed her gently aside to baste the puny bird.

She went off at last to dress, and I started the familiar panic, suddenly realizing that, as usual, I had left myself too little time to get things done. Mrs Drew didn't help by flying in in her négligée to say: 'Oh dear, you've put out the white mats and I wanted the green. Didn't I tell you? Well, never mind. Or have you got time to change them?' I found it impossible to take things calmly with her flapping around, and soon we were both rushing about like a couple of clucking hens, working each other up into a state. Mr Drew came in in the middle of it all. He was a large, helpless sort of man, with a funny little baby face stuck up on top of his lumbering body, and a surprisingly thin high voice. His wife shooed him off to change, and after a bit he came into the kitchen with a half-bottle of sherry, just one grade higher than the stuff I had put into the trifle. He poured it out with great care into six glasses and carried them proudly into the drawing-room on a tray. I didn't know what they were going to drink at dinner – I had put wine glasses out on spec – so I went in to ask him if I was to open any bottles of anything.

'Here is the wine,' he said proudly, handing me a bottle of Empire Burgundy.

'You devils,' I thought, carrying it away at arm's length.

I took a pretty gloomy view of this dinner party altogether. The host and hostess were each as nervous and anxious as the other. He was pacing the floor fingering his tie, and she kept darting into the kitchen to ask futile questions. I took an even more gloomy view when I took out the trifle to see whether it had got properly cold. The thing was tepid! Even the dish was still faintly warm. I put my hand into the frig and, if anything, it was warmer in there than in the kitchen.

'Madam,' I said despairingly as Mrs Drew came poking in again in a trailing chiffon dress, 'your frig is out of order and the trifle hasn't got cold.'

'Oh, my goodness,' she gasped, 'didn't I tell you? It's been wrong for days and the man simply *will* not come. I keep ringing them up. Oh dear, oh dear, of course, it never occurred to me about the trifle, I thought you made it cold.'

'Well, madam, custard must be made hot, you know,' I pointed out, keeping my temper and my manners with difficulty.

'Yes, yes, of course. I never thought of that. How very dreadful it all is. Couldn't you put it out on the window-sill to cool?'

Well, it was her picnic, so I balanced it precariously on the narrow ledge and she went out, rather pleased with herself, but going into a terrified scuttle as the front-door bell rang.

I didn't imagine that the two people whom I admitted were the guests of honour, as they looked more like a pair of nervous ducks than anything else. I asked the sister whether she would like to go to the bedroom and she shook her head, after throwing a scared glance at her husband, who just stood with his toes turned in, making a pinched mouth of shyness. I opened the drawing-room door.

'Mr and Mrs Mottershead,' I announced, and shooed them firmly in.

The guests of honour were a little late, which was all to the good, as it gave the carrots a few more minutes in which to become less rock-like. When they did arrive I saw at once that they were not at all the sort of people to appreciate Empire wine and tepid trifle. 'Why have you come here in your fat opulence?' I wondered. Mr Garrow had probably been dragged here by his wife to fulfil some overdue politeness, and his red-veined face was sulky with annoyance as he followed his wife into the drawing-room.

'Dinner is served!' I announced afterwards, giving the carrots up as a bad job, and the embarrassed spasms of conversation broke off with relief as the party trooped into the dining-room with much shuffling of feet and 'After you's' at the door. After more shuffling they somehow all got seated, not at all in the places that Mrs Drew had intended, but she was not really clear about it in her mind anyway.

As usual, I was too busy to notice much of the social side of the dinner, but I could see that it was one of the saddest parties ever, and my food had turned out dreary and un-appetizing, as if in sympathy with the general atmosphere. When I got as far as Mr Garrow with my reluctant chant of: 'Will you take wine?' he nearly had a stroke at the sight of the bottle. I think he thought that he would be offered something else, for I saw his eyes follow me incredulously as I filled up the last glass and went out to get my duck.

By the end of the next course Mr Garrow's conversation had dwindled from monosyllables to grunts, and his wife was struggling gallantly to keep it going. When it was time for the sweet my brain had gone as feathery as Mrs Drew's, and I couldn't for the life of me think what I had done with the trifle. It suddenly came back to me, and I fished it indoors, skimming off the black specks of soot as well as I could. Mr Garrow didn't miss much by refusing it. His eyes looked rather agonized, and I think his stomach was troubling him.

After coffee the ladies withdrew to talk about servants, and the gentlemen followed soon after as there was no port over which they could linger, and Mr Garrow's stomach was in no state to encourage jovial *camaraderie*. I was crashing away at the washing up when I heard someone come softly into the kitchen and close the door behind them. I hoped it was Mrs Drew with my pay, but when I turned round I was surprised to see Mr Garrow standing in a conspiratorial attitude with his finger to his lips.

'For God's sake,' he croaked, 'I must have a drink. Have you got anything?'

Poor man, he looked a wreck. Boredom and indigestion had played havoc with him. He was welcome to the remains of the cooking sherry, so I fished it out from behind the dustbin and, putting the bottle to his lips, he gulped it down at one draught. His eyebrows shot up as the stuff hit his stomach and his purple face became tinged with green.

'My God! What the devil – ?' His stomach now told him it was time for him to leave, and leave hurriedly. He stumbled from the room, a broken man.

Plover was resurrected in a week's time, and, wearing her black, with hair scraped unbecomingly backwards, she trotted off to Mrs Elkington's. It was evidently going to be a large party, judging by the number of waitresses and barmen who were surging about in the basement. I was shown where to leave my coat, and put on the cap that I had bought for the occasion. I had made the great mistake of not trying it on at home, so I was not prepared for the awful vision that gazed at me from the mirror when I tied it round my head. A little farther back, perhaps, more like a halo and less of that visor effect – that was better. I was just going to powder my nose when I heard cries of: 'Where are all these girls? Rose, Lilian, Plover – where is this Plover?'

I popped out into the passage and met a fat, harassed butler with a list in his hand.

'Who are you?' he said.

'Ai'm Plover,' I replied, smoothing my apron.

'Oh, you're Plover, are you? I've been looking for you. Your job is to hand round trays of cocktails, which you'll collect at the bar, see? Walking through the two rooms and filling up same place. Right now you can carry some glasses up from that pantry there to the bar on the landing.'

I went into the pantry, where a maid with a face like a pig was loading glasses on to a tray.

'Ooh,' she said, 'did you know your cap was slipping off? Let me pull it down for you before you lose it.' She rushed at me, and before I could stop her had converted my halo into a visor again. I felt an awful fool, and knew I looked it, but I couldn't very well wear it the way I wanted if people were going to come and pull it forward all the time.

Finding a tray, I started to stack glasses on to it, and when it was full, carried it carefully upstairs, wondering what would happen in the not unlikely event of my dropping the whole lot. I arrived safely on the first floor landing, a large square expanse with buffet tables round three sides of it. Three or four waiters were making champagne cocktails as fast as they could go, and I longed for one. I wouldn't have minded a *marron glacé* either; a huge bowl of them was right under my nose as I unloaded my glasses at one end of the bar, and I could easily have pinched one without anybody seeing, but 'No,' I said to myself, 'Plover would never do a thing like that.' Would Plover be above making friends with one of the barmen so that he would save her a cocktail when the party was over? I thought she might descend to it in her off moments, so I smiled seductively at the nearest one, a thin, pale youth with a protuberant Adam's apple. He stared through me unseeingly, so I tried again, and this time he just gave me a brief smile for civility's sake – a mere twitch of the lips. Poor Plover, spurned and humiliated! I hadn't realized that I looked quite so frightful in that cap. I pushed it up a bit surreptitiously as I went downstairs, but it had fallen over my eyes again by the time I got back to the pantry, so the pig-girl had nothing to complain of. I pushed it up again when she went out, but it was no good. I would have to put up with looking like a 1920 tennis player and give up the idea of a cocktail.

I carried up two more trayloads, and then somebody told me to get some cocktails and take my place in one of the two

162

big reception rooms leading out of each other, as the guests were due to arrive at any minute. The family were already standing uneasily about in new dresses and wondering whether they had invited people for the right day. I thought they looked as if they needed a drink, so I advanced carefully towards them over the parquet with my tray. Mrs Elkington was looking queenly in blue velvet with an excess of orchids.

'Have I time for a drink I wonder before we have to start receiving people? Why don't you have one, John? You look as if you needed it.'

John, I supposed, was her husband, a nondescript, nervous little man. He had to clear his throat twice before he could start to answer.

Their daughter, the girl I had met the other day on the stairs, broke in: 'Well, I'm going to have one, I feel terrible. How about you, Aunt Madge?' I gave her and Aunt Madge a cocktail and Uncle somebody thought it was a good idea, too. I looked round for the fiancé, but there was nobody in the room that I'd have had for any money. He couldn't have come yet, unless – oh dear, *could* it be this square little turkey-cock with red hair, who was even now making free with his arm about the lovely girl's waist? No wonder she felt terrible and looked sulky – who wouldn't? I grudgingly offered him a drink, and he took it in a pink and podgy hand. I couldn't think what to do now, so I copied one or two of the other waitresses and took up my stand by the wall, wearing an impersonal face. The fat butler appeared from the landing and said: 'The first guests are arriving, madam.'

Mother, father, daughter, and fiancé ranged themselves by the door, and in a minute or two the butler started to announce people in a quite unnecessarily loud voice.

'Mrs Boggan and Miss Kathleen Boggan!' he yelled, and two rather dusty-looking people shuffled in and were greeted effusively, though it was obvious that nobody knew who they were. The Boggans were well in advance of the main body of the guests, and they looked as if they wanted to go home again, but Aunt Madge and I came to the rescue simultaneously, I with my drink and she with her mauve hair and much-lifted face. She chatted to them about nothing in particular, and after a bit people started to arrive thick and fast. There was soon quite a crowd in the rooms, and I was rather scared of venturing among them with my tray, but one of the waitresses passed by me and said: 'You got to circulate, see?'

I had to leave my wall and pick my way carefully through the crowd, offering drinks here and there, and feeling as if I ought to be crying, 'Chocolates! Cigarettes!' I loaded on some more cocktails at the bar and started off all over again. It was really very amusing hearing snatches of conversation and observing people from under my cap, which was well down over my eyes by now.

'My dear, have you *ever*?' I heard one smart deb say to another. 'That horrid little man. How Ann *could* have – '

'I know; it can't be love. If you ask me it's a question of anything to get away from that mother of hers. They fight like hell, you know.' I wanted to hear more, but a large male was clicking his fingers at me a few yards away, so I had to go and give him and his lady-friend a drink. She gazed up at him with adoring eyes as he handed it her with an air.

'Oh, *thank* you,' she said as if he had bought it for her.

'Thank me, not him, he ain't done anything,' I thought as I moved away.

I was doing good work. My cocktails went rapidly, and I had to go back to the bar for more before I had got through the two rooms. I didn't know what to do with the dirty glasses that I had collected on my way. I asked a woman who was standing on the stairs directing people to the cloak-room, and she said: 'Couldn't şay, I'm sure. Ladies' cloak-room, madam? Up the stairs and first on the right, if you please.' They didn't want them at the bar and I obviously couldn't carry them down the stairs as guests were still flowing steadily up.

I felt a bit lost; I didn't like to ask the barman who had

turned me down, so I tried the next one along, who was bald and kind-looking. He jerked a thumb towards a small door leading out of the hall that I hadn't noticed before. I went through it and nearly fell down a long flight of stairs on the other side. One glass shot off the tray and bumped to the bottom where it broke with a noise like a plate-glass window.

'Struth, who done that?' said a raucous voice from below, and a creature in a green baize apron appeared, shook his head at me reprovingly, and vanished, leaving me to pick up the pieces. I kicked them into a corner, and was just wondering where to go now when Green Baize reappeared from a sort of scullery where he was evidently washing up.

'*In* 'ere, butter-fingers,' he said, and I dumped down my tray hurriedly and fled back up the stairs. I didn't wish to linger in his scullery as I felt he had me at a disadvantage, not to mention the fact that garlic had figured on his luncheon menu.

I loaded my tray at the bar again and set off on my circuit. Three more rounds and my feet were drawing as never before, but there was still quite a crowd left, so it was no good their telling me that they wanted to have the weight taken off them. It was tiring work and I began to feel a bit dazed and forgot to be Plover all the time. I offered a drink to two men who were talking together, and when one said to the other, 'What station does one go from for Portsmouth?' I answered automatically, 'Waterloo.' I was horrified, and they were a little startled, but being perfect gentlemen they smiled politely and said, 'Thank you.'

I pulled myself together after this *faux pas* and dashed about alertly, spilling some drink down a woman's back in my excess of zeal. She never noticed, so I hurried away before some kind friend could point it out.

The guests were beginning to thin out, but there were still quite a few who looked as if they would be with us for some time yet. I really felt exhausted, so next time I passed the little door I popped through it and knocked back two cocktails off my tray without drawing breath. I emerged a new

165

woman, beamingly impervious to the suspicious glance that the bald barman gave me.

'To hell with Plover and her scruples!' I thought, deftly taking a *marron glacé* as I passed, without checking my stride.

There were not many people left now and they all seemed to have drinks, so I leaned against a wall and watched them, feeling quite mellow. Ann Elkington was sitting on a sofa having an intimate conversation with someone who was certainly not her fiancé. He was strutting about at the other end of the room, talking business to an elderly bore. Mrs Elkington was having a good gossip with a woman who nodded the ostrich feathers in her hat every time they came to a bit of scandal. The host had disappeared. As one who had also been present since the beginning, I didn't blame him. I stood on like Casabianca, and some of the people trickled away, till there were only one or two groups left. A voice at my elbow roused me from the coma into which I had sunk. It was the girl who had told me to circulate. She thought me rather a poor fish and said pityingly: 'Don't you know you can go now? There's eats in the kitchen.'

I realized how hungry I was, so I threw my tray down on the bar and ran down the back stairs. I heard a lot of voices coming from the end of a passage, so I went along and there was the entire company with their mouths full of left-over sandwiches and cake. I suddenly felt fearfully shy. It may have been my imagination, but I sensed a rather hostile atmosphere. Nobody had been at all pally all the evening; Plover was hungry, but she was not popular. I spotted Green Baize, and the undesirous barman, and the pig-girl saw me in the doorway and shot a scornful glance at my head. I definitely couldn't face it, so I crept away to the room where I had left my coat and saw that my cap was sitting rather drunkenly over one eye. However, shy or not shy, I was not going without my money. Luckily the fat butler came out into the passage, so I didn't have to go into the kitchen.

'Who are *you*?' he said as I accosted him.

'I'm still Plover and I want my money,' I said, tired and cross.

'All right, all right, all right,' he said, drawing ten shillings out of his pocket in a lordly way and handing it to me with the tips of his fingers.

'Good naight!' I said, rallying Plover just once more before letting her pass into the valley of the shadow as I passed out of the back door into the area.

# Chapter Thirteen

I FRITTERED away another month or two doing occasional cooking and waiting jobs, but there didn't seem to be much demand for me in this capacity. Odd jobs like this, of course, are paid proportionately much higher than a regular place, and I suppose people thought they weren't getting their money's worth in me. The only person who ever engaged me more than once was a sour old lady, who was willing to pay me three-and-six a time to go and cook her dinner three evenings a week. After one or two treks out to her flat somewhere beyond the Crystal Palace I decided it wasn't worth it, and in any case she was becoming sourer and sourer as she got to know me better. I sat around at home and waited for the telephone to ring, but there was not much doing. In the absence of more high-class jobs I even went out once as a scullery-maid to wash up after a dinner party – a sordid pastime that turned out to be unexpectedly comic.

I was dumped into the scullery the moment I arrived, with strict injunctions not to stir from the sink. Starting with cocktail glasses, I ploughed my way through the mountains of stuff that were hurled at me by a procession of cheerfully indifferent maids as the dinner upstairs progressed. I was to do it all apparently. No one else intended to have any truck with dishcloths and greasy water – they had other plans for the evening. I gathered from the odd word thrown at me as they crashed in and out that the people upstairs were all going off to a dance at about ten o'clock.

After about two hours' slavery at the sink, with the skin on my hands becoming wrinkled and decayed-looking from the hot water, I heard attractive sounds of revelry floating down the passage from the kitchen. The noise grew louder, the blare of wireless mingling with shrieks and screams of high-pitched laughter. Although I had been told not to leave my sink, I wasn't going to be left out of it any longer. I had almost finished my work, anyway, so I threw down my sodden dishcloth and went along to gate-crash the most wonderful party that was being held in the kitchen. The butler, a sporting old devil with white hair, was taking advantage of his possession of the wine cellar key to celebrate his birthday in the best champagne and port that the house could offer. There he sat, jigging one of the parlourmaids on his knee to the tune of the foxtrot that some of the others were dancing.

'Heh!' he roared at me as I appeared in the doorway, 'what d'you think you're doing in here?'

'I've finished. Can I have a drink?' I roared back, emboldened by the gaiety of the atmosphere.

'Make yourself at home, this is Liberty 'All!' he shouted, and the boot-boy handed me a glass of champagne and said would I like to swing it with him. We swung it. We sang, we danced, we drank, we bumped into people, and played slap-and-tickle with everyone. They were a delightful lot in that kitchen, even if it was at somebody else's expense. The master of the house was a rich man anyway and could well afford it. I'm sure it was a much better party than any he had ever given upstairs for his débutante daughter, with inane girls and callow youths vying with each other to see who could enjoy themselves least.

I left before the end. I was doing fine with the boot-boy, but I suddenly felt very peculiar and thought I had better take the mixture of port and champagne home and put it to bed. A scullery-maid doesn't usually go home from her drudgery in a taxi, but this one had to. It was not until I was in bed, and hovering above the black abyss of alcholic oblivion, that I remembered that I had never finished my washing-up. Anyway, I hadn't had my pay either, but I just didn't care.

Apart from this one lively incident my jobs in various houses only served to convince me that human nature is not all it might be. I must have struck it unlucky, for apart from the fact that most of the people I went to never wanted to see me again, one meeting was certainly enough for me. I suppose I happened to go to poisonous people because they were the sort whom no maid would stand for long. I was beginning to take a gloomy view of life, but one evening I went out to cook a dinner and discovered that there was hope for the world yet.

Everything went right that evening, it was most peculiar. The egg that I put into the soup didn't curdle it, the omelettes were neat outside and runny inside, the meat was tender, and the fried potatoes crisp. Strangest of all, the cheese *soufflé* was ready at exactly the right moment. I hadn't dropped or spilled anything when handing round, nor had I gashed or burned myself in my usual style.

I was standing in the kitchen after dinner, pinching myself to see if it wasn't all a dream. I had just come to the conclusion that it was either something to do with the stars, or else my guardian angel had decided to throw his weight about, when the mistress of the house came in.

Mrs Vaughan had grown-up children – one of them was there that evening – but her hair had refused to go white or her figure to spread. She was like a brisk little sparrow, always hopping about doing things. She had even kept jumping up at dinner to get things instead of mouthing at me, like most of my employers. Her motto was, evidently, 'If you want a thing done, do it yourself' – that was probably the way she kept her figure. She pottered round the kitchen, fiddling with things while she talked.

'Miss Dickens,' she said, breathing on a glass and polishing it with her handkerchief, 'we did so enjoy your dinner tonight. Everything went off wonderfully, I thought. I suppose you wouldn't ever – ? No, I don't suppose you would – well, I don't see why not after all, it's worth asking you, anyway. I've been wondering if you could possibly help us out. Would you consider coming here as a permanency? – As cook-general, I mean? I have a girl who comes in for housework in the mornings, but apart from that we're stranded. My cook walked out suddenly – she was mad anyway, poor thing – and I can't get anyone for love or money. It's not a large flat, as you can see. The work's not hard, it's just my husband and me when there's no one staying. We never have formal parties or anything, people come into meals quite a lot, of course, and I really think you might be happy here. I'm sure we should be more than happy to have you.'

The idea attracted me, they seemed such very nice people, so I accepted as soon as I could get a word in edgeways. I felt I ought to tell her that my performance tonight had been well above my usual standard, but I didn't get a chance, because the flow of speech had started once more, and the whole thing was fixed up with scarcely a word from me. She tried to persuade me to live in, because she thought it would be less tiring for me, but I didn't want to risk any more black iron beds or smelly furniture, so I produced the widowed mother again as an excuse for sleeping at home.

It wasn't far to go in the morning, and as they didn't want to be called particularly early I didn't have to rise at crack of dawn.

I made early-morning tea, and, going into the bedroom, dumped it down between the two mounds of sleeping humanity. Mrs Vaughan woke as I drew the curtains and plunged in the most amazing way straight from sleep into conversation. All about the breakfast it was, and where I should find this and where to put that. I had a feeling she had told it me all the night before, but my brain, which had been conscious for a good hour longer than hers, wasn't nearly as awake. Thoughts were clicking around in Mrs Vaughan's mind with whirling speed, but in mine they were still groping about in a confused fog left over from the hours of darkness.

She looked rather sweet in bed, very tiny, with a wee pigtail of thin hair lying neatly over one shoulder. I stood looking at her with my mouth open, taking in some of the talk, and eventually the larger hump in the other bed heaved and said: 'Really, dearest, what a noise you make.'

'Well, I must tell Monica what to do, it's her first morning. If you'd be a little more helpful and say whether

171

you want sardines for breakfast we might get somewhere.'

'Sardines?' he said on a huge yawn. 'Not if they're like the last lot you gave me.'

'Don't be silly,' said his wife, 'those were the ones Agnes opened and left in the tin for two weeks. They've been thrown away days ago – I hope. I had the most amazing dream last night, all about Uncle Rupert. We were in Prague – ' Bird-like, her brain skipped from one subject to the next with bewildering quickness. I was still standing with my mouth open in case there were any more instructions, so I coughed to show I was still there.

'Oh, yes, Monica, sardines,' she said, hopping from Uncle Rupert to breakfast with the same agility. 'And scrambled egg!' she called after me as I went out. ' – So I knelt down in the road,' she had picked up the threads again before I was out of the door.

I started to dust the dining-room, but it was a disheartening task as there were so many things standing about. Framed photographs there were and ornaments and statues of every description, probably presents that couldn't be thrown away in case the person who gave them should die. I contented myself with flicking a feather duster over one or two things, including a few small silver cups for seaside golf tournaments. It was obviously hopeless to embark on pictures on the walls, there were so many of them that I could hardly see the colour of the wall-paper. When I heard Mr Vaughan go slop-slopping to his bath I laid the table and started to cook the breakfast.

Mrs Vaughan came soon pattering in in her little red slippers to see how I was getting on.

'Are you sure there's nothing I can do to help you?' she asked. 'I know it's difficult the first morning. Here, let me take this coffee-pot in for you.' It wasn't ready to go in yet as it hadn't any coffee in it, but I let her trot away with it and went and retrieved it when she had gone back to her room to dress. Mr Vaughan was ready before I was, and prowled about, saying, 'Why isn't breakfast in? I shall be late for the office.'

172

'Now, darling, you know we never have it before a quarter past nine,' said his wife, popping out of her room with her mouth full of hairpins and her hands busy with her small bun. 'You never leave the house before ten anyway, so don't pretend you're so hard-working.'

'I thought of walking across the park this morning. I want to see what our wonderful bureaucratic system is doing about those trenches.'

'Well, you can see tomorrow. I don't suppose they'll have done anything before then. I've told you ten times it's Monica's first morning so don't be difficult. She's doing very well; I think she'll do.'

I kept the kitchen door open to listen to their idle chatter as I finished getting the breakfast ready. I was glad to see that there was going to be no *pas devant la bonne* in this household; they either considered me so human that I was almost one of them, or so stupid that I couldn't take much in.

While they were having their breakfast there was a ring at the back door and I opened it on a large girl of greasy but cheerful aspect. She goggled at me and could have been knocked down by the proverbial feather.

'Where's Agnes?'

'She's gone. I'm the new cook.'

'Go on, you don't say. Things certainly move fast around here. One day I come and there's Agnes, and the next day I come and "Agnes is gone", says you. What's your name, dear?'

'Monica.'

'That's ever so nice, I like that. Mine's Maud. That's pretty, too, I think. Mrs Vaughan says there's a poem about me. Fancy! Ever such a nice lady, Mrs Vaughan is. A great one for a chat, too. No swank, though she does know her place, if you know what I mean. Not above sitting down to a boiled egg now and then when she's alone. Got a cup of tea for me, dear? Agnes and me, we always used to have a cup of tea before starting on the trivial round, the common task, as we say Sundays.'

Anyone could have got on with Maud, she was such a

cheery soul, and we were bosom pals by the time we had finished the second cup.

'Fortunes now,' she said, turning both our cups upside down and tapping on their bottoms with a mystic rhythm. 'Let's see what you got. Oh, you lucky girl! Look, dear, you got two spoons near the top. That means flirtations, and this ring by the handle, that's a wedding. That's a lovely cup, that is. Look at all these dots. They mean money coming to you.'

I was thrilled to the core. 'How d'you do it, Maud?' I asked.

'Oh, it's a science, dear, same as astronomy and that. Oh, look!' she said, turning up her cup, 'scissors. That's quarrels. All the leaves at the bottom, too, that means bad luck. I'm afraid you couldn't possibly call this a swan here, could you? I sail into more prosperous waters if it is. I never seem to have much luck with the cups. Cards, now, that's another story, but cups! The things I've seen! I had a coffin once. That was a terrible day.'

'Did anyone die?'

'No, dear, but they might have. You've got to think of that.'

The front door slammed. 'Ah, that's our boss off to work, bless his heart. Her ladyship'll be in directly, to order, so we'd better be getting a move on.' She explained to me how the work was supposed to be divided between us, and then Mrs Vaughan came in and told it me all over again. She and Maud were evidently old friends. They had a little chat about Maud's mother's diabetes, before she went off to make beds, and Mrs Vaughan settled down to order the food. She kept dashing out to answer the telephone, which I thought rather complicated things, but she seemed to be able to cope all right.

'Steak, tonight,' she would be saying. Ting-ting, ting-ting! went the telephone, and off she would run. She reappeared saying: 'with plenty of onions,' as if she had never been away. We got everything settled and she walked out for good, only to reappear two minutes later to say that someone had rung up and asked themselves to lunch. While we were in the middle of rearranging things slightly, the milkman arrived.

'How's your little boy getting on, Mr Finnigan?' she asked.

'Nicely, thank you, Mum. They say he can come out in a week. It was ever so good of you to send them toys. Thank you ever so much, I'm sure.'

Mrs Vaughan went off to spend the morning at a prison, handing out library books to the convicts. The woman was nothing but a communal benefactress, and I was not surprised when the lunch visitor turned out to be a woman who had left her husband and wanted advice, and, incidentally, money. She got both, from what I could hear as I handed round the cutlets and treacle tart. I was the parlour-maid, Maud only did housework and 'rough', and she left before lunch. She fulfilled the duties of a char really, though the word didn't fit her. She had another cup of tea 'for the road', and saw a lighthouse in it, which sent her off in good spirits, babbling of legacies.

One of Mrs Vaughan's two married daughters dropped in to tea, a stout, overpowering girl, about three times the size of her mother. They were discussing some rather absorbing medical details when I took in the tea, and I wanted to hear more, so I listened outside the door.

'Oh, dear, she's forgotten the sugar,' I heard Mrs Vaughan say. 'No, don't ring, Frances, we must save her legs. She has enough to do as it is. Let's do without sugar, I don't really mind whether I have it or not, do you?'

'Oh, Mummy, you know I can't drink tea without it. I suppose I'll have to get it myself. Really, you and your maids, the place might be a charitable institution. You collect a lot of old crocks and pay them colossal wages, and then proceed to spoil them, which they probably don't appreciate at all. I hope this one's not quite such an imbecile as Agnes. She – ' Here I surprised them by walking haughtily in with the sugar basin. I placed it on the tray, and stalked out again in my best Plover manner. Imbecile indeed! Old crock! I'd show her. They should realize that I had known better days in high-class kitchens.

For a little while I strove to be the perfect maid, nearly bursting myself with efficiency and correctness, but it wore off after a few days. Mrs Vaughan was just as charming to me whether I made Nonsenses or not, and the lack of formality with which all sorts of odd people tumbled over one another in the flat didn't encourage me to waste valuable energy on punctiliousness. There was a family dinner party while I was still conducting my efficiency campaign, and I couldn't make out why Clare, the youngest daughter, was reaching all round the table, opening the mustard and pepper pots.

'Look, everybody!' she cried, 'a revolution in the Vaughan household! Mustard and pepper in all the pots!' I didn't see what was funny enough in that to produce screams of joyous laugher from everyone.

'Look, Pa, that's something you've never known before isn't it?'

'I've told your mother time and again – ' he began, but nobody paid any attention.

'We've been used to shaking pepper pots fruitlessly for so long that you make us feel peculiar,' explained Clare to me as I handed her the bread sauce. I liked her. She was completely naïve and friendly, like a child, though she had one of her own, 'turned three', according to Maud. Frances was a bit more uppish, and I don't think her husband liked her particularly. He had probably married her on account of her father. He was in his office, so had hopes of advancement, but apart from that he thought Mr Vaughan quite the most entertaining man that ever walked. He was a wonderful audience for him, and would go black in the face and have to be led from the room if his father-in-law so much as said, 'Pass the salt.'

Although Maud was only thirty, she had been working for the family since she was eighteen, and knew more about their characters and life histories than they did themselves. I had a lot from Mrs Vaughan, of course, who was always ready for a chat at any hour of the day or night, and what she didn't tell me Maud supplied, with great exaggeration of detail. Once or twice a week, if there was a lot of work to be done, or a room to be turned out, she would stay a bit longer and have lunch with me in the kitchen. On these days, Mrs Vaughan, who always did us proud in the way of food, would order something for which she knew Maud had a particular fancy. Pork was her special delight. It made her face shine more than ever. Mrs Vaughan never poked into the larder, or inquired after puddings and things that had appeared once in the dining-room and only been half finished. They hardly ever appeared again if Maud and I could help it. 'Pity to leave it in the larder to go off,' we would say, as we polished off the best part of a trifle or blackcurrant tart. I got revoltingly fat under Maud's influence and nearly burst out of my uniform.

After lunch, she would relax with a long sigh and proceed to regale me with titbits and anecdotes about our employers. She was surprisingly old-fashioned in that she had quite a feudal feeling for the family. She was passionately keen that they should be kept in their place, both through our unfailing efforts and their own. She even thought that Mrs Vaughan 'demeaned herself' a bit too much, and certainly no one else might go as far.

'It's not *right*, Monica,' she would say. 'Mrs Chesterton' (that was Clare) 'didn't ought to walk about the streets without a hat – gives people ideas. But she always was one for doing funny things. D'you know – ' in an awestruck whisper, 'she has no white curtains up in any of the windows of her house! Very strange, I call that. It's not right, you know, for a young lady not to have everything nice. I used to tell her fortune with the cards before she got married. A tall, dark man, she was going to meet. Well, Mr Chesterton's fair, but he's tall all right, so it just shows. Ever such a nice gentleman he is. Always gives you your name.'

I was at the sink, washing dishes to the accompaniment of Maud's voice. 'What's the time?' I called over my shoulder.

'Half past kissing time, time to kiss again,' said Maud infuriatingly, as I really wanted to know. There was to be a tea party for the children this afternoon, and I had a lot to do. It turned out to be nearly half past three.

'Oh, my Gordon!' said Maud. 'I ought to be gone hours ago, Mother'll be getting nervy. You keep me here, chatting – '

'And I've got to start making cakes and things,' I said, breaking a plate in my haste. Maud got up and picked up a cloth.

'Come on, dear, I'll dry for you.'

'Oh, Maud, you are a love. Thanks ever so. Oh, heavens, I've hardly got any flour, I'll have to go and ring up for some. What a life this is.'

'Cheer up, dear, soon be dead,' said Maud blithely, breaking another plate, and hurling the pieces into the rubbish bin with gay abandon.

I went into the drawing-room where Mrs Vaughan was writing letters.

'May I use the phone, madam? I've run out of flour.'

'Certainly, Monica. Can you manage? I'll do it for you if you like. Did I hear Maud? She ought to have gone hours ago. She never used to stay so long when Agnes was here. She was frightened of her. She – '

I had to interrupt her, as a voice was saying, 'Hullo?' so her narrative was suspended while I put the fear of God into the grocer and made him promise to send round at once.

'She was a little mad, you know,' went on Mrs Vaughan, as soon as I put down the receiver. 'One day, we were going to have a dinner party, and I went into the kitchen about something, and there was Agnes sitting under the table, waving a burning duster, and singing "God Save the King". It *was* Coronation year, but still. She was a dear old thing, really though – '

I had to stand there listening politely, though there were masses of things I wanted to be doing. Mrs Vaughan talked and wrote at the same time, so she couldn't see me fidgeting

178

pointedly, and edging towards the door. Luckily the telephone rang, and though it was only a wrong number, it gave me a chance to escape.

When Maud had finished the drying, she heaved off to Paddington Green, where she lived with the diabetic one. Frances and her two children arrived early, only a few minutes after the grocer's boy, so I had to leave my scones to open the door to them.

'Ooh, look!' piped the eldest, a fat little brute called Angeline. 'She's got white stuff all over her face. Why has she, Mummy? She does look funny. Mummy, Mummy, doesn't she look funny?'

'Hush, dear,' said Frances, throwing me a surprised look. I had been prepared to undress the children, but I took umbrage and removed my flour-streaked face to the kitchen.

I made a lot of tea cakes and scones, and little buns, and I had made a big iced cake the day before, rather damp and undercooked, and probably fatal to small insides, but that was the mothers' lookout. I took everything into the drawing-room, where Mrs Vaughan was crawling on the floor playing bears with her three grandchildren. One or two nieces had also arrived with their young, and the place was in an uproar. To the children's great delight, and her own unconcern, Mrs Vaughan's bun had lost its moorings. I looked round for somewhere to put the heavy tray.

'Oh dear,' said my mistress, coming out from under the piano, 'I think we'd better have tea in the dining-room, then we can all sit round the table.'

Out I staggered, and bustled about finding tablecloths and extra chairs, and by the time everything was ready the tea was getting cold. I was glad I hadn't bothered to make a fresh pot, for the grown-ups didn't notice. Each mother was too intent on watching her own children, with tears of pride in her eyes, as they slopped their milk and spat out masticated gobs of bread and jam on the clean tablecloth.

Clare's little boy was my favourite, and she brought him into the kitchen after tea. I left him cold, but he felt a social obligation to entertain me, so went through his repertoire of songs with the air of one pandering to an inferior mentality.

Mr Vaughan came home before they had gone, and pretty soon he was on his knees too, and the whole flat was in such a turmoil that I couldn't even get among them to clear the tea. Screams and yells of over-excitement rent the air, and Philip, Frances' son who was a minute edition of his father, was, like him, convulsed with laughter at the ponderous antics of his grandfather. Needless to say, this turned into hysteria, and he lay kicking on his back till his mother came and took him off under one arm.

'Really, Pa, you are a nuisance,' she said irritably, 'you always work him up so. I'm going to take him home before he chokes himself or something. He'll probably be sick when we get back, anyway. Where on earth's Angeline got to?'

'Don't fuss, Frances,' said Mrs Vaughan, arriving on the scene with the other child. 'I've been wondering whether perhaps Angy's getting too much starch. Look at her little tum, it's like a football.' She prodded the offending part, and Angeline began to add her yells to her brother's. The exasperated Frances said hasty good-byes, and removed them both. Their yells could be heard floating up the lift-shaft as they descended.

When the last child had been hauled and slapped out of the front door by its harassed nurse or mother, Mrs Vaughan sank with a sigh of relief on to the sofa in the drawing-room, where I was tidying up.

'Thank goodness we're alone tonight,' she said to no one in particular. 'I'm really dead tired. Oh, that telephone!' She jumped up, though I was much nearer it than she was. I had ceased to bother about answering it when it rang, as she always came running anyway, and stood by my side saying, 'Is it for me?' while I was saying, 'Yes, madam; hold the line, madam.' It generally was for her, but even if someone did happen to want her husband, it made no difference. She carried on a long conversation with them in his place, until they sometimes forgot what they had rung up about, and rang off before she had even fetched Mr Vaughan.

'Hullo!' she was saying now. 'Oh, *hullo*, my dear – tonight? But, of course, we always love to see you. Sweet of you to want to come. Quarter to eight? – all right, that'll be lovely. Good-bye. There!' she said, turning to me, 'I spoke too soon. Mr and Mrs Fleming want to come to dinner tonight. I couldn't say no. I always think it's so touching when the young people want to come to the older ones. I hope there's enough to eat, that's all. What were we going to have?'

'Wild duck, madam.'

'Oh, dear, that won't be enough for four. We'd better have tomorrow's joint, and the duck can keep. If we've got enough vegetables, that'll be all right, and perhaps you could do us a Scotch woodcock or something, for a savoury.'

'Yes, madam. I'll go and put the joint in the oven, madam.' I spoke glumly, and I certainly felt glum. I still had all the washing up from tea to do, and then a dinner for four on top of that – my head ached from the racket of the afternoon, and my legs were not themselves at all. Anyway, I thought, I would leave most of the clearing up of the children's mess – sticky fingermarks on doors and paint, and bits of broken toys under the furniture. Maud and I could do it tomorrow. I banged out of the room, and Mrs Vaughan put me to shame by rushing after me saying: 'You poor dear, I'm afraid you're having a dreadful lot to do today. I tell you what, I'll help you with the washing up of the tea things. That'll make a little difference, won't it?'

Mr Vaughan came out of the dining-room. 'Monica! I wish you'd clear this table, I want to use it.'

'Oh, John,' said his wife, 'you're not going to work now, surely?'

'No, of course not. What d'you take me for? I'm going to paste photographs in the album.'

'Well, you must let Monica lay the table when she wants to. Mary and George are coming to dinner.'

'Oh, dearest, I thought we were alone. I wanted to listen to the wireless. There's a good concert from Stuttgart. *Why*

181

must you always ask people? Mary's so affected, she gives me the shivers.'

'She isn't, John; she's perfectly sweet. She's probably frightened of you. Some people are, you know, goodness knows why. Anyway, I didn't ask them, they asked themselves.'

'Well, it's a bore just the same. I think I'll have a Pink Gin to cheer me up.' There was a pause, followed by a roar: 'Who's taken the key of the wine cupboard?'

I had been clearing the table in the dining-room while all this was going on in the hall, and I came out now with my tray, as Mrs Vaughan pointed out that the key was in the cupboard door. 'Well, that's not its place,' he growled. 'It's supposed to live in the drawer of the hall table.'

'But, darling, that's so silly. If the idea is to stop Monica and me from drinking ourselves to death on your old brandy, there's no point in hiding the key where we know where it is. Why not either secrete it on your person, or else leave it in the door, which saves a lot of trouble. You're a sweet old man.' He screwed up his face to receive her kiss, patted her on the shoulder, and ambled off quite happily into the dining-room with his photos. He didn't seem to mind at all that no one took him seriously. I had been scared stiff at first when he shouted at me for forgetting things or leaving the lights on, but I was already coming to regard him with the same affectionate lack of awe as the rest of the family.

Mrs Vaughan followed me into the kitchen, where I was just putting the joint into the oven. I started the washing up, and she stood by me and dried, pausing at intervals to go off into a soliloquy about something that she was wiping.

'I always think this is such a dear little milk jug. It was my mother's, you know; she loved silver just like I do. Oh, dear, this plate's got rather a bad crack. I expect that was Agnes. You will be very careful of it, won't you? Perhaps we oughtn't to use it. It's the only one left out of six that we had as a wedding present.'

We were getting along quite nicely, though there was still a lot to be done, when the front-door bell rang.

'I'll go,' said Mrs Vaughan. 'Your hands are wet.' I heard her greeting somebody in the hall: 'Why, Miss Nitchin! How nice to see you! Come in and have a glass of sherry.' She took the visitor into the drawing-room, and came flying back to me.

'I'm so sorry, Monica, I wanted to help you. Poor Miss Nitchin has so few friends. I simply must talk to her for a little. I only hope she won't expect to be asked to dinner. Would you bring in the sherry and some glasses?'

I was annoyed, not with her, because she was so charming and considerate, but with life in general. Fatigue, I suppose, because really, when I thought about it, I had no grievance at all. I told myself sourly that I was unworthy of such a good mistress, but it didn't stop me taking a very jaundiced view of Miss Nitchin, who sat shabbily and diffidently on the sofa sipping sherry, and moaning about the slump in the dressmaking business. She infuriated me to the point of almost cutting off the top of my thumb, as I sliced carrots viciously, wishing they were Miss Nitchin. I found some plaster in the bathroom, and got on with my cooking as well as I could. I decided to leave the rest of the washing up till after dinner. When I wanted to lay the table, I went and stood pointedly in the dining-room doorway, but it made no impression on the hunched figure sitting within, absorbed with pots of paste and snapshots of the back view of his wife as a foreground to the Grand Canal  I tried walking round the table and tripping over the cord of his electric lamp, and jogging his elbow at a ticklish moment. This did the trick.

'Oh, God,' he said, getting up resignedly, 'is there no peace?' I helped him gather up his things, and he took himself off to the drawing-room, where he luckily solved the Nitchin problem by saying: 'Oh, hullo, Miss Nitchin! Just going? That's too bad.'

This blasted her hopes of staying to dinner, and she went off, still moaning, only about ten minutes before the Flemings arrived. Mr Vaughan was right about the affectation. Mary Fleming spent most of the evening giggling and chirruping coyly at him. He was very nice to her, however, and she sat on his right hand, and before long he was discovering how pretty she was, and feeling quite a gay old dog. His wife noticed my bandaged thumb, while I was handing round the dishes, and showed great concern. 'I'll put some iodine on it for you afterwards. Now don't forget and go home before I've seen it.'

There was not much chance of my forgetting it, as it was giving me real agony. Between my thumb, and my head and my legs, the end of dinner found me a wreck; I felt more like putting my head in the gas oven, than clearing the table and washing up. My eye fell on a decanter of sherry which was standing on the sideboard, and I considered it fixedly for some time. Well, after all, why shouldn't I? One quick nip – it would just give me enough heart to finish off what I had to do. Glancing furtively over my shoulder, I poured out quite half a tumblerful, and tossed it off. Everything went black, and then balls of fire shot up my throat, and exploded in a thousand stars before my eyes. It was not sherry at all – it was whisky! Once I had got over the first shock, I felt terrific. I reeled into the kitchen, polished off the work with the speed of a machine, and rushed off home, quite forgetting the iodine, for the pain in my thumb was miraculously cured.

# Chapter Fourteen

ONE day, after I had been at the Vaughans' about a month, the peace of an October Sunday afternoon was broken by a violent pealing of the bell, and hammerings of fists on the front door. I left the crumpets, which I had just put under the grill, and flew to open it. A distraught figure there – Clare, with her hair standing on end, and her eyes wild and red with weeping. She rushed past me into the drawing-room, screaming, 'Mummy, Mummy, Mummy!' and, flinging herself into her mother's arms, burst into floods of tears.

I wasn't going to miss a scene like this, so I took up a strategic position behind the half-open door, and waited, while Clare was gradually calmed by her mother into a state fit for speech.

'What is it, darling?' she said, when the sobs had been choked back into isolated hiccoughs. 'Tell me what it's all about.'

'Oh, Mummy, it's Alec. They've taken him to a Nursing Home. Mummy, he's got to have an operation – tonight!'

'An operation?' said her father. 'What d'you mean? What for?'

'He suddenly had the most awful sort of attack after lunch, and I thought he was going to die, and then the doctor came, and they took him away – oh, it was awful – in an ambulance! They wouldn't let me go in it. He looked all peculiar, he – ' she burst into tears again, burying her head in her mother's lap, from the smothered sound of the sobs that I heard.

'Yes, but for heaven's sake, Clare, what *for*?'

'Appendicitis!' came a muffled wail.

Her father, who had been holding his breath in his agitation, let it all out on a sigh of relief. 'Is that all? Why, that's nothing these days, darling.'

'Nothing, you call it? I think it's g-ghastly. Oh, poor Alec! Oh, Mummy, suppose something goes wrong, he's never been ill before, what if he can't take gas properly or something? Oh – '

'Now, Clare, darling, don't be hysterical. People have their appendixes out every day of the week. It's sure to be all right; especially as they've caught it at once.' Her mother was being wonderfully calm, as she undoubtedly always would be in any crisis. 'When are they going to operate?'

'Six o'clock. Can we go there, d'you suppose?'

'Yes, of course. Where is he? Wimpole Street? We'll go along at once.'

'Who's doing the operation?' asked Mr Vaughan.

'Some butcher called Wilson-Stokes. Have you ever heard of him?'

'Old Stokey? I should think I had. Why, we were at Cambridge together. Grand lad, Stokey, he'll look after Alec all right, don't you worry. Most amusing devil; I remember he and I once had a terrific row about a girl in a draper's shop. She – '

'John, dear, stop reminiscing, and go and ring up a taxi. And get Clare some brandy, that's what she needs.'

I had been so engrossed in this human drama, that it was not until I skipped out of the way before Mr Vaughan should come out, that my nose told me what to expect in the kitchen. At first sight, I thought the whole stove was on fire, but then I saw that it was only my crumpets blazing merrily away under the grill. I dashed water on to them, to quench the flames, and went out to the dustbin to throw away the blackened remains before anyone could see what I had done. I couldn't think what the faint roaring noise was, and it was not until the kitchen began to smell like an air-raid that I realized that I had forgotten to turn off the taps, after putting out the flames.

I opened the window wide, but Mrs Vaughan came in, and nearly fainted as the atmosphere hit her.

'Goodness, Monica, what have you been doing?'

'Cooking crumpets, madam.'

'Well, they smell rather funny. Never mind, we shan't be wanting any tea anyway; we all have to go out. Poor Mr Chesterton has to have an operation for appendicitis, isn't that bad luck?'

'Well, I am sorry to hear that. Who'd have thought it?' I said, feigning great surprise at the news; 'I hope everything'll go off all right, madam, I'm sure.'

'Oh, yes, of course, we don't expect any trouble. I thought it would be a good thing for Mrs Chesterton to stay here for a bit, though, it's so much nearer the Home. Would you make up the bed in the little spare room before you go? – and lay supper for three – I don't know when we'll be back. Then tomorrow Miss Clare is going to fetch little Peter and his nurse over; they can go into the big spare room, if they bring his cot. It'll be nice to have the little boy here – won't it? – ' She gazed at me anxiously, as my jaw was dropping a bit at the thought of all the extra work. She was afraid I was going to say: 'I've only got one pair of hands', or, 'It's not my work,' so I pulled myself together, and struggled to appear the old family servant, the rock – equal to any crisis.

'I'll try and get Maud to stay on for the whole day,' she went on, 'then we ought to be able to manage all right.' Wails of, 'Mummy, *do* let's go!' came from the hall, so she hurried off, throwing a few injunctions, such as 'Cold beef,' and 'Hot bottle,' at me over her shoulder.

When 'in service' one has a rather cold-blooded tendency to regard the emotions and hazards of one's employers' lives with a certain detachment – almost as if they were people in a play, and the kitchen was the back row of the pit. I was surprised, therefore, to find that the thought of the nice blond Alec Chesterton being slit open at six o'clock quite worried me.

When I arrived at the flat next morning, I didn't have to wait till I called Mrs Vaughan, to hear the news. The sight of the dining-room reassured me. They would not have made such a hearty meal, and washed it down with a bottle of champagne, if all had not gone well. I was able to greet Mrs Vaughan with a bright and appropriate smile, when she woke, as usual, as I put down the tea-tray.

'I'm so glad the operation went off all right, madam,' I said.

'Yes, isn't it splendid? But however did you know?'

'I just *knew*, madam,' I said mysteriously, 'I have a *feeling* about things sometimes.' I gave her a penetrating look, charged with psychic meaning, and went out, leaving her sitting bolt upright, staring after me in great astonishment.

I had been told not to wake Clare, and she slept on until long after Maud had arrived. She was fascinated by the whole story, and pressed me for medical details of the operation, which I was unable to supply, though I made a few up to keep her going. When Clare woke up, and yelled for her breakfast (none of this family ever rang bells – they had got so used to them not being answered), Maud insisted on taking in her tray. She was in there quite a quarter of an hour, and came out bursting with information. She was retailing it to me, when Mrs Vaughan came in, to ask her if she would be able to put in more time at the flat.

Maud sucked her teeth. 'I'd be very pleased to, 'm, I'm sure, but I'll have to ask Mum. She gets a funny head, you know, and doesn't like to be left. I think it'll be O.K. though, as a matter of fact, because my sister Ivy's at home for a bit now. She's theatrical, you know, resting before the Panto season. Principal Boy at Nottingham – *Babes in the Wood*, it is, 'm.' I had heard a lot about this Ivy, famed in the Theatre Royal or Hippodrome of many a provincial town as 'Gloria May, the Sweetheart of Bradford' (or Huddersfield, or Kidderminster, as the case might be).

'Shall I pop over at lunch-time, 'm, and see what Mum says?'

'Thank you so much, Maud. I do hope it'll be all right. It would be such a help to have you.'

Clare went off later on to fetch her nurse and child, and

Maud and I put in some good work, making the spare rooms a home from home. We had the same ideas about housework, both favouring the dust-under-the-bed method, our motto being: 'What the eye don't see, etc.' We got on very well together, especially when Mrs Vaughan was not hovering round us, making suggestions, and giving us the moral support of her conversation.

Maud 'popped' just before one, and soon afterwards the Chesterton *ménage* arrived, complete with all the etceteras that make a small child as bulky to travel with as an American heiress. I went down to help unload the car, and Mrs Vaughan and I had quite a tussle with a spring mattress, until we discovered that it came out quite easily if one pushed and the other pulled, instead of both tugging from opposite sides.

Peter sat up in a high chair at lunch, and pulled my apron strings undone every time I passed his corner of the table. He kept it dark from his nurse, for whom he seemed to have no very great affection. I didn't know her as well as he did, but from the look of her I didn't blame him. I should have thought the sight of her horse-face alone would have been enough to give any child inhibitions, apart from the fact that she exuded a most unpleasant smell of mothballs. She didn't seem to take much to me, either, and I wondered if we were fated to be mortal enemies. Sure enough, it was written by the hand of fate in my teacup that very afternoon.

Mrs Vaughan and her daughter went back to the Nursing Home soon after lunch, and the horse went for a trot with the pram. Maud arrived while I was washing up, with the glad news that her mother had given her consent, and, furthermore, as Aunt Maggie was coming to keep her company that afternoon, Gloria May had promised to shed the radiance of her presence on us, by coming to tea in the kitchen. I was thrilled at the idea of seeing a Principal Boy without tights and ostrich feathers; I had never met one off-stage, and Maud could hardly wait for me to meet her. She was terrifically proud of this sister, whom she regarded as a being from quite another world, as far removed from us in station as our employers.

Nurse was back by the time Gloria arrived, and she popped out of her room to see what she was like. She sniffed at what she saw, and went disdainfully back to her stable. I think she was jealous of Ivy's teeth, which had rushed to the front of her mouth in an even more dazzling profusion than hers.

The fame and adoration of the Provinces had not turned Ivy's head at all. She was just a very colourful edition of Maud, with the same jolly simplicity of heart. Her hair was curled in many sausages of brassy-gold, and jingling bracelets stretched from wrist to elbow over her dress of brightest emerald green – but then, you've got to have a bit of style if you're on the stage. She made a good tea.

'It's a good thing Mr Mosei likes a few curves in the right places,' she remarked, accepting a second slice of cake. 'Wouldn't suit me to have to watch my diet, I can tell you. Anyway, who wants to be skin and bone? Look at Sylvia Farrar, forty if she's a day, and looks fifty without her make-up.'

'Who's she?' asked Maud, hanging on her words, with rapt adoration.

'Principal Girl in *The Babes*. Lord, what a cat, and sour! My dear, don't speak of it. There'll be plenty of fights between her and Yours Truly before this season's over, or my name's not Gloria May.'

When we had finished tea, Maud said, 'Shall we tell the cups, Ive?'

'Not me,' said her sister, with a superstitious shudder. 'You don't catch me telling my fortune before the first night. Worst thing out for luck. You do yours though, go on.'

Maud peered into my cup, breathing heavily. 'Can't make head nor tail of this, dear. I believe this is a common quality tea. Ooh, whatever's this, though? A snake, look! Enemies and treachery. That's not a bit nice. Have another go, I should. Fill your cup up again, dear.'

'No, this is all right,' I said, 'I'd call this a horse at the bottom, wouldn't you, Maud?'

'I would, and kicking too.'

I was quite moved by this unmistakable sign from the beyond. It gave me a good excuse not to waste energy being friendly to Nurse, if fate had willed it otherwise.

Maud made a wish on hers, and there was quite a nice little crescent moon in her cup. 'Ooh, I say!' she breathed. 'Romance!'

'What did you wish about, Maud?'

'Ah, that's tellin'. Ask me no questions, I tell no lies.'

'Come off it, ducks,' said Gloria May, convulsed with toothy laughter. 'If you want to keep anything dark, you shouldn't let Mum know. She told me all about the postman looking sideways at you in Edgware Road. Lord! That reminds me, I promised I'd get home before Aunt Maggie goes; I must be toddling along.' She got up, drawing her fur-collared coat round her. 'Good-bye, all! It's been ever so nice to have met you, Miss Dixon.' She went off, with a flash of teeth, and a jingling wave of the hand, leaving us feeling very flat and dissatisfied with a life which made it possible for Nurse to summon one to the dining-room, by ringing the bell for more milk. I took it in with a glower of simmering hatred, quite worthy of the Demon King himself, in one of Ivy's pantomimes.

\*

According to the voluble bulletins that Mrs Vaughan gave us every morning, while ordering the meals, Clare's husband was continuing to make good progress, and no anxiety was felt about him. There was no reason, therefore, why a dinner party, which had been brewing for some time, should not be held.

'Are you sure you and Maud can manage all right by yourselves?' Mrs Vaughan asked me. 'We shall be ten, I think, but I can easily get someone in to help with the waiting.'

I said, 'No, no,' proudly, and assured her that it would

191

be a mere nothing to us. I didn't want to miss the amusing part, which was the handing round, and listening to scraps of conversation; also, we two fell over each other enough, as it was, without having another body to add to the confusion.

Confusion is the right word for the state we were in on the evening of the party. In contrast to the first dinner I had cooked at the Vaughans', this time, everything was going wrong.

It started by my dropping a milk bottle on the floor, leaving myself with nothing to make a White Sauce for the cauliflower.

'I'll pop out for some,' said Maud amiably, but by the time she got back, I had discovered that, though there would be White Sauce, there was no cauliflower to put in it.

'That greengrocer hasn't sent,' said Maud, 'I know his sort, I'll give him What For.' She was just going to pop again, when Clare came shouting that they wanted tea for three in the drawing-room, with Anchovy toast and Plum Cake. (How typical of Miss Nitchin to be here again today.) Would we also mind hurrying-up with the nursery tea, as Peter was screaming with hunger. Maud had to stay and help get the teas, as I was too busy cooking to be able to do more than watch the toast. I rang up the greengrocer as soon as I had a spare moment, and reviled him.

'Haven't got a boy in the shop,' he said, unabashed. 'Nor shall have before six, if then.'

'Maud, you'll have to go, we want potatoes, and onions, too.'

'O.K., dear, just wait till I take in this tea. What a to-do, eh?' She went out again, into the rain, and while she was gone, one or two bells kept me rushing about; once for more hot water, once for more jam sandwiches (Nurse), and once to open the door to a man selling tickets for the Fireman's Ball. All this meant that my Jugged Hare, which ought to have been put into the oven long ago, was making no progress at all. I couldn't find half the things to put in it, either.

'Maud, Maud!' when she came back laden with vegetables, and dripping rain-water on to the floor. 'Where's that Cooking Port we had left over from last week?' We started a frenzied searching.

'Can't see for looking,' said Maud, standing on a chair to look on the top shelf of the cupboard. 'Oh, my Gordon!' she cried, losing her balance, and staggering to the ground. 'Don't you remember, dear? We drank it that evening when I had the blues and you had the collywobbles.'

This was ghastly. I saw myself having to jug the hare with water and cochineal, and leaving the rest to the imagination of the diners. There was only one thing to do.

'We'll have to get a bottle out of the wine cupboard. The key's in the hall table. Maud, you do it, quick, while they're at tea.'

'Not me, I daren't. You go, dear.'

'No, you.'

We tossed for it in the end, and Maud lost.

'I'll take the cheapest-looking,' she whispered, tiptoeing into the hall with heavy thuds. Needless to say, Nurse chose this moment to finish her tea, and come out of the dining-room.

'Tra-la-la!' sang Maud with artificial unconcern, pretending to be sorting letters on the table, until Nurse and Peter had passed into the drawing-room.

'Here,' said Maud, rushing back a minute later, and waving a bottle triumphantly, 'this is Port, isn't it?'

After a lot of hacking and delving, she got the cork out, and it was not till then that I took a closer look at the bottle, and saw the film of dust and age that clothed it, and the tell-tale bits of crusted black seal still clinging to the neck.

'I took one of the shabbiest I could find,' said Maud cheerfully. 'Phew! You should have heard my heart beat. Haven't had such a bit of excitement since father died.'

Quite exciting for the hare, too, to be jugged in rare old Vintage Port. I used it liberally, and poured the rest into a jug, so that I could bury the evidence of that bottle deep in the dustbin.

We washed up the tea, so as to get it out of the way, and I shook a careless soapy hand in the air, and deposited a few suds in the soup. It didn't seem to make any difference to the taste, and, 'What the eye don't see – ' said Maud.

She laid the table, and then came back to help me with the last stages of cooking. You wouldn't have thought two people in one room could possibly get in one another's way so much, or make quite such a commotion and mess. Even Mrs Vaughan who, having at last got rid of the Nitchin by offering to pay her taxi, came in to see how things were going, retreated before the clamour of battle. There simply was no room for her; Maud and I had developed into about twenty people, with outsize feet.

Maud had already put on her clean party apron, as it was now nearly half past seven, and the guests were due at a quarter to eight. I was going to change in the last minute, so as to be sure of not dirtying mine, and I was justified in this precaution, when a piercing howl from her, as she opened a tin of cherries to decorate the pudding, brought Clare out into the hall in a pair of cami-knickers.

'Fruit-juice!' wailed Maud. 'All over my apron, and I haven't got another!'

'Soak it in salt water, quick!' cried Clare, running about looking like a picture on a magazine cover. 'Gosh, the bell! Let me get back to my room before you open the door.' She fled. I couldn't answer the bell, shiny mess as I was from cooking and turmoil, and it had rung again, before I had found Maud an old, but fairly clean apron of mine in the dresser drawer.

'You're too early,' said Clare, coming out into the hall again, as a loud guffaw announced that it was only Frances and husband. She took them into the drawing-room, doing up her dress as she went.

The other guests were not so punctual. This, I believe, is a source of annoyance to the good cook, who has everything ready on time, but it is always a blessing to such as me.

I cleaned myself up a bit while they were having cocktails, and carried in the soup, while Maud announced dinner. We

194

had arranged that we would each do one side of the table, and this worked quite well, except that there was one rather pathetic man at the end who didn't seem to belong to either of us, and was constantly being forgotten. I don't believe he got half the things handed to him, but perhaps it was as well, for he looked the dyspeptic sort.

Clare made Maud's face shine red with embarrassment through the thick white coat of powder that she had applied for the occasion by saying loudly, as she handed the soup: 'Oh, you got a clean apron, Maudie, dear, you do look smart!'

The hare had a success worthy of the extravagance of its ingredients. 'What a *delicious* dish!' said a large purple velvet woman on Mr Vaughan's right, 'I really must be greedy and have another helping.'

'I hope it doesn't put you under the table, that's all,' I thought, holding the dish while she spooned out a lot of the Fine Old Fruity gravy.

Serving the dinner between the two of us was quite a hectic business and we should have been even more flustered if it had not been such an informal affair. Mr Vaughan helped by stumbling about with the drinks, and his wife popped up and down in her usual style, getting bread, and thinking she heard the telephone ring. A brief lull in the babel of conversation was filled by a penetrating whisper from Maud, as she handed Frances the sweet course: 'Come on, Miss, tickle out the cherries! We haven't got all night.'

In spite of the many set-backs that had occurred during its preparation, the dinner seemed to go down all right, helped along by the lavishness of the host in the matter of alcohol. The men were so obviously dug in for a long session with the port and brandy, that Maud and I abandoned all hope of clearing the table for some time, and sat down to stuff ourselves with leavings among the piles of dirty crockery that littered the kitchen. The best part of any party is always the discussion and criticism of the guests that one indulges in afterwards, whether one has participated in a below- or an above-stairs capacity. Maud was quite vindictive for her. She had taken exception to a nut-crackery woman in a violent shade of cyclamen.

'I never did like that Mrs Holden, and I never shall,' she declared. 'I take people as they come and she comes very unpleasant. Messing about with the sweet, she was, as if it was mud pies, and then didn't take but only a spoonful. "Well!" I felt like saying: "If you don't want to buy the watch, don't breathe on the works."'

'She drank enough, anyway. I saw her fairly lapping it up.'

'That's right. Would you believe it, she had some of that cream stuff – demented cream, or whatever they call it, and then didn't say no to a glass of brandy.'

An uproar of male voices indicated that the gents were joining the ladies, and a higher, more piercing wail indicated that the noise had woken Peter.

Maud and I cleared away the rest of the things in the dining-room, and were continuing our gossip over the washing up, when Nurse came padding into the kitchen – a most unappetizing figure in black carpet slippers and a green flannel dressing-gown. Her streaky hair, smelling more strongly of moth-balls than ever, hung down her back like so much seaweed.

'They've woken my little boy,' she said, 'I never heard of such a thing.' She turned her schoolmistress eye on us as if we were to blame. 'I'm going to see if a little warm milk won't send him off.'

'Oh, Nurse, I'm ever so sorry,' I said, 'there isn't a drop in the place till the milkman comes tomorrow.'

She had never heard of such a thing as this either. She took it as a sign of personal spite. 'I shall have to speak to Mrs Vaughan in the morning,' she said. 'I shall have to make it clear to her that I'm not at *all* accustomed to this sort of thing. I've never had to do with it before, and I don't wish to start now.' She was gone, with an indignant whisk of the seaweed. I was too tired to do more than giggle feebly, and Maud was seriously shocked at such an exhibition of superiority from one whom she didn't consider Real Class.

Peter evidently soon decided that it was better to be asleep than to have to contemplate his nurse, for the wails ceased before long.

Mrs Vaughan came into the kitchen to say how well it had all gone off. I thought for the thousandth time what a mercy it is that mistresses don't see the back-stage details of a dinner-party, they probably wouldn't eat a thing if they did.

We didn't finish till well after eleven o'clock, but the next day was a Sunday, which meant that I didn't have to arrive quite so early in the morning.

I saw Nurse buttonhole Mrs Vaughan after breakfast, and tell her some long story, with much nodding of the head and raising of the eyebrows. I thought it was probably about me, so I was not surprised when I was summoned after Nurse had gone.

'I don't quite know what it's all about,' said my mistress, smiling, 'but Nurse seems annoyed about something. You must be careful not to upset her. It may be only a little misunderstanding, but I do like harmony in my household.' I was going to stick up for myself, but she, who hated having to 'speak to' anyone, hastily picked up the telephone and dialled a number, to prevent any further discussion of the subject.

I slouched out of the room, muttering gloomily, and met Peter in the hall, dressed to go out. He was amusing himself while he waited for his nurse, by methodically straightening out each separate fringe of a Persian rug. I stopped to have a word with him – here was someone, at least, who didn't annoy me. As far as he was concerned, my sole use in the world was to provide food, so he promptly seized me by the hand, and led me to his favourite biscuit tin in the kitchen. The child was ambidextrous, so it always had to be two of everything, so that he could have one in each hand. He was sitting on the table, taking bites out of each biscuit in turn, when a camphorated tornado blew in through the door, swooped down on him, and bore him off, screaming, and dribbling tears and biscuit crumbs all the way to the front door.

'Now I've told you time again, you're not to keep running into the kitchen. If you want a biscuit, you can ask Nanny for it, the kitchen is not the place for little boys.'

The door slammed on this remark, and I was left seething. I suppose she thought the child would pick up vices or something if he spent too long in my company. I was longing for Maud to arrive, so that I could unload my grievances on to her good-natured ear. Surely she was very late? I looked at the clock and saw that she was nearly an hour after her time. I was thinking that pretty soon I would be able to put off no longer the various unpleasant jobs that I had been leaving for her to do, when the back bell rang, and I opened the door to an extremely dirty small boy in trousers cut down from a full-grown man's, bunched round his waist with a bit of string. He handed me an envelope which said, 'Mrs Vaughan, by hand,' so, telling him to wait, I took it along to the drawing-room. Mrs Vaughan read it, tut-tutted in a distressed way, and handed it to me.

*Dear Madam* (I read),

I am sorry to say that Mum has taken a Coma. She lays still as she has done since 5 this morning and Dr Bright says not to leave her. Hope you can spare me Madam. Will let you know when I can come back. Please tell Monica Mr V. must have clean towels today.

With apologies, Madam, yours truly,

M. BUXTON (Maud)


This was most upsetting, especially the touching evidence of Maud's devotion to duty. Mrs Vaughan asked me to get her the medical dictionary, while she scribbled a note in reply, so that she could look up all about Diabetic comas.

The small boy was still standing where I had left him, but on one leg now, with the other twisted round it in an uncomfortable-looking way. I gave him the note, and sixpence from Mrs Vaughan, and impressed on him that he was to go straight back to Maud.

When she was worried about anything, Mrs Vaughan

always had to vent her anxiety in a flow of words, so I had to go along to the drawing-room and lend an ear. She didn't really want answers, as she was quite happy to conduct a conversation with herself, but she liked to have someone in the room, for company's sake.

I got on with polishing the fire-dogs while she talked.

'Very worrying,' she was saying. 'Poor Maud, I do feel so sorry for her. Of course, her mother's been ill for a long time, but this does seem to be a turn for the worse. A coma – rather serious, I'm afraid, but on the other hand it may be nothing much – perhaps the doctor's a scaremonger. I hope they'll take her to hospital . . . Oh, of course, they will, they always do if it's serious. Unless, of course, she can't be moved. She'd be better in hospital, though. I wonder if I could do any good by going round there? I think I will, if she isn't better tomorrow. One might be a nuisance, though, I wouldn't want Maud to think I was interfering. I wonder when she'll come back – she won't stay away long unless her mother's really bad, then we should have to get someone in to help you. I think I'll leave it for the moment, until we hear from Maud. You must just skimp the work, we shan't mind. I'll help you where I can. D'you think you can manage? I don't want to ask too much of you.'

'Yes, madam,' I said, making my first and last contribution to the conversation. I had finished my polishing, and Mrs Vaughan seemed to have temporarily dried up, so I left her, as I had a thousand things to do.

I didn't know where to start. There were so many things that Maud usually did, such as beds, baths, and boots, as well as my own share of the housework, and all the cooking. We had drifted into a sort of slap-dash routine, and, between us, had got through the work fairly easily, but my brain reeled at the thought of doing it all by myself. However, Mrs Vaughan had said 'skimp the work', so I took her at her word, and it was an understatement for the shirking I indulged in that morning.

I made beds by the simple, if unhygienic, method of pulling up the clothes without untucking them, and barely stayed long enough in the bathroom to put the tooth-brushes in the mugs and fold up the bath-mat. I closed my eyes to the three layers of dirt round the bath, indicating where Nurse, Peter, and Clare had rid themselves of some of the grime of London. The next person in would be Mr Vaughan, who was short-sighted, and would only add a fresh level anyway. Nevertheless, there was still enough that had to be done to keep me panting about the place, trying to dust, sweep, and cook lunch for four people and a baby all at the same time.

I wished it had not been the day for Peter to have brains; I always had to nerve myself for the ordeal of handling them, and this morning my resistance was weak. I thought of Maud's mother in her coma and wished it was me. There is no doubt that drudgery is embittering to the soul, and the sympathy that I should have been feeling for the Buxton family was replaced by a rather sour resentment.

'Poor Maud and all that,' I thought, starting to wash up the breakfast things, when I could stand the sight of the egg- and marmalade-encrusted plates no longer, 'but if ever there was a case of "One pair of hands", it's now.'

It was a horrible lunch I gave them. Stringy, sodden cabbage, overdone beef, and lumpy custard were among the things that made it memorable. Laying the table in a hurry, I had forgotten various things, and I had to keep running to the kitchen for them, in between handing round. I had also forgotten to make any coffee, and as they were going to a concert they had no time to wait while I made some.

Almost the worst part of the whole thing was the confounded tolerance of the Vaughan family. They didn't mind a bit, and kept making allowances for me, which was more annoying than if they had reviled me, as it put me in the wrong for feeling ill-used. However, there was always Nurse to pin a bit of spare rage on to; she was quite willing to add to the gaiety of life by demanding extras, such as a Swiss roll for Peter's tea. I made no objection as I was beginning to feel resigned, in a sort of stark Russian way, and one thing more to do couldn't possibly make me feel any worse.

Today was Sunday anyway, and I was supposed to go off at six o'clock, which I determined to do, whether I had finished my work or not. It amused me to think that there had been a time, far back at the start of my kitchen career, when I should have had no peace of mind or sleep if I had gone home leaving any jobs undone. Domestic service had had a most demoralizing effect on me. It was a very different person from that conscientious enthusiast of over a year ago who now banged the door behind her on empty coal-scuttles, a supper laid with only the bare necessities, tea-things in the sink, and three pieces of a broken plate lying in the middle of the dirty kitchen floor.

# Chapter Fifteen

LOOKING back on my last few weeks at the Vaughans' I can never make out why I didn't throw up the sponge sooner than I did. Maud's mother continued to 'lay like a log, madam', and this and other circumstances combined to result in my carrying on by myself. Mrs Vaughan and I had a heart-to-heart talk a few days after we heard that Maud was not yet coming back.

I was laying the fire in the drawing-room, a task that was supposed to be done before breakfast but never was. My mistress never said anything about it, and didn't seem to mind my crashing about in the hearth while she was writing letters and telephoning to tradesmen.

'Well, Monica,' she said, raising her voice so as to be heard above the clatter of me raking out cinders, 'I really don't know what to say. I've made inquiries, but it seems impossible to find a char who's half-way nice. I'd rather the flat went dirty than have to put up with some of the drunken old cripples they've offered me. – Yes, what is it, dear?' as her husband poked his head round the door. He didn't see me as the sofa was between him and my kneeling form, so he spoke without reticence.

'Where the hell has that imbecile hidden my nail-scissors? I wish you'd speak to her, dearest. Of all the half-witted sluts we've ever had ...'

'*Ruhig! Ist im Zimmer!*' hissed his wife, whose German education was better than her French.

'*Mein Gott*, is she? *Je n'ai pas vu,*' he mumbled, withdrawing his head hurriedly. Mrs Vaughan was so upset to think that I might have been offended that, to show I didn't mind, I had to fall in with the suggestion she now put to me.

'I was wondering,' she said, 'whether, if I gave you a bit extra, you could possibly carry on by yourself for the time being. You seem to be managing quite well – providing you're not getting too tired? It seems hardly worth trying to find a non-existent char when we don't know when Maud may come back. What d'you think? I don't want to slave-drive you. You mustn't mind Mr Vaughan,' she added, laughing uncertainly, 'you know what men are – always saying things they don't mean. I do hope it didn't upset you?' She looked so concerned that I had to say: 'I'm sure I can manage myself, madam,' in order to show her there was no ill-feeling.

She said that she would give me thirty-five shillings a week, and added the extra bait that Clare would not be staying much longer as she was taking her husband away to convalesce. Nurse was staying on, needless to say, but I was getting so used to loathing her that I should almost have missed her if she had gone.

I was in a rut altogether. Exhaustion gradually began to induce in my brain a coma quite worthy of Mrs Buxton, although my body was not recumbent like hers, but walked about in grim and automatic toil. I don't blame my mistress, for I had brought it on myself, and she really had no idea how tired I was. She merely thought me rather more than abnormally stupid and spent her time making allowances for each fresh nonsense that I made, which encouraged me to make still more to see how much she would stand.

Sometimes, in order to cheer myself up, I tried dressing-up and going out in the evening, but it was not a success. I had lost the Party Spirit – it had gone down the plug-hole of the sink, or been thrown into the dustbin and buried under tin cans and cabbage stalks.

On days when my employers were going out to dinner they generally let me go home at about seven, which gave me the opportunity to attempt a little weary whoopee. I arrived home on one of these evenings to find an invitation to go to the theatre and dance afterwards. I decided to go, although I didn't know the people very well, and I had never felt less like gaiety in my life.

I quite enjoyed the theatre because it gave me the chance of having a nice little nap. I woke up in the intervals and said: 'Marvellous! I do think it's good, don't you?' so nobody noticed that I had no idea whether the play was musical comedy or a Russian tragedy.

A good supper revived me: it was lovely to eat food that I hadn't cooked myself, and I had quite a light-hearted dance or two, untroubled by housemaid's knee.

'Thank Heaven for alcohol!' I kept thinking, amazed at the way in which those feet, which had been trailing around all day behind brooms and carpet-sweepers, were doing the rumba. My knell was sounded, however, by the voice that said, 'There will be an interval for the glasses to be cleared from the tables!'

Pretty soon after that I began to wilt, and it was unfortunate that I had to do it while dancing with a hot-blooded gentleman of South American extraction. I suddenly felt like death and drooped on his shoulder, hooking myself on with my chin to save myself from falling like a log. He thought this was the Invitation to the Waltz and got very Trans-Atlantic. His passionate grip had the advantage of supporting me and keeping me on my feet, so I could just bear it until the end of the dance released me from his greasy clutches. I staggered to a chair and said: 'I really ought to go home. I'm rather tired, I've been working so hard all day.' No one knew what at, they were the sort of people who would have raised their eyebrows and laughed uncomfortably if they had known they were entertaining a cook-general.

'I weel take you 'ome,' said Black Pedro instantly, and I had to choose between this very repulsive prospect and going on to a night club with the others. A good look at Pedro decided me. We all got into taxis and I found myself walking as though in my sleep into a dim and airless haunt of gaiety six times as sordid as any basement that ever smelt of greens.

I sat down at a corner table with the rest, and soon they all got up to dance. Pedro asked me and I shook my head, which suddenly weighed ten stone so that I had to put my, arms on to the table and drop it on to them.

The band was playing 'Boom, boom, zinca boom, zinca boom!' or was it in my head? No, because there was a bee there, singing ... singing, to the boom, zinca boom ... Ees the matter? said Pedro from the other side of London. Boom said the bee, said the boom, said the ... you eell? I am swimming in waves of rhythm ... I am sinking ... boom, zinca boom, sinking boom, sinking ...

My heart woke me by dropping out of my breast with a crash. I was instantly conscious of a strong and unfamiliar smell, and raising my head slightly, I saw with surprise that a fat white hand with crimson nails was attached to one of my elbows like a growth.

'I've brought you some aspirin, dear, make you feel better. Just the ticket when you've passed out,' said a hoarse voice in my ear. I was bolt upright now and fully conscious of where I was.

Pedro had disappeared, and the others, I suppose, were still dancing somewhere on the dim and faraway sea of the dance floor. I was alone at the table except for a raddled but motherly creature, who had for the moment abandoned her duties of 'hostess' to minister to what she thought was a Dead Drunk.

My one thought was to escape, I couldn't even thank her. I pushed her away and, leaping to my feet, made for the door, followed by the delighted sniggers of the band, who had evidently been watching the whole comedy of my disgrace.

This episode, with the consequent necessity for apologies to my hostess, whom I have never seen since, and the deathlike Hangover that enveloped me all the next day, discouraged me from much more sociability. I had to attend an occasional dinner party, and there were one or two rather pathetic incidents, such as the time when I went fast asleep with my head pillowed on the shoulder of a High Court judge, and once when I lost all chance of success with a French Count who discovered, when he kissed my hand, that it smelt strongly of that well-known perfume, 'Bouquet des Oignons'.

I had got into the state of thinking that life was bounded by gas-stoves and grease, and saw no reason to imagine that it could ever hold anything more for me. This melancholy thought made me sour and disagreeable during the few hours I spent at home, and by no means a ray of sunshine at the Vaughans'. My sulky apathy was beginning to tell on even my mistress's nerves, though she never ticked me off. I noticed her once or twice checking an impatient exclamation at my incompetence, but she was far too kind ever to suggest 'making a change', however trying I was, quite apart from the fact that she knew that the species 'Cook-General' was comparatively rare. The poor woman's flat was in a terrible state. The smuts and dust of London, which always get the upper hand unless resisted with methodical zeal, had consolidated their position, undeterred by my feeble opposition with dirty dusters and brushes clogged with fluff.

Once when Mr Vaughan had his glasses on he caught sight of his tarnished golf cups, and he also discovered that the mustard and pepper pots had reverted to their former condition of emptiness. I was just on my way in with the joint and two veg., but I waited outside the door until he had finished saying: 'Really, dearest, why don't you speak to her? You put up with anything; it's thoroughly bad for a lazy girl like that.'

There was a pause, presumably for Mrs Vaughan to tap her head significantly, and I heard her murmur something about 'Poor thing ... can't help it.'

The first of December is a date that is engraved on my memory, for it was the day on which I woke at last to the realization of a New Dawn. I can't understand why it didn't happen before; I can only suppose that it was this sort of trance of fatigue that I was in that made me accept my dreary lot for so long. It was certainly not curiosity any longer or interest in seeing Life in the Raw. I had found out all I wanted to know about kitchen affairs, and a great deal too much about the squalor attached thereto.

It was while I was washing up after lunch, always one of the lowest spots of the day, that I suddenly saw the light.

Something seemed to click in my brain. The curtain of fog went up with a rush, and it became all at once crystal clear and filled with the dazzling white light of reason.

'This is no sort of life for a girl!' The words rang in my head like a bugle call. The back-door bell rang, too, and the baker was quite startled by the joyous reception I gave him. I almost embraced him in my new-found lightness of heart. It didn't matter that he was one of the most drooping and depressed-looking creatures who ever walked this earth; I bubbled at him, hardly knowing what I was saying.

'I'm going! I'm leaving! For ever, I mean. A new day has dawned. I can't stand it any longer. Oh, baker, baker, congratulate me, I'm so happy!'

I seized him by the hand, and he suffered it to be pumped up and down, saying gloomily 'What a song and dance about getting the sack, I must say.'

'Sack? What are you talking about? I've fired myself this time. I'm walking on air, I tell you. I'm going to Live, Laugh, and Love! Can you waltz?'

'I did used to in me younger days . . .' he said hesitatingly, but with a sparkle of something almost like wistful gaiety beginning to gleam in his eye.

To the strains of the 'Blue Danube', panting and gasping as we whirled and bumped, we were rounding the table fo the third time when our progress was impeded by a solid body which had stepped in through the door just in time to make a collision inevitable.

'Monica!' said Nurse in a choking, scandalized voice as she picked herself up out of the coal-bucket, '*Get* on with your work, and don't make yourself cheap with the trades-men.'

She had got so used to my pretending to her to be more or less deaf and dumb, as I had for the last week or two so as to save myself the trouble of talking to her, that she was quite startled by the spate of words that now escaped me. She retreated before them into the hall, protesting feebly, and fending me off with upraised hands. She backed straight into the drawing-room, and I heard her say: 'I'm afraid

Monica has gone out of her mind. Shall I dial 999?'

I pushed the baker out of the back door, and just had time to seize a carrot and be discovered chopping it with sane and meticulous accuracy when Mrs Vaughan came running in.

'Nurse said – ' she began, and then stopped and looked at me wonderingly. '*Is* anything the matter, Monica? You look quite flushed.'

'I don't feel quite the thing, 'm,' I mumbled. 'Vertigo. Mother says I ought to take a rest – go away or something. "Monica," she said to me last night, "You're over-taxing your strength. You'll kill yourself if you go on like this." I never was strong from a child, you know, madam.'

Illness had got me out of the Chilford House job without acrimony, so I thought I had better fall back on it again this time.

I rather wished I hadn't, for Mrs Vaughan, though secretly rejoicing at the opportunity to get rid of me without hurting my feelings, was terribly concerned about my health. She insisted on feeling the back of my neck, which she declared was stinging hot and showed I had a temperature. I managed to convince her that I could hold together until she found someone to replace me. I tried to strike a note of wilting but courageous suffering, which was difficult when the only thing wrong with me was a fever of delirious joy.

Distressed, she went away to ring up all the agencies she knew, and I, feeling rather a cad, decided to prepare a very special dinner to salve my conscience.

Mrs Vaughan went out to follow up one or two likely trails, throwing parting injunctions at me 'not to overdo it' and to 'take two aspirins in a glass of hot milk'.

She didn't get back till after six, by which time an exotic chicken dish was simmering itself to a rich perfection in the oven. She found me in the drawing-room, whither I had gone in response to a roar from Mr Vaughan: 'Curse this infernal machine! Monica! come and get this damned number for me before I – '

The whole trouble was that the poor darling's fingers were too fat and stubby to fit into the holes of the dial. He had tried yelling: 'Operator, operator!' into the mouth-piece, and been maddened by the penetrating and imper-sonal 'burr-r-r-r' that mocked him in answer. By the time I came to his rescue he had forgotten what number he was trying to get. When he eventually found it, after much hunting through a jumble of papers in his pocket-book, I decided not to dial it, but to dial 'O' and let him ask them for it. I thought it would be good for 'O's' patronizing smugness to listen to a sample of his extensive vocabulary.

His wife came in when he was in the middle of it, so with a final shout of 'I shall write to *The Times*!' he gave it up and decided to write a postcard instead.

I left them as I thought she might want to tell him about me, for women will never learn that if there is one subject that bores a man more than any other it is the servant problem in his own house.

She came into the kitchen quite soon and said: 'Well, you'll be pleased to hear that we're going out to dinner; you can go home when you like. That'll be nice, won't it?'

I could have cried, had it not been for the spring of happiness that was still bubbling inside me. 'The chicken, madam!' I cried, agonized. 'A special dish. And the *zabaglione*!'

'Oh dear, I didn't think you would have started yet. I had said roasted, hadn't I? We can't very well get out of going to the Welds' now, I asked them if they'd have us. Wouldn't it keep till tomorrow? We could have it heated up ... Oh, by the way, talking of tomorrow, I think I've found somebody. She's going to come in during the morning to see the place, and I'll get you to show her what's what. I expect your mother would like you to go away as soon as possible, wouldn't she? Where are you thinking of going?'

'Skegness,' I said at random and thought afterwards that it might be a bit too bracing at this time of year, so added 'or Hove' as an afterthought.

The timid creature who arrived the next morning as my possible successor was called Mrs Hopper. She crept about the place with Mrs Vaughan, clearing her throat nervously when addressed, her forehead puckered anxiously under a green cloche hat.

'And now,' said Mrs Vaughan in the hall, 'if you really think you'd like to come to us I'll take you to the kitchen. Monica can explain things there to you better than I can. I'm afraid I'm no cook.'

I was spared the trouble, however, as they came in together and Mrs Vaughan, having nothing better to do, stayed and conducted the tour of the kitchen herself. I was able to go on peeling potatoes while she rattled off details of our domestic routine. She knew all about cooking and housework in theory, anyway. It was one of the many accomplishments of her extraordinarily versatile brain that she could discourse at length on the principle of any subject under the sun, unhindered by the fact that she would be unable to carry it out in practice. I had heard her telling Mr Vaughan how to play golf when he came home tired and discouraged on a Sunday evening, and really, though perhaps a little tactless, it was very sound text-book advice. She could give instruction, too, on how to drive a car, with illustrations of road signals, though apparently the only time she had ever taken the wheel had been the last day on this earth for two chickens and a baby pig.

When she had finished she left us, and Mrs Hopper, bewildered and docile, accepted her suggestion that she should stay and have a cup of tea with me.

We didn't get on particularly well together, I'm afraid, as I was feeling excited and rather distrait, and she was one of the most painfully self-conscious women who ever crooked a little finger over a kitchen cup. She was desperately anxious to make it clear that she was a cook-general only from necessity and not from station.

'Just a temporary thing this is for me,' she said, nibbling genteelly at a small crumb of bread; 'it's never been my lot to serve, you know.'

I was in no mood to tell her such things as: 'Everyone that humbleth himself shall be exalted,' which is what she would have liked to hear, or to paint a rose-tinted picture of domestic service for her encouragement. I sat silent, thinking, and she, though slightly daunted by my churlishness, cleared her throat a bit and tried to keep the conversation going.

'Of course, I wouldn't really be doing this sort of thing at all,' she pursued, 'were it not for certain unhappy circumstances. Poor Mr Hopper was taken from me all too soon; he wasn't able to provide for me as he would have wished.'

I was uncertain whether this meant that one ought to express sympathy for Mr Hopper's demise or for his incarceration, so I let it pass, and his wife became even more convinced of my uncouthness and began to show a desire to leave, but an inability to make the move. I was called away to open the front door to Clare, who had come to lunch to help dispose of last night's chicken, and when I got back to the kitchen I found that Mrs Hopper had hopped it. We hadn't arranged what time she should arrive the next day, so I ran out of the back door in the hope of catching her on the outside staircase. I was just in time to see the top of her hat, like an inverted pudding basin, descending spirally to the street below. I yelled at her with no result, so I gave it up and leant against the railing thinking about life.

Watching the green blob becoming smaller and smaller made me wonder what I should think of my year and a half of servitude when its memories had diminished too. I was still too near to it at the moment to regard it as anything but a most depressing chapter of my life, and I wondered whether I should ever find myself in the position of people who talk about their school days as the happiest days of their life with no idea of being untruthful. They forget the misery that they may have suffered – that agony of spirit that nearly all children and very young people know and no grown-up can understand, because they have already forgotten.

Our memories are merciful; they store up details of happiness much more readily than details of sorrow. We, however, respond ungratefully by indulging our innate passion for self-torture by turning remembrance into regret. In the end the memory of something perfect becomes even sadder than the memory of despair, for we torment ourselves with the thought that it can never be quite the same again.

When the first agony of a real sorrow has faded, though the sorrow may remain, natural resilience makes the mental picture of oneself in the throes of it fade too. Happiness is so easy to picture that one dwells almost morbidly on some lovely memory, harping on the fact that it is gone, exaggerating, imagining, comparing the present unfavourably, until there you are in floods of tears and almost ready for the gas-oven.

'Ah, well,' I said, turning to go in, '*c'est la vie*.'

'Ho, yes, we had one but it died,' said the grocer's boy, rounding the last turn of the staircase and handing me half a pound of prunes and a packet of soap-flakes.

Although I hadn't been at the Vaughans' more than about ten weeks it was long enough to make me quite an institution. They were a very die-hard family, hating change, and when it came to the point they thought they were sorry to see me go, and felt quite tender towards me.

There happened to be a family dinner on that last evening and I was quite drawn into the conversation, almost as if I had been sitting at the table with them instead of running round it with the steak-and-kidney pudding.

It is a curious game that people like to play sometimes, drawing out the maid (baiting the butler in some houses), in order to get amusement out of the screamingly funny idea that she may have some sort of a human life of her own. Nice people like the Vaughans laugh with you, others laugh at you; but it comes to the same thing in the end. Once you get used to the idea of being suddenly hauled out from the oblivion of servitude into the spotlight of attention, and expected to provide entertainment until they just as suddenly tire of you, and intimate that you have said your piece, it's quite an easy game to play. You have to humour them by saying amusing and slightly outrageous things so that they can retail them to their friends, or 'dine out' on quotations from your conversation.

Frances started it this evening. She was feeling arch tonight, which was unusual for her, so she said: 'I believe I know why Monica's leaving; that young man of hers has come up to the scratch at last!'

I smiled politely, waiting to see whether they wanted to play or whether they were going to start talking about something else. I was quite ready to oblige, but I wasn't going to waste any energy. Clare took it up.

'Has he proposed? How thrilling! What did he say and where did he do it?'

This was the cue for me to become side-splittingly un-conventional.

'What a thing to say, Miss Clare!' I said, handing her husband the potatoes from the wrong side, 'you know I don't care for men.'

'What about that Adonis I saw you talking to outside the lift the other day?' asked Mr Vaughan with his mouth full of pie.

'Pardon, sir? I didn't quite catch. A – what?'

'Adonis. Good-looking chap, you know. Good God!' (aside to Clare) 'don't they give these girls *any* education?'

'Oh, him,' I said, ignoring this slight on one of the most famous girls' schools in London, 'that was only the lift man in his Sundays. He's no oil-painting.'

The thing was getting a bit laboured. I hoped they'd soon get sick of it, but they were determined to give me a break on my last evening.

Frances again: 'I'm sure I saw you with a red-haired man at the "Odeon" last week. Honestly,' looking round the table, 'I was sitting just behind them. If you're not engaged to him, Monica, you certainly ought to be.'

'Miss Frances! May you be forgiven. My friend's a married man. His wife's away at the moment so I'm simply keeping him warm.' I rounded this off with a daring wink, and felt that I had done enough. I wanted to take away the pie and see whether they had left any kidneys for me.

Mrs Vaughan thought I had gone a bit too far with my last remark and hastily turned the conversation away from me before I could pollute anyone's mind, so I was able to escape gladly to the kitchen. Not one single kidney! Really, I thought, people are gross. Greed is only pardonable in those one loves very dearly or in oneself.

After dinner I was yelled for from the drawing-room to go and say good-bye to the younger members of the family whom I wouldn't see tomorrow. Nurse had drifted away with Peter during the afternoon without so much as a nod to me. To her I was one of those things that one hopes to exterminate by pretending they are not there.

I sidled in, wiping my hands on my apron, and when I saw them all sitting there, the picture of a family happy in the old-fashioned way, that is rare enough nowadays, my heart quite warmed to them and I could almost have wished that I was staying on amid this nice contented atmosphere. Almost, but not quite.

Clare was sitting on her father's knee, busily engaged in pattering the top of his bald head with lipstick. Her husband was dropping pipe-ash over a photograph album that he was looking at with Clare, who was being roared at by her father: 'For God's sake, why can no woman ever look at photographs without putting sticky fingers all over them?' Clare's husband had decided that she was, after all, quite fetching and was absent-mindedly stroking the back of her neck while he noisily appreciated the humour of his father-in-law.

Mrs Vaughan was darning socks. This was a complicated business, as she couldn't darn without her glasses, and for some unknown reason she couldn't talk if she had them on. To darn without talking would have been agony, but on the other hand, in view of the pile of socks in her basket she didn't feel justified in talking without darning. The result was a complicated exercise of taking the glasses off, losing them, finding them, and putting them on, losing her needle, dropping the sock, picking everything up, and just getting ready to attack a hole, and then thinking of something to say and starting the whole thing over again.

'There you are, Monica,' she said, removing the encumbrance once more, 'they just want to say good-bye before you go.'

It had undoubtedly been her suggestion, but they all shook me dutifully by my red and rather sodden hand – I had just been washing up – and wished me luck.

My last morning dawned in a grey drizzle of rain, but nothing could damp my spirits on this auspicious occasion of 'positively my last appearance in this or any other country' as cook-general. I walked through the streets under my father's umbrella, unchastened by the thought of what he would say when he found I had taken it without asking.

An impulsive and short-lived consideration for Mrs Hopper made me have a sketchy round-up of some of the dirt and mess that was my legacy to her. I cooked a large breakfast for Mr Vaughan as a token of my goodwill, and he lingered over it and, rushing off to the office in a hurry, forgot to say good-bye to me. His wife, when she realized this, was across the hall and out of the front door like a bullet. She caught him waiting for the lift, and I heard him complaining slightly, like a small boy who has been told to go and wash his hands. He stumped back to the kitchen and blurted out, 'Good-bye, Monica, it's been so nice having you with us,' at the top of his voice, as if he were addressing a large crowd behind my left shoulder, and hurried away again.

'What, no tip?' I thought as the lift gates rattled and crashed.

Mrs Vaughan made me ashamed of my graspingness by presenting me before I left with a most beautiful pair of bedroom slippers made of white rabbit fur that had been bought for Frances but discovered to be too small.

Mrs Hopper arrived at twelve o'clock, and was established in the kitchen in a black dress and a black full-length apron that sported a great many pink cabbage-roses but no waistline. She had a curious way of accompanying all her actions with a *sotto voce* running commentary of spoken thoughts. I left her making an apple pie, and could hear it going on in the distance while I took leave of my mistress in the hall.

'Three ounces of butter – weigh it out – that's right. Now, let me see, I must have six ounces of flour; here's the bin, it looks as if it could do with a clean. How much sugar? Sugar, sugar, where are you, sugar? This must be it; the supply seems rather low. I'll put it all in. Apples – one, two, three, four, five, six; will that be sufficient, I wonder?' and so on as a background for the kind and solicitous remarks that Mrs Vaughan was pouring into my undeserving ear.

'Now, be sure to come and see us when you're passing and tell us how you're getting on.' (This was probably what Miss Nitchin had been told, too.) 'Take care of yourself. Tell your mother from me that you ought to go on an acid-free diet; do you all the good in the world. I used to say the same thing to Maud, but she never paid any attention.'

'Oh, you will give her my love when she comes back, won't you, madam?'

'Of course. She ought to be back next week. It's wonderful that her mother's so much better. Maud won't have so much to do for her any longer. Well, good-bye, and be sure – Oh dear,' as a crash came from the kitchen followed by a feeble wailing. 'I believe that's Mrs Hopper in trouble already, I'd better go and see. Good-bye again.' She rushed away, so I had to call 'Good-bye, madam,' after her. I knew the timbre of every crash and clatter that could be got out of that kitchen, and this one was only the old familiar story of the oven shelf being pulled out too far and falling to the ground, sometimes accompanied (as in this case) by a pie-dish that had been standing on it.

I shut the front door behind me on poor Mrs Vaughan at the start of a fresh saga of contretemps. The people who deserve perfect service never seem to get it; I suppose because they are too indulgent. It seems hard when one thinks of the cantankerous devils whose staff hop round them with the immaculate efficiency of terror.

It seemed funny to be swanking out of the flats by way of the lift and the main entrance instead of clattering down the iron staircase at the back. It was the epitome of my glorious freedom and as such gave me a terrific thrill.

Returning to the family bosom, I found it heaving sighs of relief at the ending of what they had written off as a period of strange and regrettable madness. I began to realize what they had to put up with from me, in the way of exhausted and moody silences, or occasionally hysterical scenes of rage and tears.

'Oh, well, she can't help it, poor fool, she's tired,' or 'Don't tease Monica, she's not herself tonight,' they said good-naturedly, pitying me in my lunacy. It really was a little hard on them that the only repercussions they felt from my being a cook should have been such unpleasant ones. I determined to be a little ray of sunshine in future, tripping about the house, scattering joy and gladness on all who crossed my path. On this nauseating vision I fell asleep and slept, off and on, for about a week, only waking to open my mouth for food and drink and to scrub myself frenziedly in hot baths. I was haunted by the thought that the smell of the kitchen still hung about me, as if domestic service were loth to let me go from its clutches. At last I began to feel a bit more pure, and I rose from bed and bath a new woman.

I found that quite a lot of money had accumulated in the bank as the result of earning wages that I had had neither the time nor the energy to spend, and in my desire to live in a way as far as possible removed from what I had been through I went out and spent the whole lot in a very short time on the adornment of my person.

I broke out in no uncertain way in a search for the fun that I had missed for so long. With the strident cacophony of gaiety I tried to drown the cold little voice inside me which soon began to mutter disparaging remarks.

'Isn't all this just leading back to the same point of boredom from which you tried to escape before? And when you get there,' it seemed to say, 'then – what?'

# ONE PAIR OF FEET

*To*
*Doady and Denys*

# *Chapter One*

ONE had got to be something; that was obvious. But what? It seemed that women, having been surplus for twenty years, were suddenly wanted in a hundred different places at once. You couldn't open a newspaper without being told that you were wanted in the Army, the Navy or the Air Force; factory wheels would stop turning unless you rushed into overalls at once; the A.F.S. could quench no fires without you, every hoarding beckoned you and even Marble Arch badgered you about A.R.P.

The Suffragettes could have saved themselves a lot of trouble if they had seen this coming. Men's jobs were open to women and trousers were selling like hot cakes in Kensington High Street.

I could not make up my mind what to be. A lot of fanatics rushed into the most uncongenial jobs they could find, stimulated by a glow of self-sacrifice that lasted until the novelty wore off or the cold weather set in, but it seemed to me that, provided that it was just as useful, it was no less patriotic to do something enjoyable. At first sight, the choice seemed so enormous that the trouble was to decide what not to be, but a closer inspection revealed so many snags that in the end the trouble was to find something to which I had a hope of sticking.

The Services? I didn't think my hips would stand the cut of the skirt and I wasn't too sure about my legs in wool stockings. Besides, I've never been much good at drilling and all that. My school reports used to say : 'Not amenable to discipline; too fond of organizing,' which was only a kind way of saying : 'Bossy.' I might have been a success as a general, but not as a private.

The A.F.S.? I did try that for a while, but at the beginning of the war there was not much doing and I got discouraged with sitting all day in the back room of a police station knitting and eating sticky buns with six assorted women and a man with a wooden leg. At the end of a week, we all knew each other's life histories, including that of the woodenleg's uncle, who lived at Selsey and had to be careful of his diet. Messenger Dickens had once been down to Roehampton to fetch the Commandant's handbag and a small tube of soda-mints from the shelf in her bathroom.

A bus conductress? The idea appealed, but what about the questions of flustered old ladies, up for a day's shopping and an egg mayonnaise tea on the fourth floor? Anyway, although money is lovely to handle, they say that everything you eat afterwards tastes of coppers.

The W.V.S.? I once accompanied six evacuees down to Exeter. Never again. They punctuated their questions with a piercing 'Eh?' or 'What say?' One of them had impetigo, and when we arrived, they all wanted to go straight back to Dalston East.

I worked in a canteen for a while, but had to leave after a terrible row with Mrs Templeton-Douglas, who could never subtract one-and-ninepence from half-a-crown. I sold some of her jam tarts for a penny instead of twopence, thinking they were the throw-outs we had bought at the back door of the A.B.C.

The Land Army? One saw oneself picking apples in a shady hat, or silhouetted against the skyline with a couple of plough horses, but a second look showed one tugging man-gel-wurzels out of the frozen ground at five o'clock on a bitter February morning.

Ministries and Bureaux? Apart from the question of my hips again (sitting is so spreading), they didn't seem to want me. Perhaps it was because I can only type with three fingers and it always keeps coming red.

The Censor's Office I knew was in Liverpool, and I'd been there once.

Nursing? The idea had always attracted me, even in peace-time, but I suppose every girl goes through that. It's one of those adolescent phases, like wanting to be a nun. It was reading *Farewell to Arms*, I think, that finally decided me, though what sort of hospital allowed such goings on, I can't imagine. However, that was the last war. Then I saw Madeleine Carroll in *Vigil in the Night*, and that settled it.

I was going to be a nurse in a pure white halo cap, and glide swiftly about with oxygen cylinders and, if necessary, give my life for a patient and have my name on a bronze plaque in the hospital corridor. I wasn't going to be a V.A.D. either, I was going to start training and be a real probationer. I had heard that V.A.D.s never get beyond the charing stage and that however long they work in hospital it doesn't count as any training if they want a nursing job after the war. We were being tactfully prepared at the moment for a long war, and I thought I might at least emerge from it with some letters after my name and an enamel badge on my bosom. Provided, of course, that I could pass the exams, but having had all my meals for a month with a trained nurse when my sister was having a baby, I didn't see that they could be so difficult, if conversation was any guide to intellect.

Once the idea had taken root in my brain, it flourished there. The more I thought about it, the more certain I was that this was the one thing I really wanted to do. Perhaps it had been my *métier* all along and it had taken a war to disclose it. I was not discouraged by people who told me that the first year, at least, would be unrelieved drudgery. I had weathered two years of being a cook-general, and knew that there were no lower depths to be plumbed.

I wasn't particular what hospital I joined, provided it was somewhere that could take me straightaway. A decision loses its charm unless you can act on it immediately. It's like buying a new hat; you must wear it at once or not at all. I wrote to several hospitals and some answered and some didn't, and the nicest reply came from the matron of the Queen Adelaide Hospital in Redwood, a town about fifty miles north of London, famous for being the home of a certain sort of sausage pie, probably delicious locally, but disappointing in a cellophane wrapper on station buffets. A doctor I knew had been House Surgeon at this hospital and had recommended it if only for the fact that the bath water was always hot.

Miss Sarah P. Churchman (Matron S.R.N.C.N.B.) had asked me for references, so I dictated one or two to friends with solid-looking surnames, saying how reliable and intelligent I was, with a gentle sympathy of manner that would make Florence Nightingale look like an S.S. Guard at Dachau. Sarah P. wrote again, still pleasantly, asking me to go down for an interview. She sounded deep-bosomed and motherly, beloved of all nurses and patients and the confidante of doctors in their matrimonial troubles. I prayed that she would like me.

Once when I was loitering at the bookshops in the Charing Cross Road, I had bought a ninepenny book called *Sister Fairchild's Manual for Nurses*. I hadn't really wanted it, but I had been so long at the stall reading the old volumes of the *Strand*, that the proprietor, a man with sinister pock-markings, had begun to hover. I had bought the first book that came to hand to pacify him while I finished the last instalment of *Lady Bracken's Ball*. Remembering it now, I took it with me in the train to Redwood to find out what demeanour befitted a nurse.

That ninepence was well spent. It's a wonderful book, thick as a Bible and full of illustrations of nurses in high caps and birds'-nest hair doing strange things with kettles and primitive gas jets. I stopped looking out of the carriage window at the different effects that the inhabitants of Watford had made out of a sliver of back garden and settled down to 'The Ethics of Nursing. Qualities required of the New Probationer. She must be a woman of intelligence,' I read, 'healthy physique, perfect temper, obedience, punctuality, cleanly habits, able for hard and exhausting work both mental and physical.' I didn't see that I was any of these things, so I went on to 'Dress', which told me that rustling petticoats, squeaking shoes and jingling chatelaines were out of place and that outdoor wear should be neat, modest and not likely to excite comment. I was wearing a navy blue Burberry, low-heeled shoes and a hat that had once been quite a saucy sailor on the back of the head, but was now harmlessly turned up at the back and down at the front. I seemed to be all right there and went on to learn that one should never sit in the presence of superiors and that conversation with them should be limited to essentials, personal matters and opinions being kept in the background. I wondered *en passant*, what I should do if Sarah P. offered me a chair, leaned her deep bosom confidingly on the desk and said : 'Now tell me *all* about yourself !'

Then my eye was caught by : ' A Nurse's duties to herself', and I read with horror that : 'passing her life amid scenes of sorrow, suffering and the results of what she has been taught to consider sin, she tends to become morbid, introspective and cramped. She must, therefore, off duty, seize every chance of relaxation in any sphere unconnected with her work.' I shut the book hastily, before I could get melancholia, and divided my attention between the greening country and the morning paper.

I was nervous, no doubt about it. I did so want to be a nurse, and I was frightened of the alien atmosphere of hospital. The smell alone makes you feel an outsider and everyone is always so much too busy to be bothered with you.

The train swung round a curve and I saw the miscellaneous architecture of Redwood Court : crenellations, spires, bastions, curly white balconies and fake Tudor outbuildings, all jumbled together in a dip of the rolling part, like oddments in a schoolboy's pocket. Then a spur of trees rose between us and in a moment we were drawing into the station, for there are no suburbs on this side of the town.

Up till now, I had known Redwood simply as a place that one passed through on the way to somewhere else. One only stopped there to buy a paper, or a genuine Redwood pie, or because Aunt Ethel was car-sick, or perhaps to lunch at the Rowan Arms in case there might not be anywhere farther on. Now, as I came out of the station, asked my way, and struck off up the High Street, I viewed it with more attention. If I got my wish, this might be my world for the next three years – stifling thought. Every inch of this pavement, every shop, and perhaps even some of the faces thronging by me, might soon be only too familiar. I should know by heart each vase and cabinet in the window of this antique shop, every signed photograph of unknown artistes in the window of that hairdresser. My feet would wear a path round the counters of this Woolworth's, and how many cups of coffee might I not drink at the 'Blue Lady Café. Morning Coffee, Light Luncheons, Dainty Teas. Meet your friends'?

It was quite a long walk to the hospital and by the time I reached the gates I was determined to be accepted. I was not going to have come all this way and have had this uphill walk for nothing.

To visualize the geography of Redwood, you must imagine the hill on which the town is built as a rather squat pudding and the town as a sauce which has been poured over and run down the sides. A currant in the sauce has remained sitting right on top of the pudding and this is the Queen Adelaide Hospital. The side from which I approached it is the business part of the town, where the shops and cinemas and traffic lights are. The sauce has run thickly here, and collected in lumps, but down the other side, it slips into the pattern of residential Redwood : Victorian at first with large sombre houses in shrubby gardens, then brighter and more modern, a whole network of little streets of semi-detached paradises that you can own if you will only join the such-and-such building society. Beyond this, the custard has dripped on to the green plate of Suffolk plain in scattered properties that are not quite country houses, yet not of the town. They are inhabited by people who have guaranteed subscriptions at libraries and get their groceries from Harrods and give tennis parties with one court and eight people, who have to spend the afternoon protesting that they would really much rather sit and watch.

Between the business and the residential, two other streams of life run down from the hospital : on one side the long straight rows of mouldering plaster houses, where dressmakers live and little drapers' shops sell everything on earth except what you want, and women with piled up hair let rooms. On the other side, an untidy slum rackets cheerfully down to the very park wall of Redwood Court, which consequently is crowned with spikes and broken glass. Half-way down the hill on this poorer side there exists, for no apparent reason, an arty colony, full of little converted slum houses with blue doors, and women with corduroy trousers and hairnets and big dogs on leads, and grubby men in sandals.

How and why this odd little collection got here is a mystery, for Redwood is anything but artistic, but they all seem quite happy and do mimes and plays that nobody else will produce, in a rather smelly basement theatre.

Over all this then, broods the hospital, and the sight of it as I breasted the hill and crossed the road to the main gate did nothing to put me at my ease. Illness is ugly enough, Heaven knows, without its headquarters emphasizing it. Surrounded by iron railings, it stands back from the road in a gravel space, large and square and grey, with symmetrical oblong windows and a slate roof from which tall iron chimneys pour dark brown smoke. The human etcetera, like the glimmer of a nurse's cap at a window, or a man in a white coat crossing the gravel, or the geraniums in the window of the porter's lodge, seemed insignificant beside the shadowy massif. I went in at the gate, past an assortment of cars and an ambulance, drawn up with tails to the railings, and stood uncertain on the open space. Like most hospitals, it is impossible to find the way in. The main door is tight shut and says 'NO ENTRANCE', another says: 'ORTHOPAEDIC CLINIC. OUTPATIENTS ONLY', and another 'X-RAY. NO ADMITTANCE WITHOUT A GREEN CARD'. At last, in a corner I saw a notice that whispered: 'Enquiries and Visitors' and I made for it, flattening myself in the doorway to let a blanketed stretcher go by. I came to a sort of glass ticket office, which must have been built round the vast man who sat palpitating inside. His blood pressure seemed terrifying, but I supposed the hospital knew about that.

I had to show him the Matron's letter before he would believe that I had an appointment with her. He seemed sceptical, and I imagined that he too adored Sarah P. and had constituted himself her bulldog to keep off annoyance. Following the direction of his short pointing arm, I went down a corridor, turned a corner and was immediately lost. He had promised me I should see a flight of stairs with a green door at the top, but instead, there was an archway, with a choice of three passages beyond. I plunged down one of these at random, meaning to ask the way, but never actually summoning the courage. I wandered for ages up and down stairs and along stone corridors past doors behind which Heaven knew what was happening and which opened now and then to let a preoccupied, unapproachable figure dash in or out. Sexless hands on the walls pointed the way to wards with names like 'Grace Annie Sprock' and 'Herbert Waterlow', but I was too worried to wonder who these people were. I was beginning to wish I had pretended to be a cripple and made the porter take me up in the lift, when, pushing through some swing doors, I suddenly found myself in a ward full of beds. A clamorous woman with great shoes bore down on me.

'I'm in charge here,' she cried. 'You can't come breaking into the ward like this. Who do you want to see? You can't see them now.'

I thought of bursting into tears and saying : 'I've come to see me Mum,' but as I looked up at her, my eye was caught by the fantastic, equine length of her false teeth and I could think of nothing else. I stared.

'You can come back on Wednesday,' she was saying. To-day was only Monday, and I thought how awful if I really had wanted to see me Mum. Still gaping, I was being shooed backwards by her apron and great feet, until eventually, I bumped into the swing doors and recovered my speech.

'Please,' I stammered, 'I want to see the Matron. I can't find the way.'

'Good gracious !' Her eyebrows shot up and so did her top lip, revealing a sweep of shining orange gum. She turned and clicked her fingers at a scurrying girl. 'Nurse Rogers ! Show this – er – show the way to Matron's office and come straight back. Quickly, Nurse. You've got plenty of work to do here without jaunting over half the hospital.'

Nurse Rogers ducked her head and scuttled through the doors without looking to see whether I was following. I kept her in sight with difficulty. As I turned into a passage, she would be just disappearing at the far end, and up the stairs; all I knew of her was her back draught. At last I found her waiting for me on one leg outside a door that was, as promised, green, and said 'PRIVATE' across the top.

'Here,' she panted, already poised for flight, ducked her

head again and was off like a water-rat. I hoped that I should never be sent to that ward. I should never stand the pace.

When I had recovered my breath, I knocked on the green door and waited, wearing a polite face. No answer. I knocked again, still politely, and then a bit louder. Perhaps Sarah P. was deaf. These dear old bodies often are. At last, I opened the door just far enough to put my head into the room, leaving my body still politely outside. There was nobody there. It was a chintzy room with a lot of photographs and a vase of Michaelmas daisies in the grate. An ordinary drawing-room, except for the large flat-topped desk that faced the door. As there was no one in the passage, I ventured in, and wandered round looking at the photographs: groups of nurses mostly, dating from the Crimea, or visiting Royalty with wide hats and waistless coats and bouquets. I inspected the desk for anything scandalous like dope or a forged death certificate, but there was not even a hypodermic syringe. I wandered out again and leaned against the wall in the passage, wondering whether I had come at the wrong time or even on the wrong day. Supposing she had been expecting me before. She would never take me now; *Sister Fairchild* had harped a lot on punctuality. Still, having got so far, I was determined to see the Matron if it meant propping up the wall till night-time. I waited nearly an hour, patiently at first, then restless, then aggrieved and was just beginning to feel really sorry for myself when I was brought bolt upright by a clack-clacking on the linoleum at the end of the corridor.

The figure that approached was like a plucked boiling fowl. This couldn't be the Matron – not with that corrugated perm, those horn-rimmed spectacles and that scrawny neck poking out of the high collar of her black dress. Why, she was quite young – well, not old enough to be a Dear Old Body, anyway. True, she wore no apron and she was slowing down, but this couldn't be Sarah P. Churchman. Where was the bosom, where the dewlaps and the benevolent, understanding smile? She paused with her hand on the door-knob, cleared her throat efficiently and said: 'Yes? What is it?'

I told her what, and she said: 'Come in. You're early,'

and went into the room, her back managing to convey that I should have opened the door for her.

She looked sparer than ever seated behind the big desk. Her face was very lined and the thick, distorting lenses of her spectacles made expressionless marbles of her eyes. She had obviously led a life of great rigour and was determined not to allow anyone else the indulgences that she had missed. I felt very soft and stupid, and forgot all about the *Fairchild* code of manners. I didn't think she would take me. She seemed vaguely scornful and only acknowledged my answers to her questions by writing scratchily with the back of a relief nib. She didn't even say : 'I'll let you know,' or 'I'll write,' or any of the things with which people usually conclude an interview. She simply said : 'Very well, thank you,' cleared her throat again and swinging open a ledger, busied herself with some accounts. I plodded out over the thick carpet, started off despondently in no particular direction, and, surprisingly, found myself almost immediately back at the bulldog in his glass kennel. I realized now why he had been so sceptical of my appointment. Sarah P. was obviously not much of a one for callers.

## Chapter Two

OF course, as soon as my hopes had been realized, I had qualms. These were increased in the Buckingham Palace Road, where I bought my uniform. The stockings were so very thick and black, the collar so very high and hard, the striped dress so very like a 1920 Kodak Girl advertisement. I tried the whole thing on at home, and took it off again quickly, before anyone could see. It made me look like one of the Noah family – as if I ought to be on a stand. Perhaps I would pass among a lot of others all dressed the same, and the cap might help. The shop had told me that I would be shown how to make it up at the hospital, but at the moment, it was just a flat linen semicircle that bore no resemblance at all to a Madeleine Carroll halo.

Sarah P. Churchman, orderly as a calendar, would not

232

take me until the beginning of the month, so I had a few weeks to fill in before my incarceration. Following the current craze, I collected scrap-iron. I borrowed a barrow and a small hairy pony called Tiger from the local mews, and went from house to house annoying people. I usually managed to call at an inconvenient time : people were either out, or in the bath, or cooking the dinner, but even so, apart from a man who abused me for being a propagator of infernal machines, the response was soon too great for the pony. People began to unload boilers and bedsteads and garden rollers on to us, and poor Tiger just took one look and sagged at the knees. His union wouldn't allow it, he said, and I had to hurl the things feverishly on to the pavement again before he lay down in the shafts.

Then the Borough Council lent me a motor dustcart, complete with two dustmen called George and Arthur. George was waiting to be called up. He was young and earthy, with fair hair that sprang out in front of his cap like coiled wire. Arthur was older and more staid, the home philosopher type, who liked a kipper to his tea, and would trundle out quiet sagacities over the bones. We went round to all the residential hotels of Bayswater. Labyrinths of cellars under the pavement yielded tons of stuff that had been accumulating since accommodation was sold out for Queen Victoria's Jubilee. George and Arthur were just as keen to ferret it out as I. I suppose it was a change from cabbage stalks and tea-leaves wrapped in sodden newspaper.

At the Grand-Carlton, watched from behind the lace curtains of the lounge by mouldering old ladies, George kept staggering up with cistern after cistern, plug and all. Although they had been rusting there for years, they were in good shape, unused as far as one could see, and afterwards when we were knocking off for tea and hot pies at Andy's Café, we tried to fathom the mystery of the Seven Cisterns in a Cellar. Perhaps the owner of the Grand-Carlton had once come into money and had planned lavish expansion, beginning with the plumbing. In the first flush of enthusiasm, he had ordered these seven cisterns before the Will was proved, and when he found that he would not, after all, be able to build anywhere to put them, he had hanged himself with one of the chains, and his relations had not the heart to sell the cisterns. A ribald cousin called Cyril had suggested erecting one as a tombstone, but had been frowned down. Or, said Arthur, someone might've bought 'em cheap at an auction and put 'em by for a rainy day. He had a great uncle who would buy anything if it was a bargain and whose wife had left him when he came home with a mechanical bar-room piano that broke into the *Lily of Laguna* every time an underground train passed underneath the house.

After a few days, Arthur let me drive the lorry and even work the lever that tipped our load on to the dump. I could have gone on doing this for ever, but Redwood called and I had to leave off and start trying to get my hands clean again. We got a little paragraph in the local paper saying that we had collected ten tons of scrap-iron, and I got a furious letter from a man in Porchester Terrace, who said that the old bath I had removed from his cellar was his air-raid bunk.

I arrived at Redwood station on the evening of September 30th and didn't know what to do. I couldn't walk up the hill with my luggage, I couldn't see any buses, and I didn't think it would look right to sweep up to the Queen Alelaide in the dowager Rolls-Royce that seemed to be the only available taxi. I asked about buses and everyone told me something different, so eventually I decided to take the Rolls and get out before I got to the hospital. Perched on the worn beige whipcord, my nose almost touching the paper carnations, I clung on to the strap, tense with apprehension. It was drawing so near – the agony of being plunged into a new world, of being stared at and criticized, of only learning the right things to do by doing the wrong ones first. All too soon, we were at the top of the hill, and I must get out and be a nurse or else go home again and never know what it was like. The iron gates towered above me as I went through, and I felt very exposed as I lugged my suitcases across the gravel and presented myself at the glass box.

The blood pressure seemed worse. Surely more veins flamed round his nose now than before.

'New nurse?' he panted. 'Wrong door. Nurses don't use

main door. Round to your right.' He motioned with his arm and then leaned back, exhausted, against a notice board. I slunk away, thankful that at least I had not arrived in the Rolls. Following the grey wall of the hospital, past all the doors with their different prohibitive notices, I came at last to one larger and heavier than the rest, with a great lock on it.

'NURSES' HOSTEL', it said, but it might just as well have said 'GAOL'. A smaller door within the big one was ajar, but I didn't like to go in. I rang. Nothing happened, and I knocked with the same result. I was begining to feel unwanted, when I heard footsteps behind me and turned to see two nurses arm in arm, wearing red cloaks over more convincing replicas of the uniform that weighted my suitcase. They stopped giggling to give me a silent stare as I stepped respectfully back, then they pushed open the little door and went giggling inside. I followed them and stood in a dim, square hall, trying to make out what sort of a place I was in. Dusk had drifted in from outside and there was no electric light to chivvy it out. Instead, dim blue bulbs made the ghostly twilight of a photographer's dark room. Evidently this was their way of saving blackout material and I wondered if the bedroom lights were the same.

Before me, the lights made fading pools down the polished wood of a long corridor, and on my left, stairs turned upwards into obscurity. The two nurses had gone this way and looking after them, I saw a blur of face hanging over the bannister at the top.

'I say,' said a very young voice, 'did you want something?'

'Well, yes, I – er – I mean, I'm a new nurse. I've come.'

'Oh, bad luck,' she said depressingly. 'Still, I suppose you want to find your room. I wonder where they've put you. Half a mo – I'll come down and look on the board. You go and make the coff, Con,' she called back as she came downstairs, 'I shan't be a jiff.' Everything with her was an abbreviation. Striking a match by the notice board, she searched for the number of my room. 'Presuming the Ass Mat's remembered.'

'The who?'

'Assistant Matron; old Fanny Harriman. Mad as a hat.'

Nevertheless I was prepared to like her for having the same name as my mother. It was only later that I discovered that Fanny is a derisive applied to any Sister. Seeing my name on the list gave me a thrill of belonging, and removed some of that feeling of having come on the wrong day. The nurse led me down the long blue tunnel of the corridor. 'There's hardly anyone about now,' she said. 'They're not off dute. Here you are, here's your boud.' She opened the door and sniffed. 'Furniture pol. They only clean your room when you first come here. Makes a good impresh,' she said and disappeared.

The light was not dazzling, but at least it was not blue. When I had climbed on a chair and removed the green shroud from it, I could see quite a lot. Thank goodness, anyway, one had a room to oneself. I was dreading getting up at six o'clock, but it would be impossible in company. It's bad enough to have to see one's own face at that hour, let alone anybody else's.

The *décor* of my little home was simple. Wardrobe, black iron bed on wheels, chair and dressing table with swing mirror that overswung itself and reflected only your stomach. Behind the cupboard door there was a long list of rules, starting with 'Nurses must throw open their windows and turn their mattresses before going to breakfast,' and ending with : 'No nails to be driven into walls,' and 'trunks and boxes to be sent to boxroom and not kept under the bed.' That was to stop anyone flitting in the night. I felt rather harassed and homesick, did a little desultory unpacking, sat down on the bed and brooded, read the rules again and wondered whether I ought to tell anyone I had come.

Then the noise began. At first it was just an odd shout, a heavy tread, a door banging. Soon it had swelled to a crescendo of voices, door-slamming that made my mirror swing farther each time, and tramping feet that could be nothing else but the nurses coming off duty. My door burst open and a fat girl with a shiny face filled the doorway. Her apron bulged before her as if it held all the family washing.

'Oh, hallo,' she said. 'Are you a new Pro?' I supposed I was.

'D'you know how to put on your uniform?' I thought so.

'D'you know how to make up your cap?' I didn't.

'Well, you'd better come along and I'll show all of you together.' I was relieved to hear that there were other new girls besides me. It made me feel less inferior, but when we met, in the fat girl's bedroom that smelt of cheap powder and tea-leaves, I began to feel inferior again. There were three of them, two Welsh and one Yorkshire, called Gunter. They had all been nursing before – the Welsh girls at a maternity home in Caerphilly, and the other one at some hospital unspecified. She was completely silent, but managed to convey the impression of knowing a lot. Whenever our fat instructress, while she was sewing a specimen cap, told us some rule or point of etiquette, the Welsh girls would say: 'Yes, we know. Like at Caerphilly,' and the dumb one would nod and drop her heavy lids, as if it were an old story. I wanted to ask a lot of questions, including: 'When do we eat?' but when the senior nurse asked if we had had supper, the others all said they had, so I did too.

I looked hideous in the cap she made up for me, because she would try it on right down over my eyes. The others didn't look too bad; they had more curls or something, and the Yorkshire girl was hideous anyway, with or without a cap. Afterwards, she and I went out for a silent walk. At least, I went out for some air and she loomed beside me and stuck, like some large dog on a string. The air on the hill was cool and fresh. 'I like the night,' said Gunter. 'It's more quiet than the day.' With which simple truth her conversation ended and we returned in silence through the little door and were parting halfway down the long corridor, at the door of my room, before she spoke again.

'I'll call for you on the way to breakfast,' she said. 'You and I'll be friends, shall we?'

Thump – crash! 'Six o'clock, Nurse!' – crash! as the door shut again. Whoever it was had given me the shock of my life. I thought I had only just gone to sleep – a heavy,

237

weighted sleep from which awakening was unbearable. I lay for a while, stunned, unable to believe that my night was at an end. So this was what it was like to rise at six!

Only the thought that Gunter might be upon me before I was dressed, forced me out of bed and into my clothes. My fingers were still numb with sleep and fumbled with the studs and buttons that caged me in. Remembering one or two astringent remarks from Sarah Churchman on the subject of make-up, I washed my face and let it shine on. Now for the cap. The more I fiddled with it, the more shapeless it became. I pushed it forward, I tipped it back. One way I looked like a half-witted waitress, the other like a half-wit. It was all very well for Madeleine Carroll; she had probably had hers made up by Adrian, not by a girl with fingers like half a pound of sausages. A door banged and feet hurried past my room. In a sudden panic that I was late, I left the cap to its own devices, rocking insecurely somewhere on the top of my head, and trod into my respectable black shoes. No time to wait for Gunter, even if I had wanted to, but when I opened the door, there she was, waiting outside like the Rock of Ages, with her heavy jaw slightly dropped and her eyes like lead coins.

Nurses were coming out of doors all along the corridor and we followed the stream away from the entrance hall, through a door and up endless flights of stone stairs. Gunter climbed like a stayer, but I felt exhausted for the day. In the dining-room, there must have been about fifty nurses, gathering round the three long tables like a flock of white birds. It's a funny thing that whatever nurses may look like individually, *en masse* they make an oddly pure effect, like a billowing flight of doves, that belies their conversation.

Someone shoved me into a place and we all stood behind chairs while a pretty little Sister with a tired face said Grace. The tables were covered with green oilcloth and set with crockery that looked as if it ought to have G.W.R. on it. The empty table across the end of the room had a tablecloth and napkins; evidently the Sisters breakfasted later. Breakfast was strong tea, a brittle bit of bacon with the rind on, and as much bread and margarine as you could eat. And could

some of them eat it! The doorsteps that they got through at
an hour when my stomach was only just stirring in its sleep,
were staggering. Gunter told me she could never fancy
marge from a child, so she ate her way solidly through three
hunks of dry bread. I looked at the other nurses and wondered whether I should ever be able to tell them apart.
Thank goodness, they took no notice of us new girls. They
just ate and drank and passed the bread up and down the
table and said: 'Sugar, please,' more like pigeons now than
doves. Opposite me, the two Welsh girls were talking away,
unawed, about Caerphilly, with which Redwood evidently
compared unfavourably.

Degrees of seniority were marked by the number of red
stars you wore on the bib of your apron. At my table, they
had none, at the table beyond, they all had one and beyond
that, two. At a smaller table in the bay of the window, sat a
dozen awesome girls with no less than three stars and special
caps to boot. Among the two-pips, I spotted the abbreviat-
ing girl of the night before. She looked young and fresh, like
a baby waked up for its bottle. She was talking to a girl who
stood out from the others, not from particularly striking
looks, but from an enviable air of not belonging to the herd,
of looking at it from outside and probably laughing at it. I
didn't think I liked her.

When Sister called the roll, she paused at my name, which
sounded as odd as one's own name always does in public.
'You go to William Forrest Ward, Nurse,' she said. Gunter
was destined for Herbert Waterlow, which was a relief. After
Grace, I went into the corridor with the mob, which dis-
persed in all directions, while I stood lost. Someone grabbed
my arm. It was the girl I had noticed at breakfast. She had
straight fair hair, like clear honey, and a bony face, plain
but attractive.

"Come on,' she said; 'you're on my ward.' She caught up
someone on the stairs and they went down talking, while I
followed behind like a servant. I felt terribly shy going into
the ward and thought that the eyes of all the beds were upon
me. I hardly dared look to see whether they were male or
female eyes, and I was relieved to find that in spite of

239

William Forrest, it was a women's ward – that was slightly less unnerving. I felt all hands and would have felt all feet too if my dress had not been long enough to shelter them. The others stood about for a moment yawning and calling good-morning to some of the patients, then we took off our stiff cuffs, rolled up our sleeves and began to make beds. That is to say, Nurse Richardson (square, with a healthy crop of black hair on her upper lip) took one side of the bed and did miraculous things like mitreing corners and whipping draw sheets in and out under obediently raised bottoms, while I, on the other side, fumbled and muddled, tore my nails and was convinced that I should never make a nurse.

Each hour of that first day strengthened my conviction. I could do nothing right, it seemed, and everything wrong. I was always either in the way or not there when I was wanted. I had always either not given enough time and trouble to something or else should have been finished an hour ago.

I can give no very coherent account of that first day, because it was a completely incoherent day. It seemed that I had special duties – the most menial, I could see that all right. The Staff Nurse, one of those with three stars and frills on her cap, strung off to me what these duties were, but I couldn't take them all in at once. Simple items that even I could do, like sweeping the floor, and cutting bread and butter, alternated with mysteries like 'doing one's side', 'seeing to the gastric feeds' and 'getting diabetic specimens'. I spent most of the day pottering about after somebody, saying : 'What do I do next?' and in this way discovered what the nurses were like.

The Staff Nurse, who was called Nurse Ketch, was slick and soulless. She was usually too busy doing something frightfully responsible to reply. When I came trotting up with my innocent question, expecting some commendation for having finished the job before, she said : 'I told you what to do once,' and went on being highly skilled with glass trolleys and bits of rubber tubing. It seemed that no comment other than adverse was ever made on your work, and that it was not what you did but what you did not do that attracted notice. If you were told to do twice as much, and,

240

by a superhuman effort, achieved it, it would be taken as much for granted as your heartbeat.

Nurse Richardson was kinder. She would tell me, when she had time, but then she never had time. She was always scudding about, with two furrows between her heavy brows, throwing desperate glances at the clock and muttering: 'Oh, Glory, I'll never get done. I've got that ear to dress ... inhalations ... all those temps to take ... that leg – Heavens! I've forgotten the diabetic specimens. Have I got time to test them before I do that leg? I shan't go to tea. ....'

I was rather afraid of asking Nurse Parry, the girl who had brought me down. She seemed so sure of herself, and I gathered she thought me a panicking fool. She herself strolled through her work, unperturbed by crises, and letting fall appalling language, more from habit than provocation. 'For Christ's sake, woman,' she kept saying, 'calm down. We don't work very hard here on a Sunday.' That was all very well. We did, and I wanted to know what to do next before I was cursed for not having done it. I envied her her easy familiarity with the patients. She didn't mind what she said to them and they seemed to love it. I myself was terrified of the thirty odd female bodies that were our charge. *Sister Fairchild* had said, in Chapter Two : 'Never let the patient know that you are nervous or do not know what to do. You will sap his confidence in you and so delay, or even prevent his recovery.' But they could have had no confidence in me to be sapped. I didn't even know what was wrong with them and was frightened of touching the wrong end.

How did one ever learn their names? Except people like Mrs Greenbaum, whose name was indelibly printed on my mind after I had given her the wrong dinner tray. Knowing full well that it was not hers, she had eaten it and had nurtured the consequent pain until her doctor came round and she could tell him exactly how she got it.

The two other nurses on the ward were fairly junior. They had no stars and seemed to do almost as much cleaning and polishing as I did. Nurse Donavan was jolly and cockney and rather dirty and would sooner wipe a plate on her apron than walk two yards to the sink to wash it. She answered my questions with loud laughter and : 'Good Grycious, don't ask *me*. I only work here.'

Nurse Drew was saccharine. 'Ask me anything you want to know,' she kept insisting. 'I can remember what it was like to be strange,' she said, as one looking down the years and stretching out a hand from the summit of experience. She didn't have far to stretch, as I presently discovered, for she had only been there three weeks longer than I had.

These were the nurses on William Forrest Ward. William Forrest himself was a man who had lost his wife there, of a pulmonary embolism and had endowed the ward in questionable gratitude. Of Sister Lewis, the dictator of the ward, I knew no more at the end of the day than the beginning, for she had not spoken one word to me. They told me she never did under a week. Nurse Parry insisted that there was once a nurse about whom, at the end of two months she was still asking : 'Who is that?' with the same look of delicate distaste that I had seen her direct at me. She was a frail-looking woman, a mere anaemic drift, and completely unnatural. She struck poses and wove sentences of elaborate refinement. She didn't look strong enough to be a hospital nurse, unless her frailty was also a pose.

By the end of the day, my mind and body were in such a chaos of fatigue that I couldn't think of anything but my bed, black iron or not. I just had the strength to stagger to a phone box, accompanied of course, like a solid shadow, by Gunter, and tell my family : 'I love it.' Because I did. That was the one thing that emerged clearly.

## Chapter Three

FOR the first few days I groped my way through a dust-storm of new impressions, baffling orders and mystic phraseology, but gradually the dust began to settle into the pattern of hospital life. What had seemed chaos at first emerged as a routine so rigid that it superseded any eventuality. The Ward Work must go On. That locker must be polished without and scoured within, though Death and Tragedy lie in beds on either side.

Soon I could hardly imagine a time when I had not been doing exactly the same things at the same time each day. I sometimes caught myself thinking how deadly the work would be if it were not for the patients, forgetting that without patients there would be no work, for it seemed to have an independent existence, which nothing could ever stop. If all the beds were empty, one would still come on at seven o'clock and push them backwards and forwards and kick the wheels straight.

As it was, life became more bearable with each day's knowledge of the patients and the realization that they were people, not just bodies under counterpanes whose corners had to be geometrical. Of course, there was hardly any time to talk to them, but sometimes, closeted behind screens to give a blanket bath, you could get down to a good gossip, until a long white hand drew back the screen to admit the ivory face with its fluted nostrils and fastidious lips.

'Neu-rse' – Sister Lewis's voice had a kind of disdainful creak – you're giving a blanket bath, not paying a social call.' She was on speaking terms with me by now, at least on telling-off terms. I was responsible for an unmentionable little apartment called the sluice, which she would enter every morning at nine o'clock, almost changing into old shoes to do so. She would sniff delicately and touch things with her fingertips, but her eye was ruthless. There was usually something to be cleaned again and I would have to miss part of the half-hour's break we were allowed for making our beds, changing into a clean apron and having a cup of coffee.

If I had been surprised by the capacity of the nurses' stomachs at breakfast, I was staggered when I did get time to go to the dining-room for what was known as 'Lunch'. The ends of yesterday's long loaves were on the table, with a mound of margarine and a bowl of dripping. I tasted the dripping once, and tasted it all day in consequence. Gunter used to take her plate to the end of the table where there was plenty of elbow room and eat bread and dripping like a starving refugee.

This being Lunch, the next meal was called Dinner. This was at midday, except for the senior nurses, and there were all the white pigeons again, ready to make up for only two slices of meat by quantities of potatoes and as many goes of rice pudding as they could manage before Sister said Grace. Tea was at four and the bread was new and doughy and had to be cut in hunks anyway, and supper was at half past eight, when one came off duty. It was usually sausages and disguised pies, and perhaps blancmange or cold rice pudding left over from dinner. One thing that hospital taught me was to eat the sort of puddings I had been refusing since the nursery. Hunger compelled it. My appetite grew enormous and I saw myself becoming one of the doorstep-and-dripping brigade, with my apron growing tighter each day and my dress straining its seams.

Seven a.m. to 8.30 p.m. sounds a long time, but we got three hours off during the day, either morning, afternoon or evening. Evenings were the best, because there was no coming back on duty, and sometimes I used to dash down to London in order to get a decent dinner and dash back again to get in before they locked the little door. It was not until later that I discovered the bathroom window. We also had one whole day off a week – a day of eating, drinking and sleeping. Words cannot describe the joy of wearing human clothes.

All the same, I was quite proud of my uniform and was getting used to the sight of myself in it, although I still felt like somebody masquerading as a nurse. The mysteries of William Forrest Ward were being slowly revealed to me; it was a medical ward, I discovered. This sounded well to tell at home : 'I'm on the women's medical ward.' Nurse Richardson was kind to me. When we were making beds together, which was the only time she ever got a moment to talk, she would drill me in the patients' complaints. Half the time I had not the faintest idea what the words meant but it pleased her to hear me say : 'This patient is suffering from acute leukaemia with enlargement of the spleen and oedema of the lower limbs.'

'When I was a new pro.,' she told me, 'nobody would tell me anything. I know what it's like.' She had me on her conscience and was determined to bring me up right. When she was not reckoning out loud the jobs ahead of her, she would keep up a running commentary on my work.

'Now the draw sheet – straighten the mac, pull from me, tuck in – now you shake the pillows, then *up* the bed with the patient – that's right – arm under her axilla. Now turn in the wheels, pull that locker forward, has she got water? Here's a torn pillowcase ... Oh, Glory, we'll never get these beds finished and I shan't get the flowers done before Sister comes on. Off you go to the linen cupboard, Nurse. *That's* right – pop it on – open end away from the door, don't forget. Now, Mrs Brownlees. Now, Nurse, what did I tell you about this patient's hand?'

'Cellulose,' I would say sleepily, snatching at the corner of a blanket as she whipped it through the air.

'Oh, Glory, you must try and remember – cellulitis.'

'Fancy,' said Mrs Brownlees, 'cellophane,' and stored it up to tell Ethel on Visitors' Day.

Next to Mrs Brownlees was a Polish woman, a Jewish refugee from Warsaw, who when she had a pain, would keen like the lost tribes of Israel : 'Oi-yoi, oi-yoi, yoi-yoi-oi!' Her English was not good enough for her to enter into the sociability of the ward and the conversation that broke out whenever Sister was off duty. She would lie with only her chin above the sheet, following the exchange of symptoms from bed to bed with eyes like black currants. Mrs Brownlees, who was fat and wobbly, tried to jolly her along and called her Miss Clean dearie, but as Miss Klein only stared at her suspiciously, she soon turned to Mrs Russell on the other side, who would swop a fibroid for a confinement any day.

One day, I found Miss Klein crying and oi-yoi-ing as if her heart would break. 'What's the matter?' I asked, nonplussed. Sister had told me to find out what she wanted for dinner. 'Have you got a pain?'

'No.'

'What's the matter then?'

'Pleess?'

'Come on, cheer up,' I said. 'I want to know what you'd like for dinner. There's some lovely fish – well, anyway, there's fish —'

'Na!' She shrugged off my hand and turned her face into the pillow.

'Well, would you rather have meat? Would you like fish or meat, Miss Klein,' I persevered. I thought perhaps she didn't understand me because she was usually keen on her food, so, without thinking, I tried her with: 'Wollen Sie fisch oder fleisch —' She was round on me in a moment, with her hair on end and her eyes flashing in her stricken face. 'Ah!' she cried, thrusting me away, 'You too! You think it too!'

'Think what?'

'All these woman —' she darted a look round at all the figures sitting up harmlessly eating stew off painted tin trays, 'they think I am a spy.' She nodded vigorously and a great teardrop fell into her thick lower lip. 'Oh, yah,' she interrupted my protestations, 'you can say and say and say. Don' tell me. I have heard them talk about me and say: "she is a spy". They don' like I am here. How I can get well?'

'But that's ridiculous, Miss Klein. Nobody talks about you. We're all very fond of you. Who do you think doesn't like you?'

'Her, and her next.' She nodded towards Mrs Brownlees and Mrs Russell who were whiling away the time between courses with the subject of varicose veins. 'All day they talk and say: "She is a spy, she talk fonny," so now I don' speak any more, but still they talk. You shall see – they will tell the politz. Yoi-oi-yoi —' She began to sob again.

It was no use trying to reason with her. She was obsessed. Small wonder that she had this persecution mania after what she had probably been through. The Warsaw from which she had fled must have been a city of spying and treachery and suspicion, of whispers in cafés and meaning glances and abusive notices mysteriously appearing on walls.

How could you trust anybody when people that you knew, even your friends, appeared from one day to the next in Nazi uniform, and even your old servant turned informer?

For several days she lay in a huddled ball, sobbing off and on, and then early one morning, she suddenly hopped out of bed, scooted for the door and was off down the passage in her crumpled nightgown and bare feet before anyone could stop her. When she was brought back, struggling and shrieking in Polish, they put boards round the sides of the bed so that she couldn't get out, and she lay like a trapped animal, with only her eyes moving. She had no people over here and the mistress for whom she had worked came to see her once and stood looking vaguely down at the bed and saying : 'Oh, dear, it's all very unfortunate, but I don't see what I can do – I'm not responsible for her.' Soon after that, they took Miss Klein away, I don't know where to.

At one end of the ward, glass doors led to a stone-floored balcony, where half a dozen convalescents and chest cases were protected from the hilltop winds by yellow army horse-blankets. The balcony had three glass sides, like a conservatory. When the windows were open you could see the hospital's vegetable garden, full of cabbages and rhubarb, and beyond that the descending roofs of residential Redwood, and when they were shut the anti-shutter coating gave you the impression of being in a Swiss mist.

In a corner of this balcony, surrounded by fourpenny novelties, bags of gummy sweets and half-empty pots of anchovy paste, was my greatest friend, Mabel Mutch, a convalescent Appendix. She had a face like a slab of concrete, a powerful cockney accent and a sense of humour that lit up the balcony. Her husband was called 'Cicil', and was very flash with a three-wheel car and mauve trousers, and she used to tell me long stories of how he had courted her at the White City and how she had finally said yes at the Palace, while Robert Taylor was at Garbo's deathbed.

It was one of my jobs to sweep and dust the balcony in the mornings, and I used to spend as long as possible over it, talking to Mabel about food and drink. Once Cicil brought in half a bottle of port, and when Sister had gone to supper we had quite a party. The woman in the next bed had some too and it made her cough worse than ever and the bright spots on her cheeks flamed.

There was not much time for sociability in William Forrest, however, even when the Staff Nurse wasn't whisking up and treating you like dirt or Sister appearing silently with her : 'Neurse, since you appear to have plenty of spare time, you had better go and employ it in turning out the splint cupboard.' I was always in a desperate hurry to get done.

'Getting done' is the purpose of every nurse. You have so much work to do by a certain time and not long enough in which to do it. If anything untoward happens, or extra work crops up, it throws you out and you rush about saying : 'I'll never get done!' and nobody pays any attention because they are too busy trying to get done themselves. I was terribly slow at first and permanently harassed. I could cheerfully have killed any patient who delayed me by upsetting a glass of water or fancying a slice more bread and butter when there wasn't any cut, or any of the hundred things I was sure they did on purpose to annoy. Ordinary working tempo doesn't do for hospitals. After a while, I got the knack of keeping up such a speed that it was impossible to stop going. My feet became scorched by the friction and were balls of fire at night. I tried sleeping with them on a pillow, and even raising the foot of my bed on books, higher and higher, until Nurse Drew told me my heart would slip.

I was growing to dislike Nurse Drew. She and I were supposed to work together in the evenings – taking round the suppers, tidying the ward and cleaning things that all had to be cleaned again anyway in the morning. She had a happy knack of looking very busy about doing nothing, being closeted behind screens holding a leg while it was dressed, or running back and forth with hot fomentations for Nurse Ketch. By the time I had pushed round the trolley, with my chant of : 'Cocoa, Bovril, hot milk, cold milk,' gone back to the kitchen half a dozen times for things I had forgotten, weighed out the special suppers for Diabetics and opened a sardine tin with a pair of scissors for Mabel, the maid would

248

often have gone off duty and I would have to wash up. Nurse Drew would come mincing in with her head on one side just as I had finished, and offer to help me. I could have pushed her simpering face in if I hadn't been too tired.

However, she was senior to me and I had to stand back for her at doors. It was rigid, this hospital etiquette. I was always dropping bricks and addressing people as equals or helping myself to salt before someone who had a red star. Once I answered the telephone and took a message for a doctor who was doing his round in the ward. Most respectful, I went up to him with lowered eyes and hands behind my back, waited for his attention, said : 'Excuse me,' delivered the message in a hushed voice and thought I had done rather well. Afterwards, Sister beckoned me over to where she was sitting with one elbow on the desk and her fingers arranged in the air like a ballet dancer's.

'Nurse,' she said, looking at the dirt on my apron from under her mauve lids. 'You must never, never, do such a thing again.' I was staggered. I asked her what I had done, what she meant?

'You know perfectly well what I mean,' she said. 'I am exceedingly shocked.' So was I, but with surprise, not horror.

'But really, Sister,' I began, 'I don't know —'

'*How* long have you been here, Nurse?'

'Two months.'

'And you mean to stand there and tell me that you don't know that you may not address a member of the medical staff directly, but only through the medium of someone senior to yourself?' I gaped.

'How you could do it, Nurse, I don't know. How you could bring yourself to do such a thing —' She looked at me as if I were a bad smell.

I went away and cried in the sluice and Nurse Drew came and patted my shoulder and said : 'Cheer up, we all have our little troubles. I'm sure you didn't mean to break that thermometer.'

The amount of time one wasted putting on and taking off one's stiff cuffs for the sake of etiquette was endless. Once, a patient was having a terrific nose-bleed and I was sent hurrying up to the kitchen for some ice. Remembering that the only two occasions on which a nurse may run are fire and haemorrhage, I pelted off and ran into a Sister on the stairs who held me back by the arm and said : 'Nurse! whatever are you doing outside a ward without your cuffs?' Breathlessly I tried to explain, but she wouldn't even listen until I had gone back for them and confronted her again decently dressed. By the time I got back to the ward with the ice. Sister said : 'I suppose a patient might die before you'd hurry yourself,' and the patient, who was farther from dying than I was, looked as smug as was possible with a large wad of cotton wool under her nose and moaned pitifully. She was my *bête noire*, this woman. She would keep on calling, calling for me in a hoarse voice when I couldn't possibly come. 'What is it, Mrs Kirby?' I would throw over my shoulder as I dashed by. She would never answer – just beckon with a horny finger. 'Nurse, I wants yer.' As often as not when I did go to her, all she wanted was to know the time, or to ask me what was for dinner. One morning, she had been particularly trying. I had remade her bed twice, because she said crumbs were fretting her bottom and countless were the times I had trailed to the kitchen, either to refill her glass or to heat up her cocoa which she had allowed to grow cold. Two casualties were coming in and I was trying to make up beds for them and at the same time keep an eye on a mad woman who would keep tearing off her bandages.

'Nurse!'

'Oh, you can wait a moment, Mrs Kirby.'

'Nurse, I wants yer.' Out of the corner of my eye I could see her beckoning, but I pretended not to hear. I had to pass her bed on the way to get sheets out of the linen cupboard.

'Nurse – 'ere – Nurse—' It was like a hand jerking at my skirt.

'Oh, *wait* a minute, Mrs Kirby,' I said. 'Can't you see I'm busy?' She was still beckoning, undeterred, when I came back. Sister was looking my way, so I had to go to her. 'Well, what is it now?' I snapped. I was furious with the woman. Everything had gone wrong this morning. I was hot and tired and hungry and my cap would keep slipping off the back of my head. 'What is it?' I said, dumping the sheets heavily on to her legs while I jabbed at my cap.

She beckoned me closer. ''Ere,' she croaked, ''ere, dearie, I've got a stick of chocolate for you.' My soul craved for nut milk chocolate, but I was ashamed to take it. I had to pretend I never ate chocolate and she turned up her eyes at me, hurt. When she left hospital, her nephew, who was in the trade, brought her in a whole parcel of chocolate, which she distributed to all the nurses – except me, of course.

Some mornings, before she said Grace after breakfast, Night Sister would read out the names of those whom Matron wished to see. This usually meant trouble and there would be craning necks and stares of gloating sympathy at the unfortunates, who would pretend it was about holidays. One morning, it was Nurse Dickens to see Matron at ten o'clock. I froze with horror, a forkful of solidified scrambled egg substitute half-way to my mouth. What had I done? Or rather, what had been discovered? Could anyone have found out that I had been cleaning the bath with pure Dettol to save elbow grease, or about that medicine glass – had I not buried the pieces deep enough in the bin? Gunter was staring at me, the primary stage of digestion visible in her open mouth.

'It's all right,' said Evans. 'I had to go yesterday. It's only to sign on.' She and her Caerphilly colleague were not so thick these days, since they each discovered that the boy from the 2*d*. library had been taking the other one out. He must now have been concentrating on Evans, for she was quite bouncing, while the other drooped, rather spotty, farther down the table.

'What's signing on?' I asked.

It appeared that your first few months were a kind of trial on both sides. You could leave or be thrown out without notice, but once you had signed on, it was a month's notice on either side and you could not leave without a good reason.

'Do you have to sign on?' I asked the girl next to me, a little bustling body who may have had legs somewhere under the voluminous apron that would have gladdened the heart of *Sister Fairchild*.

'Well, you don't have to,' she said. 'She gives some people longer if they can't make up their minds.'

'I shan't sign on,' I boasted. It was a claustrophobian idea. When I went into Sarah P.'s office, she was scratching away at one of her interminable ledgers, the desk was littered with them and with notebooks and sheaves of lists. I thought sadly of the paper shortage and of the scrappy bundles that Bert and Arthur and I had pounced on with such pride in my salvage days. Matron gave me a quick glint from her thick lenses and said : 'You had better come back and see me in a clean apron, Nurse.' She talked like a ventriloquist – her lips rigid and her epiglottis sliding up and down her scrawny throat.

I didn't feel like a fagging all the way down to my room. 'Please Ma'am,' I said, 'I haven't got a clean one till the laundry comes back.'

'The laundry came back yesterday, Nurse.'

'Mine wasn't there, please Ma'am.'

'I checked the laundry myself. There was none missing. You can come back to me with a clean apron or a better excuse.' If there was a spark of humour in her eyes, the thick lenses concealed it.

I went. I might have known how useless it was to try and pit oneself against authority and a system that had been going on long before one thought nurses were only things with laps and warm towels. Several people had told me that they tried to resist the hospital system at first and had ideas about revolutionizing the whole thing. But you can't; it's too big and too rooted. You may think it absurd that grown-up girls who are considered responsible enough to deal with life and death should have their bedroom lights turned off at the main at half-past ten every night, but there's nothing you can do about it. After a while you get quite good at doing your hair in the dark.

When I returned, crackling with starch, Matron just handed me a piece of paper and said : 'Sign here,' and of course I signed meekly. The net was closing round me.

Once I had signed on, I realized that I had let myself in for exams and lectures. You had to attend these three days a

252

week, in your off-duty time. The final examination was three years ahead, with its remote possibilities of becoming State Registered and wearing frills and medals, but there was something called 'the Pree-lim,' which you took after a year, and could take as many times as you could afford the entrance fee until you passed. Some of the nurses had been taking it cheerfully and unsuccessfully for years. Their swotting, or 'studying' as it was known at Queen Adelaide, was done communally. They would sit on each other's beds, drinking tea out of tooth mugs and eating large dry cakes from the busmen's café across the road. They would start off quite earnestly with : 'What is a cell now, Jones?' ... 'A cell is a minute living organism consisting of a nucleus and protoplasm enclosed in a stroma, or envelope' ... 'Brilliant, now, let's have about tissues,' but the conversation would soon drift on to what I said to Sister and how Dr Pascoe said : 'Thank you, Nurse,' from behind his mask in Theatre.

The lectures were on Hygiene, Nursing, and Anatomy and Physiology. Hygiene was all right if you happened to be keen on sewage and Activated Sludge. A knowledge of plumbing is apparently essential to a good nurse and soon I could not pass a house without gauging the efficiency of its outside pipe system. Nursing was mostly practical work – bandaging each other and making the bed of a lay figure that was known as Old Mother Riley and appeared to be a maternity case.

The Sister Tutor who taught us was so fat, that once between her desk and the blackboard she was wedged there for the whole lecture. She liked to illustrate various bones on herself, and would poke and prod at her cushiony hips for ages, trying to find her Iliac Crest. She always spoke in technicalities, even in ordinary conversation : she was dehydrated instead of being thirsty, and rotated the Axis on the odontoid process of the Atlas when she wanted to turn her head.

Anatomy was fascinating. I started to write a story entitled : *The Skeleton in the Cupboard*, in which the hero was called Pyloric Sphincter and the heroine Hernia Bistoury. There was a beautiful spy called Vena Cava and a will-o'-the-wisp creature called Poly O'Myelitis, who led a gipsy life on a Cavernous Sinus. The heroine's unattractive friend, who was always tagging along as an unwanted third, was Ulna Tuberosity, and there was a dapper old gentleman called Sir Glenoid Fossa, who collected antiques and owned the inlaid ivory Malleolus, the blunt instrument that silenced the barking of Hernia's faithful Mastoid.

There were about a dozen nurses in my lecture class : the Welsh girls and Gunter, who couldn't spell, four new girls, even newer than me, and a few oddments from higher up who had arrived too late to go into the class above. One of these was a conversational girl called Kelly, with wild hair and soft brown eyes and an irrepressible sociability. She would interrupt Sister half-way through a dissertation on ears to say : 'I must just tell you about my aunt, Sister. I'm sure you'd be awfully interested. So would the class, perhaps.' Her smile flashed over our inert figures like the beam of a lighthouse on a shuttered village.

'Not now, Nurse,' said Sister impatiently. 'Afterwards, if you like.'

'Oh, but Sister, I must just tell you. It was so queer. This aunt, you see – she lived in Dublin – she'd been deaf for years and never thought anything of it, till one day, her nephew who'd just qualified at the Rotunda, said : "Why don't you let me take the syringe to it, Auntie?" She'd try anything once, she said, so he did, and what d'you think? Out came a blue bead. It must have been there for ages, because it was years since she wore that necklace. Wasn't that amazing?' The beam swung round on us again.

'Fancy,' said Sister and tapped on the blackboard with her pointer. 'Now the external auditory meatus —' I liked Nurse Kelly. She brought a freshness to the sterility of the lectures that Sister had been delivering without variation ever since she gave up the post as Junior Night Sister at the Birmingham General because of heart trouble.

'Describe this bone,' she would say, rootling in her gruesome box and thrusting one at Nurse Kelly, who would handle it like an amusing toy. 'There's a funny little knob at the end here – well more of a hump I'd call it, wouldn't you, Sister?'

'That's a tubercle, Nurse.'

'Oh, but it isn't exactly. It's more like those sorts of warts that grow on trees – and look! There's a little ditch – where the other bone fits in, I suppose.'

'I don't know what the examiners will say to you, Nurse, I'm sure. You must try and be more technical.'

'Oh, but they won't mind surely, if I explain in my own words —'

'Sit down, Nurse. Nurse Jones, go on describing the bone.'

'Oh, but I do know it – really,' said Kelly, jumping up again and waving her hand.

'This is the lateral epicondyle,' pronounced Nurse Jones, stabbing it with a dogmatic forefinger.

'Oh no, Nurse, surely —'

'Sit *down*, Nurse Kelly!' She would eventually subside and go on talking to me, unabashed, while Jones rattled crisply through the salient points. She was a menace, a know-all with a glistening face and important figure. She liked to be thought keen, and when the lecture was over, would delay our escape by asking unnecessary questions, while we muttered and shuffled our feet.

It was bad enough having to attend lectures in your off duty, but when they fell on your day off, it was infuriating. At first, I used to miss them and go home as usual, but I soon found myself before Sarah P. at ten o'clock in a clean apron. Having a lecture on my day off meant either that I could not go home for the night or that I had to come back from London in the morning. For the hundredth time I wished that nurses had a Union. No other trade would allow one's free time to be encroached upon like this. I collected a repertoire of excuses – dentist's appointments, long-lost relations, a mythical fiancé, which I trotted out from time to time in order to get my day unspoiled. The exam was nearly a year off, anyway, and I didn't think I would still be there, even if the war lasted. Every morning, as I fought my way out of sleep at six o'clock, I resolved to give in my notice, but as the agony wore off my resolve weakened and the interest of the day began to take hold of me. I made a bet with Nurse Parry that I would not stay a year.

255

'You won't have the initiative not to,' she said. 'They get you into a rut and then you haven't the energy to cut free. I used to think I'd go mad if I stayed another day, but now I've settled down, like a cow.'

It was visitors' day and we were in the bathroom making plaster bandages and having a few surreptitious puffs at a cigarette. I can't think of anything less cowlike than this leggy creature with her attractive, dark blonde hair and her casual talk. She had been trying to shock me with improbable stories of her pre-hospital life. 'I came here to expiate my sins,' she said, 'like a ruddy nunnery – look out!' We hurled our cigarettes out of the window.

'I can smell smoke,' said Sister, coming in and finding us rubbing plaster into the stiff gauze strips like mad things.

'It was that porter,' said Parry, 'when he came through to fetch the laundry.'

'You may stop the bandages now,' said Sister, still sniffing unconvinced. 'I'm going to ring the bell for the visitors to go.' She drifted away.

'Dirty swine,' said Parry. 'It's only five to four.' Sister resented the visitors and would always try to cheat them of five minutes at either end of their time. She thought they spoiled the appearance of the ward, and after they had gone we would have to mop the floor because she fancied they left muddy footmarks, even on a dry day.

I loved visitors' day. Long before two o'clock the crowd would begin to collect in the corridor outside the ward, peering and waving through the glass doors, while we were tidying and retidying lockers, changing the bedjacket of Mrs Grant who had dribbled her mince again – anything that Sister could think of to keep them out a little longer. At last the doors were opened and they poured in, making a beeline, or hesitating if they had not been before, usually too shy to ask. Straw hats with roses on, knitted berets with brooches, best black coats, paper carriers crammed with food, flowers of all kinds from great sprays to wilting little bundles in brown paper. Men with their caps held in front of them, lurching from foot to foot, girls smart and made up, chatting brightly to Ma, but looking round all the time and fiddling with their curls, old men with dim eyes, who were managing alone at home and probably not getting enough to eat.

A young husband would go up to his wife's bed on tiptoe, clutch her hand and hang on to it for the full two hours, both of them practically speechless. Children were not allowed into the ward, but sometimes they would be brought to the door to wave at Gran and hustled away when they set up a yell to see her lying there as if she belonged to the hospital, and not to them any more. That must be the worst part of having someone in hospital. You have surrendered them, body and soul, to this alien, intimidating institution, that only lends them to you grudgingly for two hours twice a week.

## Chapter Four

WOMEN were not meant to live *en masse* – except in harems. They inflate the importance of their own little centre of activity until it eclipses the rest of the world. Men manage to pigeonhole their life : work, domesticity, romance, relaxation, but a woman's life is usually as untidy as her desk. She either fails ever to concentrate on one thing at a time, or else fills one pigeonhole so full that it overflows into the others.

I don't know whether the nurses at Redwood were typical of the whole profession, but most of them had no interest in anything that happened a yard outside the iron railings. They never read a paper, except the *Nursing Times*, and only turned on the Common Room wireless when the nine o'clock news was safely over. They were only interested in the war as far as it affected them personally – shortage of Dettol and cotton-wool perhaps, or jam for tea only once a week.

The ward beds had earphones fitted to them, connected with a central receiving set, and while I was dusting lockers, I used to enquire about the seven o'clock news. 'Why d'you always ask if there's any news?' a patient asked me one morning.

'Well, I don't know – because I'm interested, I suppose.'

'Funny,' she said, 'I shouldn't have thought a nurse would be interested.' That summed up the attitude of the outside world towards nurses and of nurses to the outside world. Nurse Donavan once asked me – I remember the day well; it was a red letter one, because she had washed her hair – 'Whatever were you talking to Sister Mason about at dinner?'

'Oh, the war,' I said vaguely. 'Settling world politics.'

'Good gracious,' she said, 'hadn't you got anything better to talk about than that?' I asked her what she would talk about when a German officer swaggered through the glass doors to take over the ward.

'I'd ask him if he'd had his bowels open,' she said and laughed coarsely.

Although they were so wrapped up in the hospital, some of the nurses grumbled incessantly. 'I hate it,' they would say. 'I hate the uniform, I hate the patients, I hate the Sisters and Fanny Churchman is a mean old witch.'

'But you like the work, don't you?'

'Loathe it. Sick people disgust me and operations are boring once you get over feeling faint.'

'Why ever be a nurse then?' one asked innocently. The nurse would stare. 'Well, what else could I possibly be?'

I should have thought almost anything rather than something so distasteful. They could have left; it was only a question of a month's notice and the Matron's odium. They can't have disliked it so much. In the same way, they grumbled about the food, while packing away mouthful after mouthful.

I asked a lot of them what originally made them take up nursing. Sometimes it was that they had been ill and had a very good nurse at an impressionable age. They rushed into hospital as soon as they were old enough, without seeing anything of the world or having any of the fun that is due to extreme youth. Naturally the restricted life irked them. They would have done far better to have seen a bit of life first and settled down in hospital afterwards if they had not yet worked the urge out of their system.

The war, of course, sends a lot of girls into hospital, but in normal times, apart from hero-worship and a semi-religious call, they go because nursing is about the only profession which you can enter entirely unqualified and not only get your training free but be paid while you are training. I never can see that nurses are so underpaid in the probationer stage. Besides their training, they get their keep, uniform and all medical treatment for nothing. I agree that the wages of a fully trained nurse are iniquitous; their skill and experience, acquired after three years of comparative slavery, should entitle them to more pay than a high-class parlourmaid.

I say all this now, rather smugly, but at the time, of course, I grumbled as much as anyone and disparaged the contents of my monthly envelope. Redwood was not a hub of entertainment but one can spend money anywhere. Apart from things like stamps and cigarettes and stockings, whose life was not lengthened by crawling about dusting bed wheels, there was always food. When the stomach wearied of a diet excessive, as *Sister Fairchild* would say, in carbohydrates and deficient in Vitamins C and D, we used to live for a while on coffee and buns and snacks and whatever we could afford. At the beginning of the month we used to go to the Blue Lady Café and Biddle's Restaurant and the tearoom above Hooper's, the only department shop in the town – all places where you got a tablecloth and a couple of flowers in a vase and a reasonable amount of currants in the cakes and tea per pot, not per cup. By the end of the month, we would be sneaking out after dark to 'Fried fish, Wet or Dry, Chips 2d., newspapers urgently required', or to 'Jock's Box' and 'Jack's Snacks', where the sandcake was really made of sand and the coffee came syrupy out of a bottle, but the beans and sausages were heaven at ninepence a go. We never went to the Rowan Arms – why, there was a set price for dinner there and two ancient waiters and an idiot boy in tailcoats, not our style at all. There was a cosy bar, though, upstairs and along the passage past the engravings of the various stages of Queen Victoria's coronation, and, as the barmaid had once been a patient on William Forrest, it made a good excuse for Parry and me to call in there occasionally with coats over our uniforms. She and I had got as far as Christian names – definitely not done at the hospital, however great a friendship. Her name was Chris. I liked her a lot and wondered why I had felt an aversion to her at first. Envy, I suppose, because she seemed so at home. She told me that she had hated me, too, and thought I looked sour and conceited. There had recently been a fruity scandal at the hospital, just before I came unfortunately, and now everyone was on the lookout for people to be 'queer'. One night, the guns round the nearby aerodrome were very noisy, and I went into Chris's room for company. What with this and the Christian names, we were quite a bit of gossip until Nurse Grainger provided a fresh subject by running off and marrying Nurse Larkin's fiancé, an unappetizing man called Gander, who had had half of his stomach removed on Herbert Waterlow Ward.

Just about this time, I was feeling quite pleased with life. I had got an amusing friend to work with, and had found one or two others who were good for a laugh; I was no longer the most junior on the ward : there was a pathetic, half-drowned little thing called Weekes, who never spoke above a whisper and who knew no better than to ask me what to do; I was beginning to learn my way about the work of the ward, and had picked up one or two of the basic rules of nursing. My complacency was doomed to shock, however.

One evening, the Senior Staff Nurse, the fat girl who had initiated us on our first evening, summoned me to her room. The basin was still choked up with tea-leaves, and her smalls were drying on hangers, festooned round the top of the cupboard.

'Just a hint, old thing.' She was fearfully matey, as matey as her sister, whose photograph rollicked at me from the dressing-table. 'You won't make yourself popular here by being too friendly with the seniors. It isn't done, you know, really.' She undid her belt, and the studs popped gratefully.

'D'you mean Nurse Parry?' I was staggered.

'Oh, come on, I didn't mean anything personal,' she said, red in the face, as she struggled with her apron straps. 'Just a hint.'

'Who may I be friendly with, then?'

She released the strain from one overworked safety-pin. 'Well, your own set.' The other safety-pin relaxed and her apron bib fell forward, exhausted.

'Oh, my own set. People like Gunter.'

'Yes, old thing.' She could breathe more easily now. 'When you're as junior as you are, it's better to stick among the juniors.' I noticed that her mother and father were laughing at me from sagging deckchairs on the windowsill. She had undone her collar, and as there seemed nothing more to say, I thought I had better go before she started on the buttons of her dress.

When I had got over my amazement, I looked forward to telling Chris about it. She had gone out with an airman that night, but I would see her on the ward in the morning. We would make beds together, and I would tell her then. While we were doing poor old Mrs Morey, perhaps, who had morphia every four hours to sweeten the dregs of her life and thought that Chris and I were Snow White and Tinkerbell.

I had forgotten that it was the first of the month. I could have cried when Night Sister read out the Change List: '... Nurse Dickens to go to Herbert Waterlow.' It looked like fate. Gunter leaned across the table to say: 'I'm not changed. You're on my ward.'

I returned her widespread smile with a sickly one, and slumped down to the Men's Surgical Ward in a furious temper, prepared to hate all the Surgical Men. I thought that I had been changed because I was Too Familiar with the Seniors. How petty these women were! All right, I thought – ten times as petty myself, but one's sense of values is groggy at that hour of the morning – all right, I won't try. Sister had the day off, and Nurse Sowerby, the Staff Nurse, was a feeble creature with swollen ankles, whom everyone called Sow. I slopped through what work I could not avoid, snapping at the men and not attempting to learn their names or ailments. Gunter was always underfoot and the other nurses seemed a deadly lot. The First Nurse, a raw-boned, ginger Scotch girl called Ross, said: 'None of your dirty William Forrest ways on this ward,' before I had even started, and I knew we were enemies. She had long yellow teeth and red wrists.

The day seemed endless, because I was clock-watching all the time, and at half-past five, I dropped what I was doing, excused myself abruptly to Nurse Sowerby and rushed off the ward, only to be recalled half-way down the corridor by Nurse Ross, to come back and wring out the sheet I had left in the sink.

'I said, none of your dirty William Forrest ways,' she said. 'You dare to treat Sister Martin as I've no doubt you treated Sister Lewis.' I bent over the sheet, with tears of rage burning my eyes. I prayed that she would give a man the wrong medicine and be publicly disgraced.

The next day was my day off, and when I got out into the great world things clicked back into proportion and I saw how wee I had been and how dangerously far on the road to becoming one of those whose limitations so irked me. Thank heaven for these days off, and for the sanity of a long sleep. I returned to Herbert Waterlow prepared to like it, and soon discovered that I was on the best ward in the hospital, with the most lovable patients. I had to work like a black to counteract the bad impression I had made on my first day.

There was always something going on on this ward. As well as operation cases, we received all the casualties – the car smashes, the drunks, the would-be suicides and the accidents from all the factories within twenty miles. It was quite exciting going on duty in the morning, because hardly a night went by without an admittance, and you might find anything from another perforated gastric ulcer, propped wanly upright with a saline transfusion dripping into the vein of his arm, to an unconscious man with two black eyes in something that was just recognizable as a face.

Scottie was one of these – a brawny giant with red hair ramping all over his chin and chest. He had been embroiled with a lorry on the way home from 'The Running Horse'. He lay for two weeks like a happy baby, taking the nourishment that was fed to him and giving an occasional prehistoric grunt, but otherwise completely insensible. His tough little wife used to visit him every day and talked to him in the hope of waking him. Sometimes she would bring the baby and shake it under his nose, but he would just stare with empty blue eyes. Once, when I was pouring some Guinness down his throat, he smiled at me and winked, and I ran for Sister, thinking he was coming round at last. When we got back to him, he was more deeply unconscious than ever, possibly due to the stout, and she delivered me a short lecture on the strict observations of symptoms. I should like to be able to record that it was his wife and baby that at last pierced the Lethe of Scottie's brain, and that he opened his arms and cried 'Wee Jeanie!' but what actually happened was that he suddenly grabbed Gunter's skirt as she was passing by, and said : 'Hullo, darling, it's a dark night for a nice wee lassie like you to be out by herself.'

There was plenty of work on that ward. We always had a few more patients than we could comfortably manage. More came in, and we still managed somehow. You never got off duty to time, but you didn't mind because what kept you was real nursing – something more than going over and over the same bit of brass with a duster. Working hard with people creates a bond, and I grew to find something in common with all the nurses – Sowerby, with her air of an overworked charwoman; Ross, who was deadly efficient; little Robins, the new Pro, who used to giggle and slap the men; Howes, whose apron and deportment were always spotless; even old Gunter, who continued to be as indigestible as the puddings that were our daily diet now that winter was drawing on.

I had not been long on the ward before I realized that it was Sister Martin who was responsible for the unusual atmosphere of willingness. She had the knack of getting work out of people without goading them, and of making them feel that they were co-operating in a united effort, instead of being pawns without initiative. She was a rare specimen.

She had the energy of the small, wiry person, and shot about from bed to bed like those cash holders on wires in old-fashioned drapers' shops. Each patient was in the nature of a personal challenge to herself. If anyone could save a man's

263

life, Fanny Martin could – even the nurses admitted that. I have seen her miss all her off duty for five days, staying on the ward from eight in the morning until after ten at night, nursing a man who you would have thought was the core of her heart. When he died, she ran off and changed her apron, and was back again to see about rallying old Hoskins, who had been shrugged over hopelessly by the House Surgeon. She didn't think much of House Surgeons. She chivvied them all over the ward, and when at last they escaped, making, perhaps, for their dinner, she would run after them and drag them back to see a patient they had missed. She accorded a certain amount of deference to the Honorary Surgeons, but she was almost the only Sister who didn't either toady to them, or bridle, or hero-worship and probably make up long stories in bed about them. She treated them as equals, and if she thought they were wrong she said so, and they liked her. I once saw that eminent surgeon, Mr Harvey Watkins, pinch her in the doorway of the Specimen Room, after she had worsted him in some argument. I looked at her with new eyes, and saw that she was quite young enough to be pinched. She might be quite pretty if she would only stand still long enough for you to see.

Chris's airman had asked her to bring a couple of friends to a concert at the aerodrome. She asked me to go, and Barnett, the baby-faced girl who had found me my room on that first evening. At first I said I would not go. I was always too tired these days to do more than a few minutes' home-work for Sister Tutor, soak in a bath with the morning paper I had got from one of the men on the ward, and fall gasping into bed. Chris drew me terrifying pictures of myself in a rut, cutting myself off from the outside world through mental inertia, and ending up with social paralysis, a stammer and a twitching face when publicly addressed. I allowed myself to be persuaded, and began to look forward to it. It was ages since I had been out anywhere, and I had to spend all my off duty on the day of the concert trying to make up for the neglect of my nails and hair. Of course, the ward was busier than ever that day : two emergency cases for operation and a casualty admitted who never recovered consciousness before he died. As the evening wore on, I kept looking at the clock as I scurried about, knowing that I would never be finished by half-past eight, and ready to be picked up in the airman's tinny Austin at nine.

By an immense effort I was ready to go at a quarter to nine. I was dropping with fatigue, and would have given anything not to be going out. I kept thinking of my bed. On my way to Sister, old Hoskins called me. I pretended not to hear, but a smug man in the next bed sang out : 'Hoskins wants you, Nurse!' By the time I had attended to the old man, who fussed and fidgeted and couldn't be made comfortable, it was nearly nine.

'Please, Sister, may I —' I began.

'Nearly finished, Nurse?' she said. 'You've done that polyomyeletis boy's legs, haven't you?'

I had forgotten all about it. 'Just going to do it now,' I said, cursing inwardly, and dragged myself off to the backbreaking task, of rebandaging a couple of legs to splints, firmly and thoroughly so that the little devil couldn't kick them off.

By the time I was changed, Chris had been in and out of my room six times and had eventually gone out to appease the impatient Arthur, who wanted to go without me rather than be late for the concert. I rushed out, feeling a mess, piled into the back of the car on top of Barney, who said : 'Look out for my coiff. !' and we rattled off down the dark hill towards the aerodrome.

Arthur had provided two exuberant friends called Tom and Nigger, for Barney and me. We seemed to have a lot of drinks quickly, and I was surprised that I could ever have felt tired. That must have been some other evening. The hospital seemed very far away, and I told Chris that she was right; I should do this sort of thing more often.

'Shut up,' she said, 'there's a man singing.' So there was. We were all sitting on rows of benches in a hangar, and a huge man in uniform was standing on a platform with a Union Jack behind him, his eyes tight shut and his fists clenched, singing *There'll Always be a Nengland* as if it were being pumped out of him. After him there was a Sergeant-Pilot who tap-danced, and then a quartette harmonized interminably and nasally. They were evidently popular, because the audience stamped their feet and whistled and would not let them go until they had given a rendering of *Dinah*, cribbed from a record of the Mills Brothers. There was a conjurer, and a small thin boy who recited, and then it was the interval and we had more drink and sausage rolls. I missed the rest of the concert, as the one who was called Nigger, because he had tight curly black hair, insisted that I would like to see his aeroplane, which was standing all by itself in the farthest corner of a very damp field.

I enjoyed my evening tremendously. The thought of six o'clock in the morning left me unruffled. Barney and I slept on each other all the way home, and I woke with a start from a beautiful dream to hear Arthur saying : 'Are you getting out, you two? This is as far as we go.' He had stopped in a side street just before the hospital, and we fell out only half-awake. It was bitterly cold and the stars were scattered prodigally on a black velvet sky, but I was too concerned with getting to my bed to notice the beauty of the night. The main gates were open, but we had to creep round the edge of the gravel to get to the little back courtyard and the convenient bathroom window.

'My God,' whispered Chris, 'the night nurses are busy.' Two ambulances were drawn up outside the main door and another turned in at the gates after us, its headlamp painting an arc on the gravel as it swung round.

'I bet they're all going to Herb Waterlow,' I said. 'I wonder what it is. There hasn't been a raid or anything.'

We could see shadowy figures and the humped shapes of stretchers, touched here and there by the red glow from a tail-lamp. Muttering voices and exhortations came across the gravel, but it all seemed remote from us, like a scene in a play. We crept on, falling over things, giggling and shivering, found our window and pushed it up cautiously, to avoid its treacherous squeak. I heard a hollow clang as Chris reached the bath, and then we heard her : 'What on earth — Here, come on in, quick, there's something up. Don't make a

266

row.' I climbed sleepily in after Barney and sat on the edge of the bath to put on my shoes again. I didn't care what was up so long as I could get to bed. I didn't realize at first that all the blue lights in the passage were on, that people were running up and down and calling out, that the place was alive, in fact, at two o'clock in the morning, when it should have been dead in sleep.

I thought I had better get to my room before I was seen, but as I turned into my corridor, someone grabbed my arm. It was Nurse Ross, half in and half out of her uniform dress. She didn't seem to notice that I was in outdoor clothes.

'There you are!' she said breathlessly. 'You've got to get into uniform and go on the ward.'

'*What?*' I must be dreaming.

'Hurry, now!'

'What's happened?' But she was gone already. The door of Robins's room was open and I looked in. 'Rob, what on earth's happened?'

'Don't you know?' She looked at me with enormous eyes, as she pinned the straps of her apron behind. 'There's been the most frightful explosion at one of the factories. Everyone on the men's wards has got to go on. There's twenty burn cases coming in, they say.'

How I got myself to my room and into my uniform, I don't know. I was almost crying with tiredness and my head throbbed like a machine. Through half-shut eyes, I saw my reflexion in the mirror, grey and old, more like a patient than a nurse. I hardly had the strength to raise my arms long enough to fix my cap. No satin couch could have looked more tempting than my ugly, long-legged bed, with its jumble of cases and shoes underneath. I kept my eyes averted from it while I pinned on a dirty apron – I couldn't be bothered to look for a clean one – and stumbled out of the room, wondering how I was ever going to keep awake long enough to be any use.

The ward was in chaos. All the lights were on, and every patient awake and goggling. The two night nurses were dashing about aloofly, half resenting the day nurses' intrusion, half thankful for help in a situation with which, they told themselves, they could somehow have coped alone. Extra beds were being put up at the far end of the ward, and patients who were well enough were being moved into these so as to leave ten empty beds at the top of the ward. Four of the casualties were in already, and a stretcher was waiting on the floor in the passage. Sister was on her knees beside it. 'Quickly, Nurse,' she said, without looking up as I passed her, 'bring me the hypodermic tray – and the Adrenalin.' But when I got back, she was standing up, just going back into the ward. 'I'm afraid it's too late,' she said, with a grim little smile. There were already three screens round one of the beds in the ward. I knew what that meant. Nurse Sowerby came out from behind them. Her mouth was quivering and she was on the verge of panic. 'Oh, Sister, they should never have brought them on to the ward,' she gabbled. 'They're bringing in dead men, that's all. Whatever shall we do – oh look – there's another stretcher and no bed ready. Oh, Sister, what shall we do —?' Her hair was in wild wisps and her cap askew.

'Pull yourself together, Nurse, for Heaven's sake,' said Sister, sharply. 'You'll have to go back to bed if you can't control yourself.' Poor old Sow gasped and wavered, and eventually saved herself on the rock of Sister's astringent calm. She spent the rest of the time being elaborately composed, doing everything with maddening deliberation and telling people to keep calm who had no intention of doing anything else. Some of the burns were not serious, others were a nightmare. They nearly all had to go up to the Theatre to be dressed and treated, and the blinds were going up on a slanting winter sun before we were anything like straight. Two more of the men had died before morning. It must have been a terrific explosion. People were talking about sabotage, but it was never proved.

As far as possible, Sister gave us a man each to attend to, while she herself dashed about from bed to bed, just in time wherever she was wanted.

'Get this man into bed,' she told me, as another stretcher loomed in the doorway. 'That bed there. Get him ready for

268

Theatre; they'll all go up as quickly as they can be taken. I'll come and see him in a – Mr Briant! Here a minute!' She grabbed at the House Surgeon's white coat.

'They want me on Secker ward,' he said.

'They can go on wanting,' she snapped, and dragged him behind a screen.

Between us, the porters and I got my man on to the bed and heaped blankets on him. I was terrified. I had never seen a bad burn case before and I hardly dared to touch him. I looked round, but everybody was busy. It was up to me to look after him, and I suddenly felt proud and excited. This one shouldn't die. He was unconscious, but breathing, his face waxy and an ominous blue shadow round his nose and lips. I could just feel his pulse. His face was untouched and his eyes seemed all right, but it was his body. . . . I couldn't undress him; his overalls were burnt into his skin in places. I cut them away as well as I could. He was quite young, with a fine straight nose and curly mouth and brown, soft, boy's hair.

Sister came up to give him an injection. 'More blankets, Nurse,' she said, 'and hot bottles if you can find any. He's terribly shocked.' There was only one bottle in the cupboard, but I snatched another out of Robins's hand, cursed her as she grabbed at it, and I believe I hit her before I rushed off with it, leaving her twittering with rage. Mr Briant was examining my man sketchily when I got back. 'None of them are fit to go to Theatre,' he muttered, 'but I daren't leave them.' His long chin was dark with a stubble of beard and his eyes bloodshot. I remembered that the night nurse on Maternity had told me he had been up all the night before with a Caesarean. 'Get him up as soon as you can,' he said. 'He's got a chance.'

I saw Nurse Howes coming into the ward at one end of the Theatre trolley. She looked as neat and spotless as ever, her madonna face unruffled. As soon as she had got her man into bed, I grabbed the porter.

'Here, this one's next, come on.'

'Sister said that chap over there,' he said stolidly.

'No, no – she meant this one. Really, she told me.' I

269

dragged him unwillingly over to the bed. There was no one
free to help us, but between us we managed to get him on to
the trolley. In the lift he suddenly opened his eyes and
moaned.

'Hullo,' I said.

'Lo,' he said, and closed his eyes and moaned again, com-
plainingly, pouting like a hurt child.

In the anaesthetic room, there was another trolley waiting,
with a nurse from another ward. 'How many have you got?'
she asked.

'Ten,' I said. 'At least, ten came in. How many have you?'

'Six. Secker have got some, too. Where's yours burnt?'

'Body.'

'Face and eyes, mine.' She sighed. 'Gosh, I'm tired, aren't
you?'

I remembered with a shock that two hours ago I had been
on the point of death. I didn't feel a bit tired now; there
hadn't been time. Surely it couldn't have been only two
hours ago. I could hardly remember it, it seemed so far
away.

The sliding doors opened and one of the Theatre nurses
came through. I caught a glimpse of the usually speckless
and orderly Theatre. Chaos was an understatement.

'Hullo,' said the nurse, as she took hold of the other trolley.
It was Barney. 'How d'you feel?' I said.

'Terrif. What a night!' She grinned, and they went into
the Theatre, and the doors slid to behind them.

The youngest and newest of the House Surgeons came in,
swinging his stethoscope and looking as nonchalant as a
Harley Street surgeon.

'Is this chap identified yet, Nurse?'

I shook my head.

'Some of the relations are here. There's a woman outside
who hasn't found her husband yet. I think she'd better have
a look at him before he goes under.' He called through the
door behind him : 'Come in, Mrs – er . . .' She came in, a little
brown-eyed fieldmouse, who was going to have a baby,
clutching her handbag in front of her and tiptoeing. She
took one look and sucked in her breath, nodding and look-

ing from one to the other of us. 'Jack,' she said shyly, and touched his face. 'I'nt 'e cold?'

'He'll be all right,' said the doctor, with over-loud assurance. 'You tell Nurse his name and all that, and then you'd better go and wait downstairs.'

'Roper's the name,' she whispered.

'Right you are,' he said. 'You tell Nurse, I've got to go and —' He escaped, still swinging his stethoscope, determinedly jaunty.

I found a bit of paper and put down the particulars she gave me, to fill in later on his chart. She answered me earnestly, anxious to do the right thing, awed by the hospital. She kept touching him wonderingly, as if unable to believe that this was really the man who should just about now be calling her name as he stamped into the house, home from the night shift.

'The doctor said he'd be all right —' she whispered, as if to reassure herself.

'Yes, I'm sure he will. You'd better go and wait downstairs now, Mrs Roper. We'll look after him.'

'Yes,' she said, touching him once more before she went out of the door. 'But i'nt 'e cold ... i'nt 'e terrible cold?'

Barney came in soon, and we wheeled him into the littered Theatre. Mr Sickert, the Resident Surgical Officer, was sitting in a corner, in his sterile cap and gown and mask, with his gloved hands clasped in front of him, like a good little boy. When we had got Roper on to the table, the anaesthetist clapped down the rubber mask. 'I'll only give him a whiff of gas,' he said. 'Just enough to keep him under. His condition's pretty poor.'

Mr Sickert got up wearily. 'Better cut down for an intravenous up here, I suppose. Why wasn't it done on the ward, Nurse?'

'Well,' I mumbled through my mask, 'I don't know really, sir. It's such a muddle down there —' I had said the wrong thing.

'Muddle, muddle, muddle – it's always the same. Expose his leg, Nurse – come on, hurry up. What it would be like here in a bad air-raid, God only knows.' He grumbled away to himself as he began to cut down to the vein.

I went into the sluice to find the stand for the saline bottles. I could hardly get in for the piles of towels and gowns and dirty swabs overflowing from the sinks and bins. Through the far door I could see them operating in the other Theatre. A nurse came out with a bucket of dirty towels, and I asked her where the stand was.

'Don't ask me,' she said, as she emptied the bucket despairingly on to one of the heaps. 'I'm either going or gone mad.'

They finished with Jack Roper at last. The saline had improved his pulse slightly, but his colour was still deathly. His arms and body were dark purple where they had coated him with Gentian Violet. It was already hardening into a sheeny skin like the tight-fitting costume of an acrobat.

I had to leave him when we got back to the ward, because there was so much sluicing and clearing up to do outside. I felt fiercely possessive about him and hated to take my eye from him or let anyone else touch him in spite of their knowledge compared to my ignorance.

In the sluice I flopped. Robins was flopping there, too, and we cried with exhaustion over a pile of sheets. I discovered that I was aching all over and I could do nothing but yawn and yawn.

Sister came out while we were coping half-heartedly. 'You can leave this lot for the moment,' she said. 'Dump it all in the bath, if you like. You can go off now and have a bath. There'll be breakfast at six, and you'll have to come back on the ward for a little, I'm afraid, but I'll let you all off in shifts during the day to sleep.'

There was porridge for breakfast, and sausages and bacon, and cups and cups of glorious coffee. Coming out of the dining-room, we met the other day nurses coming in for the ordinary breakfast. They were aliens – people who had slept all night. It was too much bother to appease their curiosity.

I had got beyond being tired now. I made beds and tidied the ward just as if it were an ordinary day, feeling that I

272

didn't care if I never slept again. My legs didn't feel like my own, that was all; they carried me about like automatons. Some of the men, who hadn't slept all night, were peevish and tiresome, but most of them were grand. The ones who were allowed up helped us as much as they could : they swept the balcony and emptied ashtrays and ran errands for the other patients. They approached as near as they dared and stared in mute sympathy at the violet figures – there were only six of them now, and soon would be only five. Those that had face burns looked like niggers, and the pads over their eyes were startlingly white.

Sister sent me off at twelve o'clock. Jack Roper had woken up, and he was holding his own. He had said 'Hullo' again, and had taken a feeding cup of tea from me. I didn't dare ask Sister what she thought about him, in case she should shake her head.

I couldn't sleep for a long time, and when I did, I dreamed about him. I went back on to the ward in the evening, unrested, feeling as if I were moving about in a play. Sister was still there. I don't know when she slept.

Roper was the worst of the burn cases, and therefore Sister's pet. She nursed that man like her own son, and when she saw that I was interested in him, she let me do a lot for him. I used hardly to dare to go on the ward in the morning in case anything had happened in the night. I don't know why, but for some reason it meant more than anything to me that he should live. The oddly possessive feeling that I had for him made me almost oblivious of the other patients on the ward. I didn't care what happened to them, but Jack must not die. It was a kind of conflict between myself and the evil force that destroys youth.

Mrs Roper came every day to sit by his bed and to hold his hand mentally, since she couldn't hold his purple bandaged one. He was a cheerful boy, and used to make commonplace little jokes and smile politely when one tried to be funny for his benefit.

On the Friday evening before Sister's week-end off, Sowerby was already twittering in anticipation of being left in charge of the ward. She so far forgot her position as to show me her varicose veins in the bathroom.

'What would you do with legs like mine?' she moaned. 'Aren't they wicked?'

'Wicked,' I agreed.

'They always seem to get worse when Sister's off. Oh, dear, what'll go wrong this week-end, I wonder?' Last time, the pipes behind the sterilizers had burst and we had been practically flooded out, and the time before that, she had got a Catholic priest to give Extreme Unction to a rabid Methodist. It was just poor old Sow's luck.

However, this week-end seemed to be set fair. Sister went off quite happily on Friday afternoon, leaving the ward not overfull and all the burns progressing satisfactorily. Sir Curtis Rowntree came to do a round when he had finished operating and expressed himself as pleased with Jack Roper. Sow came beaming back into the ward after ushering him out. 'What a *nice* man he is,' she said, as she pottered back to the desk. 'He said "Good night, Nurse" ever so charmingly, just as if I'd been anyone.'

Saturday began badly. I tweaked a tube out of a man's stomach while I was making his bed, and Nurse Ross had to spend hours trying to get it back before the doctors came round.

'One little setback like this and the whole routine's thrown out,' fretted Sowerby. 'Look, you see, Nurse Ross should have started dressings hours ago. We'll never get them done before dinner. I suppose I'd better start them myself, but then the doctors'll come round, and then where'll I be? Oh, dear, I do wish you wouldn't be so careless, Dickens.'

'Well, I didn't do it on purpose,' I retorted. I was worried myself about what Mr Morris Evans would say to me if he discovered it.'

'If you speak to me in that tone of voice, Nurse,' said Sow surprisingly, 'I shall have to send you to Matron.'

'But *Sow* —!'

'Oh, it's all right, dear,' she said hastily, horrified at herself. 'You know I'd die rather than get anyone into trouble. It's just that I get so worried sometimes I don't know what

I'm saying.' She called round the screens to Ross. 'Have you done it yet, Nurse?'

'No,' said Ross angrily. 'I've a mind to leave it.'

'Oh, you'd better not do that. I don't know what Mr Morris Evans will say. Look, I'll start some of the dressings.' She sent me off to get the trolley, but, of course, no sooner had she got the bandage off the first man and her hands scrubbed, than a stout Surgeon in a hurry burst through into the ward with a small House Surgeon panting at his heels.

'Where's Sister?' he snapped, snatching down the chart of his first patient and scattering the notes all over the floor.

'Sister's off duty, sir,' said Howes politely, smoothing down her apron.

'Where's the Staff Nurse?' he demanded angrily, and Sow came hobbling breathlessly up with her hands red and dripping. Every time she started to do a dressing, something called her away, and she was still talking about starting them when it was time for her to serve out the patients' dinners.

'I've done all the dressings,' said Nurse Ross crisply, as she passed the kitchen on the way to her own lunch.

'Oh, have you? How splendid. That is a relief. I don't know how you've managed so well.'

'Method,' said Ross nastily, and went on.

'Well,' said Sowerby, on Sunday evening, when I brought her a cup of tea in Sister's sitting-room, 'that week-end's over, thank goodness, and we haven't got through too badly.' She sank into the wicker armchair and kicked off her shoes. 'I don't think Sister'll find anything wrong when she comes back tomorrow. I really do believe I'll be able to sleep to-night. What a nice cup of tea you make, dear. Just pop into the ward before you go and have a look at that appendix man! I'm not quite happy about him.'

I went and looked at the man, who was showing no cause for anxiety, said good night to Jack Roper and went off the ward.

Sowerby may have been able to sleep that night, but I certainly could not. I read for hours, and then kept dozing off into queer fragments of dream and waking in a fright with my heart thumping. I wondered whether my room were haunted; the wardrobe had a nasty looming look about it. I got out of bed and shut its door, in case a body should fall out, but it was still a sinister shape, and as the moon sailed in and out of the clouds, a tiny eye kept winking in the mirror.

I dreamed again, a vivid nightmare, and woke with a start. There was someone in my room.

I sat up, terrified. 'It's all right,' said a white shape. 'It's me, Andrews.' She was the Junior Night Nurse on the ward.

'What's the matter? Is it morning? What's happened?'

'We can't find the continuous nasal oxygen apparatus. I thought I saw you cleaning it last night.'

I told her where I had put it : in the wrong place, of course. 'Who's it for, Andrews?'

'Roper. He's collapsed.'

## Chapter Five

J u s t before Christmas, Sister went on holiday, and a temporary woman called Sister Oates took charge. She was a snob of the highest order, so superior that she could never bother to learn anybody's right name. She had been relieving on the private wards, where apparently she had spent most of the time bridling and smoking cigarettes in the middle of her mouth in the room of Lady Mondsley, who was in hospital for hypochondria.

I was not looking forward to Christmas. It was the first I had ever spent away from home and I didn't think I would be very good at communal jollity. 'Christmas is such fun here,' people kept telling me.

'What do you do?'

'Well, for one thing, the nurses all have a Christmas dinner and the doctors wait on us. It's a scream, my dear, we all throw the food about. Last year we had wine.'

'What, Graves?' She nodded, awed.

'Oh, everyone goes perfectly *mad*, you know. We do the

daftest things ... we all throw the food about!' That seemed to be her criterion of wassail.

Because I could not be at home, I pig-headedly determined not to enjoy myself, but as the preparations advanced I began to be drawn in. You can't live in a place that takes up your whole time and interest without absorbing some of the current atmosphere. The men were out to have a good time; they accepted the situation in which they found themselves and determined to make the most of it. They had been getting out of hand for some time – ever since Sister Martin removed her velvet-gloved control. They mocked Sister Oates behind her back and called her 'Wild Oats', because she was so proper. There were quite a lot of them at this time who were allowed up, and it was the hardest thing in the world to get them into bed at all.

They were not allowed up between nine and twelve in the morning. 'Nurse Dickinson,' Sister would say, 'get all those men into bed. I'm going to have my coffee now and I don't want to see anyone running about when I get back.' Having her coffee was a morning ritual which took place in the sitting-room. No one must disturb this sacred rite, but Nurse Sowerby was graciously admitted to discuss the day's work, rather as if she were a cook coming up to settle the meals.

I managed to hound some of the meeker men into bed, but others would only say: 'Come orf it, Blondie, can't a chap get shaved in peace?'

'Well, mind you get into bed as soon as you've finished, and for heaven's sake don't smoke till she's inspected the ash-trays.'

I tried to chivvy them back by the time Sister came to do her stately morning round. She would be halfway round the beds, with her 'And how are you this morning, Jenkins?' or Fox, or Stuart, or whatever the name might *not* be, when a wild pyjama-ed figure would scuttle across the floor and bound into bed, emerging above the sheets with an innocent air, while Sister Oates would stop in her tracks, staring as if she had found bugs in her kitchen.

There was a man called Toller, a railwayman, who had lost an arm in a shunting accident. He had only three fingers on the remaining hand, but he could do more for himself than a lot of the patients did with ten. After a few days of drinking through a straw, he demanded a cup and taught his fingers to hold it. He would not even use a spoon for his meals, but managed to manipulate a fork like an American. It was agony sometimes to watch him struggling to strike a match, missing time after time, but it was as much as your life was worth to try to help him. He would deliver some goodsyard language that sent you away red to the ears. He had a vital, Latin appearance – black hair, brown skin and very white teeth, and his eyes were always up to something. He kept the whole ward alive, and his cheek was colossal. On Christmas Day he kissed Sister Oates, smack on the lips, which must have needed some courage.

'Nurse Dickinson and Nurse Bunter,' she said, on the day before Christmas Eve, 'this afternoon we will decorate the ward.' Mounds of holly and miles of coloured paper-chains were stacked in readiness in the splint cupboard, and there was a Christmas tree and a whole boxful of balloons. Sister began to blow one up, her pigeon chest poutering alarmingly. The whole ward was watching open-mouthed, wondering which would burst first – she or the balloon.

'There,' she said at last, panting and holding her hand to her heaving apron, 'that's the way to do it. I mustn't do any more, because of my heart.' Soon after that, she retired to her room to eat tea and buttered toast, leaving Gunter and me to cope with the decorations, and emerging when we had finished to say : 'Oh, no, I don't fancy that at all.' Fortunately, she couldn't make us rearrange them, because two of the results of a motor-cycle accident came in and kept us busy. So she was able to spend the rest of the Christmas days saying : 'Now, if only we'd had the Christmas tree at this end of the ward —,' and 'If you'd put those balloons where I wanted them, the men wouldn't have been able to reach them with their cigarettes.'

On Christmas Eve there was a dress rehearsal of the concert that we were to give to the patients – as if their suffering were not enough. Chris and Barney and I had been asked to go to a dance at the aerodrome that night, and as the other two were not in the concert they refused to let me make us all late by staying on for the rehearsal.

'No one'll notice if you're not there,' said Barney.

'But I daren't not go. What'll Beaver say?'

'Oh — her,' said Chris, and Barney said : 'Anyone would think you were the flaming princ. boy, the way you go on.' Actually, I was in the back row of the chorus : 'The Redwood Juveniles,' in knee-length operating gowns and big white bows of bandage in our hair. After a day of running about after Wild Oats like a negro slave, I was as keen to get out of the hospital as the others. I had just decided to cut the rehearsal and was going into my room to change, when Beaver, the Senior Staff Nurse, gave me a slap on the back that pitched me through the doorway. 'That's right, old thing,' she said, bursting with Christmas Cheer, 'don't be late for rehearsal. I'm going to give you a line to say, as Jones is off sick,' she added, as if bestowing a colossal treat. I would have to go to the rehearsal now. Chris and Barney went on to the dance without me, as Arthur was champing outside, but he promised to come back for me later.

The rehearsal was held in the Common Room. Some people turned up in the strange garments that were their idea of a policeman or a soldier or a nigger minstrel; others, under the delusion that it would be All Right on the Day, had not yet thought about their costumes. Everyone talked the entire time.

Beaver kept telling us that a bad dress rehearsal made a good first night.

The House Surgeons were in the concert, too. They strolled in after dinner, guffawed their way through the sketches, but soon got bored with it and strolled out again. Miss Llewellyn, one of the female Housemen, stayed on till the bitter end, her spectacles and teeth flashing with keenness. She had been an awful nuisance all along, always having some ambitious idea about a thing long after it had been settled and wanting to argue it out. She kept urging us to have part songs, although none of us could sing in tune, much less keep a part.

'We always used to do them at the Royal Free,' she would say, with that nervous, pecking movement of her woolly head. 'They were a tremendous go, I can tell you.'

I escaped as soon as I could, and changed my silly operation gown and did something to the face which had obviously not been attended to since six o'clock that morning. On my way out, I ran into one of the Sisters and had to pretend that I was just going out to post a letter.

'There's no post out on Christmas Eve,' she said, eyeing my clothes suspiciously.

'Yes, there is, Sister,' I lied. 'Special wartime arrangement.'

'Well, in that case, you can post some for me.' I toiled up to her room with her to get the letters, which I forgot all about and found in my pocket weeks later.

When I reached the usual meeting place, out of sight of the hospital, there was no sign of Arthur and his biscuit tin on wheels. A large black car was waiting a little farther up, however, and as I approached, a head looked out of the driver's window.

''Devening,' it said. 'Are you Nurse somebody-or-other?'

'I expect so.'

'Hooray. Climb into the pumpkin, sweetheart, and I'll take you to the ball,' said the head, disappearing inside. It was obviously rather drunk.

Even I could see, however, that it sat on top of a uniform with far more stripes than I was accustomed to.

'Are you a pilot?' I probed, as we shot dangerously downhill. He laughed so long and boisterously that I didn't dare enquire any further, because it made the car lurch.

'Why did you come and fetch me?' I asked. We had left the dark, deserted Victorian streets and were levelling out into the suburbs.

'Heard someone say they were coming to fetch a nurse,' he said. 'Marvellous party, by the way. Never could resist a nurse, so I said I'd come. Chap didn't mind – too busy with a cracking blonde.' This must be one of the evenings on which Chris was being nice to Arthur.

The hangar was gay with holly and flags and hordes of sweating, pushing people dancing to a band that was only audible at one end. The shuffle, shuffle of their feet on the concrete almost deafened you as you came in, but after a bit, you didn't notice it.

'Straight to the bar,' said my boy-friend. He turned out to be a large, well-fed man, with a great head of curly, greying hair, which he held very high, like a horse.

'What is it?' I whispered to Nigger, whom I found in the crowd round the bar. He giggled. 'It's a Wing-Commander. Doing well for yourself, aren't you?'

'Here you are, darling,' said the Wing-Commander, handing me a glass.

'Thank you, angel,' I said, and he roared with laughter and kept telling me what a wit I was. He was easily amused.

'Look out,' said Nigger in my ear. 'There's its wife over there.'

Sitting at a table by the wall, hemmed in by the standing crowd, was a superior little party, with Mrs Wing-Commander in the middle, skinny and upright, with red hair piled on top of a face that seemed to go on for ever vertically. She sipped her drink as if it had been poured out for her by a Borgia. I danced with her husband and then escaped for a while, but he found me again and slapped me playfully.

'Naughty little girl to run away,' he said. 'I'll have to keep you on a collar and lead.' He was just as easily amused by his own wit as mine. He insisted that I should meet his wife, so that she could ask me to their house. He evidently didn't dare to ask me of his own accord. She was circling regally round the floor with a deferential young officer, who was under the delusion that he might thereby advance his career.

'This is Nurse What's-it, Mavis,' said the Wing-Commander – I hadn't yet discovered his name.

'Oh, yes?' she said, making inverted Vs of her eyebrows and looking at my swollen red nurse's hands as if she knew that I had corns on the soles of my feet.

'Yes,' he said, with his head higher than ever, not meeting her eye, 'she tells me they get God-awful food at the hospital, so I thought it would be fun if she came to dinner one night.' She was looking at him cannily, and he laughed uncomfortably, as much as to say : 'Yes, you're right, I am a bit tight.'

'So you're a nurse?' said his wife, and led me to a corner, where she questioned me with a kind of detached pity, as if I had been an unmarried mother. After a struggle between disinclination and her duty as a social worker, she fixed a date for me to dine on my evening off, and left me, her charitable conscience salved. I had no intention of going, but I thought it was simpler to accept now and cry off later.

Christmas Day. Noel. Sing Hey, the Holly, but I didn't feel like singing Hey anything when the Senior Night Nurse bawled : 'Six o'clock, Nurse,' maliciously across my sleep. One couldn't even go to church, to make it seem more like Christmas, because on Christmas and Boxing Day we had no off duty at all.

All the essential work of the ward, the dressings and treatments, had to be got through in the morning, so as to leave the afternoon free for jollity. Fortunately, we had only one very ill patient, but I didn't see how he was going to last out the day, with the noise that the men were already making. They had started the morning by dressing up and playing charades. Jackson, who could get about at a great rate on his crutches, had chased Gunter into the bathroom and relieved her of her cap and apron. I found her sitting resignedly on the edge of the bath, reading a two-days-old paper. She looked funny without her cap; her head was quite flat, like a boiled egg with the top sliced off.

In the middle of Toller's famous impersonation of herself, Wild Oats arrived on duty, with a majestic hangover from the Sisters' Christmas Eve party, at which they had had Empire Burgundy and Bagatalle. We had to tell her he was being Douglas Byng.

We had all to subscribe to a present for her, and Sowerby now presented it in the sitting-room, with much clearing of the throat. It was a tooled copy of Shakespeare's Comedies, which Ross had picked up cheap because it had a page missing. It was only one of the last pages and there was no reason, anyway, to suppose that she would ever read the book, and it looked handsome and expensive. She was pleased with it. She visualized it sitting behind a glass-fronted bookcase when her ex-patients came to tea with her.

Then she fished in the cupboard where she kept the tea and sugar locked away from us, and surprisingly presented us each with a bottle of eau-de-Cologne. 'A happy Christmas to you all,' she said, her gold back tooth glittering.

When she went for her elevenses later in the morning, we gathered in the kitchen to distribute our own gifts. To save having to buy five presents we had each bought one, and we jumbled them up in the bread bin and drew in turn. I had bought a bottle of complexion milk that I wanted myself. I thought I'd be able to recognize its shape. To my fury, who should draw it but Ross, whose face obviously had no dealings with such things. She unwrapped it in silence and went away to her work. I drew a beastly little memo book, with 'Lest I Forget' stamped across the cover. I was pretty sure it was Ross's contribution. Gunter drew a bit of bread the first time, but tried again and got a powder compact. Powder and scent – her young man would have had a fit if he had known. She had told me all about him. He was a male nurse in the R.A.M.C. who thought that clothes were for utility, not adornment. 'He likes women to be as God made them,' she said.

After the present-giving, she drew me into the linen cupboard. 'Something for you,' she said, fumbling under her apron and producing a very nice screw pencil. 'A Merry Xmas,' she said, taking my arm. She had a passion for touching you. Luckily she had not seen me draw the memo book, so I was able to say : 'And I've got something for *you* !' and produce it proudly.

The men's Christmas dinner was the high spot of the day. There was a huge turkey and a plum pudding, and a crate of bottled beer. The surgeons had to dress up in chef's caps and carve the turkeys. We had Mr Harvey Watkins, who wore a small frilly apron round his non-existent waist and was full of bonhomie. He carved the turkey on a table in the middle of the ward, and we all stood round him with trays, saying 'Ha-ha' to whatever he said. Sister ladled out the vegetables and sauces as if she were presiding at an East End soup kitchen, and we carried the plates round and opened the beer. There was big eating, and a certain amount of cheating among those who were on special diet. I got mixed up and gave Gastric a leg of turkey and three roast potatoes, but it didn't seem to do him any harm, and he was very difficult afterwards about his normal diet of flaked fish and purée.

The shattered turkey and the remains of the excellent rich dark plum pudding were taken out to the ward kitchen, and when Sister had taken Mr Harvey Watkins into her sitting-room for a glass of sherry and the men were busy pulling crackers, a disgraceful scene took place. All the nurses rushed for the kitchen, as fast as their various degrees of foot trouble allowed, and with silent accord we fell on the broken meats. You can get far more turkey and plum pudding by snatching it from the dish with your fingers than you ever could at table. Goodness knows how long we would have gone on stuffing if it had not been for the frenzied shouts of : 'Nurse !' from the ward. Old McGilligan had fallen out of bed and was sitting happily on the floor in his nightshirt, singing 'Come Back, Paddy Riley to Ballyjamesduff.'

Seeing that there were enough people to deal with him, Gunter hurried back to the kitchen, before the porter should come and take away the dishes.

The visitors came after lunch, bringing presents and strewing the ward with paper and string. I had to go off and get ready for the concert. I was feeling tired now, but I remembered that Chris's Maternity Ward had some bottles of port going in the Labour Ward. It was queer to find the hospital regulations so suddenly relaxed. Ordinarily, it was an appalling crime to go to another ward without a very good reason, but to-day, one could wander about anywhere and nobody even said : 'Where are your cuffs?'

By the time we had done the concert on all the five big

wards, it seemed to be getting very stale, but the audience lapped it up. They enjoyed seeing the doctors and nurses, in whose power they normally were, making fools of themselves. The House Surgeons dashed off in between every performance to fortify themselves, taking some of the more attractive nurses with them. Poor Nurse Beaver was perpetually hunting for people, and when they didn't turn up in time to go on, Miss Llewellyn, who was anti-fortification, leaped into the breach and understudied, mouthing her words and doing a great deal of miming at the side of the stage when someone else was talking. After I had said my one line : 'But look, Princess, see who's coming !' I lost interest and used to go and sit in the audience. There was never room for all the Redwood Juveniles in the space at the end of the ward, anyway. Some of them would be going through the motions right out of sight, but quite happy.

Some of the Night Nurses had stayed up as it was Christmas and were sitting yawning, their eyes bright with lack of sleep. Andrews told me she had followed us round and seen the concert on every ward. She was in love with Mr Briant, and was torturing herself with the sight of him in a borrowed battledress, with a bandage round his head.

The Nurses' dinner party was as promised, except that it was cider, not Graves. There was plenty of food, both eaten and thrown about, and Mr Vavasour, the gynaecologist, was very giddy with a bit of mistletoe. Matron looked in to see how we were getting on, and we all had to give three cheers for her, goodness knows why, as she was not even responsible for the food. She had probably had a row with the House-keeper about providing too much. Afterwards, there was dancing in the Common Room, with five times as many women as men. Etiquette decreed that the doctors should dance principally with the Sisters, and when one of them danced with a nurse, there was much jealous whispering : 'Look at Harrison. Isn't she soft? *I* wouldn't dance with Johnny Briant – conceited ass.' If a couple were so rash as to sit out somewhere, the Assistant Matron, a cushiony woman with abundant hair, would search for them and manoeuvre them back into the ballroom. With the nurses' bedrooms so close, you see ... One never knew. These modern girls ...

I enjoyed Boxing Day more than Christmas Day. Sister went off in the afternoon, and the men produced some beer from their lockers. Robins brought up her gramophone, and we moved the desk and cupboards from the centre of the ward and danced. Toller could rhumba. 'This is the other thing you don't need two arms for,' he grinned.

The ill patient had fortunately been given an injection of morphia after lunch, and slept like a log, even through the singing of the patients who couldn't get up to dance. Even Sow's varicose veins took the floor, and she polka'd with old Daddy Masters, who might never have heard of such a thing as Hernia. Jackson and I had discovered the delightful game of filling with water balloons for unsuspecting people to burst. I can't quite remember how it happened, but it ended in a rugger scrum with me underneath. I was lying on my face, screaming, when all the bodies on top of me suddenly melted away, and I rolled over to see Wild Oats looming above me in perspective. At the time, she only said : 'Put your cap on at once and go and change your apron,' but the next day she had me into the sitting-room.

'You see, Nurse Dixon, it isn't so much a question of bad behaviour. We won't go into that – that's your parents' responsibility. It's a question of your dignity as a Nurse. You're letting down the whole Profession, don't you see?'

I mumbled and shuffled my feet.

'It's playing for popularity, Nurse,' she went on, her eyes bulging like a Hyper-Thyroid, 'and it won't do. The men don't like you any the better for it – don't imagine that for a moment.'

'But, Sister —'

'I'm speaking, Nurse. I say they don't think any the more of you; they merely lose their respect for you. They remember, and they'll take advantage of you another time.'

'But, Sister, they wouldn't. After all, they are sensible.'

'They are not sensible, Nurse.' She looked up at me in surprise. 'And remember : whatever class a patient may be, and some of them may be very good class – *quite* good class –

you must always keep yourself just that little bit above them. Dignity, Nurse – without it, you may be a nurse, but you'll never be a good nurse, Nurse.' I edged towards the door, and she held up her hand. 'One more thing,' she said impressively. 'There might not always be other nurses there to back you up. Night Duty, for example. You might easily find yourself one day in a *very embarrassing position*.' She pronounced the last words with a ponderous horror, and I left her, slightly out of breath, to contemplate this interesting possibility.

The aftermath of Christmas was as might be expected. Two days of thirteen hours apiece without a break had left everyone tired and irritable, and the patients were inclined to be whiny, like children overtired by a party. There was all the clearing up to do, a lot of extra cleaning, and all the decorations to take down.

'How about leaving them up for next year, Sister?' asked Robins, from the top of a step-ladder. 'It would save an awful lot of trouble.'

'I can't hear a word you say, Nurse Dobbin,' said Sister Oates, who was in no mood for joking. 'Mind what you're doing with that holly.' Robins dropped it on to the upturned face of a sleeping man, and he sat up with a yell.

'I don't know how Sister Martin puts up with such girls. Ah, there's Mr Harvey Watkins!' She steamed towards him, the badges and medals on her apron arriving long before she did. 'Good morning, Mr Harvey Watkins,' I heard her say. 'Just clearing away the traces of merriment, you see.'

The surgeon rubbed his hands and ha-ha'd, throwing out his legs as he walked. The House Surgeon lagged behind, looking as if he could have done with more sleep and less liquor.

This reaction was general, it seemed. One would not have thought Redwood to be a town of unbridled licence, nor of the temptation or facility to make a beast of oneself. Yet into the Out-patients' Department there poured a stream of black eyes, broken heads and acute abdominal disorders. One man, who was admitted to our ward as a query concussion, was found to be merely sleeping in the comfortable lap of Bacchus, and was fetched home, as soon as he had stopped being sick, by a harridan in a hard hat.

We also had an old man who had been knocked down by a car, and a couple of motor-cycle accidents. One of these was a Canadian soldier, whose right leg was amputated soon after he came in. He was a fine man in his prime, about thirty-five, weathered and independent, a man to lean on in a crisis. And now he was leaning on me, asking me whether his leg was there, for of course he could still feel it.

I didn't know what to say. He was only just round from the anaesthetic and very shocked. They were going to give him a blood transfusion as soon as Mr Briant could get down. I hedged. 'You'll be all right. All you've got to do is just not to worry. Try and get some sleep.'

The words sounded trite and silly as I said them. He was not a man to be fobbed off with glib hospital jargon.

He gave me a look that he had probably given a lot of brainless women, and said : 'Come on now, Honey. Don't stall. I can take it.'

'We're not allowed to tell patients anything. You have to ask Sister, or a doctor.'

'They've chopped it off, then,' he said, fixing a cold blue eye on me. I nodded.

'Yeah.' It was more a long-drawn expiration than a word. 'Yeah. Thanks for telling me.'

In spite of his ability to bear pain, he was a difficult patient. He was autocratic and grumbled about everything except his leg. He had the aggressive Canadian conviction of supremacy and was quick to criticize anything that displeased him. Wild Oats mistrusted him because she felt he had got her number, and I think all the nurses except Ross were a little afraid of him. He made one feel somehow pettily feminine, and rather ridiculous for being occupied most of the day with trifling details. Unlike the other men, he would not accept a rule because it was a rule, unless he approved of it.

'If he wants to have things his own way,' Sister kept saying, 'he ought to go into a private ward. But I don't suppose even the Canadian Army is mad enough for that. The man's only a Private, after all.'

Laurence Cowley – that was the Canadian's name – had had a knock on the head that had wiped out all recollection of the accident or what led up to it. The Police had been to see him once with notebooks, and boots that resounded through the ward, but he had been unable to tell them anything. He was very tactless with them, and started to quote the Canadian highway laws and they went away, their boots a little subdued by pique.

It was more than a week after his operation before something clicked in Cowley's brain and he remembered part of what he had forgotten. I was feeding him his dinner, for one of his wrists was broken and the other hand bandaged. We had got beyond the preliminary 'Hell, where do they get this stuff, anyway?' stage, and he was taking the spoonfuls sulkily and abstractedly, as if he were trying to keep his mind on more pleasant things. Feeding somebody is very boring. Because you are impatient to be finished, you try to make them take the food faster than they want, and they either choke or take it slower than ever – on purpose, I believe. Cowley had two teeth knocked out, which did not help matters much. I shovelled in as large a mouthful as he would take without protest, and while he dealt with it, shifted my weight from foot to foot, leaned against the bed and gazed round the ward with ennui. I was watching old Daddy James trying to retrieve a piece of meat that had fallen down the front of his nightshirt, when Cowley suddenly gave the impression of having leapt six feet in the air, although he was actually unable to move.

'Jumping Jesus!' he said, 'I knew there was something!'

'What —'

'Maisie!' he almost shouted. 'What happened to her? Why in Hell didn't they tell me what happened to her?'

'What happened to who? Who's Maisie?'

'Why, the kid who was riding pillion on the bike. I forgot she was with me till just now. I guess that bang on the head

– but they could have told me about her, they could have told me what happened.'

'Perhaps she wasn't hurt,' I suggested.

'She must have been. She'd have come around to see me. Listen, maybe she's hurt bad. Maybe she's even dead – Jeeze, poor little Mais. Poor Kid —'

'If she was hurt, she's probably in this hospital. I'll ask Sister if I can ask at the Secretary's office.'

'Keep that old battleship out of this, will you? She'd have the enquiry scheduled in triplicate and sent up to the Ministry of Information. Find out yourself – it'll be much quicker. Jeeze, I'm going to feel badly if —'

'I'll try, but we're not supposed to give information about patients, you know.'

'Don't pull that on me,' he said, magnetizing me with an eye.

'All right,' I said. 'I'll find out at teatime. Look, you haven't had your pudding. I'll go and get it.'

'If you do,' he said, 'Ill sling it in your pan. Listen, Honey, it's not pudding I want, it's Mais.'

Maisie was in Jane English Ward, with compound fractures of both legs. At first they had thought she would not live, and it was nature, not she herself, who had made the effort and proved them wrong. She had been told about Cowley, though not yet about the amputation. Evans, one of the Welsh girls who had come with me, was on Jane English, and she told me all I wanted to know while we squatted in front of the gas-fire making toast. Above the fire, a notice in a looping hand was pinned to the wall with drawing-pins :

Owing to damage to the Asbestos
NO NURSE MAY MAKE TOAST AT THE GAS FIRE
Bread is more nourishing than toast
E. Harriman, Ass. Mat.

There were dozens of these little texts, all over the hospital and nurses' hostel. Sister Harriman's duties seemed to be wholly deterrent, but she was evidently of the school that thinks children should be told Why, and nearly everyone improved the occasion with a little free information. One of the notices in the bathroom read :

DO NOT USE TOO MUCH HOT WATER
There are others to come after you

also

Too hot a bath lowers the vitality
and reduces resistance to infection

and another on the board in the entrance hall read :

NURSES ARE RESPONSIBLE FOR THEIR OWN BLACKOUT
ALSO FOR ANY FINE INCURRED IN CONNEXION WITH
SAME

Carelessness in such matters is more than unpatriotic

IT IS TREACHEROUS

After I had found out all I could about Maisie, I sounded Sister Oates. I was helping her to put away the clean linen – at least, she was telling me where to put it and I was running up and down the step-ladder to reach the top shelves.

'Sister,' I said casually, with my face in the linen basket, 'does Cowley know about that girl who was injured with him?'

'No,' she said. 'He remembers nothing about her, and Sir Curtis Rowntree doesn't want him told yet. How many pillow-cases have you?'

'Forty-two.' Sister ticked it off on her list. 'How did you know about the girl, Nurse Dixon?' she asked. 'He hasn't said anything about her, has he?'

'No,' I said. 'One of the nurses on Jane English was talking about her at tea.'

'There's a great deal too much shop talked at meals, in my opinion,' said Wild Oats. 'When I was doing my training, one of the Sisters used to listen to our talk and anyone who mentioned the wards was sent away from table. We used to have some very interesting conversations, I remember.' She sighed. 'But girls these days have no social manners at all.'

'I make that twenty-four drawsheets altogether,' I said coldly.

'Correct,' she said. 'Up on that top shelf, please.'

'Sister,' I pursued, when I was at the top of the steps, making piles of the fragrant-smelling linen, 'supposing Cowley remembers about the girl and asks, will you tell him?'

'I should certainly do nothing without Sir Curtis's permission, Nurse. He has given his orders and it is my duty to see that they are carried out. Surely there was a great deal of laundry this week. I shall have to see about making the nurses wash some of the things in future.'

When she was safely away at her supper, I told Cowley what Evans had told me. He considered the information, acclimatizing himself to the idea of Maisie with a bruise on her forehead and both legs in plaster casts up to the hip.

'You won't tell anyone I told you, will you?' I said.

'Hell, no. You were great to do it. Listen, do one thing more for me, will you? Write a little note and have them give it her.'

'Quick, then,' I said, 'before Sister comes back.'

I got a bit of paper and he dictated to me :

HULLO, MAIS,
Sorry I busted you up. Keep your chin up, kid, and get well quick. Am feeling fine, but afraid I'll have to use cork on my right leg from now on.
Be seeing you soon, Honey.

LARRY.

I took the note round when I went off duty, and had to dodge in the shadows out of Sister Porter's way until Evans came out of the ward. She made some excuse to go back again, and came out after a while with another bit of paper, folded very small. 'She's crying,' said Evans.

I sneaked back to Herbert Waterlow, and gave the note to the Junior Night Nurse, who was making Horlicks in the kitchen. As I came out, Sister was just coming off duty with a great bunch of chrysanthemums that I could almost have sworn were the ones Mrs Lockyer had brought for Lockyer.

'I sent you off duty hours ago, Nurse Dickinson,' she said. 'What on earth are you doing?'

'I forgot my lecture book, Sister,' I answered. 'I was just

asking Nurse Andrews if she'd seen it, because I want to do some work to-night.' I did not want to have to walk majestically to the hostel with her, so I hurried on ahead to get dressed for the Police Dance at the 'Rowan Arms.'

It strikes me now how very often I failed to obey Sister Fairchild's injunction to 'cultivate scrupulously the habit of accurate statement.' Unless it meant harm to anyone else, it was always much simpler to make an excuse, if you had a convincing one, than to go through the fatigue of another row. I probably never deviated from the accurate statement so often in my life before, not even at school. But in hospital you have got to look after your own interests. Nobody else will.

I carried several notes backwards and forwards for Larry before Sir Curtis Rowntree decreed that the taboo subject might be broached. Larry put up a very good pantomime of surprise and gradually dawning memory, and immediately began to make himself a nuisance. He wanted to be put on a trolley and wheeled round to call on Maisie. He could see no reason why it should not be allowed. If it came to that, nor could I, but I realized that it could not be done. It was just one of those things that weren't.

'I came over here to fight for liberty,' he told Sir Curtis, who stood over him with his elegant length and proud face, his black hair flicked carefully up over each ear. 'For liberty,' continued Larry aggressively, 'and what do I get? First thing I know, I'm in a prison camp. Don't talk to me of the Motherland. When can I get up, Doc?'

'Take it easy, son,' said Sir Curtis, whose daughter sometimes took him to the cinema, 'we've got to get you a new leg first.'

'Say, do I have to wait for a cork leg before I can see Maisie? Now see here, Doc —'

Across the bed, Sister Oates threw a glance which said : 'What can one do with such a man?' but the Surgeon ignored her and turned round to ask me politely to bring screens.

Sister Martin came back at the end of that week, much to the relief of everyone, including Sister Oates, who was going to the Maternity Ward, where she hoped to find some high-class babies. She had despaired of ever finding any high-class Surgical Men.

Sister Martin made a brisk tour of the premises on the first day and announced that we had been slacking, which was true, but somehow one felt that she blamed Wild Oats as much as us. There were indigestion tablets loose in her desk drawer and a ring from a hot coffee jug on her sitting-room table. Once one got used to the idea of working harder, it was nice to see the ward return to its old efficiency and the stimulating air of enthusiasm come creeping back. Even Larry noticed that difference and became more amenable. Then, just when I had got to the stage of waking each day with anticipation instead of distaste, my happiness was neatly whisked away.

There was only one announcement after roll-call at break-fast. 'Nurse Dickens to go on Night Duty to-night. For what we have received, the Lord make us truly thankful.'

## Chapter Six

ONE of the stock phrases at the Queen Adelaide Hospital was : 'I can't stick this hole any longer.' Everybody said it, even those who were obviously destined to pass their State exams brilliantly, become Sisters and go on upwards, nurs-ing their lives away but deriving great satisfaction and hap-piness thereby. Nobody, however, ever admitted to anticipa-tion of this, or to the smallest ambition. If one wanted to pass an exam, it was only so as not to waste the fees, or be out-done by that conceited Wyman or give Toots – Sister Tutor – the satisfaction of seeing her prophecy fulfilled. However much you liked nursing, the thing was to pretend that you hated it and were only there under some unfair compulsion.

'I'm going to hand in my notice,' was another favourite remark, but it rarely came to more than an extravagant account of the interview with Matron, in which the trium-phant nurse had consented to stay out of gracious con-descension to the War.

There was one girl who lived permanently on the eve of departure, crouched, so to speak, like a runner, ready to spring off in a moment. It was said that she always kept her suitcase half-packed, and if you asked her to do anything, even if it was only a week ahead, she would say : 'My dear, I can't fix anything. I probably shan't be here by then.'

Her name was Dawlish, and she was quite handsome in an over-ripe way. She dressed her thick black hair in as many sweeps and coils as the shortage of hairpins allowed and perched her cap on top like a crown. She had a superior way of talking and a trick of slowly lowering her eyelids as if you came far below her estimation of herself. She seemed to be a good nurse, and if she were only half as skilful and knowledgeable as she thought, that still made her very efficient.

I am sure she enjoyed the work. One sometimes caught her in a complacent song, that would give place at anyone's approach to : 'I can't stick this hole any longer. I'm going to give Fanny Churchman my notice to-morrow.'

'But you did that last week,' one would say.

'I know, but this time I'm not going to relent. I'm not going to stay here and be bossed by uneducated women with no breeding. Sister was abominably rude to me this morning about the broken thermometer. She as good as told me I was a liar. "How dare you speak to me like that, Sister?" I said. She didn't know what to say to that, so she said : "I merely asked you, Nurse, if you knew anything about the thermometer." "Pardon me, Sister," I said, "you accused me of lying – I suppose because it's what you yourself would have done under the circumstances." ' Dawlish paused, to make certain that one was impressed.

'So Sister said, in that voice – you know, trying to disguise the cockney accent – "Very well, Nurse," she said, "You can go to Matron's office to-morrow morning." "I shall be only too glad to," I said, "to hand in my notice and tell her exactly why I'm leaving." '

At dinner the next day, I heard her describing the interview with Matron : 'So I said to her : "I'm not accustomed to such treatment, Matron," I said. "I don't like your tone, Nurse," she said. "No, Matron," I said, "and I'm afraid I don't like yours." 'I did, really,' she replied to the exclamations of incredulity, muted by macaroni pudding.

' "If you're not careful, Nurse," she said, "I shall have to give you a month's notice." "Thank you, Matron," I said, "but I came here for that purpose this morning." '

I had been waiting outside Matron's Office myself that morning, but Dawlish didn't like to be addressed by Juniors and anyway, I didn't think it worth asking her how she had got all this into the half-minute or so within which I had seen her go in with a shilling and a broken thermometer in her hand and come out with a new one.

Whenever, in my moments of depression or rebellion, or simply fatigue, I considered giving in my notice, I had always ended by deciding to stay until I had to go on Night Duty. I hated the idea of staying up all night from compulsion not choice, and of having to spend precious daylight hours in bed. One would be completely cut off from the world, a demi-civilized, underworld creature, out of touch with normality for three weary months. Recent notices had hinted that, owing to shortage of staff, this might even be extended to four months. 'Many factory workers have been on Night Shifts for more than a year without complaint. E. Harriman, Ass. Mat.'

I was quite willing to give the thing a try, but I didn't see how I should ever keep awake. I went off Herbert Waterlow Ward at two o'clock in the afternoon, supposedly to get some of the sleep that I should miss that night. Night nurses had rooms in a different part of the hostel, behind a baize door, but I had not yet had time to change my room. I had not been in bed ten minutes before three of the maids settled down outside my door for a long gossip, whose punctuation marks were shrieks of laughter. I stood it for a while, and then opened the door and gave them what angry people in hotels give to belated revellers who are being awfully amusing with the boots and shoes. They stared at me in silence and I slammed the door and went back to bed, feeling rather a fool.

'Ee,' said Janet, who came from Tyneside and had stunted legs and not a sound tooth in her head, 'ee, that Na-a-as

Dickens, who does shay think shay is? What a cha-ayk!'
They talked on for a bit, to make it quite clear that when
they did move away it was only because they wished to do so.
I burrowed my head down and concentrated on sleep. It
was bitterly cold; perhaps that was why I could not get off.
I went out to the bathroom and filled my hot bottle.

'Hullo,' said Richardson in the corridor, surprised to see
me in a dressing-gown, 'are you ill?'

'Night duty.'

'Oh, Glory, how *awful*. D'you know what ward you're
on? I expect you'll be on Maternity – MacDonald's off sick.
I say, bad *luck*.'

Thoroughly depressed, I got back into bed with a jersey
over my nightgown and lay tense until I could relax in the
slow return of warmth. I knew what Night Duty on Maternity meant : a baby born every night and all the mess for me,
as junior, to clear up. Anything up to ten babies yelling all
night long, and Night Sister coming round at intervals to
say : 'Call yourself a nurse and you can't even keep a few
babies quiet!'

I had just fallen into a shallow doze when somebody came
down the corridor with her voice raised in song. I dozed
again, and she returned, still singing the same song. After
that, it was the nurses coming over for their teatime cigarette. Three and a half hours until getting-up time. If I could
get off now, it would still do some good. The more I worried
about it, the more restless I became. My head was like a
factory working overtime. How often, on the ward at this
time, I had felt that I would give anything to get into bed
and sleep for ever. When the workmen began mending the
pipes in the bathroom opposite, I gave it up and switched on
the light to read. I was just nodding pleasantly over the
book, reading whole pages without taking in a word, when a
battering ram struck my door and Janet's 'Uff pust sev-vun,
Na-a-as!' stabbed me into the horror of reality.

This, I thought, as I got dressed, was the body that I had
got to drag round with me all night. Please God, don't let
any babies be born to-night. Hold up the course of nature
until daytime; it can't make any difference.

The junior night nurses' breakfast was at eight o'clock and we had to be on the wards at twenty-five past, so that the day nurses could get off. There were nine of us, and we sat at one end of a table, while a maid laid the places for the day nurses' supper.

Tea and porridge and bread and margarine did not go down very well at this hour, but I was pleased to discover that Kelly, the Irish girl who brightened Toots's lectures, was also on night duty. She arrived late, in a sweet disorder, and helped herself to an immense plate of porridge, saying : 'Just got here before Fanny Adams, God be praised.'

Fanny Adams was the Senior Night Sister, a nut-coloured raw-boned woman, who prowled round the hospital on silent feet, with a venomous fang for a tongue. When she took morning breakfast on the Junior Night Sister's night off, people hardly dared to speak. She came in to-night, just as Kelly rammed in the last of her porridge, and we all stood up as if we had sat on drawing pins. She was very tall and looked, in her uniform, like an iron column, because she had no ins and outs and her apron did not stick out like other people's, but hung rigidly tubular.

She looked us over in silence and ticked off our names in a book.

'Nurse Dickens,' she said sharply, pronouncing it 'Diggins', 'you're on Jane English.' I could not help a broad smile spreading with relief at my escape from the babies, but she wiped it off with : 'I don't know what you're grinning at. You'll find plenty of work to do there. Busiest ward in the hospital at night usually.' Then she gave us a short lecture on blackout carelessness, threatened us all with prison, and thanked the Lord tartly for our tea and porridge.

Sister on Jane English was sitting at the desk writing the report when I reported for duty. She was quite young ; she had done her training in this hospital and had only recently been promoted from Staff Nurse, and was very conscious of her status. She spoke primly, folding her mouth after each remark, in the same way that one felt she would never leave a drawer or a cupboard door open. She told me to go and ask

298

the day nurses if I could help them finish up. I found them in the sluice, reading the paper.

'Is it half-past? Thank God,' they said, and hurried away to go off duty. I could have told them there was nothing to hurry for, because I had seen the maid dumping on the supper tables the great bowls of beetroot which always accompanied the pink rubbery circles known as Luncheon Sausage.

Sister Porter told me to go round the beds to see if the patients were comfortable. All the ward lights were out, except one or two, green-shrouded, over the beds of very ill patients and the shaded lamp on the desk, which picked out Sister's small hand, writing carefully, and one side of the neat roll of dark hair which surrounded her head in front of her cap. Just behind the desk, in the middle of the ward, a fire was burning low in the tiled stove, but beyond this, the beds were in complete darkness. I knocked into one or two, and fell over a chair, but most of the women were awake anyway, and the one or two who groaned were probably chronic grumblers. They all seemed very nice, with that undefensive friendliness that unfolds when the lights are out, and they all wanted to hear what had happened to poor little Nurse Siddons. They were very upset to lose her; it seemed she had made life pleasant for them, and I suppose they doubted my ability to do the same.

'Always remembered I liked my egg more set than the others, little Nurse Siddons did,' sighed a woman who was no more to me than a vast mound, a tangle of black hair and a breathy whisper. I promised her that I would remember, too. I knew I was more likely to forget, but it seemed a pity to spoil her night.

In the kitchen, there was a list of those who had hot milk drinks before settling. I was just putting the saucepan on the stove, when Maxton, who was my Senior Night Nurse, arrived with a small suitcase and a cross expression. She went into the linen cupboard to deposit her cloak and case. I wondered what was in it.

'Good evening, Nurse,' I said politely, determined to start

out right at least, however casual I might become later, under stress or exhaustion.

'What are you doing?' she said. 'You'd better stop it now and come into the ward while Sister gives the report.' In order to hear the report, one had to put on one's cuffs, and we stood, hands behind backs, one on either side of Sister while she read it. My mind wandered. It was no use feeling tired now, I told myself, with eleven hours to go, but my whole system insisted that it was time to finish work now, not to start.

'I hope you're listening carefully, Nurse Dickens,' said Sister, looking up. 'This is the only way of getting to know the patients, you know.' I brought my brain back. 'Do you know what Osteomyelitis is?' she asked.

'No, Sister.'

'Well, why didn't you ask, then, when I was reading the report on Mrs Rudolph? I don't want any carelessness from you, Nurse. This is a methodical ward, as Nurse Maxton will tell you.' Nurse Maxton lowered her pale eyes, which were always rather red, as though she had been crying. It was now that I first sensed the faint antagonism that all Day Sisters have for the night nurses on their ward. There is the suspicion that, behind their back, one will trifle with their beloved machine. Wherever possible, the blame for a mishap is pinned on to the night nurses. It is they who have broken that syringe to which no one will confess; they who ate that jelly and stole Sister's ginger biscuits. Sister Porter was quick to champion the day nurses, as she never would be to their faces, telling us how frequent treatment had improved the condition of Miss Murphy's back and how everything possible had been done to make Miss Griggs more comfortable, and hoping, though not expecting, that we should be as conscientious.

She rose and gathered up a neat pile of books and papers from the desk. 'When I come on in the morning,' she said, looking up at me, for she was very short, 'I do a complete round of kitchen, sluice, bathroom, specimen room – everything, to make sure you leave everything clean and tidy as the day staff leave it for you. Good night, Nurses.' She walked off as if she were in a deportment class with a book on her head. The long night had begun.

She was another of these notice addicts, I discovered. You could not open the door of any cupboard without being told to replace things in it tidily, and the walls of the sluice were papered with instructions to go easy on the Vim, to keep the sterilizer filled up, and which disinfectant to use for what. Nurse Maxton told me vaguely what my duties were, but her mind seemed to be elsewhere. When I had given out the hot drinks and helped her rub the backs and heels of immobile patients, I had to do a spot of cleaning and then wash and iron some linen bandages. I was tiptoeing through the ward, dismayed to find that my shoes squeaked, which I had not noticed in the daytime, when a hoarse whisper came from the gloom at the end of the ward.

'Nurse!' Mrs Riscoe was sitting up in bed, two long plaits of dark hair hanging over the shoulders of her white nightgown.

'I say, dear,' she whispered, 'we always has a nice cup of tea round about now, them what's awake.' I was sure this was not official, but I couldn't fall short of Nurse Siddons, so I went to the kitchen to put on the kettle.

'And what is Nurse Diggins doing?' No footfall had announced the approach of Sister Adams.

'Oh, nothing, Sister.' I could feel myself blushing. 'I – I was just going to fill up the Sterile Water bottles.'

'You come into the ward while I do my round with Nurse Maxton,' she said. 'Cuffs on, please.' I had to stand sedately in the middle of the ward while the other two went round the beds, although in the kitchen I could hear the kettle boiling over and hissing on to the gas. Sister Adams carried a great torch like a lighthouse, which she flashed on to the patients' faces, waking them up to enquire if they could not sleep. Afterwards, she and Maxton went into the little room where the drug cupboard was, and I heard her telling Maxton off about something while she gave out the prescribed drugs. By the time she had gone, more than half the ward was awake and wanting tea. I resolved to take it round before eleven o'clock the next night.

If it was difficult to learn patients' names and ailments in the daytime, it was impossible at night. I didn't think I would ever get them straight; I kept coming across a patient who should not be there, by my reckoning, and the five Fractured Femurs, with legs strung up to beams, were as one to me. For all I knew, I might have been giving out tea to Gastric Ulcers, but I couldn't keep asking Maxton, who was closeted behind screens with a fomentation, and who anyway moved in a brooding world of her own.

'What do I do now?' I asked her, as she was replacing the bowls in the sterilizer.

'Oh, I don't care,' she said. 'You'd better come and sit at the desk and get on with the mending, while I write the midnight report.'

She dashed off a few words about the ill patients and said : 'Now for a bit of peace, thank goodness,' and went to fetch her suitcase. It held what seemed to be all her correspondence for the last year, an apple, a half-eaten bar of chocolate, a bag of macaroons and some khaki knitting. This knitting was her passion. She hated to be called away from it and kept dashing back to it at every opportunity throughout the night.

'Who's it for?' I asked, finishing off a darn which I knew would never satisfy Sister Porter.

'My sweetie,' said Maxton, and sighed. I would have liked to hear about him, but feared to be thought oncoming. A plaintive voice called from one of the beds and I had to get up to attend to it, and to two others who were struck with the same idea. Maxton was still clicking away furiously as I sat down and started on another operation sock. She sighed. Presently she sighed again, and said : 'Aren't men unreasonable?'

'Frightfully,' I said, and waited for more. Sure enough, it came, pouring out in a whispered torrent, to the unceasing accompaniment of the pecking needles and whirling wool. Sweetie, it transpired, was in an Anti-Aircraft unit near Redwood and had fallen for Maxton while having his tonsils out on Secker Ward. He was a man of fierce passions, and would flare up in an instant if Maxton so much as spoke to

302

a bus conductor. The quarrel which was weighing on her to-night was such a complication of misunderstandings, wrong telephone messages and female cousins mistaken for males that I could not follow it closely. This evening, Maxton had received a stilted letter saying that she need not bother to meet George same time same place Saturday. I had to read this and many others that had gone before, some tender, some disagreeable and some embarrassing, while all the time Maxton knitted away at the pullover as if it were already imbued with some of the glamour of George's person.

I was to get sick of the sound of his name before long. Never did a couple have so many quarrels, so many reconciliations or so many tedious conversations which had to be retailed to me verbatim. Never was a couple more boring.

At twelve o'clock, Maxton finished a row, dabbed a grubby felt puff on to a solid powder compact and dabbed it on her nose and went up to the Midnight Meal. I felt rather big at being left in charge of the ward and strolled importantly round once or twice.

'Where's the other nurse – the sandy-haired one?' asked one of the Fractured Femurs. 'I wish she'd come and fix my leg; it's tormenting me.'

'I'll do it,' I said, though baffled by the network of strings and pulleys and bandages.

'Don't you touch it, my girl,' said the woman. 'The other nurse understands it. I want her.'

'She's gone to her supper.' The woman groaned. 'Oh dear,' I said, 'is it very painful?'

'It's perjury, that's what it is, Nurse. Perjury.'

Someone came into the ward and I saw it was the very young House Surgeon, Mr Ridley. I went up to him.

'Anything you want, Nurse? I'm just going to bed.' I remembered that Maxton had told me that if any of the House Surgeons came down, I was to ask them to chart Mrs Rudolph for something. I had not the slightest idea what that meant, but I repeated the message, and he yawned and said : 'O.K. Where's her chart?'

Her chart? I didn't even know where her bed was. I wandered ineffectually round for a bit, peering at the names on the charts, and at last he went over to the right bed and got the chart himself. I felt an awful fool.

'What d'you want for her?' he asked, bending over the desk and shaking his fountain pen dangerously near Sweetie's pullover.

'Well, I – er —'

'Pot. Brom. and Chloral, I should think,' he said, making cryptic signs on the back of the chart. 'Yes, please,' said I, although he might have been prescribing weed-killer for all I knew. He was just going, when another groan of Perjury came from half-way down the ward.

'Oh, would you just look at this woman's leg, sir?' I asked. 'She says its painful and she won't let me touch it.'

'Hullo, Mrs Davenport,' he said, going up to the bed and flashing a pencil torch on her. 'What's the trouble?'

'Me leg again,' she said. 'Here I lay, week after week, and it gets no easier. It don't seem right, you know. You'd think they could do something.' She looked like one of those potatoes that people photograph and send to the papers because it bears a curious resemblance to a human face.

'I'll soon fix that,' said Mr Ridley. 'Hold the torch a sec, Nurse.' He began sorting out the strings that slung Mrs Davenport's leg to the beam. 'Now then, young man,' she began querulously, 'don't you touch they cords – ouch!' With a quick wrench, he had hauled her foot about six inches higher and straightened it.

'There! That's better, isn't it?' She hated having to admit it, but it was.

Maxton came back as the House Surgeon was sauntering away. 'What did *he* want?' she asked, chasing the remains of her meal with her tongue.

'He was fixing Mrs Davenport's leg; she was making an awful fuss.'

'Silly idiot,' said Maxton. 'I wish he'd leave things alone; she's not his patient.'

'Well, he made it all right, anyway,' I said. 'I think he's rather nice.'

'I could have done it,' she said, picking up her knitting. 'I hate these Housemen – stuck-up little boys, they think they know everything. Give me an older man, a man with experience —'

'Like George?' I suggested, knowing that it was time for me to go up to the dining-room, and escaping before she could get going on the subject.

'Well, how's Sweetie?' Kelly asked me, as I came into the dining-room. He was evidently a notorious figure. The night duty maid dumped a tin pie dish down in front of Flowers, who sat at the head, and she doled out an ambiguous concoction with a ladle. It was vegetables cooked in water, and then the water thickened and coloured with browning to look like gravy. Afterwards, we had cold rice pudding. We were allowed half an hour away from the ward, and we spun it out with cups of tea and desultory conversation, but they all seemed pretty bored with each other and inclined to bicker. Night duty makes you like that. For one thing, you are always tired, and the comparatively few people with whom you mix get on your nerves far more than the large, assorted day staff. After a time, you feel you must scream and throw chairs if you have to sit once more at table with the same eight girls. Every mannerism is a prong, and their table manners nauseatingly familiar. You listen for the dreadful clicking of Ringer's jaw, you long to tell Flowers not to hold her knife as if she were going to eat peas off it, and you know that at any moment Jones will say : 'I always say a cup of tea bucks you up.'

Someone once burst out to me : 'Oh, for God's sake, Dickens, don't keep kicking your chair like that!' I never knew I did it. I was devastated; I knew exactly how she felt.

When I got back to the ward, it was very cold. The fire had gone out and there was a bleak draught that hit you as you sat at the desk. I went and got my cloak and then leaned against one of the radiators for a while, yawning. Soon I was so sleepy that I had to sit down, and I put my head on my arms on the desk and floated peacefully away. The words 'Fanny Adams' dropped into my sleep like stones into a lake, and a dig in the ribs sent me jumping to my feet just in time to see Maxton going forward to meet Night Sister on her early morning round. I stood by the desk swaying and shiver-

305

ing, and when she drew level with me on the way back, Sister stopped and flashed her torch on my sleepy face. 'And who is this Nurse with the bad manners? Ah, yes, Nurse Dickens; we shall have to keep an eye on you.' She stayed a moment longer, as if expecting something from me, and then, as I wasn't worth wasting her battery on, clicked off her torch and walked on.

'You soft thing, why didn't you take off your cloak?' asked Maxton when she had gone.

'Good Lord, is that what she meant? I didn't even know I had it on.'

'Well, I'm sorry for you if she gets a grudge against you. She knows how to make life Hell.' She picked up her knitting again, and I slumped down beside her. 'Maxton, I'm so tired, I think I'm going to die. I'll never last out. Isn't it nearly time to start waking them up?'

'We're not supposed to start before five o'clock, but it's impossible to get done if you wait till then. You just have to look out one of the Night Sisters doesn't catch you. Siddons used to start by washing the ill people. They don't know whether it's Christmas or Easter, anyway.'

'Can I start now?'

'Heavens, no. Not for at least another hour.' I sat and brooded for a bit, fell asleep, woke up and sat on my hands to try and warm them. I prayed that nobody would call, because, apart from being too tired, I was too cold to move. I was numb with despair. I knew now, for certain, that the night would never end.

'D'you think that'll be long enough to his armpit?' asked Maxton.

'Uh-huh,' I said without looking. The thought of Sweetie's armpit made me quite ill.

'If I were you,' she said, 'I'd go and cut the bread-and-butter and lay the trolley for breakfast. You'll never have time later on.'

In the kitchen I was struck by the brilliant idea of a cup of tea and wished I had thought of it before. Maxton would not come and have one, because she wanted to get over a tricky bit of armhole. She kept telling me to hurry up with the bread-and-butter because while I was in the kitchen she had to answer all the calls in the ward.

On night duty, you reach the nadir of vitality at about half-past three. Your system is barely ticking over; you think you are alive but you couldn't swear to it. Soon after that, you have to start work and there is so much to do that you have to start at top speed and keep up the pace until eight o'clock or later, when you go off duty. The initial effort is agony, like the moving of a limb that has been numbed with cramp, but once you have forced yourself into motion, you can keep it up if only you go fast enough. Maxton and I scuttled about like mad things. We each had our own work to do, mine more domestic and hers more skilled, and we only spoke occasionally as we flashed past, or pushed each other out of the way in the sluice, to fling over our shoulders that despairing cry : 'I'll never get done !'

Being strange to the ward, I had no system. My hair escaped from under my cap and I could see my face shining out of the corner of my eye. To think that a short time ago I had been frozen solid ! I constantly caught the name 'Nurse Siddons' in a regretful tone as I muddled along, and when it came to breakfast time, the murmurs swelled to protest. The patients had to provide their own eggs, and in my frenzy to get the breakfasts in and out before the day staff arrived, I got mixed and gave them out at random, so that rightful egg-owners at the far end of the ward were cheated. Added to this, I had hard-boiled them all by mistake, and I pretended not to hear the murmurs of 'Wicked waste, with eggs so scarce', and 'I been looking forward to that egg for days'.

'What, no porridge, Nurse? We always have porridge.'

'I'm so sorry, I'm so sorry,' I almost sobbed, as I poured out tea and got mixed up with those I had sugared and those I hadn't and gave a sugared one to a Diabetic. The atmosphere all round me was pregnant with the uneasiness of a ship whose crew is about to mutiny, and just as I was making up my mind to the fact that they would all complain to Sister and probably even to Matron, Mrs Wilson, blessed Mrs Wilson, stemmed the growing tide and turned it in my favour. She was the woman who liked her egg well set, and she had got it; the tea was black and the sugar allowance exhausted by the time I reached her, but she liked it strong and unsweetened, and she detested porridge. So she raised her voice and stood up for me, and as she was respected for her size and the length of time she had been in hospital, they gradually came round and I loved them all instead of wanting to shoot them. One or two who were allowed up even volunteered to help me clear away, and Miss Holloway, who was very refined in a green kimono and slippers with rosettes, padded from bed to bed saying : 'Are you *quaite* sure you've finished? Ah, then I'll take your tray. Just like the cafeteeria, isn't it, Nurse?' Her giggle was like the whinny of a catarrhal horse.

The Day Staff came on at seven, yawning and aloof, and we went on making our side of beds, secure in the superiority of having kept all these people alive while the others were callously asleep. We came to a bed with a wide cradle over two legs, elephantine with plaster of paris. I looked at the chart. 'Maisie Griggs'. Of course! I had forgotten that she was on this ward. But she was not at all as I had pictured her; she was quite young, but, perhaps because pain had settled in her face and eyes, she looked as old, even older than Larry. He had told me he was going to marry her, and I mentioned it, and the women on either side took it up delightedly and teased her. I was surprised to find that nobody except Evans, who had carried the notes, knew about Larry.

'Why didn't you tell them?' I asked Maisie. 'I'd boast about a man like that.'

'What's he like?' asked Maxton, heaving up one of the cumbrous legs while I turned the pillow underneath.

'Marvellous,' I said, and enlarged on him.

'Man to leave home for, eh?' said Mrs Rudolph.

'Rather. Isn't he, Mais?'

'Yes,' she said, in her quiet, toneless voice. 'Oh, don't touch that leg, Nurse – I can't bear you to touch that leg.'

None of the other Sisters ever came on duty before a quarter-past eight, but Sister Porter arrived punctually at eight, looking as neat as a doll that doesn't undress. I had forgotten about her inspection and had to dash round trying to create order, but she arrived too soon and said : 'I will not have my ward untidied. You must work *my* way here, Nurse, whatever you do on other wards.' She had already discovered that I had given an egg to a woman on sulphanilamide tablets, an unforgivable crime, apparently.

'I'm sorry,' I said, 'I didn't know —'

'You should have,' said Sister, thoroughly shocked, although it could not have been so long since she herself had discovered this fact with equal surprise. I suspected that she was younger than me, but she made me feel half her age. It is depressing to see someone cast off Youth almost unworn. It usually means they try to dress up in it again much later on when it doesn't suit them any more.

After this, I went to ask Maxton if there was anything else I had to do. 'What a night,' I said, 'I'm dead to the world.'

'What a night?' She looked at me in surprise. 'Why, that was one of the easiest nights I've ever had. You wait till we're busy.'

I was too tired to be hungry, but I had to go up to the dining-room and face rabbit stew and ginger pudding, which, at half-past eight in the morning seemed queer eating. One of the Seniors, a girl called McLeod, with arms like a blacksmith and a blooming complexion that did not look as if it had been up all night, did miracles with the food and ate on unabashed long after we had all finished.

Afterwards, when I was changing my room to the night nurses' section, I passed by her open door and saw her sitting on the bed with a friend, eating salmon out of a tin with tin-openers.

When I had adjusted myself to living upside down, I began to like nursing at night. It meant you were free to go about during the day as long as you could stay awake, and I found that by the time I had come off the ward and had a bath, I had got my second wind and enough energy to go out. It was spurious energy, that wore off after a time, leaving one limp and dull-witted, but it was enough to start off with. Officially, of course, we were supposed to be in bed by eleven o'clock, but drawn curtains and a bolster in the bed satisfied Sister Harriman's short sight. The wife of the Wing-Commander whom I had met at the Air Force dance had twice asked me to her house, and eventually I accepted an invitation for Sunday lunch. Chris was off that morning, and she and I walked in the town and had coffee at the 'Blue Lady' to keep me awake. Then I changed and bicycled off down the hill, with the wind making havoc of my carefully set hair.

Wing-Commander and Mrs Fellowes lived on the outskirts of the town in the sort of house that you find on big golf-course estates. My heart sank at the sight of two cars outside the door. I didn't feel equal to a party. There they all were, in the lounge or drawing-room or whatever they called it, drinking cocktails and making booming conversation. Mrs Fellowes, with her hair in a lot of little curls like rusty iron filings, stressed the fact that I was a nurse, which made my hands feel larger and redder than ever. Bertie Fellowes had not the faintest idea who I was, but greeted me jovially with his horse laugh and gave me a large strong cocktail. There were one or two other Air Force officers, a pink and white soldier and a high-pitched young man from some Ministry. There were also some women in towny tweeds, and a girl for whose enhancement the WAAF uniform might have been designed. There was a broken-down relation somewhere about, and two dogs that lay on the furniture.

At lunch they all talked about the war, and as I had not seen a paper for days, I kept out of it and concentrated on the food, until Mrs Fellowes called the maid back with a dish and said loudly : 'Now, you *must* have some more. Don't worry about us, we'll wait for you. I know nurses always have enormous appetites.'

Everyone stopped talking and stared, and Bertie said : 'Yes, by Jove, remember that female we had in the house while you were having the Twins? Ate like a horse, you never saw anything like it,' he assured the company.

'Yes, and d'you remember how awful it was at meals, Uncle Bertie?' said the girl in WAAF uniform, 'how she only had two topics of conversation – the Royal Family and disgusting details of her other cases?'

'God, yes,' said her uncle. 'I never knew which I disliked most – the Little Princesses or Lady Sidebotham's operation. She began on regurgitation once, at breakfast . . .'

'They're all the same, aren't they?' said the tweedy woman with the regimental badges, 'a race of screaming bores —' She suddenly noticed what I had been aware of for some time : Mrs Fellowes making pulled-down faces and tapping on the table to remind them of me. The tweedy woman laughed nervously, cleared her throat and began to talk very fast about bridge.

It was the fact that they thought I minded which made me so furious. I resolved to leave as soon as possible. However, in a comfortable armchair in the drawing-room, I became so comatose that I had not the gumption to get up and break into the talk with good-byes. Somebody came and sat down by me and began to talk, and I had to fight to keep my eyes open. I felt stupid and plain, and I wanted to powder my nose but didn't know where I had put my bag. 'You look sleepy,' somebody said. 'Too much lunch.'

'I'm all right,' I said, 'you get tired being on night duty.'

'You mean you've been up all night? How ghastly.' But it didn't really penetrate. They all felt too well and self-confident to imagine a dreariness of spirit such as mine. With an effort, I got up and went over to Mrs Fellowes. 'I really must go now,' I began, but Bertie cut in with : 'Go? Good Heavens, what are you talking about? You can't go yet. We're all going over to see a display by a new type of Fighter.'

'Oh, but really, I don't think I —'

'Nonsense. Of course you must come. I'll take you in the Buick with me. Off you go upstairs with the other gels and do whatever it is women take such hours over.' His laughter made my head reel.

Up in Mrs Fellowes's bedroom, I sat on the bed while the other women chattered and tried on each other's hats. I felt exactly as I used to at the age of eighteen, when I had gone dumbly to parties and every female, including the cloakroom attendant, had made me feel inferior. I was out of touch with the world all right, if this was the world. Somehow I

311

survived the rest of the afternoon, tagging along and yawning when no one was looking, and then we all had to go back to tea at 'Four Winds', which was the name of the Fellowes's house. I might have gone home then, but my resistance was shattered.

Mrs Fellowes sat very upright behind silver teapots, and we sat round balancing things on our knees and there was much passing of food. They were talking about the War again, and it seemed odd that we should be eating three kinds of cake. They went on talking about the War and it seemed that the pink-and-white soldier ran the Army and the high-pitched youth ran the Civil Service and the others ran the Air Force, which was nice for them. Tea woke me up slightly and I began to talk about the hospital. I found I could talk quite a lot about that before I realized I was being a bore. I had given up all thought of ever getting to bed, when some of them began to say they had to get back to the aerodrome and miraculously the party broke up.

Bertie's niece offered to give me a lift, as she was taking the Civil Servant to the station.

I explained about my bicycle.

'Leave it here, my dear,' said Bertie. 'You can pick it up any time.'

'Oh no, thanks awfully. I don't mind a bit. I like bicycling.' I didn't want to come again.

'Now be sure and come and see us another time,' said Mrs Fellowes, smiling her charity smile at me as I said good-bye. 'Whenever you want a good meal, just ring up. We're in the book.' The niece pressed me once more to come in the car, and I again insisted that I liked bicycling and pedalled away into the biting wind that is always in your face when you're bicycling, whichever way you go. I had dismounted and was pushing the bike up the steep part of the hill, when the WAAF roared past me in an Air Force car. She waved and I waved back to show that I was happy.

Maxton and I were fairly busy these nights and Sweetie's sweater was making poor progress. We had several operations at night and one or two desperately ill patients who had kept us fussed and caused Sister Adams to be in and out of the ward all night, which was enough to break anyone's nerve.

I liked going to the Theatre at night : it was exciting, and the operations, being nearly all emergency ones, were imbued with a sense of urgency. Also, there was only one Theatre Nurse on at night, so that the nurse who brought the patient from the ward had to stay and assist in all the little things that the theatre staff did in the daytime. When I ran about with drums, brought in the saline bowl or held a leg, I felt as important as if I were doing the whole operation. It was nerve-racking, because I did not know what to do, and with a dangerously ill patient on the table, the atmosphere tense with the surgeon's nervous irritability, and someone hissing from behind a mask, 'Quick, Nurse ! Give her an injection of Atropine !' I nearly had a stroke.

Usually, Mr Sickert, the Resident Surgical Officer, or one of the other Housemen did the night operations, but sometimes one of the Honoraries was called from his after-dinner chair or even from his bed. Nurse Bonar, the Night Theatre Nurse who assisted with the cases, handing instruments and swabs, had a wholesale disdain for all these men, and the more eminent they were, the more she despised them. Each one had some idiosyncrasy in the theatre – Sir Curtis Rowntree hummed all the time, Mr Harvey Watkins would not allow iodine on the patient's skin, and the gynaecologist flew into a rage if anyone spoke. Nurse Bonar would imitate them before, during and after the operation for the benefit of the House Surgeons, the porters, or whoever was about. If the operation was complicated and took a long time, Bonar would begin looking at the clock, raising her eyes to heaven and making pushing gestures in the direction of the unsuspecting surgeon. Afterwards, while she and I were bandaging the patient, she would begin to revile him almost before he was out of the door. One of the House Surgeons would stroll in. 'Treat for you, Nurse Bonar. Vav's going to do a Caesar in half an hour's time.' He would withdraw hurriedly, because Bonar sometimes threw instruments when she was in a temper.

I personally was terrified of all surgeons and hated having to go near enough to do up their sterile gowns or to wipe sweat from their brows. Once or twice I had touched them and made them unsterile and I wished myself dead as I received their reaction at having to go through the whole scrubbing-up business again. My greatest shame, however, was when one of them suddenly shot at me through his mask: 'Fetch me the proctoscope!' and never having heard of the instrument before, I heard it as something else and came trotting faithfully back with the white coat of the night porter which I had dragged off his indignant back.

On the night after the Fellowes party, we had an acute appendix and an amputation of a finger, and it was nearly midnight before I got back to the ward. I was not feeling nearly as tired as I expected after only two hours' sleep, but Maxton assured me that I should feel worse later. When she had gone up to 'Meal' and I was sitting at the desk reading the paper in an attempt to make myself more up to date than the afternoon had shown me to be, I heard sounds behind me that required investigation.

It was Maisie, with the sheet stuffed into her mouth to muffle the tearing sobs that were shaking her. Two days ago, they had decided that her left leg was not satisfactory, and needed extending. So they had driven a skewer through the heel – right through the bone and out at the other side, and from the ends of the skewer a cord let over a pulley to a fifteen-pound weight that hung clear over the head of the bed.

'Poor Mais,' I said. 'Is it very painful? Have you had your Veganin?'

'It isn't any good,' she sobbed. 'Nothing's any good any more. I wish I was dead.'

'You mustn't talk like that. You've got to get well for Larry.'

She looked at me with her swollen eyes, her sobs momentarily checked. 'But didn't you know?' she whispered. 'Larry's dead.'

'But Maisie, he's not!'

'Oh yes, he is,' she went on in that toneless voice. 'I saw

him. There was an accident, you know. There's blood all over his head.' She began to cry again. I didn't know what to do. I thought if I talked to her steadily, it might penetrate, but she only said: 'Poor Larry. Poor Larry. There's blood on my face too, Nurse. I wish you'd wash it off.'

'No, there isn't, Mais.'

'Yes, yes, can't you see?' She rubbed at her forehead with frenzied fingers. 'All over here – blood – ugh! Horrible, sticky. Look, it's all over my hand.' She held it out and then turned it backwards and forwards under her own eyes. 'All over blood,' she said pitifully.

I took hold of her hand. 'It's not your head that hurts, Maisie,' I said, 'it's your poor legs, and they're going to be all right pretty soon.'

'No, no,' she wailed, 'they'll never be all right. I don't want anything done to them. I can't . . .' She was sobbing uncontrollably now, dry-eyed and hysterical. I went to the telephone and rang for Night Sister to come, and Sister Gilbert, who was Fanny Adams's junior, came and gave me some morphia for her and Maisie slept for a while and woke again to pain.

She had to have morphia every night for a long time. Nights and days of continual pain drew her face into sharp planes and hollows, and even when the pain was temporarily easier, she thought of nothing but its return. The news of Larry was good. He was being discharged soon to a convalescent home, but she would not talk of him now and refused to write to him. Often, in the creeping hours after midnight when Maxton was knitting away at the Balaclava helmet that was the pullover's successor, I used to sit by Maisie's bed and we would have tea and talk until someone called me away.

'Larry's going out to-morrow,' I told her one night. 'I suppose you'll get married as soon as you're well.'

'No,' she said. 'Ill never marry him.'

'But I thought it was all arranged. He told me —'

'You don't understand, Nurse. There was never any question of it before the accident – well, we were friendly, and he used to take me out because he was grateful to us when he

315

was billeted on us – but not marriage. I'm too old for him, anyway.'

'But he wants you to – he told me.'

'Can't you *see*?' she said, fiddling with the bedclothes as she always did when the pain was returning. 'It's obvious enough, surely.' She gave a short laugh. 'He only asked me out of pity – to try and make up for what he'd done to me.'

I was glad when Sister moved Maisie's bed away from the neighbours who tried to cheer her up by teasing her and calling her 'the bride'. Sister put her out on the balcony to see if she would improve, but it was a long, long time before she went home, with her left leg still in plaster. I went to tea with her once and she told me that Larry had tried everything he knew to get a Staff job but had been passed out of the Army as unfit and had gone back to Canada.

'He wanted Maisie to go out to him,' broke in her mother, untying her apron as she came out of the kitchen. 'Her father and I both think she ought to go.'

'Don't be silly, Mother. A man doesn't want a wife with a useless leg.'

'Sister was telling me that Mr Sickert wants you to come back for more treatment,' I said.

'I won't go. I've had enough of being messed about. It wouldn't be any good anyway.'

'Oh, Maisie,' said her mother, pushing the cups and saucers about ineffectually, 'I wish you wouldn't talk like that. Can't you persuade her, Nurse? She's so difficult.'

'Oh, Mother, *don't*,' said Maisie.


Instead of getting one night off a week, we got three nights running each month. When Maxton had hers, her place on Jane English was taken by McLeod, the girl with the stomach like a Gladstone bag. She ate all night long, starting with tea and toast as soon as Sister had done her first round and keeping up her strength with a succession of snacks until I had made the breakfast porridge. I learned after the first night to make a double quantity. We were officially allowed to have our tea on the ward between four and five in the morning, and as this was our busiest time, Maxton and I used to snatch at it, dashing into the ward between each sip of tea and dashing back to the kitchen for another bite of macaroon. No matter how busy we were, however, McLeod would solemnly take her full twenty minutes in the kitchen, consuming vast quantities of bread and toast, which I, to my annoyance, had to make for her, and even afterwards, wandering dissatisfiedly into the larder and picking bits off the loaf.

Maxton had stayed with Sweetie's people for her nights off, as she had wangled them to coincide with his week-end leave. A horrid scene had taken place in the drawing-room after everyone had gone to bed and of course I was spared none of the grisly details.

'D'you think you ought to be telling me all this?' I asked, fidgeting uncomfortably.

'I thought you'd like me to tell you. Of course, if you don't want to hear about it —' she said stuffily.

Anything was better than to put Maxton in a temper for the night. It made her impossible to work with; she would delay taking the temperatures because she knew I could not take the breakfasts round and give the patients hot tea before their temperatures were taken, and I would be feverishly collecting cups and plates while the day nurses were already making beds, and the Staff Nurse would tell Sister I was inefficient.

'Go on, go on,' I sighed. 'I love it.' I wondered whether Sweetie was similarly regaling the boys of the Ack-Ack unit.

At the end of the month, I had my nights off, and Maxton was due to be back on day duty by the time I returned. A certain limited friendship had grown between us; you can't work hard together for night after night without developing some sort of bond, and I would miss her macaroons.

It was terrible coming back after three nights at home. It was just long enough to give one a tantalizing glimpse of the delightful, forgotten life that used to be, before the curtain fell and one was walking down the blue-lit corridor of the Nurses' Hostel as if one had never been away. Tantalizing too to have slept at night and been civilized during the day. I had slept late on my last morning, and taken the last possible train to Redwood, and Janet's 'Uff-past sev-vun, Na-a-as!' found me dolefully unpacking my case.

'Ee, not in bed?' she said, coming in and folding her arms over a shape of which everyone was suspicious until they discovered that it remained like that, year in, year out. ''Ad a good time, Honey? How's your yoong man?' she said, referring to the picture on my dressing-table which she would never accept as my brother-in-law.

'I've given my notice,' she said, accepting a cigarette. 'I told Sister Urriman to her face: "this place is a doomp," I said.' This was a ritual that occurred monthly, just before pay-day. Sister Harriman would have felt quite lost without it. I made the necessary sounds of regret.

'Ee well, ' said Janet. 'I suppose I must go and wake the other booggers.' I could hear her knocking and yelling all down the corridor, returning with an ear-splitting rendering of *A Pair of Silver Wings*.

Same old faces at breakfast, same old shop talk. Somehow one expected them to be different each time one came back. It was disheartening to think that they had all been circling around as usual within the confines, while I had been discovering that there were, after all, things going on outside. Nobody knew who was the new Senior on Jane English, but it was bound to be somebody frightful. I went about my early duties, prepared to be sickened by what nine o'clock should bring me. Sister called me over to the desk to inform me that Nurse Jones, who had taken my place while I was away, had made the tea ration go nearly twice as far, and why couldn't I, etc., etc. Catch Jones giving the patients tea in the middle of the night, I thought, and then I wasn't listening to Sister any more, for coming through the door, shooting her cuffs in that familiar way, was – of all people – Chris! Last Sunday, the stars had foretold that I would have a stroke of luck in mid-week that would alter my outlook on life. Here it was; I only hope that the prophecy was also fulfilled for the million other children of the sign of Taurus. It was a beautiful thought to think of all our fortunes turning simultaneously, like furrows in a ploughed field, and leading on up to better things, until at the week-end, we all met discouragement in

318

our home circles and fell out, temporarily, with a Loved One.

The ward was still very busy, but the work was less oppressive when you could laugh about it. Nothing had ever been amusing to Maxton. She had not even though it funny when the drug-addict came in with a broken hypodermic needle at large in her hind-quarters, or when Sister Adams slipped on a boiled sweet and shattered the darkness with a crash like the unloading of scrap iron, or when Paraldehyde went to Mrs Saxby's head and she made passionate advances to Mr Briant.

Mr Briant fancied Chris and was constantly on the ward. She called it a 'mental affinity', but whatever it was, I was always having to get up from the desk and occupy myself with chores while they talked and talked, he with his chair tipped, his feet on the night report book and his pipe alight, and Chris with her cap off and the desk lamp making her hair look like a jar of honey in the sun. I usually had to occupy myself in the kitchen, so that I could announce the approach of Sister Adams by dropping a plate, and then Chris would jam her cap on over one eye and Mr Briant would begin furiously writing up case histories with a pen with no ink in it. Sometimes, I would answer the telephone to Andrews' plaintive voice from Herbert Waterlow inquiring when Mr Briant was coming down to see their Peritonitis boy.

'Is it urgent?' I would ask.

'Well, not actually *urgent*, really – I – er – suppose he's frightfully busy with you?' I could picture her squirming and pulling up her stockings.

'Well, he is rather.'

'Could you ask him to come as soon as he can? I don't think he ought to leave it much longer.' I knew that she wanted him to go down while the other nurse on the ward was still away at supper. Then the telephone would ring again and the hoarse voice of Tivy, the night duty maid, would pant that Nurse Parry had better come up to the dining-room quick, as Sister Adams was up there to see Oo didn't turn up.

Once Chris came back from her burnt baked beans and

waxy potatoes just in time to save me from a predicament. One of the night porters, a burly man with a cauliflower ear and an aboriginal brow, was in the habit of coming up to Jane English for a cup of tea at intervals during the night. The ward was quiet, so I stayed in the kitchen with him and got on with my bread and butter, while he drew in his tea by suction. The doings of his relations were a serial story of which he gave me an instalment every time he came up, whether on business or pleasure. I was supposed to be *au fait* with the Clan Harper, but would sometimes absently ask : 'Who's Harry?' or 'Where does Lilian live?' '*You* know,' Harper would insist over his shoulder, from the other end of the trolley that we were wheeling along from the lift. 'I told you about Harry. He's the one that's an A.R.P. Warden down Bromley way – I *told* you. And Lilian, you know where Lilian lives – not a stone's-throw from the King and Queen, as she always says. Which bed is it, Nurse?'

'Yes,' he would continue, while we bent over the trolley, struggling to get our arms underneath the unconscious body to lift her on to the bed, 'yes, she's a London girl, our Lilian. Got a nice little business, too – Ready, Nurse? *Hup* she goes – Invisible Mending.' We staggered to the bed. 'But she's not like Else. I told you about Else – Want her over on 'er side? Lilian never had her head for figures —' Thump, we lowered our burden and I pulled the blankets over her. 'Works in a cash desk, Else does. I say this old dame's a bit blue, 'n't she?'

'Yes, she is rather. D'you think you could get the oxygen cylinder while I hold her jaw up?'

'Sits in a cash desk,' he continued, trundling up the oxygen stand, 'with her hair all in curls, as smart as you like. She's the one I told you that married that chap in the R.A.S.C.' He leaned over my shoulder breathing heavily while I tried to push the thin rubber tube up the patient's nose. 'Got a nice little place out Burnham Beeches – turn it on now? Right, here it comes, Ma – or the Beeches, as some call it. But, of course, come the war they had to move out. Got a nice Let for it, though, trust Else for that – 'Ere, aren't you giving her a bit much, Nurse? She's not a barridge balloon.'

On this particular night, when Chris was at supper and Harper and I together in the kitchen, he suddenly broke off an account of Cousin Arthur's wedding to stride swiftly to the door, shut it and stand against it, breathing heavily and saying, 'You don't leave this kitchen without you give us a kiss.'

I tried to laugh it off, but he held his ground, half surprised at himself but determined to go through with it.

'Oh, come on, Harp,' I said, 'don't play the fool. Let me out. Let me *out*!' I said, getting annoyed, for I could hear someone calling from the ward.

'Give us a kiss, then.'

'Oh, stop it. Listen, there's someone calling for me. They might die and it would be your fault.'

'All right. You can go out – when you've given us a kiss.' He was still rather sheepish about it. I picked up a fork to jab into the hamlike hand that held the door knob, but as I approached him, he grabbed me, chuckling with delight at himself, and Chris opened the door on a most undignified struggle.

'I'm *so* sorry,' she said, with a bland, social smile. 'Am I intruding?'

'Yes,' said Harper, still holding my arm.

'Oh. I only looked in to say that Sweet Fanny Adams is on her way round to find out why there's no one looking after the switchboard. She wants to ring Mr Sickert's bedroom and ask him if to-night's the night, but she can't get through.'

Early that morning, while I was washing Mrs Saxby, assuring her that I was doing her early so that she could have a nice little sleep until breakfast time, a large figure shambled into the still-darkened ward and stood with hanging hands, waiting to be noticed. It was Harper, come to apologize. He was horrified at himself, for in spite of his stature he was as mild as a doe.

He was quite useful. He used to fetch up coal for us, so that as soon as Sister Porter had gone off, we could fall on the fire and nurse and nourish the dying embers into something that lasted us all night. Then, if Mr Briant came down with some beer, we could pull the settee across the fire and be as cosy as anything. Sometimes Chris and I took turns to have a sleep there, regretting it on waking to a sick headache and the sense of doom that hangs about before the dawn.

Certain nights stand out now from the endless succession that rolled by until I began to forget what it was like to work in the daytime. There was the night when a girl who had been in a collision on the way home from a dance was admitted at eleven o'clock with what was collectively called a fractured skull. Her mother didn't recognize her at first. Soon after midnight, the stertorous breathing suddenly choked on a dreadful noise and then stopped.

The kind little Junior Night Sister took the mother away, and Tivy rang down from the dining-room to say that Sister Adams was up there and creating for Nurse Parry. It was a freezing night; the fire was out, and there was a chill in the ward that seemed to have reached the core of my being. I sat at the desk, with my back resolutely turned on the bed that had three screens round it and tried to concentrate on the paper. I would have welcomed even Mrs Dummett's cough, to break the stillness of the ward. The silence was full of little half-heard sounds – creaks and rustlings and the breath of a sigh that might be only in one's head. In my imagination, I could hear the pad of feet on the floor behind me. Look round, I kept telling myself. You'll feel much better when you know it's only your imagination. You won't hear it any more. But I didn't dare look round in case I should discover that it was not imagination.

It was not imagination. I could hear it quite plainly now – the pad, pad of bare feet approaching me – I could feel it in my spine, paralysing me in my chair. Slowly, slowly, I turned my head, with my eyes following last, and then, in a moment, I had leaped to my feet with a smothered yell and my hand to my mouth, petrified by the white figure that was feeling its way up the ward from bed to bed.

Serenely unconscious that she had nearly killed me of fright, Mrs Montgomery proceeded on her way. 'Just going to the toilet, Nurse,' she whispered, as she passed the chair into which I had sunk with a cold sweat breaking out and my heart hammering. After that, I sat facing the screens until Chris came back.

When you have laid out a dead person at night, especially a casualty, you know that nothing that anybody could ever ask you to do would be impossible.

I felt shaky long after Harper had taken the girl away, and Chris and I were having cigarettes by the sterilizers, when I heard the faint creak and swish of the swing doors that led into the ward.

'Christ,' said Chris, 'who's that?' She stubbed out her cigarette and looked into the ward. 'The Terror that Walks by Night,' she said, and went out to meet her. I could see that Sister Adams was annoyed about something. She stood holding her torch like a weapon while she talked, and Chris seemed to be arguing with her. At length, she raised her voice and I heard her say : 'See that it's done at once, Nurse,' before she turned abruptly and went out of the ward.

'I'm terribly sorry —' Chris hardly knew how to say it. 'I tried to make her let me go but she won't let me leave the ward.' It appeared that we had not done our job properly; Sister had been to look, and the bandages were coming through. I had got to go down to the Mortuary with wool and packing and put it right. 'I asked her to let you take another nurse with you,' said Chris, 'but she wouldn't. Here,' she said, grimly, handing me the great torch, 'she left you this for company.'

When I came back, I looked to see if my hair had gone white. I almost wished it had; it might have got Sister Adams into trouble.

I never went to the Fellowes's house again. The nearest I got to them was meeting the down-trodden relation in the town in a hopeless sort of hat, and she took me into Hooper's for a cup of coffee. She liked to talk; she didn't get much chance at 'Four Winds'; and over the second cup she became very confiding and told me that Mrs Fellowes had married beneath her. 'The family was very upset at the time. She could have married anyone, you know.'

'But he's very nice, I thought,' I said tentatively.

323

'Yes, but there's a common streak. Also —' She managed to convey that her coffee cup was a glass.

'Oh, no!' I said. 'Surely not. He doesn't drink more than lots of people. After all, everyone drinks more in wartime.'

'Oh, my dear,' she said earnestly, pushing her glasses back, 'you wouldn't say that if you'd seen what I've seen. It's the stuff of ruin, that's what it is. The stuff of ruin. Insidious, don't you see? My social work has brought me in touch with so much of that sort of thing. It's been the cause of more unhappiness —'

'Perhaps *you* could talk to him,' I suggested.

She shook her head and pushed her glasses back again. 'I did once. He was terribly rude. As good as told me I was living on their charity. After all, as I said to him, it isn't as if Catherine hadn't insisted that I go there at the beginning of the War. I believe she wanted me, don't you see, to stand by her.' She made the lifting motion with her coffee cup again. 'Of course, I needn't stay – I've got my own place – but Catherine insisted.'

So that was Mrs Fellowes's Wartime Social Work. That and having me to lunch.

I wasn't going to repeat that experience again, but towards the end of my Night Duty time, I found I could do with less and less sleep. I was so thoroughly tired – not just a tiredness that a good sleep can erase, but a deep-seated fatigue to which I had grown accustomed. I had forgotten what it was like to feel fresh, and even if I went to bed early these days, I could not sleep for long. Once, I went up to London for the day and came back just in time to change into my uniform. I knew it would be a busy night – it always was when I had had no sleep, therefore I was not surprised to see, as I turned the corner, the blaze of light on the ward which indicated that something was up. The day nurses were behind with their work, and Chris had arrived before they had settled the ward into darkness and gone wearily off duty.

They had had several operation cases in the late afternoon and evening, and the last one, an old lady of seventy, had come back from the Theatre only just alive. 'She won't last long,' said Sister, getting up again to feel her barely perceptible pulse. 'I've rung up her people, but I doubt whether they'll get here in time.' Automatically, she straightened the sheet over the dying woman and left us. There was nothing more she could do.

Sister Adams was off that night, and Sister Gilbert came tiptoeing up at ten o'clock with Mrs Colley's relations. The husband was a humble old man with faded blue eyes and the walk of a man who has spent his life with horses. His daughter was thin and tired-looking, her face blotched with crying, but she had put on her best coat and hat and was clutching an enormous battered handbag.

'I've brought Mum's bag along,' she whispered. 'She can't bear to be parted from it, but they took her off in such a hurry.' They stood by the bed and looked speechlessly at the old lady, her nose high and pinched in her waxy face, the collar of the white gown much too big for her.

Chris wanted to look at her dressing, and the husband and daughter went obediently to wait in Sister's sitting-room. The old man sat forward in his chair, his elbows on his knees, turning his cap round and round in his hands, and the daughter sat politely, with her hands in her lap as if she were making a call.

Chris had her hand on Mrs Colley's wrist, frowning.

'Not long,' she said. 'Christ, I hate to stand by and let someone just slip off like this. Here – stay with her a minute. That Appendix'll be out of bed if I don't give her her morphia.'

The green-shaded light over the bed fell on the old woman's face. You could trace the outline of every bone in her skull and her nose was typically sharp and prominent, as if the face had fallen away from it. Her skin was cold and faintly damp, and her pulse no more than a tremor and then not even that. I listened for her breathing and called Chris over. 'She's dead.'

'I wouldn't swear to it,' she said, and stood pensively tapping her foot. 'Look, get the hypo. syringe and the coramine. It couldn't hurt to give her a shot.'

'I suppose I'd better call her people in,' she said despondently, when she had given the injection. 'Oh, damn, here's

Chubby. What the hell does he want?' Chubby was Mr Soames, the little new House Surgeon, just out of the egg, with fluffy hair that never would lie down on his round head. He was on for all surgical cases to-night, and was just going round to see if it was all right for him to go to bed. As we watched Mrs Colley, one of her eyelids fluttered and for a moment her breathing was audible.

'My God,' said Chris suddenly, 'I wonder —' She clutched hold of Chubby's arm. 'Listen,' she whispered urgently, 'couldn't we give her an intravenous? Couldn't we try it? Sister said it wasn't any use, but I don't know – *Please*, Mr Soames, do let's try. It seems awful just not to do anything when she's still alive.'

Chubby ran his fingers through his hair. 'I don't know,' he said, hesitatingly, 'it's not much good —' Chris's eyes were sparking at him, her face alive with urgency. 'All right,' he said and laughed nervously, 'I'll have a shot if you like.'

'I'll go and lay up the trolley,' she gabbled. 'Don't go away – I'll have it ready by the time you've scrubbed up. You put the electric heat cradle over her,' she told me, 'and tell her people they can't come in for a sec.'

'Is she —?' asked the daughter, getting up as I went into the sitting-room. 'We're going to try something,' I said. 'It might not be any good, but —' The old man was watching me like a trusting dog.

I wanted to stay and watch Chubby cut down into Mrs Colley's vein, where the saline was going to run in through the needle, but half the ward chose to be awake and kept me running about for the next half-hour. Mrs Davenport fussed and fretted and had me yanking her leg up and down five or six times. 'What's all that light at the top of the ward for?' she grumbled. 'A person can't sleep with all this running about.'

'We're trying to save someone's life,' I snapped.

'Poor soul,' she said. 'But me leg isn't right yet, Nurse, I don't know how it is —' I said something quite rude to her, I can't remember what, but it shocked her into silence, although she kept up a rhythmic, insistent moaning for as long as she could keep herself awake.

I went to hold Mrs Colley's arm for Chris, while she bandaged it to the splint to keep it still. Mr Soames was regulating the drip of the saline, his face flushed with excitement, for it was the first intravenous he had done since he had been here. Sister Gilbert came along to see why we had not rung her yet to say that Mrs Colley had died.

'I'll do the round while I'm here,' she said. 'All right, don't bother to come with me, Nurse,' and she tiptoed off down the ward alone.

When she came back, she found the three of us wild with excitement. Mrs Colley's skin was still cold, but it was no longer clammy. You could hear her breathing now; you could distinctly feel her pulse.

'Of course, it might be only a momentary rally,' Sister said doubtfully, but she obviously didn't think that.

'Keep her warm,' said Chubby, putting on his white coat, his chick's hair on end. 'I'll come back when I've finished my round. Let me know at once if anything happens, and for God's sake keep that drip running.'

'Tidy her up,' said Sister, 'and let her people come in.' While I was rearranging the sheets to hide a little blood that Chubby had spilt in his haste, I kept touching Mrs Colley, to feel her skin gradually losing its marble chill. Suddenly she opened her eyes and looked at me accusingly. 'Me arm,' she whispered, 'what you done to me arm?'

'Now you've got to keep that arm still, d'you hear? Don't you dare move it.' She raised a grizzled eyebrow at me.

'Hoity-toity,' she said faintly.

The husband and daughter came in, breathless with hope, glancing uneasily at the bandaged arm rigidly outflung and the gibbet-like saline apparatus. 'She may not know you,' whispered Chris, and Mrs Colley unhooded one eye. 'Think I don't know Dad?' she mumbled. ''Ere, where's me 'and-bag?'

'Here you are, Mum.' Her daughter laid it on the bed under her groping hand. 'Ah, that's more like it,' she said, and drifted off into her Limbo again. They sat by the bed for a while, and presently they went into the sitting-room and had some tea. They wouldn't go home. Mrs Colley's pulse continued to be satisfactory.

Soon after Chubby had gone to bed, the saline tube blocked. We took the whole apparatus to pieces to try and eliminate the air bubble, but still we could see in the glass connection that it wasn't dripping through. We conjured with it for hours, trying different connections and new bottles.

Chris left me fiddling with it while she went to do a Mastoid dressing. When Sister came down, Mrs Colley's colour was worse and her pulse weaker. 'Try rebandaging the arm,' she said. 'There may be too much pressure.' She spoke calmly, but I could see that she was as worried as we were. She gave Mrs Colley some more coramine, and then the telephone summoned her to another ward. I piled on more blankets, refilled the hot bottles, and tried the old lady with some oxygen.

The arm was exposed now, with the needle tied into the vein, but still the saline was not running. 'I believe we'll have to get Chubby out of bed to cut down again,' said Chris, and swore under her breath as she fiddled with the tube. I became aware that Mrs Davenport had been calling monotonously for some time and went to shut her up. When I got back, Chris was not swearing under her breath but humming triumphantly.

'Don't move, don't breathe,' she said. 'I don't know what I did, but I've done it.' One of us stayed with Mrs Colley all the time, watching her like a hawk, checking her pulse, keeping her arm still and regulating the oxygen. Presently, she was well enough to take half a feeding cup of tea and even to grumble that it was not sweet enough.

She got very naughty. That was the joy of it. As her strength returned, she began to throw her weight about, and we could not let her people sit with her because she became too lively if she thought she had an audience.

'What you done to me arm?' she kept demanding. 'Practising on me, that's all you girls are doing – practising nursing, and I won't have it.'

'You keep that arm still,' said Chris.

'Don't you order me about, Miss,' said the old lady. 'I'm very poorly. I'll have another cup of tea, that's what I'll have, and if I wants to move me arm, I'll move it, see?' Her voice rose to a squeak.

'Look here, granny,' said Chris. 'We saved your life. Now shut up.'

'Oh, don't be mean to her,' I said. 'I feel as if she were my child.'

'So do I. I feel marvellous about the old bird, don't you? We saved her life.'

'Chubby didn't do anything, of course.'

'Oh, well, he helped, I suppose,' she conceded grudgingly, 'but I feel as if I'd done it all myself, don't you.'

I couldn't describe my feelings. I was *exaltée* with achievement; I was on top of the world. We were hours behind with our routine ward work, and we scrambled to get it done before, all too soon, it was time to wake the patients and get on with the morning's work. Granny Colley was sleeping. Every time I hurried past and looked at her, my heart glowed. When I looked into the sitting-room, the husband and daughter were sleeping too, she bolt upright and he with his head on the table.

'I been praying for the repose of that poor soul,' said Mrs Davenport unctuously, as I took her washing bowl. 'Save your prayers for yourself,' I said. 'She's alive.'

'Well, I never! And all that noise too. "She's gone," I said to myself, when I saw the lights on and all the to-do. "She's gone, poor soul," I said. I don't think I feel strong enough to wash myself this morning, Nurse. I know you're busy, but I don't feel able for it. I didn't sleep, you see.'

When I was bringing in the breakfasts, Chris called to me from the cupboard where she was measuring medicines: 'D'you realize we haven't had a thing to eat all night?' Nor we had. There hadn't been time to be hungry.

'Tell you what we'll do,' she said, coming up and putting in the milk for me while I poured out the tea, 'instead of going to the dining-room when we go off, we'll go to Jock's Box and have the most enormous plate of sausages and chips ever seen.' My heart swelled to receive the idea. It seemed

329

the best I had ever heard and it kept me going through the
work that was still before us. If either of us wilted over the
bedmaking, or dropped into that half-tempo from which it
is so difficult to shake yourself when you're really tired, the
other had only to murmur : 'Jock's Box.'

Mrs Colley's husband and daughter had some breakfast
and then they came in to see her. 'It's like a miracle,' the
daughter kept saying, but they both had a bewildered air.
They had steeled themselves to meet tragedy and now they
had got to get used to this new idea. We put screens round
Mrs Colley's bed, because the Day Nurses were starting the
work of the ward. When Sister came on, with every hair in
place, she sought me out where I was doing a bit of rinsing
in the sluice.

'Nurse,' she said, 'why haven't you put Mrs Colley's mattress and pillows outside the ward to be fumigated?'

'Because she's still using them,' I said, pushing up some
hair with the back of a wet hand. It was one of the proudest
moments of my life.


There was no air at all in Jock's Box; only the smell of
food. Chris and I slumped down at a little table and gazed
dreamily around. We didn't mind waiting; it merely gave us
longer to savour the anticipation. In one corner, two bus
drivers and a Clippie were having tea and bread-and-butter.
The girl had a lot of greasy little curls anchored with hairpins. She was evidently one of the jolly ones, and she had to
keep sprightly all the time, laughing a lot, with a great display of teeth. There were two soldiers at another table. They
sucked their teeth automatically at us and then realized that
we were too tired even to be annoyed by it.

And then, here was Jock himself, in a filthy apron and
badly in need of a shave, coming out of the kitchen with a
tray that could only be for us. You could see the smoke curling out of the coffee cups. I had been looking forward to
this for hours. The aesthetic quality alone of those bursting
sausages, those golden chips, the baked beans sweltering in
their tomato sauce – it seemed almost desecration to attack

them. Or was it because one was going to eat them that they seemed so beautiful?

I paused, half-way through, to get my second wind.

'You know,' I said, for the hundredth time, 'she was dead. I'm sure she was dead, just before you gave her the coramine. We dragged her back.'

'M-m,' said Chris with her mouth full, and then, a little later : 'Often I wonder why anyone is a Nurse – all the sordid part, and the drudgery, and the impossible women, and all that. Then something like this last night happens, and you see exactly why. Let's have some more coffee, shall we?'

## Chapter Seven

SOON after the Mrs Colley episode, when she was definitely round the corner and getting perter every day, Chris and I got into a spot of trouble. I am not quite clear to this day what it was all about, but it culminated in each of us visiting Sarah P. Churchman at ten o'clock to receive the information that we should never make a nurse, Nurse.

One of the charges was that we had had orgies with the Housemen – but orgies! This figment of Sweet Fanny Adams's brain was possibly woven round the time when she found Mr Briant asleep on the couch in front of the fire, and three empty beer bottles among the Cascara, Acriflavine and Soda Bic. in the dispensary basket.

I also gathered that the authorities resented the fact that Chris and I got on well together and hailed the faintest sound of laughter as a sign that we were not working properly. It was the old story, of course; Nurse Dickens had no idea of hospital etiquette, Nurse Dickens was too familiar with the Seniors, Nurse Dickens was too opinionated. Nurse D.'s name, in short, was Mud.

I was genuinely taken aback. I was longing to stand up for myself, but I thought innocence would be safer.

'I'm sorry, Ma'am,' I said, trying to look wide-eyed. 'I'd no idea I'd done anything wrong, but if I have, I'm awfully sorry.'

331

'You don't look sorry, Nurse,' said Matron, turning her thick lenses on me. 'Is that the face you make when you're sorry?' I unwidened my eyes and tried another expression. 'I really am sorry,' I repeated. 'I'll try to do better.' I saw no other way out except this rather nauseating abjection, for I was afraid of the desiccated female Fakir behind the desk. Life had whittled off her all the human qualities and left a rigorous kernel of asceticism, which offered no contact or understanding.

'I am very disappointed in you, Nurse,' she said, surveying me.

'I'm sure we weren't quite so bad as you seem to have heard, Ma'am,' I ventured. 'And we did work hard, honestly.'

'But that's what you're here for,' she said dryly, and then I had to swallow some personal remarks, before she dismissed me with : 'Youd better go and clean your shoes now, hadn't you?'

That night, after a breakfast of jam on something that was either toast or very stale bread, Sister Adams announced with glee and an eye fixed on me to see how I would take it, that I was to go to Secker Ward. This was a small, auxiliary Men's Ward, where there was nothing much to do, and I found the inaction much more trying than the busy nights I had been used to on Jane English. My Senior was an unpleasant girl with grand ideas about herself and an undisguised scorn for anyone whom she did not consider to be on her level. I suppose that was why I was sent there, because, from the point of view of work, it was a rest-cure. I got through a lot of reading and felt always thick-headed and often bored. I heard Fanny Adams telling Nurse Varney on my first night that I was to be kept in my place, and she obeyed implicitly. That sort of thing was right up her street.

Whatever I was doing, she would come along and tell me, always in front of the patients, that I was doing it wrong, and soon I got to the stage of being uncertain of elementary things that once I had practically been able to do in my sleep. She always ordered me to do a thing just before I was going to do it of my own accord, and anything I had to do for her, from making tea to clearing up her dressing trolley, she took entirely for granted.

She spoke in a studied, high-flown voice and spent a lot of time with her cap off in front of the bathroom mirror, arranging her hair. She was trying to better herself, and sat at the desk during the long empty hours, surrounded by textbooks on grammar and elementary French. This would have been admirable, I suppose, if one had not gathered that she was activated less by a pure thirst for knowledge than by the desire to set herself on a higher plane than her fellows. Of course, I was not allowed to sit at the desk with her, but had to perch on a shelf in the linen cupboard, screwing up my eyes to read in the bad light. She would invariably find me a job just before my mealtime, so that by the time I got to the dining-room, the food was cold and the tea stewed and as likely as not, Fanny Adams waiting to condemn me for being late. When Varney came back from her meals, she always went straight to the bathroom and cleaned her teeth with her special hygienic toothbrush and the mouthwash that was kept for the Gastrics.

The men usually slept like hogs all night, and I regretted the days when there had always been someone awake and only too ready for a chat. I came to welcome the hour that I had once cursed, the hour that every sleeper-out knows, when just before the dawn, every living creature stirs in its sleep or wakes for a moment, as if Nature wanted to assure herself that everything is still alive.

On my last night, Varney unbent slightly and told me about her travels on the Continent, where she had visited several cathedrals, the Louvre and the battlefields of Flanders, which she described as grievous devastation and a standing reproach to those warmongers who might have done better this time had they seen what she had seen.

When we were consuming oxtail and haricot beans at nine o'clock that morning, Sister Adams rapped on the table with a spoon and told me that I was to get up at five o'clock and go on day duty on the Private wards. Everyone looked at me pityingly and assured me that I should be no more than a glorified house-parlourmaid, but I was not ill pleased.

'Going on the Privates', as it was called, had the charm of novelty, and, I thought, the possibilities of amusement.

I had not reckoned with the bells. They rang all day long, as provoking as mosquitoes, and each time, you had to trek to the bottom of the long passage to see what number was waggling on the indicator. If you forgot to reset the indicator, you found that next time a bell rang, there were several numbers showing, and you had to burst in and out of half the rooms on the corridor before you found the right one. In any case, you always waited for a moment, in the hope that someone else might answer it first, but as I was the most junior nurse I usually waited in vain.

I got to know the people who rang for the sake of ringing, and if I was busy, would merely reset the indicator with an oath and let them ring again. One might answer the bell six times to pick up wool, tell them the time, or assure them that yes, Sister would come and talk to them as soon as she had a moment, and the seventh time, when one decided to let them stew in their own juice for a while, they would be dying or have fallen out of bed. One morning, when I had answered No. 3's bell eight times in an hour, I let her number waggle itself nearly off the hook while I finished making a blancmange. When I did answer it, banging in at the door with an intimidating expression, I found Mr Harvey Watkins with his thumb on the bell and his blood pressure mounting. I had to pretend that the indicator was broken and that I had been panting up and down the corridor to see who was ringing.

There were twelve private patients. I often think that, except for the privacy, they would have done better to have saved their money and gone into the General Wards. The wedge of Red that nine months of hospital had inserted into my social outlook, made me resent them slightly, but I could appreciate that since they were paying it was a little hard that there were not enough nurses to give them their money's worth of attention. The majority put up with this, but a few did not, and compared the hospital unfavourably with Nursing Homes of their acquaintance, forgetting that the fees at the Queen Adelaide were only half as much. They were paying, that was the point that stuck in their heads, and a phrase that often sprang, unvoiced, to my lips, was 'This ain't the ruddy Ritz.'

As is often the case, unfortunately, the objectionable people got more attention than the pleasant, unassuming ones. Sister Graham, who was a nervous woman with a mania for lists, used to pin up in her sitting-room little bits of paper with the likes and dislikes of the more difficult patients. She lived in constant terror of a complaint to Matron and would fuss up and down the corridor like a demented hen in her anxiety that all should go well. She was terrified of the doctors and, I sometimes thought, of the nurses too. She was universally considered to be 'daft as a brush'. It is almost impossible for a Sister to hit the nail of popularity. If she is too strict and stand-offish, she is hated, and if she is too familiar she is despised. God forbid, I used to think, that I should ever be in their position, but when I got to the exams, I ceased to worry, for I saw that there was no likelihood of it.

All the Private rooms were occupied when I first started to work there and after a few muddled days of taking in the wrong trays and giving Mr Faversham's peaches to Mrs Yule, I gradually got them straight.

No. 1 was Mr Levine, a cheery little American Jew, who was retarding his convalescence by refusing to be parted from his business. His secretary used to come every day with dispatch cases full of papers and, even when she had gone, he would have his typewriter on his bed table and rattle away until the patient opposite complained.

No. 2 was a lustrous girl who managed to make even an appendicectomy seem glamorous. She always had a few strident friends sitting about on the bed, who stared inquisitively at the nurse, as if they wondered how anyone *could*. The same patient who complained about No. 1's typewriter constantly complained about No. 2's wireless. I liked Bibi Preston. She was amusing, in a slow drawl, and was always pressing impulsively on one anything from a pot plant to a lipstick. Because we were not allowed to wear make-up in uniform, I think she thought that I always looked like that, which depressed her. I didn't argue the point, because she might have stopped giving me creams and powder in the hope that I might do something about myself.

No. 3 was a mad old woman with a broken arm, who was always ringing her bell and then not having the faintest idea what she had rung for. Sometimes she could not find the bell and would thump on the wall with an ebony walking-stick which hung over the top of her bed and from which she refused to be parted. She had several relations in varying degrees of lunacy, and a friend who came every day and said : 'Here I am again, Nurse, you see, turned up like a bad penny.'

In No. 4 lived Mr Walter Faversham, who was not aware that he had passed his prime. He thought that all the nurses were mad for him and used to call us Little Girl and Sweetheart and pat the bed invitingly. He saw himself as no end of a roué and would regale me with stories of naughtinesses while I did his room in the morning. Whenever I had been to London for my day off, he would say, 'Bet you had a hell of a party,' and enquire if I had been to the good old Kit-Cat and other places long since defunct. He was married, to what he spoke of as 'the Encumbrance'. They had probably been Bright Young Things together in 1920, and he had never really grown out of it, although his body had let him down by bringing him into hospital with acute gout.

Next to him, in No. 5, was a Miss Pennefeather, a colourless and humble woman, who wished to give no trouble, and would lie and freeze to death sooner than ring for someone to shut the window, not realizing that she would be far more trouble if she caught pneumonia.

Across the corridor, No. 6 held Mrs Yule, a fat, contented woman who had borne an operation with fortitude and now spent her time writing letters to her various children and children-in-law in all parts of the globe.

Her husband was an elderly Home Guard and used to come and see her in his uniform before he went on duty, which caused Sister to call him Major Yule and ask him if he knew her brother, who was also in the Army.

No. 7 was the door that every nurse went through at every

possible opportunity. I never had to answer this bell, because someone always beat me to it. Lieutenant Oliver Carew lived inside, minus a cartilage in one knee, and with dark hair and a boy's brown face on the pillow that set the heart beneath the apron bib thumping. He was naturally polite, incapable of bad temper and altogether so like something out of 'Tell England' that nurses with boy friends began to look at them critically and those without to set their hair more carefully at night. He was also very free with his cigarettes. What more could any girl want?

Nos. 8 and 9 housed two children who had struck up a friendship without ever having seen each other by tapping on the dividing wall. The boy was angelic, but the girl spoilt and captious. Her throat only hurt her when her mother was there, and with a little encouragement she would cry abandonedly until she went over the top. Then the mother would go tapping about in very high heels, indignant there was not a doctor immediately on hand to attend to darling Dilys. Mr Garthwaite, the ear, nose and throat specialist, called her 'The Sickener' and used to hide from her so that poor Sister Graham would be at her wits' end to know which of them to appease.

In No. 10, the Headmistress of the Girls' School that was evacuated to Redwood Court, lay majestically nursing kidney trouble, and in No. 11 was an old man, who would not be there much longer, which would be a merciful release, said his family, who were getting bored with trekking out from London to see him.

No. 12 was the plague spot, the conservatory of too-exotic scents in which Lady Mundsley sheltered from the fresh air and shattering afflictions of the outside world. This was the woman whom Sister Oates had so prized. She had her own private nurse; we were not meet to handle that precious bundle of neurasthenia, and when one did have occasion to go into No. 12, she would shudder under the bedclothes and say faintly, 'Such a *noise*!' Her nurse was the sort of woman who would undress under a dressing gown even when alone, and made more commotion over her one patient than we did with our eleven. She was always in the way: in doorways, or wedged into the linen cupboard, or walking slowly down the middle of the corridor with a tray when you wanted to pass in a hurry. She used to commandeer the best crockery and medicine glasses and the only eyebath that didn't dribble. She was always cooking up refined little messes in the kitchen when one wanted to get at the stove, and if she used the last of the Liquid Paraffin, she would not dream of mentioning it until after the Dispensary was closed. Her interests centred round No. 12 and she expected ours to as well.

'May patient had a better night,' she would say, as if confiding thrilling news, or 'May patient quite fancied that junket I made her. She's going to have a little nap now, so perhaps you could see that there is *ab*solute quiet on the corridor.'

One day, when she had provoked me to more rudeness than usual, I thought I had better try and atone by a little polite conversation, so while I was getting the tea trays ready, I asked her where she had done her training.

'What do you want to know that for, pray?' she asked, measuring out Rennet to the fraction of a minim. 'Quite the Miss Nosey Parker, aren't we?'

My good intentions vanished. 'If you think I care two straws —' I began and was fortunately interrupted by the entrance of Nurse Horrocks. I went on cutting bread savagely and the Private Nurse stirred milk with pursed lips.

'My,' said Horrocks, sniffing, 'I smell an atmosphere. Is someone having a row? Don't let me miss anything.' She was endlessly tall and as bony as a horse on its way to the knackers, and she had a cheerful gregarious spirit that entered whole-heartedly into anyone's affairs. If you had a bit of gossip or scandal to impart, you were always sure of an audience from Horrocks. She fed on that sort of thing, and when there was none about would concoct some intrigue from the tiniest nucleus, to keep herself going. Let anyone mention in her hearing that they felt sick, and it would be all over the hospital that they were 'preggers', and once when she thought she detected a white ring on the holiday sunburn of the third finger of Nurse Ketch's left hand, Horrocks had her secretly married to a bigamist with a wife in a lunatic asylum.

The other nurses on the Private wards were the know-all Nurse Jones, a sanctimonious girl called Farren, whom the men on Herbert Waterlow had christened 'The Disciple', a sexy piece called Delphine Lorrimer, who used the bathroom window nearly every night, and Summers, who had one eye larger than the other and legs like quart beer bottles, but was a born nurse. She was a genius with ill people – knew how to make them comfortable and sensed what they did or did not want without having to ask. Her patience and her temper were unshakable and she did not mind how late she stayed on at night. She never seemed to have any friends, and went to bed directly after supper and spent her off time during the day mending stockings or writing up her lecture notes. She told me once that if she had the choice, she would sooner work all week than have a day off. She didn't really mind that she could never go home because the fare was expensive. Her life began and ended on the ward.

When she was speaking to me I used to wonder sometimes whether I were going deaf or whether it was her adenoids. She had a curious habit, too, of leaving out all her articles : 'I'm going down to linen cupboard to get pillowcase for new patient.' 'Has Sister checked laundry?' She talked about her night duty as 'When I was on nights.' She had worked on 'Children's, on Men's, on Women's, on Eyes.' Now she was 'On Privates, on days.'

People who told me I should be a house-parlourmaid 'on Privates' had overestimated. I was Dogsbody. There was not nearly so much genuine nursing to be done as on a General Ward and what there was never came my way, as Junior. I used to spend my day cleaning rooms, doing f.owers, carrying trays, looking up addresses in the telephone book, making hot milk drinks for the weakly, tidying the kitchen and washing up when the maid had her Bolshie days – and, of course, the bells. The Bells! The Bells! I got to feel like Irving.

Even when I was off duty, my errands were not done. There were stamps to buy for Mrs Yule, comic papers for the little boy, elusive American magazines for Mr Levine, beer for Lieutenant Carew and cigarettes for the would-be roué – 'and ten for yourself Dickie darling.'

Sister Graham had a periodical game called 'Going through the store cupboard', which I had to play with her. Somebody had once told her that she should be more methodical and this, like the lists, was one of her attempts, but it never really got her anywhere.

On other wards, it was as much as one's life was worth not to put things back in the right place, but here, everyone followed their natural instincts, and replaced things at random or not at all.

'Oh, dear,' Sister would sigh, as I opened the store cupboard doors on the chaos inside, 'all our good work last week seems to have been undone. These nurses simply make a pigsty of the place. It seems some people are naturally slovenly, doesn't it, Nurse?' Often, in an attempt to be chummy with her gels, she violated the unwritten law that a Sister never criticized one nurse to another, especially if she were not prepared also to make that criticism direct. It wasn't done to answer such remarks, so one had to pretend not to hear, even when she repeated it, a little wistfully.

She had the inevitable pad of paper and pencil in her hand and while I went through the tins, she would list them and make strange signs which meant replenishment or discontinuance, or queries, which meant that she would put off her decision until next time. There were several unnecessary tins that I had been replacing, week after week, because she could not bear to throw anything away. 'You never know, it might come in sometime,' was one of her favourite remarks.

There were tins of congealing patent food, old lumps of salt, faddish preparations that had been ordered once for a special patient and never been used, a lump of diabetic chocolate. I would solemnly open the tins, she would peer inside, we would both have a sniff at it, and I would make a movement towards the pig-pail, but she stayed me with: 'No, put it back, Nurse. It might come in.'

Then we would inspect the sugar, the oatmeal, the beef extract, the Bengers, which were littered about, some with their lids off, some retrieved from various places – underneath the dresser, on top of the plate rack, anywhere but on that portion of the shelf marked by Sister Graham with its name on a piece of sticking plaster. She could never understand why the rusk tin was always empty, even when we had no gastric patients, or why the jam and the lemonade and the sponge fingers and anything else that was nice to eat was always used up so quickly. Or perhaps she did know but didn't want to be thought suspicious.

Sometimes, after we had straightened the cupboard, we would attack the larder, where any amount of little leftovers stood about on plates until a nurse felt hungry or they went bad.

'Shall I throw away this potato, Sister?' I would ask, producing a hardened lump.

'Oh *no*, Nurse,' she would say in her Lord Woolton voice. 'You could make it into bubble-and-squeak with those greens left over from lunch and it would be a little extra for the patients' suppers.' I don't know when she thought I would have either the time or the inclination to do this, but I would probably be saved answering by one of the bells, which had been calling me away repeatedly ever since we started.

When I got back from having held little Dilys's head while she tried hard to make herself sick, Sister would be toying with the various jugs which were always standing about with the dregs of some beverage in them.

'I can't make out whether this is Bovril or coffee, Nurse.'

'Perhaps it's cocoa. Mr Faversham sometimes has some in the middle of the morning.'

'Does he?' And while I went to No. 2 to hand Bibi Preston 'that box of powder off the dressing table and my nail things, and while you're here, could you be an absolute angel and get me out a clean nightie; this one looks like the wrath of God and I've got someone rather special coming to see me,' Sister would go into her room and add: 'Cocoa in mid-morning' to the other fancies on No. 4's list.

Poor Mr Faversham. He tried so hard and got so little encouragement from the nurses, except from Delphine, who responded automatically to any male, gouty or otherwise.

One of his openings was to start an abstract discussion of the eternal theme and then work it round to personalities. We would be having quite an interesting conversation about repressions until he began to suggest that that was what I suffered from, and he was always starting on the effect of nursing on a woman's outlook, so that he could lead up to his favourite aphorism : 'You're a woman and I'm a man. You can't get away from that.'

'You know,' he said one morning, watching me idly while I fiddled around with a duster among the novels and magazines, slabs of chocolate, cigarettes and expensive fruit with which he sought to cheer his confinement, 'You know, my wife and I don't really get on together.'

'Oh, not that *again*,' I said wearily, polishing up his tooth glass. 'Say something a bit more original.' He never minded how rude you were. He liked it, in fact; it made him feel dangerous.

'So we made an arrangement,' he went on. 'She has her boy friends and I have my girl friends, and neither of us gets in the other's way.'

'Why not get divorced and have done with it?'

'Well, we've talked about it," he said, reaching over for a grape, 'but it wouldn't be fair on the kiddie. One has one's principles, such as they are.'

I strongly suspected that he and the Encumbrance had never actually been unfaithful to each other. People who talk such a lot about it seldom get farther than talking. He was probably a most domesticated nature and pushed the pram out on Sundays when he thought no one was looking. As if he guessed what I was thinking, he assumed his most wanton smile and said : 'I say, Dickie darling, are you going to be on duty this evening?'

'Yes,' I said coldly, 'probably in every room but this.'

'Oh, I didn't mean that,' he said, delighted that I should have thought that he did. 'No, that'll have to be another time. I wondered if you'd do a chap a good turn to-night.'

'Depends. Sit forward and let me do your pillows. Not that I care if you're comfortable or not, but it looks better when Matron comes round.' He loved to be talked to like this.

'I say, you are a vixen, aren't you?' he laughed, giving my arm an absent-minded caress. 'Perhaps you'll be jealous of what I'm going to ask you. I know women.'

'Get on with it,' I said. 'I've got three more rooms to do before I bring your breakfast.'

'Well, the fact is, there's a very lovely little lady coming to see me to-night. Wait till you see her, Dickie, she's —' He kissed his fingers to the air and rolled up his eyes.

'Why should I care?' I said, thumping a pillow.

'I want you to make sure that nobody comes in here. I've asked Sister if the Lovely can have a spot of supper in here, and she was dubious at first but succumbed to my charm. So if you'll be the darling that you are and see that the *tête-à-tête* is not interrupted – *voila, parfait*!' He had been several times to Monte. He spoke the lingo.

'I'll do my best,' I said, 'but mind your gout.' I was awfully pleased; I thought it was so nice for him. I did not for a moment see how I could prevent anyone going into No. 4 if they wanted to, but I didn't think it would matter if they did. Every time I went into Mr Faversham's room during the day, he made some conspiratorial remark or smacked his lips or otherwise indicated his anticipation of a delicious evening. I felt quite like a procuress.

I had told the other nurses about it. He had told me not to tell them, hoping that I would, to enhance his reputation, and we were looking forward to a good listen outside the door.

As seven o'clock approached, he had me into his room again and again, to rearrange the flowers, or push the arm-chair nearer the bed, or shade the light more enticingly. I opened a bottle of sherry for him, and had some myself out of his tooth glass. He had on his best green silk pyjamas with the frogging, and had shaved after tea. It was bad luck that his gout was especially painful that evening. When I told him he was crazy to drink sherry in defiance of orders, he said : 'My body's got to obey my desires; I've no use for it otherwise.'

It was too sad. It was too heart-breakingly sad. The Lovely arrived, and although she was no raving beauty, she was passable. I mean, she had the right number of legs and arms and you could tell which way she was going, but Mrs Faversham came with her. Not as a jealous wife determined to see what was going on – that would have been all right – but as a matter of course, because they were friends, because they were all friends, the three of them. The two women talked to each other most of the time, earnestly, about clothes.

When the suppers came down from the kitchen, I told Horrocks that the extra one was not needed after all, and she retired avidly with it into the pantry. Lady Mundsley's nurse came along in a frightful state of affront to know what had become of the yellow roses that the Honourable Mrs Fluke-Fulkers had sent that afternoon, and I told her I was arranging them and would bring them in later. I could not very well go and remove them from No. 4 just yet. It would be too poignant.

He carried it off the next day by saying : 'Devilish luck, wasn't it? The Encumbrance didn't play fair last night, but still, you can't blame a woman for being jealous, it's in the blood. We had to be careful, I can tell you. The old girl was watching us like a hawk.'

The girl friend did once come alone. Unfortunately, it was the day of Mr Faversham's first attempts at walking and she turned the corner into the passage just as he was rocking down it with two sticks and a space between his legs the size of the Marble Arch. Even he could not pretend that the situation had glamour.

Outside the hospital, Spring was waxing, as one realized with surprise whenever one went outside the gates. Changing seasons made no difference to the life within, except that one was either too hot or too cold and that there were fewer or more chest conditions. People wrote letters to the papers noting that not even Hitler could stop the daffodils from flowering, although it would have been far more noteworthy if he could.

As I walked down Redwood High Street, tenderly conscious of the pavement through my shoes, the blue sky and embryo clouds gave me a few pangs of pre-war nostalgia. Incredible to think that there had once been a time when one could go out of doors when one felt inclined, and stay out all day if the weather was like this. When the sun was shining, I always had a passing desire to throw up nursing and be a Land Girl and had to deliberately remind myself of pigswill and dirty chicken houses and sleeping in a loft with nine other girls in bottle green jumpers and shapeless breeches. On a day like this, one is always haunted by the thought that it might never happen again. Germans apart, something might go wrong with the Cosmos and there might never be any more Springs, never any more radiant Mays and basking Julys. One ought to grab at them now, in case.

That morning, while I was blanket-bathing that crashing bore, Miss Pennefeather, I had kept looking out of the window in an agony of frustration and Miss Pennefeather, sensing my restiveness, had said humbly : 'What a nuisance I must be to you, Nurse; so silly and helpless. You really shouldn't bother about me when you're busy.'

It had been one of those slack mornings, when you had time to keep looking at your watch, which you could not imagine ever showing two o'clock. Yet here it was half-past two, with the dragging morning obliterated, and I was out of my uniform and the sun was still shining. I was on my way to Redwood Court, on an errand for Miss Anstruther, the Headmistress of St Cecilia's School for Girls, late of Blackheath. One of the mistresses had brought some papers up to the Hospital for her approval and I was returning them with strict instructions to give them to nobody but the Assistant Head. I gathered that they were examination questions and it would be a major disaster if they should fall into the wrong hands and give someone the opportunity to cheat.

At the bottom of the High Street there were cross roads, with traffic lights and a policeman, who had once been a customer with us for hammer toes. To the left, the road led to the station and the factory estate, and to the right it wound its way back and up through the purlieus. I went straight ahead, on the road that quickly shed its houses and led to the country. Turning off through lodge gates on the right, I started off up the long drive which followed the ambling contours of the park, passing self-consciously a crocodile of schoolgirls in short green tunics and red blazers. Breasting a gentle slope, I saw the house below me, and in front of it, more green tunics were playing cricket on a shaved flat piece of the park, which had obviously been all too recently a hockey field.

The Rowan family, who had originally lived there, had left the place more than two centuries ago, and a succession of owners had added bizarre improvements until the place was a hotch-potch of architectural styles. The original Redwood Court, a smallish red brick house with irregular chimneys and casement windows sunk into thick walls, was practically eclipsed by the additions that had been stuck on to it. Shrouded in creeper, it huddled between the wing of a French château on one side and on the other a Victorian excrescence, hung with balconies and sunblinds and sprouting a domed conservatory of coloured glass. The front door was still in the old part, and I made for it, increasing my pace as a hard ball came hurtling in my direction accompanied by cries of 'Shot! Good Shot! Yes! No! And again! Can you? Oh, *fielded*, Mavis!' as a spidery girl hurled herself passionately on the ball just where the long grass would have stopped it anyway.

I wiped my shoes on an Italian wrought-iron scaper and rang the bell. 'To see Miss Saunders?' said the maid who was old and battered with years of service. 'Who shall I say?'

'It's from the hospital,' I said. 'Miss Anstruther sent me.'

The maid asked me to follow her, turning as we went to ask me how the Headmistress was. 'I hear she's very poorly. Miss Collis said you hardly know her.' This didn't quite fit in with the deep-voiced figure in No. 10, who radiated unconsumed energy, bullied the doctors about letting her up, ate heartily and made frequent trips to the X-Ray department in a wheel-chair, robed in a purple quilted dressing gown and overtaxing my strength. I always felt that she should be doing the pushing and I the riding.

I hastened to reassure the maid, but she didn't want to be reassured. 'They pull you down, see, kidneys do,' she said. 'Wicked things, kidneys. My sister had 'em for years, see, only they never suspected it till they cut her open after she died. She'd been a wicked colour all her life and always had trouble with her – *you* know. I always said it was kidneys. "You know what's the matter with you?" I used to say. "You got kidneys." But would she go to the doctor? And it was just the same with Miss Anstruther, see. "I don't like the look of her," I used to say. If I said it once, I said it a hundred times. And when they took her away, I said to myself: "I wonder when we shall see you back?" I said.'

'I believe she's coming out quite soon,' I said, walking gingerly on the mats that slid on the highly polished floor.

'She'll never be 'erself, though. Don't talk to me about kidneys. In here, dear.' She opened a door and showed me into what had probably been the room in which the master of the house escaped from his women. It was comfortable and shabby, with leather furniture, a lot of books, and pictures of horses with short tails ridden by men in billy-cock hats. The inside of the house through which we had made our way had been as inconsistent as the outside. The floor was all on different levels, and we had walked over red bricks, wide, uneven oak boards, modern parquet, and even a cold marble corridor, where sightless busts occupied niches in the walls, except where the drawing mistress had removed them for the studio. The miscellanea of education looked very out of place. Notice boards hung next to dark oil paintings of far-off Rowans, all with that long thin nose and little ferrets' eyes; a cardboard box on the refectory table in the old hall was marked 'PUT YOUR HISTORY ESSAYS HERE'. Red blazers and gas-masks lined the walls of a long empty room with beautiful chandeliers, and through an open door I had glimpsed a room with red wallpaper and a dark brown dado, from which all the desks and blackboards in the world could not obliterate the atmosphere of heavy Sunday luncheons.

I had not waited long in the study before the door was opened briskly by a leathery woman in a short tussore tunic, black tights and a snood. 'Good afternoon,' she said, flinging out a hand. 'You're from Queen Ad.'s, aren't you?'

'Yes,' I said. 'I wanted to see Miss Saunders.'

'That's me. Oh, ha-ha! Of course.' She glanced down at herself. 'You must excuse my rig. I've just been taking a Greek Dancing Class. This war, you know – the usual instructress doesn't come any more. Tell me, how's the Head? Do sit down.' She flung a string-coloured woolly over her bony shoulders, and I perched on the arm of a big leather chair.

'She's very satisfactory,' I said. 'She's coming out soon. She —'

'Grand, grand! Jolly good!' Miss Saunders strode up and down, rubbing her large dry hands. 'No one can afford to be ill nowadays, can they? I always say, if you can't fight for your country, you can jolly well keep fit. Who knows, Englishwomen may have to fight one day, side by side with the men. Look at the Spanish women!' She was obviously all set for the Invasion. 'I tell the girls: "You may feel pipped that you're too young to help the war effort, but there's no need to hinder it by getting flabby!"'

'*Mens sana in corpore —*'

'My hat, yes! That's the school motto. How extraordinary you should say that.' Not so extraordinary, considering I had seen it stencilled in red and green by the Art Class above the marble sepulchre that was the ballroom fire-place.

I held out Miss Anstruther's envelope and stood up. It was time for me to go if I was going to have tea at the 'Blue Lady' before I went back on duty. 'Miss Anstruther asked me to give you these papers.'

'Goodo. The Exam papers, I expect. They're frightfully important, you know. By the way, talking of exams, I've just thought of something. You're a nurse, aren't you?'

'Yes,' I said, though technically speaking I should not be for another two years, if then.

'I wonder if you'd be an absolute brick and have a look at one of our girls? She's come out in a beastly rash, and our Matron's away for the week-end. I say, is it awful cheek of me to ask? D'you mind?'

'Of course not.' I was quite ready to give an opinion, whether I knew anything about the subject or not, although I saw my prospects of tea receding. They always had lemon curd tarts at the 'Blue Lady' on Saturdays. Miss Saunders told me I was a sport, opened the door and collared a small girl who was scuttling by with a load of books. 'Don't run in the corridors, Doreen,' she said. 'Walk briskly. You'll get there just as fast and twice as quietly. Cut along now, and ask Beryl Otway to come here. She's in the Monitresses' Room at the end of Dorm. 3 passage. Don't go near her; just call outside the door.

'I've been keeping her isolated,' she explained to me, shutting the door. 'The child doesn't feel ill, but you never know with these skin things. I don't want the whole school coming out in spots.'

Beryl Otway took her time. Miss Saunders and I made desultory conversation, and I had abandoned all hope of lemon curd tarts by the time an irresolute knock sounded on the door.

'Come in, come in!' cried Miss Saunders. 'Gracious child, what a time you've been.'

'I was undressed, please, Miss Saunders,' mumbled Beryl, which explained her appearance. Her hair was scattered and her tunic bunched up under her girdle, showing green bloomers, a gap of skin and black stockings rolled above the knee. She blinked and peered, because she had forgotten to put on her spectacles. Above the crumpled collar of her blouse, a lumpy red rash crept up her neck and on to her cheeks, making her face puffy.

'Well, we won't say anything about untidiness now,' said Miss Saunders briskly, but with an underlying threat. 'Nurse here is going to have a look at your rash. I hope you haven't been scratching?'

'No, Miss Saunders. It does itch, though.'

'Calamine lotion,' I said knowledgeably.

'Yes, of course, I'll get some,' said Miss Saunders, hanging on my words. 'Let your tunic down, Beryl, and take off your

349

blouse so that Nurse can see.' She switched on the light and drew the curtains across the window, though there was nothing outside but a blank wall and a roof with pigeons on it. Beryl shuffled bashfully out of her clothes and revealed a narrow chest and back flaming with the rash. I had not the slightest idea what it might be, but as Miss Saunders expected me to be a trained nurse, I tried to behave like one. There was an awed silence while I took Beryl's pulse. 'I've taken her temp,' said the mistress. 'Nothing wrong there, and she feels all right, don't you, Beryl?'

Beryl mumbled, crossing her arms over her chest. 'Appetite?' I asked, and this gave me an idea. Perhaps it was food poisoning. I made her tell me everything she had eaten just before the rash appeared, and as it mostly seemed to be stews or shepherd's pies, there was no knowing what she might not have taken into her system.

'Nothing but wholesome stuff,' said Miss Saunders proudly. 'Unless the child's been eating too many sweets or chocolates.' Beryl was heard to mutter that she hadn't tasted chocolate for a year and only wished she could.

'Don't scowl,' said Miss Saunders, and turned to me. 'It can't be food poisoning,' she said triumphantly, 'because some of the others would have got it. They all eat the same.'

'Yes, of course, that's what I was thinking,' I said, glad that she had thought of it for me. I inspected the rash again from every angle, half-remembered words running through my head – Eczema, Erysipelas, Scabies, Urticuria – or was that something else? – Dhobie's Itch. Poor Dhobie, or was it better to be immortalized for your itch than not at all?

'Well?' Miss Saunders was tapping a bronze-slippered foot.

'It's hard to say,' I said, judiciously. 'It might be one of two things. I've seen them both often before, but never quite as virulent as this.' Beryl looked scared.

'The point is,' said Miss Saunders, 'is it catching?' As I didn't want to be responsible for the whole of St Cecilia's dying of the plague, I thought it would be safer to say 'Yes'.

Miss Saunders exchanged a look of horror with Beryl. 'Oh, but that's awful,' she said. 'The child's taking a scholarship exam the day after to-morrow. She simply must sit it. She's got a very good chance; she's been swotting like mad, haven't you, Beryl?' The girl nodded and blinked and looked as if she were going to cry. 'What do you think? Should we let her go to London? Even if we covered the rash up, it wouldn't be playing the game to let her go about spreading something.' Here was a dilemma for me. On my word, apparently, hung the fate of hundreds of unknown girls, and also the future career of Beryl Otway. Her whole life might be affected if she did not go to this college. On the other hand, the youth of England might be ravaged by Spotted Fever. I sent up a quick prayer to *Sister Fairchild*. If only I had her tucked under my arm!

Miss Saunders was watching me avidly, her eyes passionate under the snood that bound her dust-coloured fringe. I was just taking a deep breath, hoping that words would come of their own accord, when Beryl herself saved me.

'Perhaps I'd better see a doctor,' she suggested, hesitatingly. Of course! It had not occurred to me before. Miss Saunders's acceptance of me as the ultimate oracle had made me forget that I was not. I intimated that Beryl had taken the very words out of my mouth, and suggested that she should come back to the hospital with me and go to Out Patients, where we might just catch the Medical Clinic. This was frightfully sporting of me. Miss Saunders was thrilled to bits, and insisted that we should go back in a taxi at the School's expense. Beryl pulled up her clothes, and the pigeons were allowed to look in at her again. Then Miss Saunders rushed her off to put on her outdoor things, and appeared at the front door with her, muffled like a leper, as the same old Rolls that had first taken me to the Queen Adelaide tricked gently down the drive, past the cricket match that was now giving Three Cheers.

'Who won?' called Miss Saunders, making a trumpet of her hands. 'Tchk,' she said, as the reply came faintly back from the Games Mistress, 'The Fifth Form'll never win a match till they get a bit sharper in the field.' She packed Beryl and me into the car, commanded the driver to wait and bring the girl back, and watched us off, waving cheerily, with her skirt fluttering above her knobby knees.

351

Beryl was silent, gazing out of the window, and unresponsive to conversational openings. I hoped she would be more expansive with the examiners. I also hoped she wasn't infecting the beige whipcord of the Rolls.

As we passed the Town Hall, halfway up the hill, I saw to my horror that it was already twenty to five. I would never be changed and on duty by five. Sister was off, and I would have to explain it all to Nurse Farren, leaving out the part about being taken for a trained nurse, and she would be righteously understanding and probably moved by her conscience to report me.

'I say,' said Beryl suddenly, in a small voice, 'I think I ought to tell you something.'

'Go ahead,' I said abstractedly, my mind still occupied with the time.

'Well, I did eat some tinned lobster the day before yesterday.' It was difficult to see whether she were blushing or the rash was getting worse.

'You did? Why on earth didn't you say so before?'

'Well,' she looked at me pleadingly through her large tin spectacles, 'how could I, with Miss Saunders there?' I saw that. I couldn't have myself.

'You see,' Beryl went on earnestly. 'She might have given me a Report, and then our class couldn't have won the shield this term.'

'D'you think it was bad, the lobster?'

'It might have been. It tasted a bit funny.'

'Where did you get it? In the town?'

'Oh, no. We're not allowed to go to the shops. I found it in my locker. It had been there ages and I'd forgotten about it.'

'How long?'

'Oh —' Beryl squirmed. 'About two years.'

I was horrified. I told the driver to go even slower than he was going, so that we could have this out. 'I can't understand why you weren't sick,' I said.

'Well, I was,' she mumbled. 'Ever so. But nobody knew, 'cos I was in a room by myself. I did it out of the window. I say, you won't tell Miss Saunders, will you?'

'Of course not.'

'Cross your gizzard and hope to die?'

'If you like. Look, there's not much point you going to the hospital now I know what's wrong. They'll only tell you you've got smallpox and put you to bed and observe you.'

With an effort, I pushed back the unwilling glass panel between us and the driver, and told him to turn round and drive back to a chemist. I was going to be late anyway, so a little later wouldn't make much difference.

'I'll get you a Dose,' I told Beryl, 'and you'll have a ghastly time to-night and probably all day to-morrow, and serve you right, but you'll be able to take the exam.'

'What'll I tell Miss Saunders?'

'Tell her you saw the doctor and he said it was – let's see, something harmless – Nettlerash. That'll do. I expect it looks quite like what you've got.' To help the illusion, I also bought her some lotion which said : 'For heat rash, nettle-rash, stings, bites and all skin irritations', got the Rolls to drive me back to the top of the hill, and sent Beryl off, well primed with what the doctor had said to her, looking small and scared and holding her medicine as if it were a Time Bomb.

I was so late by now that there was no point in rushing my dressing and appearing on the ward with studs gaping, stockings wrinkled and cap awry. While I was doing my hair, it occurred to me that if Beryl had ptomaine poisoning and became sick unto death, the doctor would be blamed for not having spotted it, it would all come out that he had never seen her and I should probably be charged with taking his name in vain, if not with Manslaughter.

I concocted my excuse for Farren on the way up to the ward. The trouble that I expected for being late seemed negligible compared with what might be coming to me. I climbed the stairs at a comfortable pace and found, on arrival, that everyone was waiting for me to take a case to Theatre as there was no one else to go. The porter was there with his trolley, the Theatre telephone ringing every two minutes, the patient drugged – Private Patients were never taken conscious to the horrors of the Anaesthetic Room – and

Nurse Farren taking up an attitude that surely was not Loving her Neighbour as Herself.

When we got to the Theatre, the Surgeon was pacing with gloved hands clasped in front of him, all ready scrubbed up, and Theatre Sister's thick black eyebrows were beetling at me over her mask. The porter, who disliked all nurses on principle, was only too pleased to explain why we had kept them waiting, and as well as the floor being wiped with me on the spot, I was ordered to leave my card on Sarah P. next morning.

I lived in a state of great anxiety for the next few days. I was longing to ask Miss Anstruther whether she had heard anything about Beryl, but I thought that the less I said about it, the less was likely to come out. Even if everything was all right, I didn't want anyone to know that I had posed as an authority. However, the next time Miss Saunders came to visit her Headmistress, she romped out with the whole of her side of the story, praising me to the skies in her delight that Beryl had been able to take the exam, and had been understood to say that she had done all right, she supposed, which probably meant that she had sailed through the papers. The fact that she had continually to leave the room, under vigilance, in case she was making an excuse to crib, was attributed to the nervous strain of the occasion.

I had to go and have my hand wrung by Miss Saunders and be told how jolly I looked in my uniform and be thanked for my help by Miss Anstruther. She knew that the House Surgeon who took the Medical Clinic was the same one who attended on her, and, to my dismay, said that she would ask him about the cause of the rash next time he looked in. I hastily told her that Beryl had not been to his Clinic, as she had been lucky enough to catch one of the occasional visits of an outside skin specialist.

'It was so sensible of Nurse to consult another opinion,' said Miss Saunders, sitting bolt upright in the chair, with her thin legs planted well apart, showing beige Directoire knickers. 'So many trained nurses are so jolly conceited that they'll say anything rather than admit that they're not sure.'

Miss Anstruther agreed, but I could see she was laughing

at me. She knew perfectly well that I was nothing like a trained nurse, knew, in fact, exactly how unlike, for she had experienced my ineptitude in various ways. But she never let on. I blessed her for that, and hoped fervently that, for the honour of St Cecilia's alone, Beryl would get the Scholarship.

The old man in No. 11 died quietly and unobtrusively in his sleep one afternoon and Sister told me to ring up his people. I spoke to his daughter and she forgot about it being a merciful release and began to cry over the telephone because she had not been there when it happened. 'Shall I come up there?' she said. 'I could come straightaway.'

'If you wouldn't mind bringing a suitcase,' I said. 'His things. ...' I hated this part of hospital deaths; it always seemed so callous to ask grief-stricken people to attend to practicalities. Especially on the General wards, where a new patient was into the bed as soon as a clean mattress could be brought. You had to intrude on people's sorrow with a brown paper parcel of pathetic trifles and unforgivable inquiries about rings and false teeth. It was a necessary routine, but hatefully inhuman.

When Horrocks had finished with the old man, Sister sent me to tidy the room and make a list of his belongings. While I was in there, the daughter came in, her fur wet from the rain and her eyes leaping at once to the sheeted bed. She was a tall, immature woman of about thirty-five, with uncertain, clumsy movements. She was the sort of woman who tries quite hard with her appearance, but always just misses, because she can't bring herself to risk a new fashion until it's going out, and never manages to be dressed completely suitable for any occasion. She wore black now, with a hat whose inappropriateness was somehow pathetic.

I made a movement to go, but she said breathlessly : 'Don't go. I don't want to be alone.'

'Would you like to see your father?'

She laughed nervously. 'It sounds awfully silly, but – I'm a bit afraid. I've never seen anybody dead before.' I lifted the sheet from the old man's face, because I knew she would find her fear unjustified, as mine had been the first time.

'Oh,' she whispered, and came up to the bed. 'Why, how funny, he isn't there at all. It's his face, but it – it just isn't him.'

That's why one doesn't mind. When you read in books about dead people looking happy, or agonized, or male-volent, it isn't true at all. Their faces may be fixed in a cer-tain fashion, but they have no actual expression. Expression comes from within and what was within has gone, fled in-stantly on the moment of death. Nor do they look as if they might at any moment speak, any more than their garments might, or the house in which they had lived. I never can understand how anyone who has seen a person after death can make a fetish of their grave. Reverencing it as a memorial is one thing, clinging to it for what lies below is a sham. The person simply isn't there.

We were to have a patient transferred from Jane English Ward. She was a woman who had been in a motor accident and was brought into hospital unconscious. When she woke up and found herself surrounded by thirty other women, there was Hell to pay. She demanded to be put in a private room immediately and on being told that there were none vacant, clamoured to be removed to a Nursing Home. When she was told she could not be moved, as apart from other injuries she might have a fractured skull, she laid herself out to be impossible. The nurse who brought her down to us as soon as No. 11 was vacant, wiped imaginary sweat off her brow and made a long nose at the closed door behind which Mrs Gordelier was recovering from the ardours of the journey and considering the defects of her new abode.

Her bell rang, not once, but as if she were giving the Victory sign in Morse.

'Bitch,' said the Jane English nurse and went thankfully back to her ward.

Mrs Gordelier's face was covered with very white powder, in case she should not look wan enough.

'I simply must have another pillow, Nurse,' she said, 'the discomfort is excruciating.'

'I'm sorry,' I said. 'I'm afraid you're not allowed to be any higher, because of your head.' She must have been told this on the ward upstairs; she was simply trying it on. She moaned. 'I shall have to ask you to do *every*thing for me. I'm too weak to do a thing, you know.'

'Of course,' I said pompously. 'That's what we're here for.' However we were not there to be treated as that woman treated us. She rang and moaned and requested and complained and demanded all day long and the Night Nurses said that if it wasn't for the invention of Barbiturates, they would have gone raving mad.

When it was discovered that her skull was not fractured, and she was allowed to sit up, she immediately rang to be laid down again: 'Or I shall faint, Nurse,' she said threateningly, though I would have preferred that she did, so that I could get on with the teas. Ten minutes later, she had to be sat up again, and all that day she was like a Jack-in-the-box; up and down, up and down, with two nurses needed to move her every time, until Sister finally got Mr Ridley to say that she must sit up and stay up, or she would never mend.

'I shall never get better anyway,' she told me with a face of tragedy. 'I've been a hospital nurse and I know.' If this was true, she should have known better how to behave as a patient. She would allow nobody to touch her except Sister and the Staff Nurse, and when Summers went in once to dress the cut on her leg, she said: 'Don't touch me. Are you trained?' Me, of course, she treated like a moron slave and alternately chivvied, patronized and corrected. One day, when I was bathing her, I saw that the Elastoplast on her leg was coming unstuck, so I fetched some more and prepared to strap on a new piece.

'My child,' said Mrs Gordelier. 'Are you doing this of your own initiative, or did someone tell you to? Surely you are not experienced enough yet to touch dressings. At my hospital the Juniors never did anything like this except under supervision.' I intimated tersely that I thought I was old enough to apply a piece of sticking plaster and she watched me anxiously, ready to scream at the first suspicion of pain. Of course, the Elastoplast would have to behave like a demon, sticking to itself and getting twisted, and my scissors would choose to have a screw loose, and merely collapse on themselves instead of cutting. Mrs Gordelier's triumph grew as she watched the mess into which I was getting. The plaster kept snapping back and folding itself together so that I had to cut the end off and start afresh. In the end, the gauze and wool dressing slipped off Mrs Gordelier's leg, exposing a small healing wound, and with a short sharp scream, she rang the bell and demanded of the nurse who came that she should not be used as a practice dummy by incompetent novices.

She treated Mr Ridley like a dog, summoning him at all hours of the day and night and detaining him in her room with endless stories of her ego, as if he had been a psychoanalyst. He suffered it all urbanely, because he was cultivating a bedside manner, with a view to inheriting his father's wealthy practice.

Mrs Gordelier's injuries were not serious, but they were multiple, and the fracture of her wrist was an uncommon one. Sir Curtis Rowntree, being not entirely satisfied with its progress, called a bone specialist into consultation. This was a big day for Mrs Gordelier. When I took in her X-Rays, she was lying back wanly with a grey chiffon scarf wrapped round her head, looking from one to the other of the men with big eyes while they discussed her. Sister was standing in a corner, fiddling with her fingers, darting forward to turn back a sheet or hand a towel, trying to anticipate their wishes. The Osteopath was a smug, dapper little man with shiny pointed shoes, who called her 'Dear Lady' and Sir Curtis looked as scornful and unassailable as ever, which of course made it heaven for Mrs Gordelier that he should be obliged to concentrate on her. Before I left the room, she whimpered a little and asked for her smelling salts. Across the corridor a thumping began. 'Oh,' said Mrs Gordelier, 'I hope I'm not going to faint.' Sir Curtis, I was pleased to see, pretended not to hear, but the Osteopath spoiled it by telling her how brave she was and she looked at him out of the grey chiffon with swimming eyes.

I went to see what the mad woman in No. 3 was making such a noise about and to remind her for the hundredth time that there was a bell pinned to the front of her cambric nightgown. She had to have everything pinned on her: handkerchief, spectacles – even her book was attached to her by a string through the back of the binding. Otherwise she either dropped things on the floor or lost them in the bed and sat on them. I was getting tired of posting broken glasses to the oculist. It always took quite a time to get out of her what she wanted. When you answered her bell or her thumping stick, she would pretend that she had not summoned you. A secret look would come over her face and you had to question her patiently or guess. If you lost patience and went away before you had discovered what she wanted, she would set up an infernal commotion with bell and stick, and when you came back would scold at you under her breath like an angry cat. This morning, it transpired eventually that the splint on her arm was uncomfortable. No wonder. She had been fiddling with it until she had managed to skew it sideways, so that the edge cut into her arm. While I was undoing the bandage, I taxed her with this and she looked sly and began to mutter at me.

Her friend came in with an umbrella twice the size of herself and a cracked leather shopping bag trailing on the ground. 'Here I am, Nurse,' she said brightly, 'turned up again like a bad penny, you see!' As the majority of her conversation was on a par with this remark, she had got so used to not getting an answer that she automatically repeated everything.

'Showery weather for June – I say, showery weather for June,' she chatted, putting her shopping bag on the bed and beginning to fish out various crumpled parcels and torn paper bags.

'Are you rolling up that bandage – I say, are you rolling up that bandage?' she said, producing a vest like a long woollen tube and holding it against her for her friend's approval. 'Bandaging up Lottie's arm – I say, you're ban-

359

daging up Lottie's arm.' I was tempted to say : 'No, playing the piano,' but she wouldn't have seen it. So I went on bandaging Lottie's arm as tightly as I could with her jerking it at critical moments. I would be glad when she had some more plaster of paris put on. They had had to take off the last lot, because she had picked at it so much that it was falling into the bed in lumps, which she sat on and gave herself a sore bottom.

'Where's the biscuits, Ellie?' she snapped, trying to bend up her thumb so that the bandage would loosen when she straightened it.

'Hey presto, here we are – I say, hey presto!' said Ellie triumphantly producing a brown paper bag with no corners. 'I couldn't get your favourite Petty Bewers, so I got you Nice and Mahree. What a terrible thing a war is when you can't get what you want isn't it, Nurse – I say, what a terrible thing a war is.' Lottie stretched out her sound hand greedily for a biscuit and mumbled away at it while Ellie and I discussed rationing and the iniquities of shopkeepers. Lottie wouldn't wear her teeth, so she had to suck the biscuit into a pulpy mess, which she then swallowed and usually choked herself.

'Choke up, chicken – I say, choke up, chicken,' piped Ellie cheerfully. 'Raise your left arm,' this being the broken one. A bell rang and I left them pecking over the contents of the shopping bag with ejaculations from Ellie and grunts from Lottie. Ellie gave me a packet of blancmange powder to make up. 'She always had a sweet tooth – I say, she always had a sweet tooth.'

Mrs Gordelier was ringing, ostensibly to have the window pulled up and down until it was right to the fraction of an inch, but really to impress me with what the Doctors had said. 'Being a nurse, of course I can understand what they tell me,' she said, 'but Mr Fennimore said that if it had been anyone else, he wouldn't have risked telling them, with their nerves in such a state.' It looked to me as if she had mauve powder on to-day. What with that and the chiffon scarf shrouding her face like ectoplasm, she looked like a banshee.

'Of course, no one knows what I've suffered,' she said complacently. 'Just lower the blind a fraction, child. My eyes ... Yes, the Doctors say, with what I've been through, it's a miracle that I've kept my sanity.' I refrained from the obvious retort and let the blind down with a rush that made her call for her smelling salts again.

She kept me standing by the door, itching to get away while she gave me some more verbatim extracts. That was the worst of private patients. You had to waste such a lot of time listening to them. I opened the door and began to edge out. Her parting shot was : 'In a way, I'm thankful for my pain. I'm offering up my suffering as a prayer to the Almighty.'

She and Nurse Farren got on splendidly. They both knew the Bible slickly and sycophantly, and could make the most shaming remarks without turning a hair. When I first came on to this Wing, I wondered what it was that Farren was always singing under her breath. Then I made beds with her, and found that it was the Psalms. She intoned them as she worked in the quavering, back-of-the-throat voice with which vicars' wives encourage a sheepish congregation. Once, when we were making Mrs Yule's bed, we got on to the subject of holiday clothes. Mrs Yule was telling us about a bathing dress with which her youngest daughter intended to startle the inhabitants of Bigbury-on-Sea, so I told her about the new shorts that I had just got for tennis. Nurse Farren suddenly stopped in the act of pulling through the drawsheet and seemed to stiffen all over. She leaned towards me, her nostrils quivered and her muddy eyes intense. 'The Woman who putteth on Man's clothing,' she hissed, 'is an abomination before the Lord. Isaiah 70. 19.' I drew back, startled. 'And I'll tell you another thing,' she continued, fixing her gaze on my head. 'The Woman who cutteth off her hair is also an abomination before the Lord. Job 53. 8.' Mrs Yule broke the tense silence. 'Could you pull the draw-sheet, please,' she said plaintively. 'I can't hold myself up much longer.' As soon as we had finished, and Farren had gone out, lifting her eyes to the hills whence cometh, Mrs

Yule said : 'Quick, give me my writing case. I must write to Angela before I forget it.'

Mrs Yule enjoyed everything, from her food onwards. She always appreciated a good story about one of her patients, and would retail it to the Home Guard when he came in the evening, and get it wrong, and have me in to tell it again, and he would take out his cigarette case and scoop all the cigarettes into my hand. After she left the Hospital, she had Summers and me to dinner and filled us with food and drink, and Summers, who turned out to be called Yvonne, quite blossomed forth in a green silk dress with her hair tonged up, and revealed an unsuspected talent for the piano. She played, and we sat in deep chairs on a sort of loggia and watched twilight deepen into dusk until the midges drove us indoors. There was a son on leave from the Army, who was clever and shy, and after a bit he sang one or two of the things that Yvonne played, and her hair looked clean and fluffy with the light on it, and her strong nurse's hands moving over the keys were full of grace.

She never would admit it, but I believe he was going to take her out. She kept her hair in its curls and suffered the personal remarks which always abounded if anyone changed their appearance, but in a few days we heard that he had suddenly been sent out to the East, and Summers let her hair go straight again.

Bibi Preston left about the same time as Mrs Yule and their rooms were taken by a scarecrow of a woman with pernicious anaemia and a diabetic Professor of Mathematics, who was a constant worry to me, because he would not eat the food that I weighed out so meticulously, under strict instructions to see that he took it all. We used to have terrible tussles, while I got hotter and the food got colder and the Professor retired under the blankets and put a pillow over his long grey head and snarled like a hibernating animal.

Miss Pennefeather got duller, Lottie madder and Mrs Gordelier more exasperating than ever, and to crown everything, Lady Mundsley, who was recovering in spite of herself, sent away her private nurse and announced that she would get her money's worth out of us.

It had now been diagnosed, for want of anything else, that her trouble might be gastric, so she was accordingly put on hourly feeds of milk and harmless puddings, for which I had to be responsible. Sometimes, even now, when I see the clock pointing to the hour, my mind automatically registers a curse. I could never start doing anything without having to leave it in the middle to take a feed to No. 12. No sooner had she drunk that milk, with delicate sips and a lot of fuss if there was skin, than it seemed it was time to take along the baked custard. I used to spend nearly an hour in the morning concocting the little nonsenses with which the private nurse had always been so tediously occupied. But she had only that to do, whereas I had the maiding of eleven other rooms besides. Also, invalid cooking is not my speciality and many is the rasher of bacon that has owed its richness to curdled custard or a watery junket or lumpy blancmange. Matron came round once in a nosey mood, and with Sister Graham twittering nervously at her heels, went into the kitchen and fired a salvo of complaints in every direction. With her face set in a censorious sniff, she snatched the lid off the pig bucket and poked at the contents with a long-handled spoon. Unfortunately, that was the day that I had burned both the porridge and the milk pudding, and she had also found a decomposing blancmange which had been there for days, sticking to the bottom every time the bucket was emptied.

Once I forgot the hourly feeds. Lady Mundsley would give me exactly two minutes and then reach for the bell. Nurse Jones, who was much too superior to answer bells as a rule, used to make a practice of answering on these occasions, so that when I panted up with something slopping over on to a tray, she could be standing there with her mouth pursed like a snapdragon, receiving complaints about me and promising to see that I was suitably reprimanded. I beat her up once in the bathroom with a back brush and she fought back meanly with nails and feet and eventually pushed me out into the passage into the arms of

363

Mr Morris Evans, who merely set me aside, removed a speck of dust from his trouser leg, cleared his throat and walked on.

When Lady Mundsley was allowed to get up, it was ordained that she should be wheeled into the garden to take the sun in an invalid chair. This involved as much preparation as a Continental journey. Eiderdowns, pillows, handkerchiefs, scarves, rugs, sunshades, sunglasses, book, magazines, Gastric Barley Sugar, Eau-de-Cologne and a foot-stool, all had to go out as well, which meant several journeys up and down stairs and round three sides of the garden to the spot which Lady Mundsley had selected as not ideal, but good enough until she saw somewhere she liked better. Then she would ting-a-ling her bell, for which I always had to keep one ear open and I would have to leave someone in the middle of a blanket bath and go and push her all over the grounds until her restless spirit found somewhere in which it could settle and by that time the sun would probably have gone in and she would want to go back to bed. By the time I got back to my blanket bath, the patient would either be resigned but shivering, impatient, or ringing bells according to temperament.

Lady Mundsley didn't like me much, because I was always knocking things over. I was clumsy enough in the other rooms, but in hers, it seemed I could never touch a vase without spilling the water or tipping the flowers out on to their heads. If I had to break a medicine glass, I would always break it in No. 12 and Lady Mundsley would draw in her breath and say : 'Such a *noise* !' The list of her idiosyncrasies was far longer than any other in Sister's room, even than Mrs Gordelier's, which might have been condensed into : 'Whatever you do, it's wrong.' Lady Mundsley apparently had some influence with the Governors of the Hospital and even Matron had to kowtow to her. Sister Graham was in and out of the room all day, with creased forehead and fluttering hands. She always had to have the best vases and the newest linen, and clean pillowcases far more often than anyone else. It was a good thing she was not on a normal diet, or she would have got all the best food.

At night, Sister would never go off duty until she had paid Lady Mundsley the ten minutes' social visit which she thought was due to her status. Neither of them enjoyed this session. Sister Graham never knew what to say and if Lady Mundsley knew, she couldn't be bothered to say it. Sister would come out of the room flushed, shut the door with noiseless care, and go off down the corridor, her shoulders straightening with relief at being free from the cares of the Ward, but her mind already busy with to-morrow's worries.

It was about this time that Horrocks began to circulate the rumour that Sister was engaged to be married, but nobody paid much attention. She had no real evidence to offer, but merely tried to look like Mona Lisa and said : 'I *know* certain things,' which always meant she knew nothing.

I don't know who it was who suggested that Lady Mundsley should be taken on a tour of the Hospital for her diversion. It was most embarrassing. I had to push the wheelchair, while Sister walked by the side, pointing out features of interest. Lady Mundsley had on her best velvet dressing gown and a soft Angora rug over her knees. Her high-nosed face was carefully made up and her blue-grey hair, which her coiffeur came every week to keep blue, carefully set. Thus she was wheeled round the wards like a district visitor, being wheeled up to one bed or another to exchange a few gracious words. In Herbert Waterlow, some of the men began to mutter and scowl, but most of the patients got the impression that she was Royalty and took it quite well. I don't know whether Lady Mundsley enjoyed it. She said afterwards that she was worn out, and when I went to settle her that night, she said : 'I feel, Nurse, that I'm going to be difficult.' She was always difficult on the nights when I was going to a dance. To-night, I was going with Delphine Lorrimer to a soldiers' dance in a hall on the Factory Estate. I didn't really want to go but she assured me that we were going to have 'a hot time with some cracking fellows'.

While I was just finishing the alcohol rub without which Lady Mundsley swore she could not sleep, the Junior Night Nurse came in and winked at me as I was rubbing the wavy white back. She was a friend of mine, a girl called Lister, who would sit on my bed for hours in a gaudy silk dressing-gown with feathered slippers tucked underneath her, talking, talking about anything that came into her head, from religion to the life history of her Aunt's cat at Thorpe-le-Soken. Sometimes I would drift off, waking again to the weight on my legs and the voice still going on. When we heard Sweet Fanny Adams's rubber soles squeaking along the passage to see who was up to what, we would turn out the light, and a quarter of an hour later, when they came squeaking back, having done the round of the hostel, we turned it on again and continued the session. Round about eleven, we would make coffee with the milk that one of us had sneaked off the Ward. I missed Lister now that she was on Night Duty, but I got a great deal more sleep.

'No. 7 wants you before you go off,' she said, and Lady Mundsley, looking over her shoulder to tell me not to rub so hard, caught another wink and thought it was meant for her.

'Are you being rude, Nurse?' she asked distantly.

'I don't know,' said Lister. 'Am I?' Some nights, she met her boy friend at the pub across the road before she came on duty. This was one of the nights.

'Your upbringing should tell you that,' said Lady Mundsley. 'Rub the back of my neck, please Nurse. I think I got into a draught along those corridors.'

I hoped Oliver Carew didn't want me to go to the fish-and-chip shop and get him fourpennorth of fish with batter and twopennorth of chips, which he sometimes did when the supper had been fiddling little messes in tiny dishes. Not that I minded going in the least; I usually bought some for myself and ate them with him, but to-night I had promised Delphine to be ready for the dance at half-past nine. She had an evil temper, and if put out at the beginning of the evening, could wreck any party. However, when I went into No. 7, there she was, sitting in the armchair and showing a great deal of sheer black stocking. It was Oliver's birthday and Lister had brought him up some champagne. At a quarter-past nine, we turned out the lights and crouched behind the bed, and he grunted sleepily as Sister put her head round the door to say good night on her way off duty. Lister came in and had a quick drink in between answering bells, but the Senior Night Nurse, who was a joyless flat-chested girl, only came in with a few impersonally professional remarks. She couldn't say anything to us, because she set too much store on riding my bicycle which was her greatest, if not her only passion.

After the second toothglass of champagne, Delphine became very society and put on her special voice and took off her cap and kept pinching up her shiny auburn hair. After a while, Mr Sickert came in, which was what she had been waiting for, and it transpired that they were on Christian name terms. Horrocks, who had been off for the evening, came sneaking back in a striped dress which made her look endless, and Oliver lay back and smiled happily and enjoyed his party. Delphine didn't know which to sparkle at, him or Mr Sickert, so after a while she solved the problem by saying : 'Well, I suppose we'd better go on to this party. Felix gets *raving* if I'm more than an hour late,' and we left, she glancing back at the door, as if almost expecting to see it bulge with the seething atmosphere of jealousy which she felt sure she had created within.

The only way of getting to the dance was on our bicycles, and when I went to draw the inadequate blackout of my room, I saw that it was raining. Chaps have got to be very cracking indeed to be worth bicycling through the rain for, even downhill. Also, the champagne had made me delightfully sleepy. I saw my bed, and thought I would make myself some coffee and go to bed with a pile of magazines that Mr Levine had given me. I kicked off my shoes, undid my stiff dogcollar which had branded me with a permanent mark on each side of my neck, and went along to Delphine's room. She was sitting on the bed in black chiffon knickers and an uplift brassière, putting orange varnish on her nails. Her friend Peterson was in there too, in a grubby cotton dressing-gown, washing her hair in the basin. She was also sexy, but without attraction. No amount of hair washing could ever make her anything but intrinsically dirty.

'Delphine,' I said, 'I don't think I'll come.' She looked at me with blazing eyes, jerking her head back aggressively.

'Well, of all the bitches —' she said. 'Of course you must come. I'm not going alone.'

Peterson raised her head from the basin. 'Of course you must go,' she said thickly, through a curtain of seaweedy hair. 'I think it was damn nice of Delphine to ask you.'

'Why don't you go yourself, then?'

'Haven't got anything to wear. Besides, my hair's wet.'

'You could put it in a snood. You might go. I'm much too tired.' I didn't want to go a bit. Delphine was now at the dressing-table, larding on orange lipstick. 'I don't care which of you comes,' she said crossly, hunting among the litter of smeared pots, broken combs and crumpled face tissues for her powder puff, 'but I'm not going alone.' She found a moulting puff and proceeded to dab white powder carefully all over her face and neck.

'I'll go,' said Peterson to me, 'if you'll lend me that green hair net and that dress with the pleats. Oh – and a pair of stockings.'

That settled it. I had to go. Delphine and I, furious with each other, bicycled down the hill a short distance apart with scarves over our heads. When we arrived, after riding up a muddy lane with potholes which she managed to avoid and I did not, she flung her bicycle against a fence and stalked in. A ladder zipped down my stocking as I dismounted and my bicycle fell down twice before it would stand up. I followed her, barking my shins on a small blast wall, which I didn't expect to find outside the entrance, and came into a narrow dark space like the place where you leave your coats outside a squash court. Two military policemen and an ordinary one were chatting in the gloom, and a couple of Tommies pushed past me with a noisy blur of song. Beyond the wooden partition came the sound of a band with too much saxophone.

'Tickets, please,' said a man sitting at a table by the door.

'Oh – I think my friend inside —'

'One-and-six, please,' he said pityingly, as if he had seen many more efficient gate-crashers than me. I certainly wasn't going to pay; that would be the last straw. I was sure Delphine would not let the cracking fellows get away with that. They had probably taken our tickets. 'I think my friend bought my ticket,' I said. 'It's probably inside.'

'No one's bought no tickets for nobody,' he droned, holding out his hand for my money. Curse Delphine! She might have waited.

'I'll go in and see,' I said haughtily, and stepped forward to find my way barred by one policeman of each sort. I was furious. It might have been eighteen pounds at issue instead of eighteen pence. I flung the money at the man at the table and flounced into the hall, which rose up and hit me with heat, smell, noise and unshaded electric light. I pushed my way through a crowd of soldiers gaping on the edge of the floor and saw Delphine dancing with a hairdresser in khaki. They were evidently having a row. She saw me and pulled him out to the edge of the floor.

'Where the hell have you been?' she asked, scowling. 'This is Felix.' She indicated the hairdresser contemptuously, and he smiled with rabbit's teeth beneath a thin black moustache and said : 'Pleased to meet you.'

'The other chaps haven't turned up,' said Delphine casually, 'but you'll find someone to dance with if you stand around a bit. You've got a ghastly ladder in your stocking, did you know?' Felix, who had been tapping his feet rhythmically, suddenly pulled her close to him and whirled her into the crowd of dancers. I watched them dance out of sight, with a great deal of hip-swaying and Palais-de-Dance footwork.

At the far end of the hall was a stage on which the four members of the band sat playing a bit of uninspired strict tempo. Down the sides of the room were chairs on which girls sat, trying to look as if dancing were the last thing for which they were here. Soldiers and airmen stood about in groups, staring at the dancers and at the girls but not doing anything about it. In a corner on my left the crowd was thick. There were trestle tables here, behind which two or three havocked-looking women were wiping glasses and dispensing drink, a lot of which seemed to be on the floor. I

369

wished I were a man. I would then have had a drink and gone home. As it was, I would just have to go home. I was turning away, preparing a dignified face to wear going past the man with the tickets, when my eye was caught by a couple on the floor and I stood transfixed. They had disappeared into the crowd before I could see them properly. Perhaps it was my imagination – but no, through a gap in the dancers, stepping sedately and slightly out of time to the music, were a stooping, spectacled officer in khaki, and – Sister Graham. It was always a shock to see a Sister out of uniform. Somehow, one didn't imagine them ever wearing anything else; it seemed so much a part of their character. She was wearing a nondescript brown dress, with a suspicion of petticoat showing at the back, and she looked quite human – soft and plump. Just as she looked wrong out of uniform, the man looked wrong in it. He was in early middle age, an indoor type, with a kind, tired face.

As I was staring at this phenomenon, a throaty voice beside me said : 'Excuse me, but might I have this dance?' and before I could think whether I wanted to, I was out on the floor in the arms of a sturdy, ginger-haired man in battle-dress, the top of whose bullet head came on a level with my shoulder. He breathed heavily and didn't want to talk. He was too busy trying to see his way over or around me. I kept trying to steer away so that Sister should not see me. He tried to steer me the way he wanted to go, and we battled silently, while the drummer, looking anxious, sang *Johnny Pedlar* into the microphone.

When it was over, my partner wiped his forehead and said : 'Coom and have a drink,' and there at the bar was Sister Graham, sipping beer with a wrinkled nose, while her spectacled man talked to another officer.

We smiled at each other. I don't know which of us was the most sheepish. Farther down the bar, Delphine had three men round her, none of which was Felix. She was making a lot of noise and tossing her hair about.

'Don't worry,' said Sister, 'I won't say anything about either of you. I should, of course – oh dear, I wish I hadn't seen you —' Her partner turned round to see to whom she was talking. 'This is one of the nurses, Godfrey,' she said. I saw that he was a doctor. He asked me to have a drink, and as I could see no sign of bullet-head, I accepted. Soon after, my partner came pushing through the crowd with the tumbler of grapefruit squash which he evidently thought met my case. I couldn't do any introducing, as I didn't know anybody's name. He was furious at finding me in an officer's party, and stuck out his jaw and went pink about the ears. Sister did nothing to help the situation, and Godfrey was vaguely at a loss as to who we were. Bullet-head drank the grapefruit himself, looking at his boots, then mumbled something and disappeared. I felt like a blackleg and wanted to go after him, but I think he was glad to be rid of me. He had not bargained on being quite so much shorter than I was.

Godfrey went on talking to the other officer, while Sister and I searched desperately for something to say to each other, and I was thankful when he took her away to dance. I felt happier after my drink, and thought that perhaps I would stay and have another dance before I went home. I went and sat down in the row of girls, but nobody came near me. I got up and looked for the ugliest girl in the row and sat down next to her. Presently, quite a nice-looking soldier came towards me and I smiled politely and half rose.

'Will you dance?' he said to the ugly girl, and waltzed her away with a large hand in the small of her back hitching up her skirt behind. I got up and then wandered about and then stood in a conspicuous place, fixing likely looking men with my eye, but I might have been a leper. Delphine was dancing now in a rather abandoned way with a red-haired Sergeant-Major. Sister was dancing with Godfrey, his face solemn with the concentration necessary for reversing. I *would* dance. Delphine had seen me, and I wasn't going to please her by ringing up 'No Sale' and slinking defeatedly away. I felt uncomfortably exposed standing about in the open space in which I had chosen to display myself. I went and mingled by the bar, and presently a man who saw at least three of me swept me on to the floor just as the band finished the tune. 'Never mind,' he said, 'Time for a little drink.' We had a little one, and another little one. Delphine came up with her Sergeant-Major and hailed me like her dearest friend. She put her arm round my shoulders and nearly wept over me, then in a moment was roaring with laughter at something perfectly ordinary that I said, and shrieking: 'You are a scream, Dickens, honestly you are! My dear, I think it's the funniest thing I ever heard!'

'Listen to this, then,' I said, and told her about Sister. She laughed herself nearly sick, but not because she took it in properly. She was just laughing. 'Sargie,' she said, pouting up at him and nestling against his sleeve, 'ickle Delphie wants a drink.'

For a girl who aspired to sophistication, ickle Delphie held her liquor worse than anyone I have ever seen. About an hour later, when I was just beginning to enjoy myself with a blond A.C.2 whom I had picked up in the Paul Jones, the red-haired Sergeant tapped me on the shoulder and said: 'You'd better go and see about your friend. She's not quite the thing.'

I found Delphine outside, being sick over a wire fence, which she thought was the rail of a ship. She was quite happy afterwards – too happy. She was long past bicycling, and I didn't see how I was going to get her home, much less get her through the bathroom window and into bed without waking the whole hostel. As we stumbled back into the Social Hall, we collided with two people coming out.

'Whoops!' said Delphine, and pinched me. It was Sister Graham and Godfrey. He flashed his torch on us and grasped the situation.

'Could we give you a lift if you're going back to the hospital?' He glanced at Sister for agreement, and she made a few nervous beginnings of sentences. I was very relieved. I was only too thankful to leave our bicycles and hope that they would still be there to-morrow.

Delphine and I sat in the back of the car, and I tried to sit on her when she burst into song.

'Have you got late passes?' asked Sister.

'Well – not exactly,' I said.

'How are you going to get in?' I didn't like to mention

372

the bathroom window; it might spoil it for future occasions. I hedged a bit, and she said: 'You'd better come in through the front with me, then you'll be all right.' Delphine looked like being sick again, and Godfrey, turning round to look at her, drove on faster. He stopped outside the railings, and I lugged her out of the car and into the geranium bed. The Night Porter looked at us in surprise as we walked through the front entrance, with Sister looking the guiltiest of the lot. She rushed us along the corridors, terrified of meeting Fanny Adams.

I had a trying time getting Delphine to bed. She made such a noise that she woke Richardson, who slept next door and came in looking very square in pink cotton pyjamas to see what was going on. Between us, we got her on to the bed and left her, fully dressed and moaning weakly that she wanted Sarge.

'I'll get her up in the morning,' said Richardson grimly. 'It'll be a pleasure.'

Delphine at breakfast, combined with over-ripe kippers, was a sight to put you off for the day. She and I made beds together, communicating only in grunts, and she nearly bit poor Oliver's head off when he asked her if she had had a good party. She got more and more ravaged-looking as the morning wore on, and finally retired to bed at twelve o'clock and lay inanimate for several hours. Sister let her go without a word. She had not said anything to me about the night before and had avoided being alone with me in case I might talk about it, which would embarrass her exceedingly.

A few days later, she came up to me in a great state of confusion after lunch, hemming and hawing and finally coming out with : 'I've got someone coming up to tea with me this afternoon, Nurse. Perhaps you could make some sandwiches – or something – or toast.' She was more uncertain than ever these days. She seemed to have no control over her hands, started nervously at the slightest sound and dithered over any decision. She appeared to have something on her mind, and I wondered if it could still be the dance.

I was in the kitchen, washing up the plates that Maggie had left as a protest against their being brought out of the rooms five minutes late on her afternoon off. Having told me about the tea, Sister seemed reluctant to go. She stood twiddling the doorknob, obviously wanting to say something. I went on scraping off mustard, hoping that she would either come in and say it, or else go away and shut the door, because there was a draught.

'As a matter of fact,' she ventured at last, 'it's Captain Hope – the friend who was with me at the dance, you know.'

'Oh, good,' I said. 'I mean – is it?'

'Yes. He's coming to say goodbye, you see. He goes up to Scotland to-morrow – oh dear,' she put her hand to her mouth, 'perhaps I shouldn't say that.' There was silence after that, and I thought she had gone, but when I turned round to get the dishcloth, there she was, still twiddling the doorknob, still trying to make up her mind to say something.

Actually, I don't suppose she was so very much older than me, but the gulf that etiquette had put between us was greater than any disparity of age. She wasn't very friendly with any of the other Sisters. She was obviously dying for a confidante, but she was a Sister and I was a Nurse, and East is East and West is West.

I was still in a draught. I tried to get her started. 'I expect you'll miss Captain Hope,' I hazarded. And then, suddenly, out it all came in a rush. She fell over her words, trying to get them out before she lost courage. She didn't look at me and I didn't look at her, just went on drying dishes with my auricular timpani, as Sister Tutor would say, popping with surprise.

He had asked her to marry him. He had been asking her repeatedly for several weeks. He had actually asked her the last time while Delphine was in the geranium bed.

I congratulated her delightedly. I supposed she had said 'No' at first, because that was how she reacted to any proposition, coming round to it afterwards if you gave her time.

'But I haven't said I would,' she said in an anguished voice. She had shut the door by now, and was standing by the stove wringing the oven cloth into a rag.

'Oh, but Sister, you *must*.' He would be perfect for her, so

374

stable. Even if he had not been so nice, there seemed to me to be no question between getting married and withering away your womanhood in a hospital.

'I simply can't make up my mind.' How she must madden him with her inability to make a decision. But I expect he thought of her as a helpless little woman-thing. If he had any sense, he would just sweep her off to church before she could get her breath.

'You see,' she pursued, turning the gas-taps on and off with little roars, 'I love this work so much, I don't know that I should be happy without it. If I could marry him and still stay on here – but I couldn't. It would mean going away with him, you see.' I had no idea her work meant so much to her. It always worried her so much, I should have thought she would be only too thankful to shake off responsibility, but I suppose that was part of the fascination.

It wasn't my place to tell her that I thought she was daft as a brush, and anyway, she suddenly recollected who she was and who I was and where we were.

She drew herself up, patted her apron and settled the belt round her cosy waist. 'Two o'clock,' she said, putting on an unnatural voice. 'I must go and check the laundry.' The laundry had come back yesterday and long ago been checked and put away, but it got her out of the room and out of the situation. She would be more embarrassed than ever with me now. Perhaps she would have me moved to another ward. I opened the window and door to let out the smell of gas that her fiddling with the taps had created, and went to tell Mrs Gordelier that no, I was not deaf : I had heard her bell, but had been giving an intra-muscular injection, in the middle of which one could not calmly walk away, as she, as a hospital nurse, must know. We brought this allusion up now on every possible occasion, ever since we had discovered from her husband, who had come to try and persuade us to keep her a bit longer, that the sum of her hospital experience came from two half-days a week as a V.A.D. at the Red Cross Convalescent Home.

Captain Hope arrived, walking purposefully down the

corridor like a man who has come for his final answer. When I took in the tea, he acknowledged me vaguely, not sure if he had met me, and if so, where.

I know it was unforgivable of me to listen outside the door, but I couldn't help it. I had caught the habit when I was a cook-general, and I couldn't miss a drama like this. Jones and I had taken in all the patients' teas and she had gone off to her own. I applied my ear to the door and had just heard him say : 'Now, Edith, once and for all —' when Horrocks came out of the sterilizing-room and said : 'What on earth —'

I flapped a hand at her. Her eyes lit up and her nostrils quivered at the scent of scandal. She would have to know now, though she was the last person who should have, if Sister was going to stay on. She crouched beside me and we listened, shivering with excitement, when Godfrey, fortified, perhaps, by the strength of my Bovril sandwiches, said : 'Once and for all, Edith, you can choose between me and the hospital. I won't stand being fooled about like this.' There was an awful hush, and all we could hear were the basket chairs creaking. I thought I heard Sister begin to cry, and then she gave a little gasp, and just at that moment, Lady Mundsley's bell exploded above our heads, shattering our taut nerves and drowning every other sound for miles. She kept us both in the room fixing her bed, so that we missed the exit, triumphal or frustrated, of Godfrey.

I went into the sitting-room to get the tea things, hoping that Sister would disclose what had happened, but the minute I went in, she rushed out of the room in a panic. She had been crying.

It was gratifying the next morning, when it was all over the hospital that Fanny Graham – of all people, my dear – was going to be married, to be able to say : 'Of course, I've known about it for ages.' Not that anyone believed me, any more than they believed Horrocks, who said it too, or Delphine, who gave minute descriptions of the man, although, until I told her, she had no recollection of ever having met him.

# Chapter Eight

FOR some time after Sister Graham had left, we were without a sister. Nurse Farren was in charge, and being a girl
with a mania for cleanliness, got down at once to repairing
the results of Sister's *laisser-faire* policy. We were not busy,
as two or three of the rooms were empty, and I spent several
days doing practically nothing but spring cleaning. Nurse
Farren had been a Staff Nurse for over a year and fancied
her chances of being made a Sister. When it was observed
what a good job she made of this temporary responsibility,
she saw herself in the near future as Sister Farren of the
Private Wards.

So I had to scrub and polish and tidy, and take down
from the top of the splint cupboard antique apparatuses that
had been there so long they had grown on to the shelves.
She tried to rope Maggie into this holocaust, telling her she
must turn the kitchen and the larder upside down and scrub
every available inch of both. Maggie had no intention of
obeying, but she said nothing. She never answered anything
she didn't like. She was a sour, knotted woman, dispirited by
years of service as a Ward Maid, with degenerate feet that
had no thickness through the instep and turned out at right
angles to her legs, so that she looked as if she were on a
stand. It was one of the sights of Redwood to see Maggie
waddling down the corridor between the private rooms, with
her toes pointing straight at the walls, her cap on the back
of her head and a great rusty hairpin hanging down her
back on a loose tail of hair. She was anti-everything, except
such of the patients who were good for a gossip while she
was sweeping their room. If you lost her in the morning, you
could track her down by the brush and dustpan lying askew
outside a door, and inside you would find Maggie, leaning
on the broom handle expounding some Crying Shame.

While I was turning out the medicine cupboard as
ordered, she came shuffling into the room for her cough
medicine. Sister Graham had allowed her to have it last

377

winter when she had slight bronchial trouble, but although it had cleared up months ago, she refused to give up the syrup. She adored taking medicine. She was not allowed to take anything out of the medicine cupboard, but she was always on at one of the nurses to give her some senna, or Epsom salts, or iron tonic. I once caught her fishing about in the dispensary basket, looking for dregs in the empty bottles which were waiting to be taken down for refilling. She had just uncorked a small dark bottle and was about to dose herself with a drachm of nitric acid.

I got down off the chair from which I was exploring the top corners of the cupboard, uncorked the bottle of Mist. Expect. and poured her dose into the handleless cup which she always carried about with her. She brought it on and off the ward every day, saying that she was not going to risk her death by drinking out of something that somebody with the Dear-knows-what had used. As she did the washing up, perhaps she was right.

'I think you're cracked,' she said, smacking her lips over the syrup. 'I wouldn't break my neck for that stuck-up, 'ymn-singing young Madam. "Scrub out the larder," she says, if you please. "Wash the paint, Maggie. Put all the saucepans and bowls on to boil with soda."'

'Aren't you going to do it?'

'That I'm not. No one's going to put upon me. What was good enough for Sister Gray-ham is good enough for any la-di-da, even if she is gone on God. I don't hold with churchiness and such. I 'd like to see Nurse Farring bury a husband and two kids, and see whether she's still got a mind to praise the Lord.' Her voice was funereal, every vowel a wail and every consonant drawn out.

'You'll go to Hell,' I said, scraping at an encrusted lump of something on the top shelf.

'I dare say. The company might be an improvement on some I could mention. Got a taste of bismuth there, Nurse? I haven't had any all day.'

Nurse Farren fussed and fretted about the state of the kitchen, and in the end, I had to do it with one of the V.A.D.s on Maggie's afternoon off. The V.A.D. was a pert, pop-eyed girl, who worked all week in the Habby Department at Hooper's and gave up her Sundays to what she had thought, in common with many others, was vital work, but turned out to be either doing any dirty job that could be thought up or feeling very much in the way. Although they exploited them, most of the Sisters disliked the V.A.D.s. They made dirty digs about them being untrained and irresponsible, but would never give them a chance to be anything else by letting them see what was going on. I have often heard Sister Lewis say about some job like sewing on pillow covers or scraping and oiling trolley wheels : 'We'll leave that for the V.A.D. to do to-morrow, it will keep her out of the ward, at any rate.'

The nurses welcomed the V.A.D.s. Apart from being a help they brought with them a breath from outside and relieved the tedium of knowing the conversational repertoire of one's colleagues by heart.

Nurse Farren was off that afternoon, so the V.A.D. and I only tidied the kitchen perfunctorily and wiped over one or two shelves with a wet cloth to look as though they had been scrubbed. The rest of the time we spent having tea and toast, and Horrocks came in and polished off half a cold rice pudding and a jelly that wouldn't set.

Farren came on at half-past five to the tune of *Jerusalem the Golden* and seemed quite satisfied with the effect we had created. The V.A.D. wanted to give a blanket bath for practice, so Farren found her a nice little job sitting in one of the empty rooms and marking the bundle of new linen that came from the proceeds of the Linen Guild's American Tea.

Nurse Farren was thrilled with her achievements on the Private Wing, and was smug enough and rash enough to point out the improvements to Matron on her morning round.

'I should hope you *are* keeping it clean,' said Matron, through rigid lips. 'That's what you're here for.' I laughed inwardly, remembering how she had once said the same thing to me. I laughed again, but not quite so inwardly, because everyone on 'Privates' was laughing, when it was announced that Staff Nurse Beaver was to be Sister of the

Private Wards. Poor Farren was sent to be Staff Nurse on the Maternity Wards, whose Sister was the hospital terror, and was later reported to be going about crooning darkly to the babies about the Lord confounding his enemies.

It seemed strange to see old Beaver in a dark blue dress instead of a striped one and the pointed Sister's cap, which she had not yet quite mastered. The square, strapless apron bib was an improvement. There was not so much strain. It jutted straight forward and was fastened at the salient point with vast safety pins where the other Sisters wore gilt tiepins.

. The ward gradually settled back into the comfortable disorder from which Nurse Farren had roused it. Sister Beaver was earnest and competent, but she was also short-sighted and too eager to be jolly girls together to command any discipline. The Private Wards were heaven to her, because she could indulge her sociability to the full. Lady Mundsley, who had chosen to have a relapse and looked like being with us for ever, discharged herself within a week because she could not stand any more of Beaver's conversation.

Mrs Gordelier was still with us, however. Her husband kept persuading her to stay on. Not that she needed much persuading, although her injuries were sufficiently healed. She was quite annoyed when the plaster cast was removed from her wrist and she was told to exercise it. The most she would do was to waggle her fingers feebly, and that not without much groaning and a nurse in the room in case she fainted.

It was July, the month when one ought to be planning holidays. We were supposed to get three weeks' holiday in the year, which meant that I ought to get mine at least by the end of September. People told me, however, that there was not a hope. I would be sure to have to wait. Often one went for a year and a half without the smell of a holiday, and it was said that Fanny Churchman tried to wangle it so that you caught up with your next year's holiday, and at the end of your three years you found you had only had six weeks off. I had several reasons for wanting a holiday in August. One morning, I was foolish enough to go and tell Matron so. It needed a lot of courage to bring myself to it, but I did want that holiday, and in any case, she couldn't kill me. Or could she, I wondered, seeing my turn approach outside the door and wishing I had not come.

She only said : 'I suppose you think you're the only nurse in the hospital, Nurse,' but it was the way she said these things.

It was much too hot to work. The rooms filled up, Nurse Summers went off sick and was not replaced, and we toiled on, with the starch melting in our high collars. At the end of the day, one was too limp and tired to go out and enjoy the lovely pastel evenings. I sweated up and down after the bells, with a cross red face and a molten area round my waist under my stiff belt. We had a patient in with Shingles, and when my waist got hot, I used to think I had got them, too. She had them all round her back and under her ribs, and Maggie said that when they met in front she would die.

One morning, I suddenly felt very dizzy and reeled against the Professor's wash basin. I put it down to blowing up his rubber air-cushion and thought no more about it until I felt dizzy again in the sluice, without having blown up anything. Perhaps I was going to have a heat stroke; my head felt very muzzy. We were very busy and I didn't have much time to feel ill, but I had a vague sensation while I worked that it was all a dream and that I was using somebody else's legs. When I got a moment to think about it, I hoped that I was going to be ill. It would be a rest if nothing else. Presently, I hoped more fervently; I didn't want to feel like this for nothing. My head was swimming, but I put off taking my temperature in case I should be disappointed. By tea-time, I couldn't take in properly what was said to me. Surely now I was ill. But as I went to the medicine cupboard to get a thermometer, I remembered. To-morrow was my day off. My father was fetching me at half-past eight to-night and driving me up to London. I couldn't be ill yet, otherwise they would keep me here in my black iron bed. If I could stave it off, I could be ill at home, which would be lovely.

I sneaked off with a thermometer and locked myself in somewhere to see whether I was dying. I was over a hundred and two, and my pulse was trotting along like a pony trying to keep up with a horse. Joy and a faint sense of pride mingled with alarm at the prospect of bearing up for four hours more. I felt worse now that I knew there was something wrong.

A merciful haze lies over those hours. Only the passionate longing for home, which is one of the symptoms of illness, kept me going. I kept taking my temperature, and watched it creep beyond a hundred and three with morbid satisfaction. The others were too busy to notice if I looked peculiar or talked at random, and when Beaver said once : 'Are you all right, old thing? You look a bit flushed,' I was able to pass it off as the heat. By half-past eight, I felt so ghastly I didn't care if I stayed on all night, I couldn't feel any worse. Beaver – now, of course, known as Fanny Beaver – sent me off punctually, saying that I looked tired which, I thought resentfully, was underestimation considering that my temperature was nearly a hundred and four.

I found that by going about it very slowly and deliberately, I could just manage to get changed, though I couldn't get as far as packing a case. My ordeal was not yet over, because if I told my father about it before we got home, he might refuse to take me and put me straight back to bed at the hospital. I would have to keep up the pretence for another hour. I would lie back and pretend to be asleep, so that I didn't have to talk.

Luckily, it was dusk when I got out to the car and his sight wasn't good enough to see what I looked like.

I had forgotten about his sight. 'You can drive,' he said casually. 'I can't see a thing in this light.'

We got home somehow. My performance merely confirmed his previous opinion of my driving, but how we missed that island at the junction of Hendon Way and the Finchley Road, I shall never know.

A few days later I felt strong enough to open *Sister Fairchild* to see what she had to say on the subject of chicken-pox. She showed me a terrifying photograph – no, that was smallpox. Chicken-pox was on the other side, almost as bad, but in different places. I couldn't think how I had caught it. There had not been a whisper of it in Redwood.

'May be contracted,' I read, 'through contact with a case of *Herpes Zoster*.' I was sure we hadn't got any of that – wouldn't be seen dead with it. I looked it up in the index : '*Herpes Zoster*, or *Shingles*.' I felt like writing to the *Lancet*. It is always so surprising when the written word is proved by experience.

When I returned to Redwood, I learned that I had started quite a run on chicken-pox. Nurse Donavan, in fact, had made a palindrome of *Sister Fairchild's* theory by subsequently getting shingles.

Whenever you had been away, you had to report to Matron's office that you were back. What did one say? 'I'm back,' was so obvious and was liable to elicit the retort : 'Where from?' for Matron could not be expected to have the comings and goings of some hundred odd nurses at her finger-tips. Labouring up the hill in the bus, I considered : 'Here I am,' 'Please, Ma'am, I'm better,' or just walking into the room and presenting myself for inspection like a child in a new dress, with feet planted and stomach well out. Sarah P. was one of those people for whom one always rehearsed beforehand. Not that it ever got me anywhere. I never went into that room, with its misleading homey chintzes, without saying the wrong thing.

I was lucky to-day. Matron was out, and I had only to report to Sister Harriman. I found her in her narrow office, which abutted on Matron's like a junior clerk's, putting a lot of art work into a notice which I read upside down across the desk :

**LOST ! !**

Nurse Jepson has lost a small gold watch
Any nurse possessing information likely
to lead to its whereabouts to report same

**IMMEDIATELY**

to     E. Harriman, Ass. Mat.

Unless nurses can exercise more care over
personal property, valuables must be
deposited in the office.

This was not so much a dig at Jepson as a mild allusion to the number of petty thefts that had occurred recently. Nobody was ever caught at it, and everyone suspected everyone else. You could not leave a pair of stockings drying in the bathroom if you wanted to see them again. If you laid down a pair of scissors in the ward, they were gone in an instant, almost from under your nose. Before I bought a padlock for my bicycle, it was always disappearing, sometimes for two or three days at a time. Although it found its way home, it was not the girl it had been when it started out. First, it was raped of its pump, then the lamp and basket, then the bell. When there was nothing else to take, it used to come home with a puncture. We had no keys to our bedrooms, and pens, underclothing, aprons, books – not money, because we never had any – were constantly disappearing. Once, I came off duty to find my drawers half open and the contents obviously disturbed. Not that I had anything worth stealing, but the fact that someone had been poking about was infuriating enough. In a towering rage, I checked up on my belongings, but the only thing that seemed to be missing were two cups that I had brought off the Private Wards for evening coffee.

Next morning, I burst upon Matron to protest, but my righteous indignation was somewhat damped to find that I had let myself in for a row about the cups, because it was she herself who had discovered them on her periodical round of the nurses' rooms.

I could never get used to this absence of privacy. You were given a room of your own, but it was not your own. The authorities considered themselves responsible for us and made that an excuse for snooping. It was probably even their duty to read any letters we might leave lying around if they looked interesting enough. You did not belong to yourself any more; you were a cog in community life. It was a wonder we did not have to throw all our clothes into a common wardrobe at night and draw at random in the morning, like nuns.

I had arrived back just in time for one of Sister Tutor's Question Papers, with which she periodically tested our chance of passing the Prelim. Exam, now only three months away. Although I had missed three weeks of lectures, I had to take the paper, and Toots pursed her sorbo lips over the result and had fears for my future. I could not see why being able to trace the passage of waste from the lavatory pan to the main sewer, or write notes on (*a*) upland surface water, (*b*) shallow water, (*c*) artesian wells, should make me a better nurse. Nurse Jones, who had got top marks and had her answers read out for our edification, was, as far as I could tell, one of the worst nurses on the wards. She was lazy, disobliging, unsympathetic and heavy-handed, but she could write a short essay on 'The Ethics of Nursing' and knew the difference between ventilation with Tobin's tube, Cooper's disc and Galton's grate, all of which had been out of date when Sister Fairchild was a probationer. I pinned my faith in her tripping up over the practical exam.

When I first came back, I was sent to the Theatre for a few weeks. I thought this would be exciting, but I was not there long enough to get much farther than sluicing out the gowns and towels which piled up round me all day as I toiled with sodden hands in the sluice. Things that had been taken out of people used to be brought out here in bowls until they were sent down to the Laboratory, and though at first they made my hair rise, I soon got blasé and could pass an appendix or a kidney or even a finger without having to peep with horrified fascination. Some people liked to have their bits and pieces pickled as a memento. A private patient once insisted on having her spleen bottled for her treasure cupboard. They tried to dissuade her, for the thing was abnormal, the size of a football, but she made as much fuss as if she were being robbed, and eventually took it proudly home, where I believe it reposes in a kind of goldfish bowl among the Wedgwood and Ming.

Theatre Sister was trying. She had a wicked temper, which had to be watched like a barometer, and prided herself on being unable to suffer fools. I was quite glad to be obliged to spend most of my time in the sluice, because in the operating theatre it was possible to do more things wrong to the minute than anywhere else. Even the Surgeons were susceptible to Sister's moods. If she were feeling jocular, the operation might be performed with something of the party spirit, but if those eyebrows were drawn down like bars of iron and that foot was tapping, the atmosphere became so thick you could hardly get in at the door. The Surgeon was irritable, the House Surgeon nervous, the Anaesthetist monosyllabic and we Nurses sweating with anxiety.

Sister would snap a demand for something from behind her mask, and I never knew which was the most dangerous : to ask her to repeat it, or to run briskly off and return with what I thought she had said. If she did not fell you verbally on the spot, you knew it was only a pleasure deferred. If she happened to be feeling sunny that day, she would save her castigation until such time as her temper was bad enough to do it justice. It wasn't really safe for her to be loose among all those razor-sharp scissors and scalpels. Once, when I had been particularly silly, she brandished a villainous instrument at me, declaring that she would love to use it on me. I discovered afterwards that it was an instrument used for crushing a baby's skull.

Theatre Sister had once left nursing to be married, returning on the death of her husband. Consequently, she was either called the black widow spider or the Praying Mantis, the female of which, according to Sister Tutor, was given to killing the male.

Apart from the Praying Mantis, I loved working on the Theatre. Operations were enthralling, each one a scientific drama, and daily I marvelled at the things a body will stand. When I saw Sir Curtis Rowntree removing clots from a femoral artery as easily as he would clean his pipe, I thought that nothing could be more miraculous until I saw Mr Vavasour do a Caesarean.

I was quite prepared to come over queer. I had read stories of nurses and students thudding to the ground right and left and being left to lie there while the white-robed, inhuman figures with their shining knives bent over the still, shrouded figure on the table, oblivious to all save their glorious task of saving life. I found, however, that if you are near enough to see anything, interest overcomes nausea. Sometimes, especially in summer, the heat, combined with the fumes of ether and the necessity of standing motionless for two hours or more, makes you feel slightly dizzy. You dare not lean against a wall, so you stand on, feeling noble, a swaying figure in the shadows outside the cone of light which throws up the dramatic grouping of the concentrated figures. All light, all eyes, all minds, are magnetized to that one point, the small uncovered area which for that hour is the centripetal focus of existence.

Although I was disappointed when Sister Gilbert announced one morning that I was to go to Martin Callaghan, the Men's Medical Ward, I was relieved to have escaped what was coming to me for letting the sterilizers boil dry the day before. I underestimated Theatre Sister. She made a special trip down to Martin Callaghan and took care to let Sister Tarling know what kind of vermin I was.

Not that Sister Tarling paid much attention. She was a kindly old body, who steered her own unhurried course oblivious of distractions. She had been nursing for more than thirty years and knew exactly what she was at, and if she sometimes favoured the Fairchild rather than the modern idea, she seemed to get just as good results as people who were always talking about psychotherapy. She called all the patients 'Dear,' from little boys with infantile paralysis to cracked old men with disseminated sclerosis. She moved about the ward slowly, because her legs hurt her. She would have been retired if it had not been for the war.

There were two nurses on this ward junior to me, so after having been only a bad smell on the Theatre, I felt quite important. The humble Weekes was the Senior Pro, and an insolent girl with a tight shiny skin and a bouncing figure was the Junior. I was Relief Nurse, which meant that I did the work of whoever was off and brought a welcome variety to life. One day I would be bustling importantly about with dressings and forceps, and the next I would be back at my old game of scouring the sluice. The First Nurse was Dawlish, still talking about leaving, but with even less intention of doing so now that she had passed her Prelim, and felt her-

387

self eminent. The Staff Nurse was a girl called Jackman, who had been at the hospital as long as anyone could remember, waiting to be married. She was engaged all right, with a ring that she wore round her neck on a piece of wool, but her fiancé could never actually bring himself to come within touching distance of the altar. Jackman went on patiently getting her bottom drawer together. She had the nature and appearance of a trusting dog. Her long face drooped like a bloodhound from triangular, weepy-looking eyes, and brown loops of hair flopped on either side like ears. All she needed was studs and a name-plate on her high starched collar.

We had a nice lot of men on the ward. They were a gentler, quieter lot than on Herbert Waterlow, and being a medical ward the whole tempo was slower. We had fewer emergencies and casualties and more chronics. Patients were admitted at respectable hours into beds that were ready for them. There were no stretchers constantly arriving in the middle of dinner, with mangled men on them who had to be given a blood transfusion immediately by a House Surgeon who could not be found. Some of the men who were only in for observation needed hardly any nursing. Many of them were allowed up and did a lot of our housework for us. They seemed quite pleased with any job that broke the monotony of a day that began at five o'clock.

There was one particular man, a Gastric called Siddons, who had been in for weeks and weeks to see whether an operation could be avoided by treatment. He was short and stocky, with hair like a carpet brush, and all the hospital dressing-gowns were too long for him. He flip-flapped about in a pair of carpet slippers, pouncing on any job that was going and looking after the other patients like a mother. The men called him 'Auntie.' He would do anything for anybody, but he kept them in order. He had been there so long that he regarded the ward as his own, and was determined to see that it was properly conducted.

He was solicitous with the old men and tender with the ill ones. Each new arrival would soon find Siddons at his bedside, jollying him along in case he felt homesick, and if anyone was in pain, he would be along to comfort him and to hurry Nurse Jackman up with the dope. When anyone was coming round from an anaesthetic, Auntie, who had been hovering close by, peering anxiously at the mottled face for the first signs of returning consciousness, would be up to the bed in a flash, growling : 'All right, Chum. Take it easy, you ain't dead yet,' and muffling the half-insensible oaths with the palm of his hand.

There were a lot of Gastrics on this ward. I had been harassed enough over Lady Mundsley's feeds, but these would have driven me demented if it had not been for Siddons. Some were on milk only, some on pre-digested milk, some hourly and some two-hourly. There was a list up in the kitchen, but Sister had taken the paper shortage too seriously, and whenever the diets were changed would cross and recross out and overwrite rather than start a fresh piece of paper. The result, in her illegible handwriting, was chaos, but Auntie had it all at his fingertips. He knew when a patient's diet was changed, either from hovering about listening to the doctors, or from studying their charts, which he was strictly forbidden to do. He took a deep interest in everything that went on and loved nothing better than to settle down to a medical discussion, propounding a mixture of the old wives' stuff on which he had been reared, and technicalities that he had picked up during his long sojourn in hospital.

'Poor old Forbes,' he would say, coming into the kitchen and seating himself on the table while I was cooking up the milk for yet another round of feeds. 'Occult blood, I see on the Path. Lab. report.'

'Auntie, you're not allowed to look at people's charts. Who's on milk only?'

'Smithers, Gold and Forrest. Forrest is starting a three days' test. Oh – and that new boy'll be on milk only for the first few days, won't he?'

I peered at the list and scratched my head, but it was simpler to trust Siddons. 'D'you have milk or custard this feed?' I asked him.

'Milk. I've had a bit of a nagging pain all to-day, nurse. You know, I think that ulcer's travelling.'

'Don't be silly, it couldn't possibly.'

'Couldn't it? What about my uncle, then? He had the Barium meal and Hex-ray, and they diagnosed an ulcer in the duo*odd*enum. Month later, they opened him up and there it was, right up at the top of the stomach. Travelled, you see – they do.'

'You tell that to Sister Tarling,' I said, setting out cups on a tray.

'Bless her heart,' said Siddons. 'She'd say "Yes, dear," and get me a bottle of barley sugar out of her cupboard. I reckon she's got Oedema in the legs, don't you, Nurse?'

'How on earth d'you know that?'

'Oh, I get around.' He hopped off the table, tripping over the hem of his dressing-gown. 'Carry that tray in for you? Better let me. You'll only go and give 'em out wrong else.'

Siddons was subjected to all the indignities and discomforts of gastric investigation. Tubes were forced down his throat and the contents of his stomach sucked up for inspection. X-ray after X-ray was taken and various different diets tried, from the insipid to the nauseating. He was sustained by his absorption in everything that was done to him, and used to ask pertinent questions which sometimes left even Mr Morris Evans stumped. One day, turning his cocky little snub face up to the Surgeon's, he said : 'Come on now, sir. Out with it. I seen on me chart "Query Operation". When you going to carve me up?'

He had a week in which to get used to the idea of being carved. He spent this time coaching a young Diabetic to take on his duties when he should be bedridden. His wife was inclined to be tearful when she came to visit him the day before. 'Cut it out, Norah,' I heard him say. 'This what they're going to do to me is one of the miracles of the age.' He proceeded to give her a detailed description of the operation which he had got from a medical book, concluding with : 'And if I konks out, I wants me body given to the hospital for research.' Mrs Siddons, an anaemic woman who had worked too hard all her life, came over faint on the way out and had to be revived with cups of tea and a sit-down in Sister's room.

When I took him to the Theatre the next day, he was

furious because he was going to be anaesthetized outside. 'I been looking forward to seeing the Theatre,' he grumbled, lying on the trolley looking clean and innocent in the high-necked operating gown. 'Fancy not letting a chap see the slaughter-house. It's a bit rough.'

'Good morning,' said the Anaesthetist, breezing in, followed by the porter wheeling the gas and oxygen apparatus. 'Now, old man, you're not going to mind this a bit.'

'Course I'm not – I don't mind,' Siddons waved that aside. 'What you going to give me, though? Ether, gas, general anaesthetic?'

'Now just *breathe* in,' said the doctor, taking no notice and clapping the gauze mask over Siddon's enquiring face.

'Yes, but what you —' He raised a hand to push it aside.

'All right, all right, old chap – nothing to be afraid of. Just breathe in and see what you can smell.'

'I want to know —' came thickly from under the mask.

'Better watch out he doesn't struggle, Nurse,' said the Anaesthetist. 'Nervy type.' He did struggle. He had told me he was going to take the anaesthetic slowly and calmly, so as to notice his reactions, but he was so infuriated at not being in the know that he tried to resist the gas, and went under choking, and finally turned dark blue and stopped breathing. 'The damned ignorance of these people,' said the Anaesthetist, after we had got him going again with artificial respiration and a gale of oxygen, 'If they knew a bit more about it, they wouldn't panic so.' Mr Morris Evans poked his head through from the Theatre. 'What the devil are you doing?' he asked. 'We're all scrubbed up and I've got a nephrectomy to do after this and an old woman to see in Cambridge by three o'clock.'

The operation started badly and everyone was in a temper throughout. The Surgeon cursed the Anaesthetist because Siddons was heaving, and the Anaesthetist cursed Siddons. Sister cursed Miss Llewellyn, who was assisting, and Miss Llewellyn cursed me. I cursed the heat and my feet.

The operation took longer than they expected. The nephrectomy was waiting in the anaesthetic room, getting more hysterical every minute, and Mr Morris Evans sent me telephoning all over the place : to his wife, to say that he would not be home for lunch, to Cambridge, to tell the old woman he would be late, to Callaghan Ward to tell them to prepare for a blood transfusion, and to the porter to tell his chauffeur to go and buy some sandwiches – ham, if possible – if not, beef, but for God's sake no mustard – and a bottle of beer.

When he was coming round, Siddons gabbled about Oxygen and $CO_2$ and Ethyl Chloride sprays. When he woke up, he was thrilled to find his leg splinted and to see the blood dripping in through the glass connexion in the tube. He was very disappointed that he had been asleep while they cut into the vein. He had his morphia, watching the syringe critically, and presently began to mumble restlessly.

'All right, dear,' Sister said. 'You'll be all right. Just sleep now, quietly,' and the well-trained Diabetic approached as near as he dared and said : 'Everything's O.K., Mr Siddons.' Still he mumbled and complained. It was quite a time before I discovered that he would not settle until somebody told him what his blood group was.

The next day I had to tell him everything, leaving out about the atmosphere. 'Took three hours, eh?' he said proudly. 'I must have been an interesting case. Something a bit out of the ordinary. They like that. Reckon they had a rare old time playing about with me up there, eh, Nurse?'

'Rather,' I lied.

Every pain he had, he studied and mentally charted. 'The stitches in the abdominal wall tweaking now,' he would say, or 'That's me peritonitis. Reckon I got a bit of wind lodged in the hole where the ulcer was. You can, you know.'

'You can't,' I said, but he produced his Uncle again as proof. I gave him *Sister Fairchild* to read, and he followed the nursing treatment with grave concern, always holding the medicine glass of citrated milk that was all he was allowed at first up to the light to see whether the amount was correct. He kept a strict eye on the Diabetic, and from his regal position, propped up on pillows, would direct him up and down the ward, wherever his sharp eye noticed something that wanted doing.

'You taking your diet right, son?' he would enquire. 'You

swear you got no sweets in your locker? What was that I saw your girl bring you in a paper bag last visitors' day?'

'Water biscuits, Mr Siddons.'

'Where'd she get 'em? You can't get 'em in Redwood. If you been eating sweets – how was his sugar this morning, Nurse?'

'My girl comes from St Albans. She got 'em there,' said the boy, peevishly kicking the wheel of the bed.

'Don't kick my bed, you'll burst all me stitches else. Then there'll be trouble, and I'll tell you for why. All me organs'll fall out into the bed. Won't they, Nurse?'

'If you say so.'

'It's time for me feed. One and a half ounce milk and one and a half ounce water this time. I go up half an ounce at twelve o'clock. Here, son, you go with Nurse and bring it back. She's got plenty of other things to do, without you hang around like a sick headache.'

I felt sorry for the Diabetic, whose main object in life was to get back to his earphones as soon as possible in case he should miss a moment of 'Hi Gang' or Sandy Macpherson. He was a tall, drooping boy, with a small face and long eyelashes, and he knew the words of all the dance tunes, especially the ones about rain in a lane and the sun smiling through, which were his favourites. He had been admitted to the ward late one night, in charge of a policeman, who had mistaken an Insulin coma for a drunken stupor. As he had been officially charged with this, it took weeks of form filling and consultation of sects. and paras. before the idea could be uprooted. Even the doctor's evidence left them unconvinced, and the wretched boy was always receiving visits from ponderous blue figures, looking undressed without their helmets, come to question him just once more, with almost wistful hope. There was so little doing in Redwood.

Life trickled gently along. Sister started knitting a pilch for her niece's baby and frequently had to have the stitches counted or picked up for her. When Sister was off duty, Jackman stitched away at the nightgown that she was embroidering for the problematical bridal night, for we were not at all busy. Dawlish went about her work in a dignified

393

way and added another layer of curls to the pile on which her cap reposed. Weekes seemed as busy as ever and scuttered about with a puckered face even when there was nothing to do, and the Junior flounced about yawning and saying : 'Am I bored? Gosh, what a deadly hole this is. Gosh, I'm fed up. Oh, ask somebody else for your feed, Saunders. I can't be bothered.' We wanted to write to her mother and ask if she didn't think it was time the girl was put into corsets.

Like someone who has lain too long in bed, it was almost more than we could do to rouse ourselves when it suddenly became necessary. One morning, we were fiddling away the time between cleaning the ward and going off in relays to have coffee and change our aprons. Twenty minutes was allowed for this, but Sister didn't treat you like a criminal if you took half an hour. As long as the work was done, she didn't mind occasional petty infringements. The years had given her a more balanced idea of these things. I was off duty that morning, and was doing the flowers in the bathroom, spinning them out until it should be half-past nine. The telephone rang and after allowing a decent interval for someone else to answer it, I went through the ward and picked up the receiver. It was Sister Harriman. When she had rung off, I felt almost like ringing her back again to ask if she had really said that. It was too fantastic. It was impossible. Where's Sister? I must find her at once. Quickly! Not a moment to lose! I was in a fluster. I didn't see how we were ever going to be able to cope.

'Nurse, Nurse, whatever are you rushing about like that for?' said Sister placidly, as I cannoned into her coming out of the kitchen. She accepted the news rather like a cook being told there will be two extra for dinner : it's a nuisance, but we'll manage.

'But *twelve*, Sister ! We haven't got half those beds – and air-raid casualties – most of them'll probably have to be operated on. It must have been last night's blitz. The wireless said London had got it badly. I suppose they daren't leave them there another night. But *twelve*, Sister – and two hours' time ! You'd have thought —'

'Poor dears,' said Sister tranquilly, 'we must try and make them as comfortable as possible. Let me see, now.' She stood with one fat finger to her lip, deliberating, refusing to be hurried. The thought of the swarm about to descend on her at eleven o'clock left her unmoved. 'You and Nurse Lawson had better start getting the extra bedsteads out of the cupboard, while I go and see which of the men we can move. Poor things, it does seem a shame to upset them. Nurse Jackman —' I heard her call, as she went into the ward, 'there are one or two things I want you to do.'

One or two things! The Junior and I toiled away in the cupboard, heaving out the folding iron beds that the Government had provided at the beginning of the war, presumably for just such an occasion. Who says England is never prepared before the event? When they were not pinching your fingers, they were barking your shins or biting your ankles. Lawson kept saying: 'Why should we have to do this? It's not fair. I didn't come here to do this. They ought to have men to do it.' I told her to go away and join something with a Trade Union. 'I may tell you I needn't stay here if I don't want to,' she said, kicking a bed which had just kicked her. 'I can get a commission in the W.A.A.F.'s any time I like. My uncle's in the Air Ministry.' One of her favourite patients, a Guardsman with ear trouble, came along to ask if he could help, and I left her to unload her grievances into the sound ear while I went to see if we had enough pyjamas for the new patients, for we had been warned that they would come with no belongings.

Sister Harriman came along, red in the face and all of a dither, to say that no one was to go off duty. 'Government order,' she said impressively, as if she visualized Churchill himself dictating it. She and Sister Tarling talked for a while in the corridor, looking, through the glass doors, like two comfortable countrywomen gossiping on a doorstep. The ward was in an uproar. It was almost as bad as the night the burns came, though it had not the same nightmare quality. A lot of the men were helping – too many of them. In spite of Siddons sitting bolt upright with his hair on end, giving directions, there was no sort of organization.

Beds were being pushed up and down without purpose, sometimes travelling all round the ward and ending up where they had started from, with the patient inside crying 'Nice day for a sail,' and 'Thanks for the buggy ride' – anything to add to the uproar.

Dawlish had the day off that day. She would. Jackman was paddling up and down, the loose skin of her forehead corrugated with worry. Weekes was pushing lockers about with a hideous squeaking of wheels, trying to trace the beds to which they belonged. Lawson and her boy friend came staggering in with the end of a bed under each arm, her face shining like a polished apple and his bandage cock-eyed. Sister went on calmly chatting. When I went past on my way to the linen cupboard, I heard her insisting on having an extra ration of tea sent down. 'It will be the one thing they want after the journey, poor dears.'

'There'll be all sorts of things they want,' said Sister Harriman. 'but I don't know about tea. All the House Surgeons are standing by, and Mr Harvey Watkins and Sir Curtis are coming at eleven. There'll be a terrible lot to do, I'm afraid, a terrible – do you allow Nurse to use hospital sheets on government beds, Sister?' she asked, as I staggered by under a bundle of linen. 'Surely you were issued with government sheets?' Sister had never bothered about this before. So long as the patients had plenty of clean sheets, that was all she cared about, but she had to send me back to the linen cupboard now, with an apologetic look to show me that she thought it was as silly as I did. Sister Harriman checked up my new bundle as I passed her leaving the ward. 'Even in an emergency like this, Nurse,' she said, 'these little things are so important. It's just the difference between a good nurse and a bad one.' There would obviously soon be another notice up about which sheets to put where, and why.

Miraculously, and without agitating anybody, Sister managed to create order on the ward. By eleven o'clock, we were ready, and we looked at our handiwork proudly and mentally rolled up our sleeves, thinking: 'Let 'em come!' I was exhausted already, but I supposed I should somehow last out the day.

The twelve empty beds were ready at the top of the ward, hot bottles in, bedclothes turned back so that a patient could be slid in from a stretcher. A pair of pyjamas, a towel, soap and face flannel were in each locker, and clean charts hung in the holders on the wall, ready to be filled in. The sterilizers were boiling like cauldrons, the blood transfusion instruments were laid out on the trolley under a sterile towel, gauze, wool and bandages were heaped on the low cupboard in the middle of the ward and the hypodermic syringes lay ready in a dish of sterile water. All the men had been got into bed, rather cramped together at the far end of the ward, but they seemed to like it : it made card-playing easier. Nurse Lawson had been sent to the hostel for clean aprons for all of us, and Jackman had even cleaned her shoes.

All we needed now was the patients.

At half-past eleven, I asked Sister if I might dash away and telephone to Mrs Yule to explain why I could not come to lunch.

'Don't be a moment longer than necessary,' said Sister, 'they may come any minute now.' On my way to the telephone box, I passed the doctor's sitting-room and saw an impressive display of white coats sprawled in chairs or standing about, waiting for the casualties. I was glad I was not on Theatre now. They would have a terrible day. Sister Harriman and the Out-Patients Sister, porters, nurses, the Dispenser and various hangers-on, were milling round the entrance hall like a reception committee waiting for a film star. Even the enormous, apoplectic head porter had levered himself out of his glass hutch and was filling the front door, doing a Sister Ann act. As I came out of the telephone box, someone said : 'Hurry back to your ward, Nurse, I can hear the ambulances coming up the hill now.' I fled like Mercury and created a gratifying stir on the ward with my announcement. Everyone ran about doing some little last-minute job, and then we all stood ready again watching the corridor expectantly. It was just like a music-hall act, when the orchestra keeps working up a terrific roll of drums to announce some stupendous entrance, and nobody comes, so they start the crescendo again and still nobody comes, and they roll again even louder, and just when you know your head will burst if they don't stop, the noise ceases, suspended in mid-air. The stage is still empty, people laugh uneasily, and then, suddenly, Nobby Navarino turns anti-climax into climax by crawling meekly out from under the back curtain or climbing out of the french horn, or being spot-lighted hanging by his hands from the stage box. The only difference with us was that the protagonists never appeared at all, even after the fourth and fifth roll of drums. At half-past twelve, Sister got so tired of hearing that the ambulances were in sight, that the stretchers were being lifted out, and other alarums that came to nothing, that she sent us off to dinner. She was getting tired. 'If they come now, they'll have to wait till my nurses have had their lunch,' she said quite testily to a porter who had only come innocently down to borrow a piece of string.

I had missed a good feed at Mrs Yule's for nothing. Chris was at lunch, and she told me that Johnny Briant had told her that the no off-duty order had nothing to do with the Government but was entirely Matron's idea.

Something did happen after lunch. It was visitors' day, but Matron had decreed, naturally enough, that with all the commotion of casualties arriving – at least fifty were expected altogether – it would not do to have visitors thronging the wards. The men understood that and had not grumbled above an undertone when they were told, but when two o'clock came and there were neither casualties nor visitors, the undertone was an ugly rumour of war. The rumour rose on all the wards and grew to a clamour that was answered by another, shriller clamour from without. When I went along to the porter's desk with a message from Sister, I saw a remarkable sight. Sister Harriman was standing on the step of the front door, arms folded, feet planted, keeping at bay a rabble of relations. They were mostly women – at least it was the women who were making the most noise. The men were tweaking at their coats and obviously trying to persuade them to come away and leave the thing alone, but the wives and mothers and sweethearts were not going to be cheated of their rights. It was visitors' day and they intended to visit. Equally, Sister Harriman intended to keep them out and the result was deadlock – institutional authority versus outraged possessive instinct. Black coats and best hats dipped and surged in argument on the gravel. Umbrellas and paper parcels waved. Those behind kept pushing, so that those in front had their noses almost touching the enemy's skirt. An untidy, hysterical woman with a jumping face kept waving a paper carrier and shouting : 'What about my Fred's clean pyjamas? What about that, I say?' For one moment, I thought they were going to storm the hospital. A common impulse suddenly swept through them like the wind through corn, and as they all pressed forward, Sister Harriman made a sort of defensive movement with her hands and took a step backwards. And then suddenly the forward movement stopped, the noise stopped, the mob instinctively fell back a pace, as Sarah Churchman appeared silently on the step above them and quelled them by the mere expression on her face. It was most dramatic. I expected her to say : 'Down, you rabble, you gutter curs – back to the sewers where you belong and rid us of your stench !'

They listened quite reasonably to her explanation of why they could not come in, and such was her power that some of the sycophants actually started to back her up and to turn to their neighbours and say that the Matron was quite right, and didn't they know there was a war on.

One nurse was to be sent from each ward to collect the things that the visitors had brought for the patients, and as I was on the spot, I was loaded with flowers, books, food, clean vests, and personal messages of every sort, from Sid having written at last to say he'd got there and it's stifling hot and lots of sand and where might that be, to Em and Baby sending their fond love and when are you coming out?

I had to make several trips before I had collected all the parcels and given out the dirty washing and messages from the patients. The entrance hall by now was like a madhouse, with nurses and relations yelling at each other across the crowd, paper bags bursting, apples rolling over the floor, and two women fighting for a dirty pair of pyjamas that each claimed came off her husband.

And still the casualties did not come.

We took the ward teas round early, so as to get that done while we could, and soon afterwards Sister said that we could go off in relays for an hour's rest. I trailed off at about six. I had been excited at first about the casualties, feeling that at last we were in more tangible contact with the war, were taking part in it in a second-hand way. But now I hoped they wouldn't come at all. Perhaps they were already dead. I was too tired to take any interest in them, far too tired to cope with the many hours' work that their arrival would entail. They would probably arrive in the middle of the night and we would have to get up.

I kicked off my shoes and lay down on my bed with a cigarette. After having got up twice for my book and an ashtray, I had just got comfortable when Janet's thump nearly stove in the door : 'All Naa-assis got to go buck to the wards !'

Before I went through the door and up the stairs to the hospital, I turned the other way and looked out of the hostel door on to the gravel to see what was doing. As I looked, a khaki woman on a motor-cycle skidded in through the iron gates as if a whole Panzer division were after her. She hurled herself off at the front door and plunged into the hospital, a canvas bag swinging on her hip. A despatch rider, hoping to be mentioned in despatches. Then I turned and ran, for I had seen the nose of the first converted bus sliding past the porter's cottage. Everyone was alert again now. The atmosphere had sprung back to eleven o'clock that morning, and we were on our toes, ready to do our best for them, forgetting how we had cursed them all day, now that they were actually here.

When the first stretcher came in with a very old man on it, we all thought 'Poor old man to be blitzed,' but when another one came in only a fraction younger, and then another and another, all old dotards and all, as far as one could see, without a scratch on them, realization began to dawn. Some of them began to get up as soon as they were put to bed and start to prowl tremulously about. 'Been out of bed for months,' they said, when we remonstrated, 'we was never in bed at the other 'orspital.'

They were dear old infirmary chronics, who had been evacuated to make room in London for the real casualties. The only arrangements that we had made that still stood were the cups of tea, although one old man threatened to walk back to London if he couldn't have cocoa. He was destined to be a nuisance; one could see that. He had a long, curly grey beard, and looked just like Judas, with small glittering eyes. Nobody could find out what was wrong with him, because all he would say was : 'You mind your business, gel. Ask me no questions, I tells yer no lies.'

The Surgeons went home, and the House Surgeons either went or sent out for beer. We turned off the sterilizers, put away the bandages and instruments, and took down the six beds that were not needed. By the time we had got the ward straight and tucked in the old men, who, incidentally, had a suitcaseful of belongings apiece, it was nearly nine o'clock and the sirens were going. All the old men sat up, and you could see by their eyes what they had been through last night. Sister went round explaining to them that the siren was a mere formality and probably praying inwardly that the Germans would not choose to-night to have a go at Redwood aerodrome. 'It's all right, dear, you're safe now,' she said, just like a mother whose child had woken up with night terrors. It seemed to work. Even Judas lay down and consented to go to sleep, though not until he had made someone get him another cup of cocoa.

None of the Old Daddys, as Sister Tarling called them, seemed to have any address other than the hospital from which they had been evacuated, or the one they had been in before that, or the one before that. Hospitals to them were like South Coast hotels to Colonels' widows – the only home they knew, and, like Colonels' widows, they dug themselves in almost immediately and managed to establish prior claims to the best chairs and least draughty corners. From the cardboard suitcases and canvas bags that they had brought with them, they produced photographs and china ornaments and other knick-knacks, which they arranged on their locker tops to make themselves at home. They were nearly all allowed up, as there was nothing much wrong with them except senility, and they used to sit round the fire in the ward, for it was a chilly October, smoking foul blackened pipes and conversing in monosyllabic grunts. They gave a homey atmosphere to the place which orderly rows of spotless beds and the smell of antiseptic normally failed to provide, but we were after all supposed to be a hospital ward, not a Home of Rest.

They had been in hospital so long that they had almost forgotten any other life, and most of them had been likewise forgotten by their relations. They hardly ever had any visitors, but they didn't seem to mind; they were perfectly self-contained between the four walls of the ward. The oldest of them all was Daddy Johnson, who was nearly ninety. He had a cherubic face with faded blue eyes, a scarlet button nose and a fringe of grey beard that went right round his face to where baldness suddenly started above his ears. When he had the wireless headphones on, he looked exactly like a baby in a bonnet. He was the goodest old man, and made far less trouble than some of the others who were not confined to bed as he was. He used to crack very feeble jokes with the younger patients, at which Siddons always laughed, even if nobody else did, and the old man would cackle delightedly at the back of his nose. As he had nobody to bring him extras, Sister used to buy him chocolate cakes, which he ate so slowly that the chocolate used to melt and run into his beard. She called him 'the Bladder Daddy', because of his complaint.

When I asked him the name of his next-of-kin, to fill in on his chart that first evening, he only stared at me innocently with his china eyes. He had no idea. He had once had a daughter, it transpired, but she was in Australy now.

Much as she loved the old men, except Judas Iscariot, whom nobody could stand, Sister spent her time urging Mr Sickert to arrange for their disposal elsewhere. We were not supposed to keep people who required no nursing and the beds were wanted for other patients who were waiting to come in. The Infirmary eventually took most of them, and

Mr Sickert managed to get the Bladder Daddy into a very superior convalescent home that was chiefly staffed by voluntary ladies who wore the Red Cross uniform as fancy dress and made up to it accordingly. Nobody would take Judas Iscariot; it seemed we were stuck with him for life. He had the most irritating, as well as the dirtiest habits. His locker was an offensive glory hole which nobody could bring themselves to turn out, even if he had allowed it. He was an inveterate hoarder, and the night nurses said he used to be opening and shutting the drawer and cupboard all night long, gloating over his scraps and oddments under cover of the dark. Every evening, we had to collect the newspapers and put them by the dustbin for the porter to clear away, but Judas would never give his up. Even after three or four days he would insist that he was still reading it and would curse you venomously if you removed one while he was out of bed. He used to fold them up meticulously with his crooked, bony fingers, so that there were only about four square inches of print showing. This he would pass up and down in front of his avid, glittering eyes, folding it again as carefully to the next section when he had got his money's worth out of every word. He only had to buy a paper once a week; the Sunday paper lasted him for seven days. When he had finished it, he would tear it into squares and line things with it: his locker shelves, the soles of his slippers, his dinner tray, anything so as to get every ounce of value for his twopence.

We had got the ward straight again, government beds stacked away, and the other beds returned to their proper places, when the old Bladder Daddy suddenly turned up again in a wheel chair. There appeared to have been some mistake. The convalescent home was only for the military. They had been expecting some handsome young lieutenant with curly eyelashes, and who should turn up but old Daddy Johnson with his cherry nose that Siddons insisted was due to drinking bad beer. He was glad to be back. The convalescent home, he said, had been too fiddle-faddle. He settled down gratefully into his old corner near the fire, and spread out his spotted china dog and his turnip watch and his ashtray with the Broadstairs Arms on it.

Not all the other wards had been able to dispose of so many of their evacuees. Herbert Waterlow was still overcrowded with them, and the consequence was that when Sweetie's Anti-Aircraft unit brought down a German plane in a ploughed field five miles outside the town, we were the only ward that had beds to spare for the two survivors. Sister Tarling, who was so patriotic that she cried when the wireless played *There'll Always Be an England*, hated the idea, and had to summon all her professional sense of duty and innate compassion to conquer her racial instincts.

'After all, Nurses, a case is a case,' she told us, all gathered in her sitting-room before the arrival of the Germans. 'I want you to look on it like this. To us has been given the privilege of healing the sick. It's a responsibility that transcends all other issues. The science of medicine is universal; it's far greater than any political upheaval or any war that was ever fought. These men are sick men. That's all you've got to think about – don't think about their nationality, and if you can't stomach their language, don't talk to them.' She paused. She had come to the end of the piece which she had prepared as much to convince herself as us.

We had not given much thought to the matter before. The mental apathy engendered by hospital routine had dulled the patriotic fervour which was responsible for half of our presences here. War news could no longer get us worked up; in fact, we seldom studied it, and as for discussing it – there were far more absorbing topics much nearer home. So the idea of two German patients had not moved us to murderous frenzy. It would be something new; you could say that for it. Now that Sister was making a Thing of it, however, we began to feel those very reactions which she had called us in here to eradicate. We saw how strongly she objected. Her usually smooth, untroubled face showed traces of the struggle between her obligations and her instincts.

'After all,' said Dawlish, in her slow, resentful voice, 'they did come here to drop bombs on us. I don't see how we can

404

be expected to forget that. I think it's awful cheek myself to expect us to nurse them,' she added, twizzling up a curl. 'I shall give in my notice to-morrow. I didn't come here to toady to a lot of Nazis. I shall tell Matron so.' Sister made a shocked, hushing face. 'I know it's difficult,' she said, 'but it isn't easy for me, either, and I look to you to back me up, as I know you will.' We all made *esprit de corps* noises. 'They'll be nursed behind screens, of course,' she went on, 'and there's no reason why the men should know who they are. You are strictly forbidden to mention them to the other patients. Is that clear?' she added, with a burst of severity, which she hoped might stop Dawlish humming and cleaning her nails with the nails of the other hand.

It didn't make any difference. The men found out within a day. Trust Siddons not to be kept in the dark about anything that was going on in his ward. He was allowed up by now, and one had to keep constant watch on him to prevent his sneaking behind the screens to 'see what the bleeders looked like'. It was all rather embarrassing. The Germans were quite pleasant, well-mannered boys, not too badly injured to be perfectly aware of the effect of their presence on their unseen fellow-patients. Naturally, they hated being here as much as we hated to have them. They both had fractures and were difficult to move, and anything one had to do for them, like bathing them or making their bed, took a long time. I suppose if I had been a good nurse I should not have grudged this time, but I did. Even if there was nothing particular to do on the ward, I felt I would have been better employed talking to Daddy Johnson about the Crimea. Whenever the men saw one going behind the screens, they would yell out : 'Cut 'is bleeding throat, Nurse'; and other suggestions unprintable. Sister used to come into the ward and flap her hands at them, and although they stopped out of regard for her, they broke out again as soon as she had gone. The night nurse said that it was dreadful at night when there was an air raid. The men had never taken much notice before except to curse sleepily, but now they would all wake up to hurl abuse over the screens, and the Germans would lie blushing and silent, contemplating the irony of having a bomb dropped on them by their own side.

Judas Iscariot, of course, nursed as big a grievance as anybody. He would lie with his glinting eyes trained on the screens, muttering Hebraic imprecations and complaining to the nurses that there was a bad smell in the ward. If anyone smelt, it was he himself. We told him so. It didn't matter what you said to him; he was uninsultable. That was the creepy part about him.

Dawlish had been to Matron and complained. 'So I said to her : "Matron," I said, "I don't see why I should be expected to surrender my patriotism for the convenience of your hospital. You can get some other nurse to do it. I feel too strongly for my country." And Matron said : "But you must stay, Nurse," she said, "I count on you for the smooth running of that ward."' Jackman, of course, believed this and was in a torment of worry for days at the thought of the aspersion cast on her.

When she had exhausted the limelight of rebellion, Dawlish thought there might be a certain piquancy in discovering the good qualities of the Germans. Everyone else was too bigoted to appreciate them. She alone had the discernment to realize their intellect. She became more boring than ever with endless verbatim reports of conversations she had held with them, usually ending up with : 'Of course, you think it's appalling of me to treat them like human beings, but I'm afraid I've never been able to develop this unthinking, automatic patriotism that everybody goes in for in wartime. I can't help seeing them as people, you see. I'm funny like that.' She would take up any attitude which she thought would disassociate her from the common herd in thought or deed. I told her she'd better marry one of them and see how far individualism got her in Germany.

We used to tease Dawlish about being keen on them, but the joke turned to ashes on our lips when Lawson announced one day in all seriousness that she was in love with Oberleutnant Himmelheber. She came and cried into the diabetic specimen that I was testing and told me all about it. Now that I came to think of it, I realized that she had got thinner in the last few weeks and was not so frequently to be found in the kitchen filling up the corners left by steak pudding and hot jam roll. To quote Godfrey Winn when he saw an egg being boiled : I turned away, sick with disgust. I suppose she was attracted by the novelty. There were plenty of perfectly good Tommies in the ward on whom she could have sublimated her adolescent desires, but no, she had to go and pick on a German who, by the time he was discharged from the ward, was strong enough to 'Heil Hitler' at Sister as he was being wheeled past her on the trolley.

She went scarlet in the face as if someone had hit her, and a perfect fusillade of oaths was hurled from all sides at the glass doors as the trolley went through. Siddons leaped out of bed and ran down the corridor in pyjamas and bare feet before anyone could stop him. He lost the trolley after it had gone into the lift, and, hareing about the hospital, found himself at the front door and was brought back by the fat porter, like a policeman bringing home a stray. He then retired to bed with indigestion. And all this time, Nurse Lawson was leaning her soft bosom on the draining-board in the sluice, crying her eyes out and swearing she would never smile again.

She may not have, for all I know, because the next day I was moved to another ward, and became so oppressed by the unparalleled afflictions of my new existence that, as far as I was concerned, everyone wore a face like a boot.

## Chapter Nine

I WAS on Grace Annie Sprock, the maternity ward into which I had blundered when I first came to the hospital for my interview. My brief, informal meeting with the female cataclysm who ran this ward had left me reeling, and whole days of her now were devastating. She ran that ward as if it were a totalitarian state, and although the result was full-tilt efficiency, I could not help thinking that a little less commotion might have been better for the mothers and babies.

'You on Midwiff?' Barney asked me at supper. I nodded,

with my mouth full of toad-in-the-hole that was all hole and no toad. 'Oh, yes,' she said, 'your apron's all over babies. How's mad Maria Ramsbotham?' I shrugged my shoulders dejectedly.

'You'll get used to her,' said Barney. 'You mustn't take her seriously. She's mad, of course – quite starkers.'

It was the energy of the woman that was so shattering. She never stopped going from morning till night, and even when there was nothing much doing, she would frequently miss her off duty and even her meals because of her mania that we did not work properly without supervision. When babies were born, she was a dynamo of activity. She was here, there and everywhere – admonishing the doctor, exhorting the mother, slanging the nurses, telling you to do something and then snatching it away to do it herself, and altogether raising such Cain in the Labour Ward that when the baby arrived, his first breath was a gasp of astonishment.

The only time when she was unenthusiastic about the arrival of a baby was when it looked like being born between nine and ten at night. It was a moot point whether this was her responsibility or Night Sister's, and although she would have overridden anyone else and if necessary stayed up all night, she and Fanny Adams were such sworn enemies that she was only too pleased to present her with a little bit of extra work to start off the night and upset her routine.

The work on this ward was confusing at first and arduous, compared with Martin Callaghan and his well-behaved Gastrics. Apart from the fact that many of the women were in a nervous and difficult state, the babies required endless attention. There were usually about five or six of them sleeping or yelling or threatening to choke in the white cots that hung over the end of their mothers' beds. There was bathing them and changing them and feeding those that were on bottles, and 'putting up' and 'taking down', which involved much shifting of screens and frequent visits to the mother to prevent her and the baby falling into a bucolic stupor of contentment at the mere fact of each other's existence. Each baby wore its name on a piece of tape round its wrist, but when two were born close together, the fracas was such that one was never sure that Sister had not labelled them wrong in her excitement. Well may Mrs Finnucane say to her son as she clips him over the head in a few years' time : 'You unnatural child !' I always had a suspicion that he belonged to Mrs Duff. He looked much more like her, and the baby that crowed and squeaked in the cot at the foot of her bed was so markedly unlike Mr Duff that one seemed to detect a slight coldness in his manner towards Mrs Duff on visitors' day.

Even when I began to get accustomed to the work of the ward, Sister still followed me about admonishing me. She would always tell you to do a thing just when you were about to do it, so that you got no credit for initiative. Even if you managed to forestall her and got on with a job of your own accord, you would see her making for you, her whole being itching to interfere. 'That's right, Nurse. Change Mrs Larkin's sheets.' She could let nothing pass without comment. Before she had even had time to notice whether you were doing it wrong, she would embark on a voluble exposition of the correct method, which she had already told you ten times, while you listened without being able to concentrate on anything but those amazing false teeth. There was a legend that once, when she was upbraiding a nurse with particular vehemency, the teeth had slipped their moorings and shot into the kitchen sink and down the waste pipe, whence they had to be retrieved with long Cheatle's forceps.

Lawson, who was First Nurse on the ward, prayed that if it happened again she might be there to see it. She said that Sister Ramsbotham was a Hyperthyroid, and certainly she had the characteristic popping eyes, the fine, dry hair, the nervous excitability and restlessness. Perhaps she was taking herself as the norm when she accused me of having Myxoedema, which *Sister Fairchild* translated as thyroid deficiency, characterized by slowness of mind and speech, a defective memory, excess of adipose tissue and abnormally large hands and feet.

It seemed incredible to think that I had been in hospital for more than a year. I had never worked for so long with-

409

out a break and was beginning to think that here was a concrete example of eternity, but when I was summoned to Matron's office one morning, I thought it must be my holidays at last.

'Well, Nurse,' she said, not looking up as I came in, 'you've been here a year now, haven't you?'

'Thirteen months, Ma'am,' I corrected her respectfully. She ignored this. 'So do you think you're entitled to a red star?' she pursued, looking up. I made modest noises, but she ignored these, too. She was evidently going through a formula. 'A red star is a sign of responsibility, a sign of increased authority,' she went on. 'You should by now be a trustworthy person to have on a ward; you should be able to carry out nursing treatments without supervision, and you should realize your duties in regard to upholding hospital discipline. A red star will give you a certain amount of influence over the Juniors, you know. As you gradually become more Senior, you are expected to help the Juniors and to assist in their training. Do you think I should give you a red star?'

Put like that, an answer obviously was 'No', but I said 'Yes', and smiled obsequiously. The whole thing was a farce, because she had obviously had reports on my work and knew perfectly well whether or not I was worthy to decorate my bosom with the scrap of red felt which she then handed to me with as much condescension as if it were the D.S.O.

'You can sew this on to your apron for to-morrow,' she said, 'but you must buy some red felt and make the stars for your other aprons.'

Mean old devil, I thought, while verbally licking her boots.

'I trust you to be worthy of it, Nurse,' she said in her thin, unresonant voice. 'Don't let me down.' It was just like being presented with one's hockey colours by the headmistress. I went out, clutching my bit of felt proudly, but sceptical about its ability to transform me suddenly into a miracle of efficiency, on whose every word the respectful Juniors hung.

The trouble was that most of them seemed to know more than I did. The Junior on Grace Annie Sprock had been at a Maternity Home in Bedford, and I was always having to ask her how to do things like putting on a nappie, about which I couldn't very well admit my ignorance to anyone else. It looked so uneducated. It was as bad as not knowing how to herring-bone when I had to pad splints on night duty.

Sissons was always telling long stories about the Maternity Home, where she had had a crush on the Matron. I got sick of hearing what a Saint she was and how she had made the place a home from home, with everyone mealing together to the accompaniment of bright conversation, and afterwards bringing their sewing to her sitting-room to listen to the wireless. Often, on her day off, she would dash back to Bedford for twenty-four soggy hours of bliss. I wondered whether she would come rushing back to Redwood all the time after she left the Queen Adelaide. She would not be put up if she did, that was certain. Matron had once allowed the mother of a very ill nurse to stay in the Nurses' Hostel for a night, as she had travelled from Cumberland and could not find a room. The next day, she informed her crisply that she must find lodgings, and when the mother mentioned the difficulty of finding accommodation, Matron said: 'I shall have to get the Lady Almoner to fix you up.'

'Thank you,' said the offended mother, drawing quite a good mink-marmot coat around her, 'but I don't think I need fall back just yet on Charity.' She spent a whole day tramping the town in search of a room, and was so tired when she visited her daughter in the evening that she cried over her, and the daughter cried too, and worked her temperature up two points.

When I started on the Maternity Ward, there were six babies, varying from cherubs to wizened old men. Besides their mothers, there were half a dozen or so other patients who would either soon fill a cot or were else in for some essentially female complaint. I felt sorry for the latter. It must have been awful to be kept awake at night by the crying of babies, none of which were your own, especially if, like one or two of them, you had just had an operation which ensured that now you never could have a baby.

I was particularly sorry for little Irene Hicks, who had

been brought in on the point of death and even now, with nearly a gallon of somebody else's blood in her, was waxy-pale. I remember the afternoon she came in : it was visitors' day, and the ward was full of staring women, their sense of drama deliciously titillated by the livid figure being wheeled into the ward. Outside, stood Irene's mother, bearing something in a pudding basin covered with a bath towel.

Poor Irene had wanted that baby, but had allowed herself to be persuaded by her young man to visit someone that a pal of a fellow he knew swore by. Before I was a nurse, I was not in favour of legal abortion. Now I think that anything would be preferable to some of the ghastly things that are perpetrated outside the law. If women could see what some of their sex have to go through in consequence, nightmare old women in basement flats would lose their trade.

Irene would lie turning her peaky little face from side to side, watching the women with their babies. She wouldn't be able to have one now.

Quite a different proposition was Bella, a Streatham girl, whose only thought was to get back into circulation as soon as possible. 'Me for some fun, as soon as I get out of this dump,' she said, sitting up in bed in a bright yellow jacket that clashed with her hair. 'Little Bella was not quite so clever this time as she thought she was.' She had a deep, rich, unashamed laugh. I once heard her say to Chubby : 'I bet you think I'm an awful naughty girl, you naughty boy.' His ears went magenta; he was highly embarrassed. Mrs Dewey in the next bed listened open-mouthed. She was unable to shut her mouth, because as she only had half a set of false teeth, she wore the one plate half-way between her upper and lower gums. She was eccentric before her baby was born and more so afterwards. One rather trembled for the child. She told me that she had three others – 'and one I buried last March, dear, lovely little coffin, 'e 'ad' – and that one day, when her husband had thrown a cup of tea at her, saucer and all, her eldest son had hurled a fork which had made three holes in his father's chest.

'So what did you do?'

'Well, I picked up the first thing that came to hand to stop

Dad going for young Ern. It was an O.K. sauce bottle; luckily it was nearly empty, else we should have had a mess.'

I hoped that next time they had a row the first thing that came to hand would not be the baby.


Farren was still Staff Nurse on the ward, somewhat chastened by Sister's constantly-voiced opinion of her but still keeping her end up with canticles. If you asked her a question, she would always finish the phrase before answering, which was maddening if you were in a hurry, which you always were with Fanny Ramsbotham chasing you about like Simon Legree. We all used to look forward to Sister's week-ends off. The ward, though perhaps not so smartly run, took on quite a different, friendly atmosphere, and you had time to chat to the women, without hearing : 'Come along now, Nurse Dickens : if you've got time to gossip, I certainly haven't. Come along now, Nurse, you've got two hours' work to do in one !' We paid for our freedom when she came back, however. She went through the ward and the sluice and bathroom and specimen rooms like a devouring flame, flinging a finger towards neglected corners, banging the lid of the dustbin, picking up an imperfectly cleaned bowl and hurling it into the sink so that enamel chips flew, routing in the cupboard for dirty dusters and flinging them in my face with a savage cry. If any patient in the ward was worse, or a baby had been born dead, Farren was in for trouble, even though the baby might have been dead long before it was born. I once heard Sister say to the Night Nurse : 'Now, Sister, if that woman dies in the night, I shall hold you entirely responsible.' A nice comforting thought for poor Rogers, who was as nervy as a squirrel, to start the night with. After she had finished with us, and sworn as usual that never again would she take a week-end off while such imbecile nurses were on her ward, Sister would roar into the kitchen to have a go at Dora, the stunted little Ward Maid, who didn't care a hang and showed it, which incensed Sister still more. There would be a cacophony of spoons and forks being counted and hurled into drawers. 'Prison's the place for a waster like you in wartime,' she once said to Dora. 'All those crusts are to be buttered and sent into the ward at teatime.'

'Can't do that,' returned Dora stolidly. 'They're hard as old boots. I wouldn't give 'em to me own grandmother, let alone anyone that's not quite the thing.'

'Some of them are quite well enough to eat them,' said Sister. 'I will not have perfectly good food wasted.'

'Eat 'em yourself, then,' said Dora, turning with a shrug to her sink and beginning to run the taps noisily. Sister pretended not to hear. She couldn't treat Dora quite as she treated us. Ward Maids were not so easily come by.

'If you was to give me out a bit of jam now, to put on them crusts,' said Dora, who was fond of anything sweet.

'I have exactly one pot in my cupboard to last two weeks,' said Sister, picking eggcups off the dresser to see if there was dust underneath. 'You people don't seem to have heard of rationing. Sometimes I wonder whether you even know there's a war on – all these drawers want fresh paper, and you'll have to wash the walls down one day this week. A nice surprise you'll get, when the Germans walk in and you find yourself in a concentration camp, which is the place where they put people like you.'

'Wouldn't be much change from this,' said Dora, as Sister swung out to see what she could find wrong with the linen cupboard.

'What d'you think of that?' said Dora, as she and I were clicking our teeth over the crusts while we prepared the teas. 'Wouldn't give 'em as much as a spoonful of jam. Mean? She wouldn't give you the drippings from 'er nose.'

'I can't think how you answer her back like you do,' I said. 'I wouldn't dare.'

'Oh, well,' said Dora, flinging a mildewy crust into the pig pail, 'I never was one to mince my bones.'

Nurse Lawson was in love. Or thought she was, because when you're in love for the first time, how can you tell whether you are in love? You have nothing to compare it with except a furtive romance with a stable boy when you were fourteen, and it is certainly an advance on that. You have not yet realized that because a man has a sports car and knows what to say to waiters, it does not necessarily mean that he is your soul mate. To Lawson, whose idea of a night out was three ports at the station hotel and a giggly walk back up the hill in the dark with the dispenser's assistant, a man who took her up to London – first class and a taxi at the other end – was heaven indeed. He had been a patient on the private wards, while she was on night duty there. He came in two days before I got my chicken-pox, a glib man, with eyes like those green marbles that used to come out of the neck of ginger-beer bottles. He was an astute business man and had a finger in many pies : a chain of grocery shops, canteens in some of the factories, one or two small hotels, and even an interest in a local film unit. This enabled him to talk with authority on many subjects, as indeed, he talked about everything, whether he knew anything about it or not. He was not unpresentable, and probably did possess some of the qualities that Lawson saw in him. If he had been born dumb, he might have been quite a nice person.

The first time I met him and Lawson in the bar of the 'Rowan Arms', I thought I should scream if he said once more : 'I know for a fact.' There was an older man there, the manager of a cigarette factory, who kept producing packets of ten out of concealed pockets, and a friend of his, a soldier who had been out in France. However, this John Davenant evidently knew more about the army and commerce than either of them, and everything that was said he capped with a story which centred round the word 'I'. He aborted any discussion by being unable to keep it impersonal, and the only heed he paid to anyone else's opinion was occasionally to wait without listening until they had finished talking and he could go on undisturbed. The story of the B.E.F. was embodied in the experiences of a boring friend of his at G.H.Q., and when somebody mentioned Dunkirk, he knew the skipper of what one might have thought to be the only vessel of that conglomerate fry. He also knew a great deal about armament factories, but as there was a large picture of Hitler dressed as an eavesdropping ancestral portrait above his head, he was able to convey a sealed-lips omniscience, without necessarily having any knowledge to back it.

Lawson watched him round-eyed over the top of her glass, and when we went to the 'Ladies', pounced on me with : 'What d'you think of him? Isn't he marvellous? He's awfully good in company, don't you think? He makes me feel terribly ignorant, I hardly dare say a word.' She circled a powder puff over her smooth, freckled face that never succeeded in looking made-up whatever she did to it. 'Oh dear, my hair! D'you like it taken up at the sides like this? John's used to going about with such sophisticated girls, it's really rather a strain. The other day, when we were in Town, we met a girl he told me he once had an affair with. He's had lots, you know, he told me, but I don't mind; I think a man ought to be experienced. Well, this girl – I had been feeling quite smart up to then, I had that blue suit of Barnet's and some decent stockings – but as soon as she came and sat with us, I felt a mess. She was fearfully sophisticated. Red hair and green eyes and a marvellous fox cape – oh dear, my *hair*!' She wrestled to make a bang on top of her head *à la* women's fashion magazines. 'I think I shall go and have a platinum rinse next payday.'

Long after I was in bed and asleep that night, I woke to see the door opening cautiously and to hear the floorboards creaking like mad with Lawson's efforts to be silent.

'Oh, were you asleep? I didn't mean to wake you. I just thought I'd look in in case you were awake. D'you mind if I come in for a moment?' She flopped on to my feet. 'Had a good time?' I asked, yawning and fishing for my hot bottle and finding it cold.

'Marvellous!' She breathed an ecstatic sigh. They had been up to Town – first class. They had been 'up West'. John had taken her to a club – 'Everyone knew him there, I was awfully proud' – and there had been fruit machines and Lawson had had several gin and tonics. They had come back again – still first class – and John had half a bottle of whisky in his coat pocket and had tipped the guard to lock their carriage. What possible answer could there be to his proposal?

'I'm so happy,' she purred, picking feathers out of my

416

eiderdown. 'Don't you think I'm terribly lucky? You do like him, don't you?'

I tried to conceal my dismay with suitable enthusiasm. Lawson was sweet and naïve and clean. She would have made somebody a marvellous wife. She could have been deeply and faithfully in love.

'When are you going to be married?'

'As soon as we can. John's got to go up North and he wants me to go with him. He's going to get a special licence. Its awfully difficult to get nowadays, I believe, but he knows a man who'll wangle it for him. He knows lots of people. Gosh, to think of getting out of this foul hole! I can't think how I've stuck it for two years.'

'Still, in a way, it seems a waste —'

'Oh, no, I'd never have passed my Finals in any case – not that I really wanted to. It would be ghastly to be a Staff Nurse, and think of being a Sister! I was always terrified of becoming like these frightful women – think, one might even turn out like Fanny Ramsbotham. Oh, no, apart from John being so marvellous, it's a merciful escape!'

Escape. So many nurses marry the first men who ask them, because they have had neither the time nor the opportunity to meet anyone else or to realize that life holds other alternatives besides hospital and marriage. They are thrilled to escape from a monotony which they know only too well into something of which they know nothing and therefore expect a great deal.

Lawson had a grand time telling everybody and giving in her notice to Matron, and buying clothes and showing people her ring and introducing John to people as 'My Fiancé', and talking, talking about him in a boastful but legitimate way. After all, he was a man, and quite a personable one at that, even if he was a crashing bore. People swanked about the runtiest of boy friends so that anyone who landed a real man was entitled to boast.

Lawson lived in a whirl of excitement that left her no time for doubts and eventually got married at St. Anne's Church, in a pale blue dress and coat and a small round hat, to John in a brown pin stripe suit with a double-breasted

417

waistcoat, making the responses very loudly, while hers were barely a murmur. Afterwards, I went to the reception with five or six other nurses who had managed to get the morning off, and we all trooped in, branded as nurses by our awkward hands, red from the early morning's scrubbing, our air of having borrowed bits and pieces of clothes, which we had, and the alacrity with which we attacked the buffet, as if we hadn't tasted decent food for weeks, which we had not. Lawson's mother and father were there, looking rather baffled, Lawson was stammering with pride, and John took the half-hearted cries of 'Speech!' to mean that people really wanted him to speak and held forth pompously for several minutes, while everyone stood round interjecting polite 'Ha-has' and 'Hear-hears' and wishing that he would stop so that they could get on with the drinking.

I seemed to be dogged by spouters. To replace Lawson on the ward, we had a wide-hipped girl called Jobling, who called every one 'Kid' and babbled on like a moorland stream about anything except what she happened to be doing at the moment. I wondered that Sister did not treat Jobling to her: 'If you've got time to gossip, I certainly haven't' line, but apparently Jobling was popular because she was good with the babies, which none of the rest of us were, except Sissons, who didn't count, because she was the Junior and mere. I suppose the babies appreciated Jobling's maternal shape, anyway, they behaved much better with her than with us, and we were constantly treated to: 'Look at little Nurse Jobling there. There's a girl who knows how to bring up a baby's wind.' Anyone whom she liked was always 'little'. I dare say a psychoanalyst would explain this as some sort of inhibition about her own size. Mountainous Mrs West, who had fulfilled Sister's prophecy by producing twins, was always 'little Mrs West', and a tall V.A.D. who came three times a week and bathed the babies with the skill of manifold personal experience and had a brother who was a Baronet, was 'the little V.A.D.' I liked the days when Mrs Finney came. It was refreshing to work with someone who had other things to talk about except shop and boy friends and uninteresting family histories. As she was not on the pay-

418

roll, she was in a position to stand up to Sister. If she did not agree with something she was told to do, she would argue it, and while at first we stood with bated breath expecting to see her crushed like a beetle, I soon realized that Sister responded better to being answered back than to having her boots licked. However, while appreciating that the best way to deal with a bully is to bully back, I never quite had the nerve.

Looking back, I could remember a time when I might have been more rebellious and less blindly acquiescent. Hospital life does alter your character. It dims any personality you might have once possessed. Through working to routine and never to initiative, your brain becomes like a car with a bad pick-up. It ticks over fast enough to cope with what is required of it, but its acceleration deteriorates until it is almost impossible to rev it up sufficiently to keep pace with anyone not similarly affected. One did not notice this in the hospital, where the conversation was unambitious and the humour unsubtle and chiefly lavatorial, but the moment you went among outside people, you felt dull and inadequate. I had never been to the Fellowes's house again for this reason. The nearest I got to them was occasional meetings with the down-trodden relation, with whom, as she told me that the 'Four Winds' set gave her an inferiority complex, I felt a certain bond.

It was a different matter going to Mrs Finney's. She had a dear little slice of a house in the arty corner of the slums, with a red door and window boxes and half a dozen small dogs to whom she was a slave. If I was fed up, I could always go there and get the hospital out of my system by talking about it, and if she was bored, she never showed it. She understood what it was like to be always tired, and sometimes, when I arrived yawning to dinner, she would put me to bed for an hour or two and then wake me with drink and food, and we would sit over the fire on a sofa that was almost as big as the entire drawing-room, and pick everyone at the hospital to pieces, an occupation of which it took a long time to tire.

Once, at her house, I met Sir Curtis Rowntree and his

wife. They were charming, and it seemed funny to think that only that morning I had been calling him 'Sir' and scuttling out of his way, and that he had thrown a pair of rubber gloves at me because I had put them away wet and he couldn't get his hand into them. I reminded him of this, and as it seemed to go down well, I told him what a to-do his coming always created and how Sister always careered round practically measuring the set of his patients' counterpanes with a micrometer – 'Because Sir Curtis is so particular about these things. He always notices whether a bed is correctly made.' He promised that he would try and remember to notice next time.

The following morning, he came along to see a new patient, and Sister, standing by the bed like a duenna, snapped her fingers at me to bring screens.

When I brought them, Sir Curtis smiled the beautiful curved smile that relaxed the sardonic lines of his face and said : 'Good morning, Nurse. How are you?' – just, as old Sow would say, as if I had been anybody. Sister's eyebrows shot into her hair, I went red and mumbled, and Sir Curtis said : 'I've brought you that book we were talking about,' and fished it out of his bag. Sister's teeth were flashing at me like a heliograph and I mumbled again and slunk away, tripping over a tear in the screen and enabling Sister to say : 'Why wasn't this screen cover changed this morning? You see, Sir Curtis, what a dirty lazy lot of nurses I have to put up with. Don't you think it's a disgrace the way the modern girl goes about her work? Work! They don't know the meaning of the word. Get away and get on with your babies, Nurse. They should have been put up ages ago. You don't seem to —' But I had gone, so that if Sir Curtis wanted to agree with her for the sake of peace and quiet, he could.

Later, when I went into the medicine room for Sister to give me Mrs James's post-operation morphia, she paused, with the bottle in her hand, and said incredulously : 'Do you *know* Sir Curtis, Nurse? I mean, do you know him *socially*?'

'Yes, I do, as a matter of fact.' I handed her the syringe.

'*How* do you know him?' The idea seemed fantastic to

her. A scullery maid might as well have claimed acquaintance with a duke.

'Well, I met him out at dinner,' I said sullenly. 'I'm going to a cocktail party at his house next week,' I added, knowing that this would infuriate her.

'Oh!' She jabbed the hypodermic needle viciously into the rubber top of the bottle. 'There, six minims – one sixth. Check this, please.' I checked the level of the liquid in the syringe. Her eyebrows were in her hair again; she was looking at me unbelievingly. 'Do you know the Rowntrees *well*?' she persisted. She couldn't get over it.

'Yes, quite well,' I lied.

'How strange,' she said rudely, and turned to lock the morphia in the drug cupboard.


When one of the first remarks of a new patient is : 'Now, I don't want to be any trouble,' you can bet your shirt they are going to be more trouble than anyone else in the ward. Mrs Drucker said it when she was brought in, pale but brave, to have her second baby. She had had her first in a nursing home, but this time, patriotically, she had decided for economy's sake to face the horrors of a general ward. She took great care to let us know that she was used to better things. How different it had all been when she had her Rosemary – but we were to make no difference for her – absolutely no difference at all. She wanted to be treated just the same as all these brave women, she said, and then proceeded to take umbrage because she was.

It wasn't that she complained or objected or made a fuss outright. She annoyed in a much more subtle way. If she wanted anything, she would not ask for it until she could say, with a brave little deprecating laugh : 'I wanted so-and-so two hours ago, but you looked so busy, I didn't like to ask.' Perhaps I forgot that she didn't take sugar in her tea, and instead of asking for another cup, she would drink it, so that she could say, preferably within earshot of Sister : 'I managed to get it down, Nurse. I know how easy it is to forget all our little fancies when you've got so much to think about, but it does seem a waste with sugar rationed, doesn't it?' If she could put you in the wrong in front of Sister, her day was made.

Her baby was not expected for another two days. 'It'll probably be late,' she said, with that irritating little laugh. 'Anyway, whenever it comes, I know I shall have a dreadful time; I went through torture with my Rosemary. I'm sure I don't know how many stitches I had. I dare say I shall cry out, Nurse, but you mustn't take any notice. I shall try not to, but sometimes these things are bigger than oneself, aren't they?' To hear her talk, you would think that nobody had ever had a difficult birth before, and after the baby came – a disgruntled, alcoholic-looking old man – nobody, as far as she was concerned, had ever had a baby before. This sentiment is common to all mothers, but whereas with others it is due to glorious pride, with her it was self-pity.

As she had a very easy time, she did not have to have any anaesthetic until the last moment, so that this gave her a great opportunity to gasp, in between pains, how wonderful they had been at the nursing home and had given her a very special sort of dope right at the beginning, but, of course, she realized that when one was in hospital one naturally couldn't expect any sort of extras, and she wanted to be treated ex*act*ly the same as the other mothers. 'Oh, dear – oh, Nurse – oh, the pain's starting again. I'm trying to bear it, but I've always been more susceptible to pain than other people. Oh, Nurse, I can't – I shan't scream – Oh!' – a piercing yell – 'Oh, d'you think Mr Vavasour will come soon? I'm sure he knows best, but he does seem to be leaving it rather late, doesn't he?'

'Don't worry,' I said, hating myself for not being able to feel sympathetic, 'you're not going to have it for hours yet.'

'Oh, Nurse, I'm sure you're wrong. Not that I question you for one moment, but if you could just go and ask Sister – no, no, don't leave me. I think the pain is going to start again at any minute. Let me hold your hand. I don't want to make any noise or disturb anybody. I don't want to be any bother to you, Nurse.'

Her screams were the most piercing ever heard in that Labour Ward, even from Mrs Morgan, who never lived to tell the tale of her terrible suffering. Rogers said that she kept everyone awake all night and then got one of the House Surgeons out of bed because she declared she was starting a haemorrhage. 'But don't worry about me. I knew something like this would happen.'

Her soldier husband came a few days later to see the baby and tell her what a brave little woman she was. He looked fresh and healthy, and was probably benefiting by his life away from her. I heard her say to him : 'Now, whatever you do, you're not to worry. I dare say it's silly of me to be nervous, but you know I can't help it. I seem to sense these things. I dare say I shall be quite all right, after all, and as for Baby's little squint, perhaps I *am* imagining it. Anyway, don't worry, and don't feel you've got to write to me if you don't feel like it. I shall understand perfectly that you've got so many other things to think about. After all, Baby and I can't expect to come first with you all the time, can we ?' I was glad to see that Sister collared him as he was leaving and told him that his wife was the healthiest mother in the ward and would be out as soon as we could get rid of her.

Nearly all babies have some charm, but Master Drucker managed to avoid it. He would not cry in chorus with the others, but would wait until they had quietened down, so that he could raise his voice and start them all off again. No one would have minded his mother thinking him beautiful if she had kept her opinion a bit more to herself. When you went to fetch him from his feed, in a hurry, probably, to get him back to his cot and get on with something which Sister said you have done hours ago, Mrs Drucker would keep you hanging about while she pointed out the monstrosity's attributes, and the only way to make her give him up was to say : 'Oh, *let* me hold him, the darling,' as if it were the world's greatest treat. Although it was hard on the mothers, it was an understandable rule of the ward that, for both their sakes, they could only have the babies with them at feed times. Mrs Drucker was always pleading to have baby Philip in bed with her. 'I like to feel him near me,' she said, adding 'I'm funny like that,' which was a remark she was fond of appending to the most ordinary inclinations. She was what the Germans call '*Ich bin so*'. She was the sort of person who says : 'Of course, I'm frightfully interested in people. I find them fascinating' – which usually means that the speaker's interest is confined almost wholly to the fascination of herself.

'Of course,' Mrs Drucker once said to me, 'I have a horror of war.' Everyone else loved it, of course.

Mrs Drucker's conviction that she was the only woman ever to give birth was belied by the spate of maternity work that flooded our ward that autumn. They say that war always increases the birth-rate – it's a form of compensation. They say that, for the same reason, more boys than girls are born in wartime. I don't know. They say a lot of things. They also say that a baby cries for exercise. They evidently have never been on a maternity ward. It cries to annoy, like the Duchess's baby. Otherwise, why should it stop when you pick it up and start again when you put it back in its cot? It could exercise itself just as well in your arms.

We were so busy that Sister kept going to Matron's office and insisting that she should be given another nurse. She was always having rows with the authorities, chiefly as a vent for her energy, and would be quite capable of storming a board meeting if it was the only way of getting a new clothes-line for the nappies. As she was promised an extra nurse, she thought she had won this fight, and then she was not so sure, because all she got was Gunter.

When I first came to the hospital, Gunter had seemed to know a lot in a silent way, but having worked with her, I saw that she was incapable of putting it to practical use. What she had learned at her Northern hospital was about as far as she could go. After more than a year at the Queen Adelaide, she was as awkward as if it were her first week. It may have been because she was slightly deaf. She was always hearing things wrong, and, with a bland smile, doing what she thought she had been told to do and causing Sister Ramsbotham to speak of her without lowering her voice as 'that fool'. She took a passionate dislike to Gunter from the moment that she set foot in the ward, trod on some spilt liquid paraffin and trod it all over the floor, which made her contempt for me affectionate esteem by comparison.

Perhaps the east wind got on her liver. I was often tempted to send her anonymously a box of Beecham's pills, for she was absolutely impossible these days – to the patients as well as to us. She was even occasionally rude to Jobling, who was so surprised that she talked endlessly about it, as if it had never happened to anyone else. 'Listen, kid, she said to me, she said : "I don't know why you go on, Nurse. You'll never be a nurse." '

'That's nothing,' I said, 'I get that every day.'

'Yes, but listen, kid, she said it to *me*. So I said to her, I said ... and she said to me, she said ... I was absolutely frosted, I can tell you – Oh, and what d'you think, kid? Who d'you think asked me to go out to tea with him on Saturday? Well, I was surprised, I said "Whatever next?" I said, and listen, kid, I must tell you what he said —'

'Who?' I and the woman whose bed we were making yawned simultaneously.

'Who d'you think, kid? Chubby, of all people ! I'd no idea – well, I mean he used to come down and yarn when I was on night duty' – I could imagine who had done most of the yarning – 'You know, kid, I really do believe he's quite keen. Tee-hee-hee —' Her giggle really did sound like that. Poor little Chubby. He would be rather overlaid.

I was so tired these days. The increase of work and Sister's incessant and noisy nagging were enough to damp the most selfless enthusiasm, which mine certainly was not. I used to snap at any patient who asked me to do something which would delay me for a moment, and I never had the energy to go out at night. I tried to work for the pending exam, but I so constantly fell asleep over the book, and even in lectures, that I saw little hope of passing.

Gunter had become more fumble-fisted than ever under Sister's scorn, Sissons was monosyllabic and couldn't be bothered these days to tell me things I wanted to know, Farren behaved as if she were a candidate for canonization and bore any adversity with a lift of her eyes to heaven, as if to say : 'Don't miss this, God. Chalk me up another pip on martyrdom.'

Even the patients that Sister liked felt the repercussions of her autocracy in our work. A hospital ward can be such a friendly, cheerful place, but this was a place of nervous, scudding feet, of jumps and starts and whispers, and conversation that broke out with a pent-up rush when Sister went to dinner and ceased as suddenly at the sound of her feet on the corridor linoleum. Even the babies were subdued when the east wind blew.

We began to have fears for her sanity when the appalling news came that an inventory was to be taken. Every single movable thing on the ward was to be counted by Matron; every bit of linen, every bowl, every kitchen utensil, every last hot-water bottle had got to be collected together so that Matron could view it all with the least possible inconvenience to herself and the greatest to us. I cannot convey the work that this implied, but anyone who has moved from a twelve-room house in which they have lived for twenty years into a bungalow with no cupboards will have a faint idea if they double that and add twelve women and eight babies who normally made overtime work.

It was over at last. Matron had checked everything with a list as long as her arm, and we had been on the ward until after ten, putting everything back.

At last we went to ask if we might go off duty. 'Quite finished?' said Sister, who was writing the report, which most Sisters wrote three hours earlier so as to get out of the Night Nurses' way, but with Sister Ramsbotham the opposite desire prevailed.

'Everything's done,' we said, with tired pride, but instead of commendation, all we got was a tirade about the condition of the mackintosh sheets which Matron had said were a disgrace both to the hospital and the nursing profession, and how Sister was expected to run the ward with a lot of vicious imbeciles – 'And Nurse,' exposing her orange gums at me, 'You've let me down. Oh, how could you let me down like that? Matron was disgusted.'

'But, Sister, I – what have I —?'

426

She pointed to my wrist. 'How could you do it, Nurse, I simply don't know. Wearing a watch in uniform. No!' She held up her hand. 'There's simply no excuse. If you have been too stupid to learn the hospital rules in the time you have been here, there's not much hope for you. I can't see why you go on, really I can't.'

Nor could I. I was too tired to think it funny, but there I was, back on the job at seven the next morning, disliking more than ever the cheesey shine of Gunter's face and the equine back view of Jobling. It was visitors' day, which Sister always hated, except that it gave her a few more people on whom to sublimate her dictatorial instincts. Mrs James's mother was foolish enough to take down Mrs James's chart and study it in full view of Sister, sitting at the desk writing out medical 'Cerstificates'.

When Sister went to tea, murmurs broke out from all sides. 'It's not right' ... 'The way she spoke to her. I wouldn't speak like that to a dog' ... 'Talk about old man 'Itler' ... 'Streuth, you can't call your soul your own.' Even Dora came in from the kitchen and egged the women on. Mrs James was in tears. Of course, we had to stand up for Sister and try to appease them by telling them what a marvellous nurse she was. She was, technically; it was her manner, as governesses say. 'She may have pulled me through me operation,' said Mrs Fisher, 'but streuth! I'm not sure I wouldn't be better off pushing up the daisies, after all. It sours the food in me when I see how she treats you girls. I 'eave, honest I do.'

Farren told Mrs James that these things were sent to try us, and Mrs James cried harder than ever. When Sister came back, she told her that if she didn't stop she would harm her milk and probably make baby James gastric for life. The murmurs faded, of course, as soon as she was back in the ward, but there was still an uneasy, resentful atmosphere. I wished Sister would say or do just one thing that would destroy the antagonism. The women could be so easily swung round to friendliness. They had no real conviction of antipathy, any more than workers would have if it wasn't for Trade Unions.

427

It was Gunter who achieved it in the end, through sheer puerility. She had the methylated spirit lamp alight in the test room, and because she wanted to fill it up with methylated, she uncorked the bottle and tried to pour it in without blowing out the flame. I was in the sluice opposite, having a lecture from Sister about the glycothymoline stains on the toothmugs, when we suddenly heard a kind of aboriginal yelp and, turning with one accord, saw that what had been Gunter was now a sheet of blue flame. For a split second, Sister's eyes met mine, and I saw my horror mirrored in them. Intimacy leaped between us, and then, before I had time to think, she had hurled herself across the passage and borne Gunter heavily to the ground.

Gunter somehow escaped with only superficial burns and a wordless dread of fire that made her incapable of lighting the gas stove, but Sister was not so lucky. She had bad face and hand burns and had to go into one of the private rooms for two weeks. She was the heroine of the hour. Everyone was talking about her and either withdrawing their previous opinion or saying that they had known her true worth all along. There was even a small paragraph about her in the local paper: 'SISTER RISKS LIFE TO SAVE NURSE.' The women on Grace Annie Sprock were wild with excitement and could not wait until she came back so that they could show her what they thought of her. All their animosity was forgotten. They classed her with people like the Queen and Gracie Fields, and never tired of talking about what they had said to themselves when they smelt burning and heard a crash, or how they saw the heroine borne from the ward by two House Surgeons. They would talk about it for years.

On the day that she was due to come back, we laboured to make the ward spruce. All the women had clean night-dresses and the babies clean shawls and cot covers. She was a different person in our eyes. I felt that in that one instantaneous flash in intimacy in the sluice, I had seen what sort of a person she really was. I was looking forward to working with her now, and hoped I would not be moved off the ward.

It was eight o'clock. From round the corner of the corridor

we heard the familiar speeding footsteps, so different now that we were waiting for them with a welcome instead of anathema. As she turned the corner and Sissons pulled open the glass swing doors, the women struck up *For she's a jolly good fellow* and Mrs James stepped forward with a large bunch of flowers.

Sister swept into the ward. There was a large piece of sticking-plaster on one cheek and she had no eyebrows. 'Stop that noise this instant,' she said. 'I will not have my ward turned into Bedlam. Mrs James – back into bed at once.'

The song withered and died. From the unseeing patients beyond the balcony doors came the ghost of the refrain : 'And so say all of us.'

With malevolent inevitability, the exam drew near, and with it came the news that as Matron was tired of people failing, anyone who did not pass would be thrown out. We were in too much of a state to realize that she would be unlikely to do this in wartime, and our 'What is a cell?' took on a feverish note. 'What *is* a cell?' One had known once, but had ousted the knowledge with so many other fragments since.

Sister Tutor was not much help. She despaired of us, she said, and spent most of our valuable revision time telling us that we were paying now for the slackness earlier on about which she had warned us. Before she came to Redwood, she had been teaching in a hospital in Wales, and such time as she did not take up in disparaging us was spent in eulogizing the Welsh nurses. 'My girls could roll up a bandage twice as quick as you,' or 'My girls wouldn't have asked a question like that,' when Kelly, with her brain in a whirl, announced that the sternum was the bone on which you sat.

I prepared my parents for my probable return home and almost ordered myself a pair of landgirl breeches. Two days before the exam, I felt like ordering the jersey as well, because I was told that while Rogers was on holiday I had got to go on night duty on Grace Annie Sprock.

Being on day duty there, one would have thought that the babies exhausted their lung power in the daytime. Being

429

on night duty, one didn't see how they had the energy to carry on during the day. Their crying and my futile efforts to quiet them was the background pattern of all my nights, whatever else was going on. Sometimes, when a baby was being born and I was rushing round in stricken circles, I would not hear them for hours on end, and when it was all over and one more potential taxpayer lay mouthing in its cot and the mother was having her cup of tea, I would suddenly realize that the other babies had been crying solidly all the time. Presently, Sweet Fanny Adams would come down and tell me that I was the only night nurse on Maternity so signally lacking in lullaby qualities.

The women would not have slept well anyway, because we had several nights of air raids. I felt that I did not much care if a bomb did come through the roof. It would at least stop the babies crying, and it might silence Miss Carmichael. At first, I couldn't fathom the clanking and jangling that always followed hard upon the last dying wail of the 'Alert'. Then I traced it to Miss Carmichael and found that she was sitting bolt upright, with a hairnet well down over her forehead, telling her beads. She had some sort of idea that the whole hospital might collapse round her bed and it be left intact, so long as she was at this pious occupation. It reminded me of my father's story of how when he was a little boy he used to clutch the bedrail while he was saying his prayers in case he should be transported to heaven.

There was no question of doing any more swotting. I slept like the dead all day and although I took a text-book to the ward with me at night, I never had a chance to open it. It was all I could do to wangle a quarter of an hour in which to sit down and write my report.

The exam was at eleven o'clock, so that there was no time to snatch a little sleep beforehand. I had to go to it with all the hours of the night piled on top of my brain. Everyone had on their starchiest aprons and had done their hair as uncompromisingly as possible, which apparently was what went down well with the examiner. Mine was done in the unsuccessful bun to which I had had to resort since Matron

430

had sent for me and told me I must either cut my hair or leave the hospital. We were only having the oral exam to-day. The written paper was a treat in store for to-morrow. We all sat in a row of chairs in the passage outside the room in which the torture was to be enacted. Toots came along and looked us over without enthusiasm and said : 'Good luck' as if she were convinced that only that could get us through. One or two idiots started a last-minute frenzied discussion about cartilage, but for the most part we sat numb and hopeless. Each name called out was like a knell. We went in at half-hourly intervals, and the ones who had finished went out by a different door, so that we had no chance of seeing them. It would have been equally encouraging to hear from a nurse coming out either that the ordeal had been a pleasant surprise, or that she had done so badly that no one could do worse. At last I was sitting next to the door. My brain had no medical knowledge in it. It had nothing in it at all, I discovered when I tried to think about something – anything to shake myself out of this vacancy. When my name was called, I found that my left leg had gone to sleep, and I had to stumble into the room like a cripple and endure agony when it came to during the interview, like the Spartan boy with the fox inside his jacket.

Our lecture room looked strange without the desks and chairs. There were just two tables in opposite corners, behind which sat two terrifying women in navy blue coats and skirts, writing busily and seemingly unaware of my one-legged presence. The fattest one looked up. Surprise! She looked quite kind, like the sort of cook who would open the oven door and give you a red-hot scone.

'Over there first, Nurse,' she said, pointing with a pencil, and I limped over to the corner where sat the thin one, who if she had been a cook would not have given you so much as a potato peeling.

She had a face like granite, unmoving but irregular, as if the sculptor's chisel had slipped here and there. Her mouth opened crookedly half an inch, and she shot a few words at one like pebbles.

'What do you know of Personal Hygiene?' I was entirely unprepared for this. I could have told her about sewers, ventilation, even the endearing habits of the bed-bug, but – What do you know of Personal Hygiene! I could only think of the advertisements.

This was the point when my foot began to come to. I can't remember what I said; I blurted out a few banalities and managed to save myself from bringing in 'Often a bridesmaid, never a bride.' Her face gave no sign that she either approved or deprecated the secrets of my toilet as embodied in my halting answers. When I stopped, she said : 'Anything more?' so that I wondered whether I had missed something out or whether this was a ruse to get me worried. My foot had reached the pinnacle of its agony and was now subsiding into the ever-increasing bliss of relief. The stone woman wrote something down, and attacked with relish the subject of sewage farms, which I welcomed with equal relish as being one of the few things I knew. Still no sign, however, as to whether my knowledge of sludge impressed her, and I crossed the floor to the kind woman with relief. If the other one had been disconcertingly hard, this one was disconcertingly kind. She was so kind that if you hesitated for a moment she began to prompt before you had a chance to say the stuff. I only hoped that she would confuse her knowledge with mine and get the impression that I had imparted most of it. 'Yes, yes,' she kept purring. 'Now tell me, what would you do in a case of shock?' I took a deep breath. I could answer this; I had had enough practical experience of it. Before I got farther than 'Well, you keep the patient warm' – remembering too late Sister Tutor's injunction not to start every answer with 'Well' – the old cook had started like the prompter in a Chinese play, who says every word half a second before the actors. I followed her along, like someone trying to race the Vicar with the prayers in church, and we both finished level on blood transfusion. 'Very good, dear,' she smiled. I think she thought that she had been following me.

That night I took all my notebooks on to the ward, determined that the mothers and babies could stew in their own juice for an hour or so while I put in some solid revising. Often enough, I had bemoaned my life, had said that I lived only for the end of the war to get me out of this prison, but now that my existence there was threatened, I did not want to leave, although recently I had been turning over the idea. Mr Bevin's continual appeals to women had reminded me uneasily that his need was perhaps the most urgent of all. And how satisfying to feel that one had played a part, however infinitesimal, in the manufacture of a tank or an aeroplane. The Germans whom it killed would be almost a personal bag.

Somebody had to nurse, though. Yes, but somebody had to make munitions – and quickly. Wars go so fast these days. In the Hundred Years' War nobody put in overtime on cannon-balls and crossbows. They probably knocked them up at their leisure, but nowadays a country could be overrun before it had time to turn round. Ought one to do something about it?

My conscience gave a little whistle and said: 'Honestly now, are you restless because you want to kill a German or because you are getting fed up with Redwood?'

'A bit of each, I suppose.' Redwood did irk me occasionally. I loved the work, but not its appurtenances. Nursing was fascinating and in a way fulfilling, but the life which it entailed was unnecessarily tiresome. And yet, when one stripped away all the pettinesses and tyrannies and discomforts and looked at the essence of the hospital and the core of its purpose, one saw that it had power to hold and bonds which it would be hard to break without regrets.

Sister greeted me with: 'Come along now, Nurse. Two minutes late and you've got a busy night in front of you. Mrs Arthur is in labour.' My heart sank and I laid my notebooks on the desk with a gesture of farewell. If only I could get an obstetric question to-morrow, I should be all right.

Mr Ripley and Fanny Adams and I fought all night for that baby. At about two o'clock, when it definitely decided to live, the mother decided to die. We thwarted her, however, and in the morning there they were, grey and unsubstantial both of them, but definitely there and likely to stay. I looked forward to telling Sister Ramsbotham of our achievement. Not that she would believe what a fight we had had. She expected everybody to be immortal, and however ill they were, was far more surprised if they died than if they lived, which I suppose was the right spirit.

'How did you get on yesterday?' she asked surprisingly, when I had given the report. I made some sort of deprecating answer.

'Sister Tutor told me that she thought everyone had passed,' she said. 'Good luck for to-day.' What was wrong with the woman? Everything seemed to be conspiring to show me that it was desirable to pass the exam and stay.

Thinking about this, and feeling increasingly tired as the sustaining excitement of the night evaporated, I decided that it indicated that the paper was going to floor me. If everyone had died in the night and Sister had been so unfair that I had decided to join something with a Union, I should have passed with honours.

Perhaps I tried too hard. I wrote so much that I had not time to read through it and delete the rubbish. The questions looked all right at first sight and one dashed ahead to put down every bit of knowledge connected, however remotely, with the subject, only to find, when it was too late to do anything about it, that the question had a catch or a tricky codicil, obviously intended to test the alertness of the candidates.

When it was over, I did not feel equal to the frenzied comparisons and post-mortems that broke out immediately we got into the corridor, so, as I was too tired to go to bed, I went out alone to have some coffee. Of course, Mrs Fellowes's sister had to be in the 'Blue Lady' in a more irritating hat than ever. It looked as though she had gone to bed in it. I pretended not to see her, but she came over to me, carrying her cup of coffee and spilling most of it over the 'Blue Lady's' coconut matting.

I let her talk. I felt terse and depressed. She was wearing

434

a dreadful gunmetal skirt, a green jacket trimmed with a chewed bit of fur, and the shaming hat. She had a drop on the end of her nose and was very excited because she had read a story which I had written months ago to while away the night on Secker Ward. It had gone the rounds and finally come to rest in a woman's magazine, glamorously illustrated and with the heroine's name changed to Hyacinth.

'Such a lovely little tale,' she maundered, 'the doctor falling for the nurse – I don't know how you thought of it. You ought to write a book about Hospital, dear. It's such wonderful work. I'm sure I would give anything to be able to follow such a noble calling.' In her mind, I could see the etherealized figures, people like Hyacinth, flitting about in spotless aprons, shaking pillows, smoothing brows and doing nothing more familiar to the patient than feeling his pulse. Sadistically, I tried to replace these figures with others, jaded, discouraged and dragooned, sickeningly familiar with dawn and the less attractive functions of the human body.

'But those dear little babies,' she said pleadingly. 'You're still on the Maternity Ward, aren't you? The miracle of childbirth —'

I was thinking about the exam and remembering one thing after another that I had forgotten. Venting my dejection on her, I told her about the miracle of childbirth, as specifically as I could with a woman in a mauve hat sitting at the next table drinking in every word.

Mrs Fellowes's sister clung bravely to her convictions. 'No, no,' she said, shaking her head so that I was terrified the drop was going to fly off into my coffee. 'You mustn't think of it like that. It's so noble ... healing the sick ... Florence Nightingale ... the miracle of birth and death ... Yes, yes. You really should put it all into a book.'

'I don't get the time,' I said, not feeling inclined to tell her about the tentative schemes which I had already sketched at the back of my hygiene book and the notes scribbled on the backs of old charts, Path. Lab. reports and slips of Litmus paper when an idea struck me in the middle of the day.

'Ah yes, that's the trouble, of course,' she said. 'You know,

I always say I would write a book myself if I had the time. I've thought of a very good title for it too : "The Travels of a Civil Engineer's Wife." ' As I had no idea that she had been married, nor that her travels had been much more extensive than from Redwood to the Army and Navy Stores this revealed her in a new light, even if it did not promise very enthralling reading.

Until the examination results were announced, I joined in the common worrying and the repeated assurances which answered the same purpose of touching wood : 'My dear, I *know* I haven't passed.' It was the bleak time of year between invigorating winter and freshening spring, when everyone feels below par. Hair will not go right and skins bear witness to too much fugging and too little fresh air. I was thankful to be moved from the maelstrom of Grace Annie Sprock.

I was back on Privates again and now I was increasingly beset by doubts. It seemed so unbearably futile to be pulling curtains backwards and forwards for neurotic women, asking them how they had slept and whether they fancied jelly or tinned peaches for lunch. In the end, it was Sarah P. who decided me.

One morning, with the examination results still unknown, I went to Matron for a sleeping-out pass.

'Oh – Nurse,' she said dryly as I was feeling behind me for the doorhandle, 'I hear that you wrote a magazine story about Hospital.' She stretched her neck with that movement she had, like a chicken swallowing, and jutted her sharp chin : 'Is that true?'

'Yes, Ma'am.' Heaven forbid that she had read *Hyacinth*.

'Well, kindly, Nurse, never do such a thing again.'

'Why not?' I asked, red in the face with all the things I wanted to say and didn't dare.

'Apart from being an unforgivable breach of etiquette, you only make yourself extremely ridiculous. So please don't try to write any more foolishness about what you see here. If you do, I shall certainly not keep you. Now you may go back to your work.'

That settled it. I had to write the book now, and if she

didn't want me, I would go to someone who did. Having dismissed me, she was busy with the lists on her desk again and I cleared my throat and announced in a voice which came out several keys higher than I intended: 'Please Ma'am, I should like to give in my notice.'

The head shot up, the glasses flashed coldly, and the thin lips ejected an impatient, toneless 'Why?'

'Please, Ma'am,' I said, 'I want to go and make a tank.'

# My Turn to Make the Tea

*To*

MARY

# Chapter One

THE telephone rang. I picked it up, glad of something to do, for there was not much stirring in our office that afternoon, except the spoon in Joe's teacup.

'*Downingham Post*,' I said crisply. 'Reporters' room.'

'There's a lady down here wants to see one of the reporters,' said Doris, who worked our little switchboard in an untaught, haphazard way.

'Oh good,' I said. Perhaps she had brought us some hot news.

'She wants to see whoever it was wrote that piece about the cold potatoes.'

Oh bad. I had written it. I was afraid at the time that I might not have all the facts right, because I had been dozing at the Petty Sessions, but the editor had wanted the story in a hurry and there was no time to check up.

I had hoped to get away with it. Ninety-nine times out of a hundred one did, but this was the hundredth. The lady was in the downstairs office, pacing the linoleum in a threatening hat. She was not the plaintiff in the case I had reported, who had been suing a truant husband for what the police called maintainance. That one had been quite a sympathetic blonde character, and I had been on her side, but this one was swart, with a trembling shadow of moustache.

I kept the counter between us. Doris and Mrs Banks, who handled the advertisements, were on my side of it doing their accounts, and I hoped they might give me support, but they only stared, and Mrs Banks shook out her sleeve in a fastidious way and drew a lace-edged handkerchief from the end of it. I rested my hands on the counter like an obliging shop assistant and prepared to sell the lady whatever she wanted.

'Are you the one who writes the court reports?' she asked, jittering her chin at me. She had some kind of affliction of the mouth, which made her look as though she were chewing all the time on seeds left over from raspberry jam.

'Yes,' I said, although the maintenance case was the first court story I had been allowed to do by myself, and that was only because Joe had wanted a drink before the magistrates did, and had gone away and left me on my own for half an hour before the lunch interval.

'You've made a libel of me,' said the lady. 'Look here.' She put a copy of our last week's paper on the counter, jabbing her glove at my story, which I could not read upside down.

' "Plaintiff, Mrs Jessie Parkins," ' she read, ' "alleged that during a quarrel, her husband emptied a bowl of cold potatoes over her head." '

'Didn't he?' I asked. From what I had seen of the husband, he looked capable of it.

'He may have, or he may not,' she said. 'That is neither here nor there. What is here is that I am Mrs Jessie Parkins. The woman in this unpleasant case' – she rapped the paper again – 'dreadful creature. We know all about *her* – is Mrs Nessie Parkinson. So you see what you've done with your vulgar publicity. You've made a libel of me and Mr Parkins, and it's set him right back, just when his legs were getting right. Thirty years we've been married and never a sharp word. Our name will be a laughing-stock when people read this. I've already had the milkman looking at me sideways.'

My heart sank. 'I'm terribly sorry,' I began humbly.

'Sorry isn't enough,' she said, chewing more rapidly on the raspberry pips. 'They oughtn't to let people like you have such licence. What are you going to do about it?'

What indeed? I could feel Doris and Mrs Banks concentrating on me from behind. I was getting nervous. The editor was always lecturing me about libel. I had made many mistakes since I had been on the paper, but none as ominous as

444

this. I apologized to her. I told her that I had meant no harm, that it was a printer's error, a proof-reader's error, a fault in the machines, an Act of God. . . .

'I could sue, you know,' she said with relish, and I thought of dashing upstairs for my coat and leaving the office for ever, although tomorrow was pay day.

'Unless you print an apology. Big enough for everyone to see, though I doubt whether even that will get Mr Parkins over the shock. Thirty years we've been married and never –'

'Yes, yes, we could do that. How would it go? "We regret to announce that in the report of a case in the Magistrates' Court last week, the plaintiff was erroneously stated to be Mrs Jessie Parkins, instead of Mrs Nessie Parkinson. We offer our apologies to Mrs Parkins for any distress or embarrassment caused her." ' I had seen it done in the daily papers. They seemed to get away with it all right.

'Distress, yes.' She nodded the hat. 'And Mr Parkins. His name too. And the address. I'd like his activities for the British Legion to go in as well.' It was going to be quite a saga.

'It will have to go in for two weeks,' said Mrs Parkins. 'Two weeks, or I take action.'

'All right.'

'Very well.' She picked up the paper and her jaw slowed down and was still. The tension in the office broke. Doris giggled and Mrs Banks let out her breath with a little hiss like a tin of coffee being opened. I got away quickly, vowing to take Benzedrine to the Petty Sessions next time.

Upstairs, Joe and Victor wanted to know what it was all about. Someone had drunk my tea, and the office cat had got my biscuit on the floor.

'Apology?' said Vic. 'You're for it. The old man hates putting them in. Says it's the hallmark of second-rate journalism.' He imitated Mr Pellet's crusted accents to the life.

'Well, but surely, if it saves a libel action –'

445

'I said, he hates putting in apologies,' repeated Vic, who could be annoying when he liked.

'Perhaps I might get it in without him seeing.'

They laughed scornfully. The editor saw every word of copy that was written.

'I could take it in to Harold and get him to set it and fit it in somewhere after Pelly had passed the page.'

'What a hope. Don't you know this paper is the old man's Bible? He lives with it all week and then takes it home Wednesday evening and sits up all night reading it. Cover to cover. All the ads, too.'

'Oh well, I suppose I ought to go and tell him now.'

'Yes, I suppose you did.' Vic picked up a pencil, sucked it, flexed his wrist, made a few passes over a sheet of paper, and started on a headline for the Bowls Club Dinner. Joe sighed and went back to the morning paper.

'Ought to what?' asked Murray, who had just kicked in through the swing door and was hanging up his coat and scarf.

'Go and ask Pelly for a raise,' said Vic, underlining his heading with artistry.

'Useless. I asked him myself last week.' Murray lifted the lid of the teapot. 'You horrible people,' he said. 'You might have waited for me.'

'You can make some more,' Joe said.

'You know the tea doesn't last out if you keep making fresh brews.' Murray had a domestic mind, and worried a lot about whether the tea and sugar would last the week, and whether the milk would go sour if we lit a fire, and whether we could get any more coal.

'I'll make you some more when I come back,' I said. I was sorry for Murray, who never felt well, and who had the sort of wife one would not wish on any man.

'It doesn't matter. I'll go without.' Murray would rather be offended now than have a cup of tea.

I went out of the long, chaotic room where we five reporters wrote and argued and laughed at rotten jokes, and bickered and made our private telephone calls and boasted about what we were going to say to the editor when we asked for a rise. I went along the dark little corridor, which was so narrow that two people could not pass, so that you had to back out if you met anyone, and up the twisting stair, which was also narrow, like belfry steps. You did not have to back down these, because you could always hear if anyone was coming. They made such a noise on the hollow wood.

Mr Pellet made more noise than anyone. He was a short and heavy man, with no waist, no neck, and no spring in his ankles. I was a little afraid of him. No one else was, because they knew that they knew their work and he needed them. I did not know my work and he did not need me, but when he was feeling cosy, he would tell me that in about ten years' time, if I did what I was told, I might make him a useful reporter. The thought that in ten years' time I might still be in Downingham writing notices of Women's Institute concerts and school bazaars was not exhilarating.

The editor was sitting at his desk by the window subbing some copy. It looked like Vic's handwriting – what you could see of it after the mutilations of Mr Pellet's soft black pencil. Although it was a raw March afternoon, with a hint of fog coming in with the dusk, he had the window wide open. Mr Pellet never felt the cold. It was said downstairs that he had a steaming blood pressure, but he was never ill, and had no understanding for anyone who was. It was enough to make you ill if you had to spend too long in his office. Even in summer it got no sun, and in winter your hands turned blue and your face stiffened as soon as you opened the door.

It was a little odd-shaped room stuck in a top corner of the ramshackle old *Post* building. There was only just room in it for a claw-foot coat-stand with one foot missing, a kitchen chair for visitors, the editor's swivel chair that swivelled on a slant, and his scarred old roll-top desk, whose bursting drawers would no longer shut, and whose leather writing surface was chewed into a relief map where he had worried it over the years with his paper-knife. The electric light, with a shade like a dirty white china plate, hung in the wrong place and was hoisted to shine over the desk by a piece of string tied round the curtain rail.

The peeling walls were lined nearly all the way up with reference books, unreadable sagas on Downingham's history, and old, old ledgers and files. Nothing much newer than the turn of the century, for since the paper started in 1890, nothing had ever been moved or thrown away. The shelves and cupboards had long ago reached saturation point, so that all the up-to-date stuff had to be kept inconveniently in the basement. Our reporters' room was half silted up with rolls of old galley proofs which had been collecting dust there since the Relief of Mafeking. No one had yet discovered that I was systematically using them to light the fire, but I would have to do it for all of those ten years Mr Pellet said it would take to make me a reporter, before I made any impression on them.

I was surprised when I first came to this room for an interview. I had expected the editorial office, even of a provincial weekly, to be more impressive. I had expected Mr Pellet to look like an editor, not like a man who prods pigs with a stick on market day. With his large head, broad and curly at the poll like a Hereford bull, his thick clumsy fingers, seasoned by years of cigarettes, like old oak in a smoky cottage kitchen, and his healthy bright blue eyes, he was the most unliterary-looking person I had ever seen. Journalism is not literature, he was always telling me. I thought it ought to be, although the others downstairs told me that when I had been there as long as they had, I wouldn't waste my time thinking up original adjectives which the old man always replaced with some of the tried favourites from stock.

When I told the old man about Mrs Jessie Parkins and the

cold potatoes and the apology, he put down his pen, sunk his neck deeper into his shoulders, looked at me like a bull, and then roared at me like a bull. Victor and young Mike, who were always being roared at, told me that this meant nothing, but it unnerved me. I stood my ground, wondering whether it was the cold or Mr Pellet that made my legs feel weak. I was afraid that he would sack me. I had been thrown out of nearly every job I had ever had in my life, and wanted to hold on to this one a bit longer. I thought he was being unnecessarily righteous about Mrs Parkins, but suddenly he stopped in the middle of a sentence, leaving a vacuum in the air where his voice had been, gave me the sucked-in smile that made him look as if he had not got his teeth in, and muttered, 'Silly bitch.'

'Me?'

He wheezed, which was all he could do about laughing. 'No, her.'

As I stepped back over the icy linoleum to the door, he said, 'Had your tea yet?'

'I was just going to make some more. Would you like a cup?' It seemed wrong that no one took him tea every day, but if ever I took it up unasked, he would wave it away and say that he was too busy to drink tea, even if some people were not.

'Aye,' he said. 'Bring us a mug, there's a love,' and I knew I was forgiven. It was always a good sign with him when he tried to talk North Country.

# Chapter Two

ALTHOUGH many people graduate from local papers to Fleet
Street with some success, between working on a provincial
weekly and working on a big London daily there is a gulf as
vast as the Grand Canyon. On a London paper, you are either
a reporter, or a sub-editor, or a proof-reader, or a sports
writer, or a political commentator, or a woman's angle expert,
or any one of the hundreds of specialists who go to make up
the staff. That is your job, and that is all you do. You only
see your own particular bit of the paper. You don't know
and usually don't care what everyone else is doing, and if
you were to get a bright idea about someone else's department probably no one would listen to you, so you don't
bother to get bright ideas. You are not interested in the paper
as a whole. It comes out, you suppose, since you see it being
sold next day – although you usually read another one – but
of all the infinite details and technicalities that bring it out
you are happy to remain ignorant.

You hardly ever see the editor, and almost never see the
proprietor, except at the Christmas party, and the annual pep
talk, although you feel his presence, because you have to
angle your writing his way, and sometimes you have to walk
upstairs when the lift doors are chained back after his Lordship's butler has rung through to say that his Lordship's car
is on its way to the office.

On a paper like the *Downingham Post*, things are very different. You don't have only one job, you have dozens. You
probably have a try at almost every job in the office before
you are done, because when Joe is on holiday, someone must
do Kiddies' Korner, and when Murray is off sick, you might
have to do the leader (non-political), and when Vic is away

at Worcester with the town's football team, and Mike covering another match, someone must go and view Plastic Novelties 1st XI v Bingley Engineering Reserves.

Apart from that, in the natural course of events, you do a thousand and one things besides your official job of reporter. You think up headlines for other people's stories, you read proofs, and recorrect corrected proofs, you reword ill-written advertisements and Birth, Death, and Marriage notices (only In Memoriams are inviolate and have to be printed just as they are sent in), and worst of all, you have to rewrite some sense into the rambling reports on darts matches and whist drives sent in by local correspondents from the villages. You also have to take your turn at filling inkwells, fetching copy paper, washing-up yesterday's cups in cold water, and making tea. If you are the only girl, it is nearly always your turn. The only thing you don't have to do is dust, because, although there is an old man who sweeps the floor once a month and disappears no one knows where for the other twenty-seven days, nobody ever dusts a reporters' room. Nobody ever has, and nobody ever shall.

Although you do more work for less pay than on a London paper, you get more fun, because you are concerned with the paper as a whole, and are more directly involved with the adventure of its appearance every week on half the doormats in the county. In Fleet Street, you don't know one-tenth of the people who work with you. In the provinces, you not only know everybody, but you know all their life histories, their moods, their maladies, and can give advice at the drop of a hat on anyone's love problem, having listened to all the telephone conversations and read most of the correspondence relating to the affair.

You see the editor all the time – too much, if he is one of the clubbable sort, who gets bored cooped up alone in his office and comes to lean on your mantelpiece and gossip when you are trying to get some work done. We did not have this

trouble with Mr Pellet, but we did suffer sometimes from
the proprietor who, far from being a Lord who had to have
lifts waiting for him, was an old lady in top-heavy hats and
fur round the hem of her coats, who would come tottering
through the office whenever she had nothing else to do at
home, and tell us tales of her bygone family, who had been
known as the Madcap Murchisons.

Then, too, in the provinces, you are not really a newspaper
in the strict sense of the word. You are more like a parish
magazine. You do not give your readers the news, but only
the news that affects them locally. Tremendous events may be
afoot in the great world outside, but you are only interested
in what happens within your fifteen-mile radius. World-
shaking speeches may be made in Parliament, but you are
only concerned with what your local M.P. said to the
Mothers' Union about the cost of living.

Even when something important enough to be featured in
the London papers happened in our district, it was no good
to us, because although we tried to persuade Mr Pellet to let
us make a big splash with it, he would always say that by the
time we went to press, people would have read all about it in
their morning papers. He was probably right, but it did seem
a waste that time when we had a runaway Duchess, and
when a real sex murderer came up at our Assizes. We reported the case, of course, but with scarcely more *éclat* than
any other. The sensational stuff had all been done by the
London papers, and our lead story that week, which might
have been 'RED-HAIRED KILLER SLAYS WIFE, MIS-
TRESS IN SAME BED,' was 'COUNCIL VETOES NEW
SEWAGE PLAN FOR BUNGALOWS.'

Poor Mike, who was keen, had gone to visit the red-haired
murderer's Mum, and had written an impassioned Human
Interest story, but Mr Pellet would have none of it. In any
case, he said, Mum lived two miles outside our boundary. She
belonged to the *Moreton Advertiser*, which supplied news

for the other half of the county. This boundary was rigid, and what happened even just beyond it was considered to be of no interest to our readers. If they thought it was, then let them buy the *Moreton Advertiser*.

One Sunday, when I was bicycling back to Downingham from a visit to some friends, I came upon an accident at a crossroads some way outside the town. One car was on the grass verge with its back wheels in the ditch, and the other was buckled all down one side like tinfoil. There was a body in the road – not a badly hurt one; it was sitting up quite animatedly rubbing its leg and cursing – but still a body. There was the usual miraculous collection of gapers from nowhere, a road scout, a lorry driver, two flushed and vociferous women who had been in one of the cars, and me, fishing my notebook out of my handbag. I had been told to take it everywhere with me, because you never knew. This just showed. You never did know when you might not stumble on a red-hot bit of news.

I had not been on the paper long, and was dead keen. It was just after the *faux pas* of the cold potatoes, and I thought that coming in on Monday morning with a sizzling eye-witness story like this would be just the thing to blot out that memory from behind Mr Pellet's deceptively ingenuous eyes. Licking my pencil, I edged my way among the little crowd. I was not sure how a reporter was supposed to behave on occasions like this; whether to be diffident, or brash, with hat on back of head, as in American films. The road scout, who was trying to pull the wing of the smashed car away from its wheel, looked kind.

'Excuse me,' I said, 'I'm from the *Downingham Post*. Could you tell me how the accident occurred?'

'Press, eh?' said the scout, lifting a face scarlet from tugging. 'You're quick on the job.'

'Just a part of our news service,' I said modestly. 'Could you tell me –?'

'I'll tell you,' said the body sitting on the kerb. 'By God, I'll tell you. Here am I, driving quietly along this main road, which any idiot within miles knows is a main road, even if it wasn't marked Major Road Ahead on all the side roads – and just as I get to this crossing, out comes this lunatic woman, full bat – crash, bang! and I just had time to think: "a woman driver, of course," and then here I am with a leg like a bolster and getting bigger every minute. Look!' He pulled up his trousers to show me a white and waxy leg with a bruise coming up below the knee and a broken sock suspender. I tutted at it.

'Might have killed me,' he went on. 'There am I, driving quietly along this main road –' I scribbled away in my home-made code substitute for shorthand, which sometimes made sense to me when I came to transcribe it and sometimes did not.

'Oh, look here,' said one of the flushed women, coming across, 'this isn't good enough. You know quite well the accident was all your fault. If you hadn't been going so fast, I'd have had plenty of time to get across. Don't print what he told you,' she implored me. 'It isn't true. It was all his fault. You say that. It was all his fault. It isn't fair!' She seemed about to cry, and the other woman came and put her arms around her. 'Leave her alone,' she told me accusingly. 'She's had a shock.'

'Had a shock!' exploded the man in the gutter. 'What do you think I've had? Here am I, driving quietly along this main road, which any idiot within miles –'

'Now, now,' said the road scout soothingly, 'don't you go making wild statements, neither of you. Save all that for the police court. And you be careful what you write, Miss,' he told me, 'else you'll be in trouble, too.'

'But I can say what I've seen, can't I?' I forgot that I was pretending to be a seasoned reporter, who would know such things.

'Oh yes, you can say what you seen, but you can't say how it come about, since we don't know till His Worship the Magistrate tells us.'

That seemed a pity, since having seen the woman, I could imagine how it came about, and would have liked to say so. However, I could do a descriptive story, teeming with human interest and emotional conflict. I bicycled home as fast as I could, locked myself in my room and spent two hours writing four hundred words. I headed it 'CALAMITY AT THE CROSS-ROADS'. Joe had told me: 'When in doubt for a head, use an alliteration. Sure fire.'

I had written the story ten times, polished it, sweated over it, decorated it with telling phrases and colourful adjectives, until it seemed to me to be just the sort of thing I should like to read in my local paper on a Thursday morning. I thought it was pretty good – better than any of the others could have done, anyway. Murray, for instance, would have started it: 'At half-past five last Sunday evening –' as he started all his stories.

When I got into the office on Monday morning, Mike was there, sharpening pencils with his overcoat on, for our room was always like the morgue after the week-end. 'Hear about the accident on the Downingham–Glenfield road?' I asked him.

He shook his head.

'Did you?' I asked Victor, who had just come in.

'Do what?'

'Hear about the accident at the Insham crossroads yesterday. Terrific smash. One car in the ditch –'

'The ditch is where I nearly was last night. Near as a toucher,' he said. 'Gosh – coming out of the White. Lion – bloody great long-distance coach – missed me by inches.' He was not interested in my accident.

Some reporters, I thought. Never know what's going on right under their noses. But I did. I had been on the job, and I had got a story that would make them jealous.

455

As soon as I heard Mr Pellet's feet clattering up his little staircase, I took it in to him. Although the room was like an ice-chamber, he was flinging open the window and grumbling about fug.

'Some copy for you, sir.' I laid my effort carefully on his desk, and put his dictionary on it, so that it should not blow away.

He grunted. 'All right,' he said, as I lingered. 'What's the matter? You put any libel in it? You've got to be careful with those darned Guild concerts. The women are after me like hens after a rooster if we don't get in the name of every last one who helped to pull a curtain or shout: "Ho to France!" in the big historical scene.'

'It isn't the concert,' I said, 'it's a news story. Something I saw myself.'

'Good girl,' he said. 'Always keep your eyes open.'

I expanded to his praise. 'It was so lucky,' I burbled. 'I was bicycling along, you see, and there was this smash, so of course I got off, and I had my notebook, and –'

'Where was it?' He leaned forward to read my writing. 'Insham crossroads. Sorry, that's a mile outside our area.' He handed the papers back to me. I could have crumpled them up and thrown them at him, only they would not have hurt.

'What's the matter with *you*?' asked Mike when I went downstairs. I told him.

'Insham? Of course it's outside. That's the *Moreton Ad.*, not us. I could have told you that.'

'Why didn't you?'

'You didn't ask me.'

'I *told* you about it.' We always squabbled first thing on a Monday morning. It was quite stimulating to have something concrete to squabble about.

I remembered that I had to go and cover a cookery demonstration. 'Where are you off to?' asked Joe, as I kicked open the swing door, which had no paint on it for two feet above the ground, and nearly laid him out as he was coming in.

'I'm going to sell a story to the *Moreton Advertiser*,' I said.

'Not worth it. They wouldn't pay you enough to cover the bus fare.'

It would not have mattered if I had sold the story to the other paper. There was no rivalry between us, but a cooperation that I had not expected to find in local journalism. We sold, or even gave each other stories and bits of news quite cheerfully. There was not even much rivalry between us and the *Downingham Messenger*, a smaller paper, which functioned in the same town. We both had our static circulation. Some families took the *Post*, some took the *Messenger*, some took both, had done for years, and always would. The few new people who came to the town were not worth competing for.

We were friendly with the three *Messenger* reporters – a disillusioned man, who had been twice round the world and ended up in Downingham, a callow youth, and a girl with orange lipstick. Although we naturally thought our paper was better, and told them what we thought of their stories, the only serious rivalry between us was in darts matches at the White Lion. Their editor was a middle-aged lady with loops of hair, who had once trained as a lawyer, so we sought her advice on court matters, and she came round to Mr Pellet with furrows in her brow whenever she got in a muddle with her local politics.

The *Messenger* came out two days before us, which was useful, because we could copy some of their stories. Not word for word, of course, but paraphrasing. On a Tuesday morning, we would all read the *Messenger*, scoffing gently at some of their items, but Mike secretly admired the Letters to the Editor, which were much snappier than ours, because their staff were allowed to write some of them, and I secretly admired their Woman's column, which told of such things as new knitting leaflets and spring modes at Harrisons the drapers.

Mr Pellet, who had been disappointed in love long ago and was a misogynist, was sternly against anything like this in the *Post*. I was biding my time. When I had been there a bit longer, I was going to start persuading him to let me have a little bit of space for women. Joe had a Korner for his Kiddies. Why should I not be allowed a niche for house-wives? The time was not ripe yet. I was still an encum-brance, but when I should be more firmly established, I was full of plans for revolutionizing this diehard old periodical. The others had all thought like this once, but had long ago given it up, except at wild moments when their broken spirits showed a rare flash of revolt.

I, who was new, and Mike, who was very young, were always planning how we would run the paper when every-body else was dead or in prison. Between us, we would turn it into the brightest thing in print, which would sweep the country. After all, the *Manchester Guardian* had started as a local paper, hadn't it? We would turn the *Post* into a tabloid if necessary, but not with Mr Pellet about. He was the rock against which all waves of enthusiasm broke and fell back with a frustrated sigh.

On Tuesday morning he came down to us with his copy of the *Messenger*, and marked the paragraphs he wanted to filch. I had always thought an editor was God Almighty, and when I first joined the paper, I used to get up when Mr Pellet spoke to me, and call him Sir. But no one else did, and it seemed to embarrass him, so I remained sitting with the others at the great dishevelled yellow table which was a desk for all of us, and was the wrong height for the chairs, so that everyone except Victor had to sit on telephone books or volumes of the out-of-date encyclopedia.

'Schoolmaster died,' said Mr Pellet, tapping the *Messenger*'s rather blurred print. 'Used to be a great football player. We'll use some of this. Not all this crap, of course. I sometimes suspect dear old Ruby doesn't know what's news and what isn't. And that Methodist centenary. Have you got anything on that yet from the minister?'

'I thought someone might go round and see him this morning,' Joe said lazily, looking at me, and I made a face at him. I did not like visiting ministers of the Church. Their studies were always cold.

'Don't bother,' said Mr Pellet. 'All the facts are here, and you can get the orphans' party from this too, and Mrs Milliter's funeral. Someone can do those this morning.'

'Poppy,' said Victor, when he had gone. 'Nice little job for you.'

After the first few days in the office when everyone was still being reasonably polite to me, I had been called Poppy, for no better reason than that a Sunday paper was running a crude cartoon about a blonde called Poppy Pink. Humour was as elementary as that on the *Downingham Post*.

Rewriting was supposed to be easy. That was why I was given it. I found it more difficult than writing something from scratch. When I was first given the job, I asked how to do it.

'Change the headline and the first sentence,' Victor said. 'Then you can copy as much of the rest as you want.'

'Oh, no,' said Murray. 'That's plagiarism.'

Vic made a rude noise. He did not like long words.

'You know a lot of our readers take the *Messenger* too. You must make the story different.'

'But how can I when the facts are the same and I don't know any more about it?' I asked.

'Guess, girl, guess,' sighed Vic.

'You use the same facts, of course,' said Murray craftily, 'but you put them in a different order, d'you see? That way, you get an original story.'

'It did not sound like it to me, but I got a pile of clean copy

459

paper, reached for one of Mike's toffees, and prepared to cerebrate. After ten minutes, I still had not got the headline. The one that the *Messenger* had chosen appeared to me to be the only possible one in the whole of the English language. If I had not seen it, I could have thought of a dozen headings, but to see something in print and have to avoid it is to stultify the brain. 'DEATH OF GRAND OLD MAN OF DOWNINGHAM' seemed to be the perfect title for the passing of a ninety-year-old councillor. I tried a lot of other things, but they did not look like anything you might read in a newspaper. Joe finally got tired of my sighing and fidgeting and throwing balls of paper at the litter round the wastepaper basket, which had been overflowing for days.

He looked up from his melancholy reading of the entries in his children's Funny Stories competition. 'Want any help?'

'Oh yes,' I said. 'I can't think of what to call it.' The morning was passing and I had done no work at all.

'Let's see.' He glanced at the front page of the *Messenger*. '"DEATH OF GRAND OLD MAN OF DOWNINGHAM." Easy. You just put: "GRAND OLD MAN OF DOWNINGHAM DIES."'

It was as simple as that. It looked well, too. I spent the rest of the morning juggling with the details of the grand old man's career, and there again it seemed to me that the *Messenger* had put them in the only order possible. Life was very difficult, and there was more in journalism than met the eye. At a quarter to one, Vic came back from the magistrates' court and asked who was coming for a drink. Joe had already gone, and Mike was putting on his scarf and bicycle clips. He rode home half an hour to lunch every day, because his mother said he must have a good hot meal.

'I can't come out yet,' I said. 'I haven't finished these rewrites.'

'You're mad,' Vic said. 'Finish 'em this afternoon. What d'you think this is – a stop press edition?'

'But there'll be lots more to do this afternoon. Proofs to read, and Births and Deaths and –'

'Relax,' he said. 'When you have been here as long as I have –'

This was a favourite remark with all of them. It was never completed, but it always meant more or less the same thing. In this case: when you feel like a drink, go and have one.

We went and had a drink.

## Chapter Three

ONE week passed very much like another on the *Downingham Post*. Since we went to press on a Wednesday, Thursday was the beginning of our new week. We all came in late that morning – later than usual, that is – and whiled away the time grumbling about Mr Pellet, choking up the fire with rubbish from the week before, and filing cuttings in the obituary morgue about people not yet dead.

Joe always filed his nails on a Thursday. He was particular about his hands, although the rest of himself was going to seed along with the brain that had once been going to write novels. He had a trustful, lopsided face, usually badly shaved, with a ridge of sandy whiskers in the groove of his chin. Streaks of damp pinkish hair were spread over the top of his freckled head, and his eyes were a slightly different size, and faded. They became more watery in inverse ratio to the strength of his drinks. Joe was lazy and selfish and a terrible old soak, but everybody liked him. He was so deplorable that you felt that underneath it all he must have a heart of gold, like the prostitute of popular tradition.

461

Mike always wrote to his girl Sylvia on a Thursday morning – at least, she was supposed to be his girl. They had been going out together for a long time, but when he tried to take things a stage further, Sylvia shied away and left him clutching air.

Mike would not believe the rumour that she was seen out with airmen. 'She's no good for you,' we told him.

'No, no,' he said. 'She's pure. That's why she sometimes won't let me kiss her good night.'

'Ought to be no let about it,' grumbled Vic. 'If you want to kiss a girl, you don't ask her. You just mucking well do it.'

'It's all very well for you,' Mike said, looking very young and despondent. 'You don't wear glasses. If I make a dive at Sylvia, my glasses go for six, but if I take them off first, she knows what I'm up to and gets the garden gate between us. How'll I start the letter this week? Last time I met her, she wasn't going much on me, so do you think she'd take it funny if I put "Darling Syl", as per usual?'

We all gave him a lot of advice, and wrote most of his love letters for him. He rang Sylvia up at her work two or three times a week. She liked that, and would converse quite seductively for the sake of the other girls in her office, and Mike would sit with a silly moony smile on his face, instead of saying the things we told him to. Once, when he was out, Victor had rung up Sylvia and said: 'Hullo, sweetness, don't you remember me? You weren't so stand-off when we met the other night. Gee, we had fun, didn't we?'

Sylvia gasped and said: 'Barry! I thought you'd gone to the Isle of Man.'

'Just leaving, sweetness,' Vic said, and hung up thoughtfully. We did not tell Mike about this. There was no point, for he was besotted with Sylvia's purity, but it confirmed our ideas about her.

Victor did not write to his girl friends on Thursday or any other day. He had several of them – or talked as if he had –

but he would never risk anything on paper, except over-developed sketches which he pinned round the office walls, and Murray hung galley proofs over them. On Thursday mornings, Victor made up his expense accounts, pondering long over how much he could get away with, and rang up one of the fire brigade, who was assistant to the local bookmaker.

Murray pottered about on his narrow feet, filing things that no one would ever want to look at again, checking the tea and sugar tins, emptying the wastepaper basket and tidying up his bit of the table, which was fruitless, for no one else ever tidied theirs, and as soon as he had made a clear space, their litter would overflow on to it. Murray was the chief reporter, because he had been there longest, and on Thursday mornings he would spend some time with Mr Pellet in conference about next week's paper, and come down looking smug. His spare and secret face drawn down to pursed lips could easily look like that.

I always read the *Downingham Post* on Thursday mornings. This seemed to the others the height of folly, but although I had lived with the thing all week and read and reread proofs until I knew most of it by heart, I never could resist seeing my own efforts in print, although they were sometimes scarcely recognizable after the mutilations of Mr Pellet's dusky pencil. I tried to read them with a stranger's eye, and wondered whether they looked amateurish, or whether readers might detect the stuff of genius in the report of Miss Alice Tufton's wedding, over which I had tried so hard, but which had come out exactly like all the other wedding reports that ever had been and ever would be in the *Downingham Post*. It was a curious process, like a sausage machine, that made our individual efforts, the product of a variety of brains, go in at one end and come out in print at the other as if they had all been written by the same person.

At half past twelve on a Thursday, Mr Pellet, crowned by

the black Homburg that was too small for him and rocked a little on his curls, would look round the door, wish us Good day and go off to his Fellowship lunch. We would all go round to the White Lion for our weekly darts match against the *Messenger*.

On Thursday afternoons we were free, unless there were any outside reporting jobs. I always had my hair washed. This may not seem very thrilling news to you, but it was to me, after a week in that dusty office, where the desperation of our labours made one frequently rake the hair with fingers that were covered with printer's ink from handling wet proofs.

On Friday morning we prepared to face the fact that we were bringing out another paper in five days' time, and things began to hum a little. That is to say, Joe rolled a fresh batch of cigarettes on his little machine that turned them out like frayed rope, got out his collection of fading notebooks and tried to think of an idea for a children's competition. He had been doing Kiddies' Korner for ten years and had long ago run out of new ideas, but as a fresh lot of Kiddies was always coming along, he could use the old ones over again in due season.

Somebody rang up the ministers of all the various churches and asked them the leading question: 'Post here. Got anything for us next week?' If they could not be reached by telephone, somebody, and it was usually me, had to go and visit the cold homes of the holy, but if you went at the right time, you sometimes got a cup of tea.

It was also somebody's grim task to ring round the hospitals and find out who had died. If there was anyone worth writing about, and we had nothing about them in the morgue, we would ring up the *Messenger*, and if their morgue yielded nothing either, somebody, and it was usually me, had to go and visit the homes of the bereaved. I jibbed at this at first and said I would not go, but Murray said who did I think I was, so I went and, curiously enough, most of the bereaved did not mind. Many of them actually liked it, and here too there was a good chance of a cup of tea. There is always tea brewing when someone has died.

Saturday was one of the busiest days of our week, because there were always a lot of goings on that had to be told in print. Sport, plays, concerts, weddings, meetings, dinners, dances, political speeches – you sometimes had five or six things to go to during the afternoon and evening, and then had to spend most of Sunday writing them up at home.

On Monday, there were all the weddings and funerals and christenings to write up, week-end notices from correspondents at the outposts of the *Downingham Post* empire to be turned into readable prose, and the beginning of the interminable proof-reading, which went on relentlessly whenever you had a spare moment from now until Wednesday evening. It was like the broomstick of the sorcerer's apprentice. Just when you had laboured through a batch, Harold, the foreman, would come in from the comp room next door with a fresh roll of galleys, smiling amiably as if sure of the welcome he never got.

On Tuesday the pace increased and the lino men who made the type on their improbable jittering machines, became a little rattled. Not so much Ernie, who had been doing it for twenty years and could skim over the keys in his sleep, but Ricky, who had only been on the job two years and was neurotic at the best of times. He made mistakes when he was hurried, and this made reading the proofs even more toilsome. They had to be corrected again and again, because Ricky did not always get our corrections right, and when Joe and Vic cursed him, he cursed back and said it was our lousy handwriting. Once he walked out of the building and was seen no more for three days, and Mr Pellet, who had been everything in his journalistic career, took off his coat and put on one of the black ink-saturated overalls and rattled away at the machine until the sweat stood like seed pearls on his brow. We had some rum type that week, because we could not correct all his mistakes. There was not time, and there just wasn't room on the proofs, and there is a Mrs Cody at Insham, who will never forget that she was once called: 'Our Hot. Treasurer, Mrs Cosy.'

So the week went round, with press day, Wednesday, coming round all too soon and catching you napping because you always thought you had plenty of time to write things up.

Much of our time, of course, was spent not in the office writing the news, but out and about collecting it. Apart from Assizes, Sessions (petty and quarter) and Council meetings (urban, rural, and arts and crafts) there was always something doing in Downingham. Not, perhaps, things that you would have attended from choice, but other people did, and so you had to be there to chronicle them.

We shared out these jobs between us. A huge diary was kept in the office and was filled in every week with what was going on, with our initials pencilled against what we were to report. Only Mr Pellet was supposed to fill in the initials, because he liked to be sure where everybody was, but you could suggest yourself lightly in pencil if there was anything which you particularly wanted to attend, which did not often happen. What did often happen was that someone would quickly pencil your initials against something they did not fancy, before Mr Pellet could put them down for it.

Even when he had put them down, they were quite capable of changing the initials when no one was about. I would look through the diary at the beginning of each week, see what I was down for and make a note of it in case I forgot, like that time I forgot to go to Lady Nethersole opening a bazaar, and she was insulted. One Friday afternoon, I saw that I had nothing, so, knowing that Mr Pellet was going away for a

466

long week-end, I arranged to do the same myself. On Friday morning, he came down to us with a green ticket.

'Who is going to the Girl Guides Tableaux this afternoon?' He looked at the diary. 'Oh, you are.' He gave me the ticket. 'Only about four inches, and for God's sake, don't forget the accompanist.'

I looked at the ticket in my hand, which bade me welcome to Olde Tyme Scenes and Fantasies at 2.30 that afternoon. My train for London went at two. 'But I –'

'Sorry, girl. I know it's murder, but it's a living. I don't remember putting you down for it, because you've been a good girl lately and I thought I'd spare you, but I suppose there was no one else.'

I looked at the diary. The baseness of Victor. Not only had he altered his initials to mine, but he had done it with one of Mr Pellet's soft black pencils to look more genuine. He knew I could not say anything, since we were in league against the boss. One always is, however much one likes the boss and hates one's fellow workers.

When the boss had gone, I got my own back by rubbing out my name from opposite the elocution competition and substituting Victor's. He could not say anything either, and had to suffer eighty children between the ages of seven and twelve reciting 'Milk for the Cat', and 'Incident in a French Camp'.

He retaliated by coming in early one day and putting me down for the Grantley Village Drama Circle in 'Quality Street', and so we went merrily on.

Wednesday was the worst day of each week. We went to press, or, as we liked to say in our nonchalant Fleet Street jargon, we put the paper to bed. Each page was built up in a 'forme', a heavy metal frame with screws round the sides to hold the type in place. The feature pages and the small ads page and some of the news pages were completed as the week went on, but two pages were left open until the last moment to take late reports and advertisements, and the stop press news of people dying or running into each other on motor cycles and anything else that was inconsiderate enough to happen on a Wednesday.

Harold, the foreman comp, never got these pages finished until seven o'clock or later. Two of us reporters had to hang about, playing cards or reading or nagging Harold. When he got to the end of his material, there was always either too much or too little to fit into the last page, so we either had to take something out of a paragraph already in type, or fish out of the wastepaper basket the notes of some rejected function, and write that up. With the presses champing at the bit and the whole paper waiting on us, it seemed incongruous to be filling in that all-important gap with a parish council meeting from a village of two hundred inhabitants, or the birth of a fine boy to some woman of whom no one had ever heard.

'Surely you're not going to waste good space putting in *this*?' I used to ask when I was new to the paper and still thought I was part of a vital news service, but I would be told: 'Just you try and find enough news in Downingham to fill a sixteen-page paper.'

It was nearly always I who had to stay on and help put the paper to bed, because Mr Pellet said it was good experience for me to see it to its completed form. No one wanted to stay on late, so the others agreed with him.

When we had written our last paragraph and Ernie or Ricky had turned it into type, we then had to read a proof of it, recheck the corrected proof, and finally correct a proof of the whole page. There were always one or two mistakes which had been missed before, and Harold would bend over the forme and pick out a line with a pair of eyebrow tweezers It was then reset and dropped delicately back into place again and the forme screwed up.

We were supposed to look through all the page proofs

again before they started printing, in case any mistakes had got through. No one bothered except Murray, who was always in a fever of anxiety lest the eyes of Downingham should be shocked by the smallest misprint. If he found one on a page whose forme was already in place on the machine downstairs, Harold would take a hammer and knock the offending type, so that it would print blurred, and no one would ever know that we did not know how to spell Appellant.

The paper's bedtime had now arrived. With groans and cries of Hup, Harold and Maurice, the apprentice, would lift the almost unliftable formes from the steel table and stagger with them to the lift. It was hand-operated, pulled up and down by a rope, like a service lift in an old-fashioned restaurant. One always expected Harold to shout down for two tomato soups and a spaghetti, but when he put his head into the hatch, it was to shout at Bob, the old man who swept the floor, whose job it was on Wednesdays to pull the lift up and down.

Like everything else in the *Post* office, the lift was very old. One day, the rope would break and the lift would crash into the basement and the type would fall out of the formes and we should have printer's pie. We had had it once when Maurice was away and Bob had come upstairs to help Harold carry the last forme to the lift. Just as they were hoisting it in, Bob dropped his end with a hoarse cry and the forme fell through the gap between the lift and scattered its type all over the basement.

Harold was never put out of temper by anything. It would have been better if he was. He whistled and sang cheerily as he tried to salvage as many paragraphs as possible from the printer's pie, and then bounced upstairs on his toes to break the glad news to Ernie and Ricky, who were putting on their coats, that they would have to stay on and reset the rest of the page.

469

Ricky had a nerve storm and had to go home. Ernie lit the gas which melted the metal for his machine and sat tapping away there for an hour with a face like the end of the world. They had to keep Bob away from him in case he might do the old man harm. Maurice, who had a date with his girl, had to stay on and pull proofs of the reset type, and Vic and I had to stay on and read the proofs. They were full of mistakes, because Ernie was so cross, and we hardly dared hand him back the proofs so covered with our corrections.

There were still a few mistakes the next time, but they were not important, so we let them pass. Ernie had the kind of spare dark face and glittering eye that made you think of a knife at the belt and dark Sicilian alleyways. It was a good thing Murray was not on that night.

The press, which squatted in the basement like a monster waiting for its weekly feed, was an old-fashioned machine of the rotary type. Archaic, they told me, but it seemed the latest miracle of science. The machine minder pressed a button and away it went, roaring and clanking, the endless paper rolling and passing and crossing and folding back so that you could not follow the progress of any one page until it turned up at the end neatly in place among its fellows. I loved to stand at the vomiting end of the machine and see the pages slide down together open, have the middle fold knocked into them by a rod and then another fold, to be spat out exactly as they would appear on anyone's doormat.

The machine minder's mate, who wore a seaman's jersey winter and summer, carelessly threw aside the first few dozens because the ink did not mark so well until the monster got going, and then we had to grab a paper and take it upstairs to look through it yet once more for mistakes before the edition started printing in earnest.

The boys downstairs were supposed to wait until we gave them the all clear, but when neither Murray nor Mr Pellet was there they sometimes did not bother. Although we dutifully skimmed through the paper, and sometimes found a few mistakes which could have been blurred out with Harold's hammer, we knew that if we went downstairs we would probably find the press already rolling and the piles of copies being made into bundles for Mrs Hogg, the Post Office, Insham, and J. Jacks, Corner Stores, Marking Green.

We went downstairs and said O.K. just for the look of it, and then we shouted Good night above the voice of the machine and let ourselves out by a side door into the Downingham night, grumbling about not being paid overtime.

At home, Mrs Goff would not have kept my supper. You had to be on the dot if you wanted to be fed, so I usually went with one of the others to have cheese rolls and beer.

I was in the Plough one night with Joe. He would never go to the White Lion, except for darts matches, because in the evening, there were apt to be women with corduroy slacks and clotted make-up, who laughed like jackals. Joe liked peace and quiet when he was drinking. He got it in the Plough, which was too squalid to attract more than a few morose men, who would rather be there than at home, and an old lady stunted by gin, who lived on the corner bench in a collapsed hat, surrounded by all her possessions in oilcloth bags.

This night, Joe had been eating pickled onions with his cheese, which always made him sad, because they gave him indigestion. Later on, when he had had a lot more to drink, he would get sad anyway, but he was starting early tonight. He told me about his wife who had gone away years ago and taken their child with her. He had told me on other occasions that he was well rid of her, and if his description of her was true, I agreed, but tonight he chose to think of her as Circe.

'Fascinating devil she was, Poppy,' he kept telling me. 'Fascinating little devil. Never been the same man since she went away.'

I did not remind him that he had previously told me that it was because he was the man he was now that she had gone

471

away. He was low tonight, and would probably get very drunk. I would go home soon and leave him to it. He was just in the mood to be upset, and when a man in a pullover came in and started insulting the *Downingham Post*, Joe sublimated his uxorious sorrowing into anger.

What the man was saying about the paper was the kind of thing I had heard Joe say about it many times. He always maintained that it was the foulest rag on earth, but no outsider might say so. Not tonight, anyway. He growled and his bald head began to sweat, which was a bad sign.

The newcomer, who was quite sober and thought he was being funny, laughed at him. 'Can't think how you can stand to work for a set-up like that,' he mocked. 'Reading it is enough to drive me round the bend, so that writing for it must be –'

'Oh look,' I said, before Joe could answer. 'It's not as bad as all that. After all, thirteen thousand people read it.'

'*Buy* it, you mean,' he corrected me. 'Of course, everyone takes their local paper, but that's not saying they read it. Oh, I daresay they look at the small ads, but if you could take a census of all the unread copies of the *Post* that go to light fires the day after it comes out –'

I agreed with him up to a point, but one has one's loyalties. He had a silly smile. He was beginning to annoy me. 'It's a better paper than the *Messenger*, anyway,' I said. 'They can't even write journalese, let alone English.'

'Yerrs,' said Joe, on a horrible note that was half a word, half an animal noise. 'You read the *Mess . . . enger?*' he asked the pullover threateningly, belching in the middle of the word. 'You would.'

'Of course I read the *Messenger*,' said the pullover, proudly, his smile growing even sillier. 'My young lady is one of their reporters.'

So this was the famous Len, about whom Nancy, the girl with the orange lipstick, was always talking. When I sat next to her on the press bench in court, she would invariably whisper to me one of her 'Len thinks' or 'Len always says' just when a witness's name and address were being announced. I can't think how she ever got any of her stories right, for she always seemed to be in a dream of Len and the caravan home they were to share together next summer. She probably did not get them right, and as I had to copy a lot of her work, mine were probably wrong too.

I was so intrigued to see that the famed Adonis was only a man with hair on the backs of his hands and ill-fitting false teeth, that I forgot we were having a row. Joe did not. He said something really very rude about Nancy (though possibly true) and pullover stuck out his negligible jaw at him.

'Don't you square up at me, sir,' said Joe. 'If you want to fight, I'll –'

Still sitting down, he took a tremendous swipe at the man, fell off his stool, and landed on the floor still clutching his glass, which was empty, but intact.

'A fight, a fight!' yelled Len hysterically, backing off. 'Take him away!'

'Now, now,' said the landlord, oozing calmly through from the public bar. 'No harm done gentlemen, and let's have a drink on the house. Get up off the floor, Joe. You'll do no good there.'

Joe was sad again now. He hitched himself to his feet, hand over hand up the rungs of a stool, and leaned morosely over the bar in a little puddle of beer.

'Shake,' he said to the man in the pullover, making no effort to hold out his hand; but Len had gone, making a great windy swish with the door.

'Are you all right?' I asked Joe.

'I expect so.'

'Then I think I'll go home, if you don't mind.' A farmer had just come in, whom I knew to be one of his enemies. I did not want to go through the whole thing again.

'Leave me,' he said. 'I would grieve alone.'

Outside the Plough, the man in the pullover was waiting for the bus that I wanted. I stood on the other side of the post.

'All the same,' he said, 'what I said in there about your paper –'

'Oh, shut up,' I said. It had been a long day, and tomorrow morning I had to get up at crack of dawn and travel twelve miles to interview a woman who had lost two children in the current flu epidemic. I was fed up with local journalism.

'Shut up, is it?' he asked, and I remembered that Nancy had burbled about his getting his eyes from an Irish grandmother.

'It is,' I said, and decided to walk home.

## Chapter Four

WHEN I first came to work on the Post, I lived with some friends in Downingham. We thought we were friends, but when I had been there a few weeks, we discovered that we were not. The Munts were quite different from what they had been on that cruise to Jamaica, and I suppose I was different too.

You can like almost anyone when the sun is shining and you have nothing to do but eat. There was not much sun in Downingham that winter, and all the Munts' meals tasted of gravy powder, so it was a relief when they went abroad again and gave me a polite excuse to leave.

I had made one or two attempts before, but although they thought my conversation silly, and were always making veiled references to footmarks on the hearthstoned doorstep

– was one supposed to jump over it? – if I ever hinted at a change, the Munts would not hear of it.

'We should never forgive ourselves,' they said, 'if we left you on your own in Downingham. It can be a lonely place. I always say one can never be so lonely as in a crowd. Lawrence dear, on your way out, just ask Mary to do over the step before the Fishers come, will you? No, my dear girl, we should never forgive ourselves if we thought we weren't looking after you.'

However, they suddenly announced one day that they were going to let their house and go to Switzerland. Whether they managed to forgive themselves, or whether they ate their hearts out with remorse in Neuchâtel, I do not know, because I never saw them again.

I had not very long to find a new home. I scanned the small advertisements in the *Post* and put in an 'Accommodation Wanted' myself. Gladys told me I could have it at Reporters' Rates, which sounded grand, but cost only threepence less.

I was pleased at the idea of no more gravy powder and no more of that chilly room, where the light hung in the one place where you could neither see to read in bed nor do your face, but soon I began to be worried. I could not find anywhere else to go.

To look at Downingham, you would not think that it was the Mecca of all the world. It had few factories, indifferent shops, an incurable bottleneck at the traffic lights, and no more antique charms than any other market town, yet there seemed to be nowhere left to live in it. The best hotels were much too expensive, the next best were too expensive and full of sad old ladies, and the next were still too expensive for a reporter's pay, and full of men with samples. I could have had a room at the White Lion, but it was separated only by a curtain from someone else's room, and I did not know who the someone else was.

I only had two answers to my advertisement. One was from a family who would take me as a paying guest, but when I got there, I found it meant sharing a room with the eldest daughter – and I saw the eldest daughter. The other was from a man, who wanted me to stoke the boiler, clean out rabbit hutches, and help to sell his herbal tea, in return for my lodging.

A few days before the Munts were leaving their house, I still had nowhere to go. I talked about nothing else in the office, and took time off when I should have been working to tramp the streets looking for notices in fanlights. Mike said that his mother would put me up in her sitting-room, but when he approached her, she said it would be asking too much of that poor old sofa, and anyway, Dad would not like to find me there when he came down to do the grate. I put another advertisement in the *Post*, and Doris told me with her boiled stare, that Reporters' Rates only lasted for one week. I paid the extra threepence, but I got no more answers, and trunks were already beginning to stand in the hall of the Munts' house, and the curtains were down in my room.

The curtains were also down between the Munts and me now that we were going to part, but I was now thinking desperately in terms of a caravan or the agricultural hostel, and although we were barely civil to each other and the meals had degenerated into picnics, their house seemed like home, sweet home, and I would have welcomed a change in their plans. I almost made up my mind to go back to the man with the herbal tea. I got as far as his gate once, but the wind was blowing from the back garden, and I got the scent of the rabbits. I even ventured to ask Mr Pellet, although I was still rather afraid of him then. He seemed to know everything about Downingham, but when I offered him that as flattery, he told me that he was trying to run a newspaper, not an advice column for distressed women.

How did he expect me to work for him if I had nowhere to

live? I was furious with him, but that was no use. He never noticed if you were cross, even if you were deliberately rude to him. I banged his door, crashed down the wooden stairs, ran into Joe in the passage and made him stagger, and went out with my notebook to get the details of all last Saturday's nuptials.

I had just been honoured with the job of writing the lesser wedding reports, but I felt far too worried and irritable to care who had married whom, and encased in what, and where. When a bride's mother, whose complexion looked as if she had had more port last Saturday than the doctor allowed her, sat me down and held forth to me about peplum waists and burgundy accessories, my mind wandered, and she pulled it back, accusing me of not taking full notes. 'And the report will be wrong, and then no one will be pleased, least of all Sonia's Dad. He's a marvel like that. Off like a flash at anything he doesn't like the look of,' she said, as if boasting about a watchdog.

The next house on my list was empty. It rang void to knockings on front or back door, and all the curtains were drawn. A neighbour put her head out of a top window and called to me that Thompsons were gone. All together on the honeymoon?

The next house was guarded by a snap-jawed woman with her hair tied up in a scarf, who was still clearing up after the wedding reception. She had her drawing-room furniture out in the hall, and there were mats and cushions in the garden, as if she were fumigating the place after disease. When I asked her if she would like to give me some details, she said: 'A piece in the papers? Oh no, we don't want anything like that.'

She tried to slam the door, but the mat was rucked up at one corner, and as it bounced open again, I handed her one of our wedding forms, which had a space for everything, including 'Presents to bride and/or bridegroom from employer',

477

and suggested that she might fill it in at her leisure. She recoiled from it as if it were subversive propaganda, and I went away. We were supposed to do at least a paragraph about everyone who got married, even if nobody had ever heard of them, but I did not feel like being insistent. If I could not find anywhere to live, I would not be on the Post next week, anyway. I should have to go back to being a cook.

I had one more house on my list. Rain was falling through the dusk and I wanted my tea. I had half a mind to drop a wedding form through the lettter box and catch a bus back to the office, but I hardly liked to return with only the trophy of the peplum waist and burgundy accessories. I was supposed to have a ten-inch column of bridal news to be written up and set in type tomorrow morning.

Miss Marjorie Goff, before she became Mrs Cecil Salmon, had lived at the Victorian end of the town, in a tall, flaking house with a flight of draughtboard steps spanning a basement area full of overflowing dustbins. Into the riser of each step was set a slit of opaque glass, to bring a gleam of hope to whatever dungeon lay beneath.

There was a small front garden of mossy earth and old iris corms, screened from the street by a high brown wall, in which a spiked gate hung at the warp and grated the ground as you opened it. From gate to front door, over the path and the steps ran a curious glass roof, supported by pillars of cast-iron barley sugar. Some of the panes of glass were broken, and where the arcade joined the house above the front door, it had pulled away and left a large gap, through which the rain fell on to me as I waited for someone to answer the bell.

The bell was a knob shaped like a pineapple. Above it were three electric buttons with stamp-paper labels, which said: 'LING', 'HAWKINS' and 'CASUBON'. The pineapple did not say anything. I pulled it, and hours afterwards, something jangled miles away. I waited. I did not like to pull the pineapple again, because it had felt as if it might come right out of the wall into my hand. I could hear people moving about, and voices, so I tapped on the glass panel that was let into the door behind a curly grille, and presently a large flat face like a turbot looked at me through the glass and the door was opened.

The hall smelled of shoes and soup. Mrs Goff, mother of the bride, took me into the untidiest sitting-room I have ever seen. It was glutted with papers, books, handbags, teacups, dog collars, bits of clothing, and everything that anyone had put down and never bothered to take away. The piano stool was stacked so high with music that you would not be able to reach the pedals if you sat on top of it, but if you removed the pile, there would be nowhere else to put it. The top of the piano was loaded with dead potted plants and tobacco tins. The mantelpiece was a welter of photographs, vases, spectacles, a bottle of vinegar, a pile of coppers, and a jack-in-the-box hanging head down out of its box on the end of a broken spring. In the mirror above, which you could see had once been gilt, were stuck curling snapshots and grocers' invoices. The curtains were coming off their rings, in a picture high up was a piece of holly from last year's Christmas, and someone had had a meal of unfilleted fish and bottled sauce, perhaps today, perhaps a week ago.

Mrs Goff, who was slightly less untidy than the room, was a short, wide woman, not exactly fat, for her bulk was more sideways than from back to front, like a drawing in a child's picture book of the unpopular nanny run over by a tram. She wore a black openwork cardigan and a brown home-knitted dress, which had never been designed for shapes like this, and appeared to have been miscalculated in the casting on. Her grey hair, stained at the front with nicotine, was bundled insecurely into a hair-net. Her fingers were not stained, for when she smoked, which was from the moment she banged at her alarm clock in the morning to the moment she set it again at night, she held the cigarette in her mouth, shifting and

479

rolling it about and chewing on it until the last wet brown half inch was surrendered reluctantly to the brimming ashtray, or a flowerpot, or misfiring into the grate.

She lit a cigarette now, from the packet in the sagging pocket of her cardigan, cleared two leather chairs on to the floor, poked at her leaking hair-net, spread an infatuated smile over the spaces of her face and settled down to tell me about her darling daughter's wedding to *that man*. Fascinating though it was, I had to keep steering her away from the subject of Cecil Salmon in order to get the details I wanted. I could not print in the *Downingham Post* that Cicil was not good enough for Marjorie, never had been from the day they met at the Outing, and never would be, for all his reckoning to be chief buyer, thank you very much. I could not tell my readers that Cicil was common, and his mother, who was she? and that the ring he had bought Marjorie was nothing but paste, dear, and she so fond of gems, and that although the wedding had been a beautiful occasion mind, at the Coach and Horses, with everything as it should be and a cake they would still be eating a twelve-month hence, it had been the saddest day in Mrs Goff's life.

Her stays were too high in the front, and she had to push them down when she wanted to raise her bosom in a sigh. She was doing this when the door burst open and two tufted airedales came in on a double leash, pulling Mr Goff. If he had gone on all fours, he would have been about their size. Upright, one of them standing on its hindlegs could easily put its paws on his shoulders, which it did, and pushed him backwards on to the piano stool, scattering the music. The other dog slipped its collar over its head and went under the table with a yellowing copy of 'Chili-Bom-Bom'. Mr Goff was a bald, puckered man with a large Irish mouth and a whistle in his speech. He would have looked like an old jockey, if his face had not been innocent of a jockey's bitter history of striving to keep himself that size.

'Here's the Press, Waldo,' his wife told him, 'come to put Marjorie in the *Post*. We always take the *Messenger*, dear,' she told me kindly.

'Yes, indeed,' said Mr Goff, taking the airedale's front legs on his knee and crunching the back of its ear, which made it grunt.

'There's to be all about the ceremony,' said his wife, 'and what Marjorie wore, and that Cicil's sister too, with her awkward shape.'

'Yes, of course,' whistled Waldo, 'and who's to pay?'

Mrs Goff shook her head at him and made a shushing face. She pointed to my notebook, which after nearly half an hour had hardly anything in it.

It appeared that there was a mouse in the dresser. 'It's the biscuits, dear.' The airedales kept leaping towards it and backing away stiffly with little moans. One of them got its front half under the dresser and stayed there with its bottom half in the air and its stump of tail quivering. The other one put its front paws on the table and polished off the fish bones.

Mrs Goff jammed another cigarette into her mouth and talked on, but I could not pin her down to the details I wanted. The clock on the mantelpiece, which was propped up one side with a matchbox, said five o'clock; I did not think it was going, but I knew it must be getting late, and I had to get back to the office before Mr Pellet put on the black Homburg and locked up. I showed her a form and suggested that she should fill it in and I would call for it next day. She shook her head. 'I've lost my glasses.'

'Perhaps your husband –?'

'He can't write.' She pushed down her stays and laughed, hanging the cigarette on her lower lip and screwing up her eyes against the smoke, while Waldo grinned and looked coyly proud, as if he had done something clever. 'He's a lovely man, but he never could write.'

'Not a syllable,' Mr Goff said. 'Marjorie used to do the

481

necessary for me, and now she . . .' His rubber mouth dropped and his eyes pinkened and grew triangular.

Down must go the stays. You would have thought Marjorie was dead. 'And there's her room, you know, at the top of the house with all her bits and pieces, where she used to dream her girlhood dreams. . . .' The bride's mother was off on a long quote from a magazine story, but I was not listening. Remembering the three bells and the stamp-paper, I had an idea.

The Goffs cheered up a little when I suggested it, especially when we talked about the rent. 'A press reporter,' Mrs Goff said once or twice, as if trying out the sound of it. 'Well, I'm sure.' She inspected me, and I could not tell if she was impressed or disapproving. I thought she was impressed, until she took her eyes off me with, 'Oh well, it takes all sorts.'

We climbed up to see the chamber of girlhood dreams. I hardly looked at it, because it was a room, and it was empty, and it meant that I should not be on the street in two days' time when Rogerson's Rentacar came to take the Munts to the station. Mrs Goff would feed me, as she fed Ling and Casubon, though not Hawkins.

'They're difficult folk.' She gathered her mouth into an elaborate smockwork round the cigarette. 'They prefer a gas-ring. A great mistake. You can't feed a man on a gas-ring, say what you will. We have the meters, of course.'

'Not in *her* room,' put in Mr Goff, nodding his bald dome down at me. We were on the stairs then, discussing the other lodgers at the tops of our voices. A door on the landing below opened and a woman in a bath cap and a kimono looked out. She looked at me for a full minute without blinking or moving a muscle. She couldn't, because she had a mud pack on her face.

'Are you much on gas?' Mrs Goff quizzed me from the stair below.

'Have to have the meter put in *her* room,' Mr Goff repeated. For a long time, he never called me anything but Her and She, not disparagingly, as his wife spoke of Cicil as That Man, but as if I were a thing in a zoo that had not been classified: amorphous, not quite real.

The following evening after work, I moved from *chez* Munt to *chez* Goff. There was a slight dissonance with the Munts over a towel of mine that had got in with their laundry, but Mrs Munt said we must live and let live – she having got the towel – and gave me a Toby jug with a broken nose as a memento of my happy stay.

I put it on the mantelpiece in my new room, where it was not alone, for Marjorie had left some of her girlhood bric-à-brac behind, including a pot full of hairpins, a mug full of black hair and a photograph of Tyrone Power. Her books were on the window-sill. She appeared not to have read anything since she left school. There were some of her underclothes and a bag full of damp knitting in the chest of drawers, and a mackintosh and a hot pink dress in the cupboard.

When I asked Mrs Goff if these could be removed, the look that I was soon to know so well came over her wide face. It was a completely blank look, the mouth hanging a little and eyes half closed against the rising smoke, and it meant No. It was a face against which there could be no argument, for there was no one behind it. Mrs Goff had gone away out of reach of opposition, and would not return until the coast was clear.

First, the look said to me wordlessly that it was sure I had not as many clothes as all that, and then it said to me with words, many words, that Marjorie's things could not be moved, because Mrs Goff had it in her bones that one day Marjorie would come home again. I was beginning to feel sorry for Cecil Salmon. I did not know that next week his conversational value would be lowered in favour of something else. Mrs Goff would run a subject to death for seven days, and then suddenly switch over at Sunday dinner and start hounding something else, which would last her all the next week.

My room was narrow but adequate, with a window which looked out on back gardens, a wooden bed with a slipping green eiderdown and a gas fire which screamed for two minutes after you turned it on. The bed was too near the fire. It kept the heat away from the rest of the room, and if you wanted to dress before the stove, you had to sit or kneel on the bed. I would probably have to do all my writing on or in the bed until the warmer weather came. In any case, there was nowhere else in the room to sit.

I put away my things and tried not to feel bleak. The first night in that room stretched before me with too many hours, and I found that I was looking forward to going to work tomorrow. At the Munts', I had often craved solitude, and dreaded hearing the creak of the stair and the whimsical tattoo on my door that meant Mrs Munt had come up for a pow-wow, but up here on the top floor, a stranger to the rest of the house, I felt unwanted and alone. I wrote a letter home and that made me feel worse.

All my life, ever since I was old enough to realize the unlimited possibilities of the inside of one's own head, I had never got enough of being alone. I had loved to be with people, but I had loved, too, to be away from them. I had treasured the release of my own room as a monk treasures the spiritual liberty of his cell. That was when I did not have to be alone. I had only to open a door and there were the voices and the familiar jokes and the feet going about their small, predictable affairs.

This kind of solitude was different. I was alone whether I wanted it or not, and nobody in the house cared whether I opened my door or kept it shut. I desperately wanted to talk to somebody. I felt that if I did not at least see someone before the night sealed me into that narrow room, I should be shut away in myself for ever and never make contact with the world again. People went mad like that. One had heard of it.

I went out on to the landing, and cautiously down the stairs, hoping that one of the chipped chocolate doors would open, yet ready to scuttle if they did. In the front room on the first floor, a wireless was playing: low, throbbing music, tuned down so that it sounded far away, like dance music in the Palm Court heard from a hotel bedroom above. In the first-floor back, which was below mine, two people were having a murmured, spasmodic conversation. The woman would say something in a light, rather lifeless voice. After a long pause, the man would answer. Another pause, and she would murmur again. It sounded as if they were busy with something else while they talked: she doing her hair or her nails, he perhaps mending something, or cleaning a pipe, or sticking stamps in his album. I could not tell, not knowing what he was like, and their seclusion deterred me, as did the intimate throb of the dance music in the front room.

I hesitated on the landing, which was stacked about with chairs and chests and other unwanted articles, such as a doll's pram and a mottled tin sea trunk, with 'L/COM. D. B. K. RINGWOOD, R.N.' painted in white on the top. There was also a bamboo table with a frayed rush top. Not the ideal writing surface, but I could do with it in my room, and I decided to ask Mrs Goff for it. I did not know her so well then.

I leaned against a knobless chest of drawers, which smelled of maids' bedrooms in old country houses, and wondered whether I could knock on one of the doors and ask for a stamp, or the time. Could one, in lodgings, call on people whose front doors were their bedroom doors as well?

The man in the back room coughed nearer the door, and I fled on down the stairs, afraid that he might come out with his braces hanging down, and share my embarrassment.

I did not know whether anyone lived on the ground floor except the Goffs. I did not think anyone would want to, for the congestion on the upper landing was nothing to this. Their untidiness had flowed out of the rooms into the hall and garden passage, and you could hardly move for all the coats and shoes and cardboard boxes, brooms, a tin of paraffin, a bucket of coal, two hat-stands, a vacuum cleaner without a bag, and pictures with broken glass and trailing wires leaning against the wall. It looked like one of those junk shops where nobody ever goes, and where it would take an hour to get at what they wanted if they did.

Casubon lived in the basement, whatever Casubon was. If I went down those dark, narrow stairs in the hope of meeting it, I could not casually appear to be just passing by. It would seem even more like intrusion than on the first floor. Stamps? The time? I wavered on the top step, looking down. I thought of my home upstairs that was not yet a home, and hated the idea of climbing back to it without a word or two of contact with someone. But Casubon might be doing something down there. Might be forging bank notes, or entertaining a lover, or practising Yoga.

As the kitchen door opened, I jumped towards the garden door, and pretended to be looking out into the blackness. A very small boy in square knickers and a congealed bib hanging back to front round his neck came round the door and stood clinging to the edge of it, a hand on either knob. At sight of me, his eyes contracted and his stained mouth dropped, but just before he could yell, a woman's voice remarked, without emotion, 'Barry, come back in here, you little sod.'

Barry suddenly gave me a beautiful smile, let go of the outer door handle and slid back into the kitchen. I went up the stairs, which were linoleum after the first flight, wondering about the Goff family and what they were doing in the kitchen, and who were Barry and the cold, unmotherly voice, in the fruitless way that one does tease one's fancy over people one is bound to know all about sooner or later.

The gas fire roared in my room, but the air was thick with silence. Now I really did want to know the time, for my clock had stopped. I did not think there was anyone in the front room, but I went across to look. It was a larger room than mine, but with less furniture. On the unmade bed was a piece of paper, which said, 'Mr Z. No money, no room. Pay tonight or never.' There were no clothes or possessions about, so I concluded it was never.

When I returned to my room, I traced the curious atmosphere in there. Marjorie's mackintosh smelled of fish. I hung it on the door in the bathroom, which was a mere slit, presumably once part of my room, for it was separated from it only by a wooden partition with misted glass at the top. When someone was in there, you could see the silhouette of their head and neck, unless it was little Mr Goff, but I don't think he ever went into the bathroom. He had tremendous washing sessions at the kitchen sink, sometimes while we were having a meal in there.

As well as the door into the passage, there was another door in the bathroom, oddly situated behind the side of the bath. I did not see where it could lead to, for there was no other room on that floor. When I looked at the house from without, there was only a blank wall on that side, with no windows above the ground floor, and certainly no trace of the other side of the bathroom door. When I lay in the bath unable to get out of the lukewarm water, I used to watch it all the time, for I dreamed on my second night there that the brass handle turned and the door opened, on to – what?

The next day, I was woken by sounds from behind the wooden partition, and I lay and watched the dim shadow of a man shaving himself in the bathroom. I could see that he was going carefully round a moustache. The church clock, which had been striking every quarter all night long, as dramatically as if anyone cared, told me that it was only seven o'clock. Was the moustache going to wake me at this hour every morning? No wonder Marjorie had left home.

I went to sleep again. I was in no hurry, because it was Petty Sessions today, and the magistrates did not sit until ten-thirty. There was nothing I ought to do in the office before that, except rewrite one of the stories for Murray, which I did not intend to do. It was about an Old Folks' Tea, and it played on the heartstrings. Murray did not like too much of the human touch. He had been brought up in a news agency, and liked his news straight and cold.

He had thrown my copy back at me and said that people in Downingham did not want to read stuff like that. I said that people in Downingham did not want to read any of the stuff we wrote, only there was nothing else, except the *Messenger*. Murray asked: Who did I think I was? That was a favourite question of his. I sometimes tried to think up funny answers to it, but they amused nobody, least of all Murray, who would slide away with his oblique walk and pretend that he was going up to a conference with Mr Pellet.

It was after nine o'clock when I woke again. Mrs Goff had told me that breakfast was at eight sharp, or earlier if desired. I believe she would have provided breakfast at five a.m. if necessary, for she never seemed to go to bed. However late one came home at night, there was always a light under one of the doors on the ground floor, and the sound of Mrs Goff's voice. If her husband was asleep and she had not managed to keep any of her family or friends as long as she wanted, you might meet her on the stairs, prowling about with her great ginger cat in her arms, looking for someone to talk to.

I tried the water in the bathroom. It was cold. I dressed quickly, with several jerseys, for the police court was one of the oldest in England, and full of draughts. I went downstairs. There was no one about. The front door and the door which led down a flight of iron steps into the chicken-soured garden were both open, and half a gale was blowing through the hall.

I went into the kitchen, where the small boy was sitting in a puddle in the middle of the floor. His mother came in from the scullery, said: 'Look at the little bastard,' in that same unemotional tone, picked him up, and carried him out, holding him well away from her.

'Good morning,' I said, but she had gone.

I stood in the kitchen and looked at the littered table, which looked as if many people had all eaten different meals on it at the same time. There was a faint smell of haddock on the air.

Mrs Goff came in from the scullery, holding a wooden spoon as if it were a sceptre. She was tautly polite to me, as if she had never seen me before. 'What can I do for you?' she asked. 'Breakfast is over, and everyone off and gone about their business hours ago, except Mrs Ling, of course.'

'Of course,' I agreed, for she said this confidently, as if I ought to know.

'Porridge there was,' said Mrs Goff, 'but porridge there isn't now. I clear my table at eight-thirty sharp.' It did not look as if it would be cleared until the next mealtime, and perhaps not even then, if room could be made by pushing the dirty plates aside.

'Oh, that's quite all right,' I said. 'I never eat porridge. If I might just have a cup of tea or coffee –'

'Everyone eats my porridge,' said Mrs Goff. 'I'm afraid the kettle is off the boil and coffee I don't make, except sometimes, after supper if we have company. You'll have to come down punctually to breakfast or not at all. I'm not running a cafeteria here you know, whatever some people seem to think. Eat, eat, eat, meals at any old time and all day long and this wanted, and that wanted, and please, Mrs Goff, may I have another bulb for my light? I tell you, dear, it's murder, letting rooms. It's keep on all day long, work, work, work, and no time to call your own. It will kill me at the finish.' She pushed down her corsets.

I longed to say, 'Well, nobody asked you to let rooms,' but I did not dare, any more than one dares say, 'Nobody asked you to be a butcher', or 'Why be a grocer then?' when shop-keepers complain about The Public.

'Anyway,' said Mrs Goff, 'shouldn't you be at work?'

'Well, you see, in a newspaper office, you don't keep regular hours. It just depends what's on. This morning, for instance, there's –'

'I know,' she interrupted. She was always doing this before you could finish what you were saying, although she could not possibly know. It grew to be very irritating. 'Lunch at one-fifteen punct.,' she said. 'My Kedigree today.' Of course. Always kedgeree when there had been haddock.

She ate a toast crust off somebody's plate, and waited for me to go, her face blank. Barry's mother came in again. She was a tall flat girl, with a bad-tempered face, which was made devilish by eyebrows plucked into a slant and greasy black hair parted in the middle and curled on either side like horns. She stared at me. 'Who's this?' she asked quite rudely.

Mrs Goff introduced us. The devil girl was Alice, Marjorie's elder sister, separated from an unsatisfactory husband and now living at home again, as Mrs Goff hoped that Marjorie soon would be. It seemed to me that it would have saved a lot of trouble if the girls had not got married in the first place.

Alice picked at her nails and listened dispassionately, while her mother expounded to me the sins of her husband. I did not want to hear about Hubert and his so-called cashier, and I edged towards the door. I did not dare ask again for tea, or even a bit of bread and butter. I would get something in a café on the way to the court. It was monstrous, when I was paying for bed and board, but I was not strong eough to fight it out now. Mrs Goff had a sapping effect on you, particularly when she had breakfasted on porridge and haddock and you had not.

As I went out, Mr Goff and the dogs came through the

back door like a chariot race, and I heard Mrs Goff greeting the dogs with high-pitched screams, promising them din-dins, and fondly begging her husband to 'Sit in, lovely, and I'll bring you something hot.'

It was somewhere to live, however. It would do until I could find something else.

Vic and Joe were already in court when I arrived. I was only there as a student, to watch and listen and learn how to report a case, and perhaps, as a great treat, to write two or three lines about a maintenance order. Ronnie, the callow youth from the *Messenger*, was also on the press bench, and a dumpy female from the *Moreton Advertiser*, who had been sent over because one of her residents had shoplifted in our town.

I slid on the hard seat next to Vic, and put my notebook on the scarred old table, which was as mutilated as a school desk. It was made of some very soft wood, so that you could do initials and drawings on it with a pencil, if you had not got a penknife. Victor was finishing off a female profile that he had started last week. He grunted. Joe was dozing.

While we were waiting for the magistrates to come in, I told Victor about finding somewhere to live, and about the Goffs. He displayed slack interest, but I was used to the morning torpor of everyone in the newspaper world. If it did not come naturally, it had to be assumed, like a bedside manner, or the tight-lipped smile of a bank clerk. He became a little animated when I mentioned the name of the road.

'That was where the murder was a couple of years ago, wasn't it, Joe?'

'Search me,' said Joe, without opening his eyes.

'Ronnie,' said Victor, leaning across, 'wasn't it Bury Road where they had that bread-knife murder?'

'That's right,' said Ronnie. 'Lots of blood. Bury Road. Number five.'

'Number five,' I said. 'But that's the house where I am. It can't have been.'

'Well, it might have been six,' said Victor. 'I only know I got a peach of a story there. A gift, it was, because it happened on press day, so we had it as soon as the London papers.'

'Number five,' said Ronnie, nodding as to a happy memory. 'I remember it well.'

My spine crept. I thought of that bathroom with the sinister door to nowhere. Anything might have happened there. 'Which room was it?' I asked.

Nancy came busily into the court with a rattle of her heels, and leaned over the bench behind Ronnie. 'There are half a dozen cases in the children's court,' she said. 'One's that Martin boy with the airgun. Shall I do them?'

'O.K. dear,' said Ronnie, knowing that she would anyway, if she wanted to. Nancy was very bossy, and always knew everything. Often, she knew it wrong, but she still went on bossing.

'You going then, Joe?' asked Victor

Joe groaned. 'I suppose so.' He picked up his untidy bundle of notebooks and copy paper and lumbered out past our knees.

'Victor, which *room* was it?' I repeated. 'Ronnie, do you know? Which room was the murder in?'

'One of the top rooms, wasn't it?'

'Which one?'

'Oh, Lord, I don't know. Don't make such a row. You'll get turned out. There's old Nobby looking at you now.'

'But which –'

'Silence!' yelled Police Sergeant Clarke, unnecessarily loud in the small room, and we all stood up as the high door behind the Bench opened and the magistrates trooped in.

There were four of them, an unprepossessing bunch by any standards, and I have often thought, here as in other country courts, that if I were a malefactor, I should wonder what gave these humdrum characters the right to judge over me. They would be harmless enough in their own homes, no doubt – the chairman a gruff but kindly father, the lady in the black hat a popular hostess. If you met all four of them on a bus together, you would not be disturbed about them; but here, stuck up in majesty on the Bench, they seemed too ordinary, too like the rest of us facing them in the body of the court, to be set thus in judgement on their fellows.

The chairman was a well-known local character, who had once been lord of a large mansion and park. He now lived in a villa just outside its gates, from where he could watch the heedless schoolboys rampaging in and out of the lovely old stone house, and churning up the park with football boots.

Like the one old deer, which escaped when the rest of the herd were rounded up for sale and still ranged the park, suspicious and aloof, Colonel Burrows would not move away from his family home, nor accept the new régime. Although he lived in a little creeper-snug house with a peaked roof and lattice windows and a lawn that took only half an hour to mow, he still dressed and behaved as if he were lord of the cold old manor, with bow-legged men touching their caps in the stable yard and a booted donkey pulling the mower all day over the slopes and swards.

The two elderly maids who had remained with him were still called by their surnames, still smelled of linen cupboards, and were treated as if they were a whole servants' hall in themselves. When the Colonel dined alone, they both had to come in with the port decanter, and stand behind his chair while he drank The King.

They were used to him and they understood, and the jobbing gardener, who came once a week from the village, was so deaf that he never knew that Colonel Burrows shouted at him as if he were a fool or a damn foreigner.

The Colonel's clothes had also outlasted the change, for

their cloth had been the best that Harris could weave. In stifling plus fours and green socks with yellow tassels under the turn-ups, he stumbled about the small rooms of his villa, bumping his head. When he shopped in Downingham for household articles he once had never heard of, he wore breeches and gaiters and a yellow waistcoat, and hectored his way round the ironmonger's, as if small boys were holding his horse outside, instead of tracing irreverence in the dust of his car.

In court this morning, he wore the plus fours, with a fox-patterned silk scarf tied like a hunting-stock, and a general air of having left a tweed deer-stalker and a knobbly stick hanging on the pegs outside. The front of the Bench was solid, so you could not see his feet, but when he took the children's court, where the magistrates sat behind an ordinary table, juvenile delinquents were fascinated by the sight of enormous ankle boots, well dubbined and studded on the soles, inanimate at the end of surprisingly thin and shapely legs.

Next to the Colonel, the top of his head on a level with the bristly tweed shoulder, sat a neat old man in a wing collar, who never contributed anything to the proceedings, and seemed not quite to know why he was there. His hair was parted in the centre and eked carefully over his clean pink head, and his eyes were round and mild. He looked lost, but patient, as if his wife had sent him there to be out of the way until lunchtime.

On the Colonel's other side were two women, who took the whole business more seriously than anyone else, and did not like witnesses to make jokes. One was flushed and heavy, with a jaw like a boxer. She always wore the same felt hat, punched into shape and held on by an elastic that made her bun stick oddly up and out behind. She looked like a Socialist M.P. about to ask a question in the House about fish prices.

The other lady was much younger than her colleagues, and had only recently been sworn in. The weekly Sessions were still quite an occasion to her, so she dressed for them in smart town clothes and a careful make-up, although there was nobody to fascinate among the joyless collection of bareheaded policemen, bored solicitors, and witnesses and relations of defendants, who were scattered on the public benches with mackintoshes and large, misshapen handbags. Everyone dozed from time to time in the magistrates' court, because none of the windows would open, but Mrs Chance, being a new girl, kept brightly awake all the time, and kept raising minor quibbles, or saying things the other way round, to show that she was not just the chairman's yes-woman.

Police Sergeant Nobby Clarke, his grizzled head rising massively from the numbered collar which identified him like a dog, opened the proceedings with various requests for extensions of licences for dances, for Christmas was approaching and Downingham was putting on the motley. Nobby had been running the magistrates' court for years, but it had not improved his diction. He read in a monotonous drone that ran the end of a phrase, and often of a sentence, into the beginning of the next. When he came to the extension of licensing hours for the Police Ball, he paused for the expected shifting and murmur of laughter. The old chestnut never failed, although the police had been holding dances twice a year for as long as anyone in Downingham could remember. The magistrates smiled graciously, and even the woman in the pummelled hat relaxed her jaw perceptibly.

Colonel Burrows said, as he had been saying twice a year ever since he had been made chairman fifteen years ago: 'Well – mph, mph –' (He could not speak without constantly clearing some imaginary strangulation.) 'Well, I suppose we need not ask the police whether they approve of that extension – mph?' He glanced round blinking, to receive the polite laughter. A very young constable, who had not heard the quip before, laughed a little too loud, and Nobby turned slowly round and looked at him. The young constable suddenly remembered urgent duties outside the courtroom and took his red ears away through the swing door.

After this jollity, we settled down to serious business. Maintenance orders and applications for legal custody of children came first, and the witness box saw the usual dispiriting procession of bedraggled wives and shiftless husbands. Whether the women looked bedraggled because they were deserted, or whether their husbands had deserted them because they had been bedraggled all along, one did not know, but the fact was that the women in these cases were mostly so unpalatable that one wondered why the husbands had taken them on in the first place, and felt a sneaking sympathy with them for having walked out. Until one saw the husbands. Then it seemed that they had been pretty lucky to get a wife at all, even one like this chewed-up little viper, who was whining out her dreary story in the witness box now.

Victor was putting a body on his female profile. Ronnie was cleaning the nails of one hand with the thumbnail of the other. The magistrates may or may not have been listening, but the large woman looked as though she were planning her menus for the week. I felt depressed. I had not yet been to enough Petty Sessions to become immune to their bitterness. Hearing only about the marriages that went wrong, and never about the ones that went right made one think that all marriage was a hopeless proposition doomed to rancorous failure.

The viper's story held all the unloveliness in creation. You could write a shelf full of existentialist novels without ever seeing more of the world than the inside of a magistrates' court. Stupidly, ineptly, she told it, contradicting herself and leaving out the most important details, but you could see behind it all those years of bitter life in the grey, degraded street, where the main-line trains threw soot at your back windows and drowned your voice a hundred times a day.

496

You could imagine the wife with her spiteful mouth still moving unheard while the train thundered past, the galling nag going on day after day, until the husband heeded it as little as the noises of the railway. You could imagine him coming home drunk, and the smell of him in the airless passage. You could imagine what he looked like on the mornings when he refused to get up and shave and go to work. You could imagine her and her mother, who lived with them, talking, talking about him with the same sunken mouths, and the paralysed father crying when they cursed him for wetting his bed. . . .

Victor dug me in the ribs. 'You're supposed to be taking notes, Poppy. You can write this one up if you like.'

I scribbled madly, filling the pages of my notebook. I would write a moving, shocking story, a slashing indictment of the housing conditions that lurked unheeded at the back of our town.

'Not all that,' muttered Vic, leaning back and yawning. 'You've only got a few lines, not the whole mucking column. Just the name and address and that.'

I asked Ronnie if he had got those details. He pushed his notebook across with a superior smile, and in trying to decipher his writing, I missed the magistrates' verdict. Ronnie took his notebook back and scribbled something, and before I could see what it was, he had closed the book and gone out for a coffee, as he did not want the next case. I would have to ask one of the policemen, which was a pity, because they called me the New Girl and did not take me seriously, and I was trying to show them that I was a seasoned reporter.

At last the matrimonial cases were finished. The magistrates were holding out well. Colonel Burrows had had his eyes closed some of the time, but that did not prove he was asleep.

The lady in the felt hat looked at the clock and asked the usher for a glass of hot water. She took two tablets with it, and settled down again to frown on the raw youth with the shifting Adam's apple who stood accused of riding a pedal cycle without lights at Marking Green.

'Mph – this is – mph – a very serious offence,' Colonel Burrows said, leaning his stomach on the Bench and pointing his wiry brows at the defendant, who chased his Adam's apple more feverishly up and down his neck, not knowing that this was one of the few remarks in the Colonel's magisterial repertoire.

The girl from the *Moreton Advertiser*, who had so far been sitting looking down her nose as if she were slumming, set herself in motion for the next case. It was a theft from a café by a 'foreigner' from her town – as if we had not enough thieves of our own, without importing them from pottery-shadowed Moreton.

The poor man had gone to endless trouble to break in, and then all he had taken was two threepenny ice-creams and a tin of baked beans. It did not seem worth it. The tin of beans appeared as an exhibit, but not the ice-creams.

The little story took a long time to tell, with policemen and detective constables and several witnesses all saying the same thing in different ways, which confused the magistrates. It took a long time to settle too, because even after they had stopped the Colonel talking at cross-purposes, Mrs Chance felt it was about time she made her presence felt, and quibbled about the fine.

The old gentleman in the wing collar sighed and took out his Albert, but it was not nearly lunchtime.

When the thief in the frayed brown coat had finally been disposed of, with Mrs Chance victorious, the girl from the *Moreton Advertiser* shut her notebook with a plop, shut her handbag with a loud click, and left to catch her bus. It seemed a long way to come for half an hour of ice-cream and baked beans.

'Must want a job,' Vic said. 'Doing us out of our lineage.

I might have got three bob for sending them that story. Here, you do the next case, Pop. I'll die if I don't go out for a beer.'

At lunchtime I went to a café, instead of going home to Mrs Goff's kedgeree. After what I had heard about the murder, I did not feel like going back to the house sooner than necessary.

I went back to the office early, because I thought that the case which Vic had given me would take me all afternoon to write up. It was an order for possession of one of a row of cottages, in which the tenant's wife had been registering her dislike of the neighbours by such practices as spitting on the ground when she saw them and trampling in her spittle, calling names out of top windows for all the road to hear, and directing a garden hose at them over the back fence. Victor had told me when I joined him in the White Lion that it was worth a lead story of half a column, and I was as nervous as if I had been told to write a leader for *The Times*.

The problem was how to keep the full flavour of the story without putting in the operative words? Or could one? Alone in the office with the morning's dirty ashtrays, I searched through old files of the *Post* to see if such words had ever got past Mr Pellet before, or whether one put the first letter and a dash, or only a dash, or just: 'Defendant used insulting language,' which took all the life out of the story.

I found nothing to help me. I sat down at the table, cleared a space, found some copy paper, and started to sketch out a story. The others could sit right down, flip through their notebooks, and skim off a finished report, without having to copy it out and alter it again and again, but I laboured painfully. I wished that we had a typewriter in the office. There was only one in the building. That was Mr Pellet's and no one was allowed to use it, except occasionally Murray, who would bring it downstairs like a high priest carrying the sacred calf, tap its keys reverently, and lock it up ostentatiously if he had to leave the room for a moment.

It was a relief to be in the office alone for a change, but I wished that someone would come and help me with my opening sentence, which would be printed conspicuously in bold type. I had tried ten, but each one looked less like journalism than the last. In the comp room next door, I heard them come back from their lunch. Maurice the apprentice was whistling 'The Mountains of Mourne' and presently the others took it up in song, dragging the slurs. I threw an empty ink bottle at the dividing wall. They threw back what sounded like a lump of type, and went on singing. The lino-type machines began their hysterical chattering, and outside the grimy windows a dog fight started, a woman screamed, and several cars hooted in the traffic jam at the crossroads.

I took off my jacket, ran my hands through my hair, and felt like a typical battered journalist. I should have had a green eyeshade and elastic bands to hold up my sleeves. Joe came in, looking cold and old.

'Joe,' I said. 'Good. Look, when you want to write Bloody, do you put B dash Y, or what? But actually, it wasn't Bloody.'

Joe went over to the corner where the gas ring was. 'God, girl,' he said, 'haven't you even got the kettle on yet? I thought you'd have the tea made by now.'

'You make it,' I said. 'I'm in the middle of something frightfully important.'

'Not my turn.' Joe sat down with his overcoat on, took out half a bent cigarette, looked at it glumly, and started to roll another. The comps next door began to sing 'I'm Dreaming of a White Christmas.' Joe threw a book at the wall.

Murray came in, rubbing his hands with a dry sound. 'Come along then, Poppy,' he said, like a kindergarten teacher. 'Your turn to make the tea today. I should have thought you would have had it brewed for us by now.'

It was not my turn. I went on writing.

Victor came in, banging the door. He blew on his hands,

stamped his feet, slammed some chairs and books about, and yelled: 'Shut up!' at the comps.

'Tea up?' he asked me. 'Come on, girl. Get cracking.'

'It's not my turn.'

'It's always your turn. You'll have to get up, anyway. I want that phone book you're sitting on.' He pulled it out from underneath me.

I turned my copy upside down so that no one could see what I had written, took the kettle, and went downstairs to fill it in the lavatory. The little room was ice-cold, because nobody had been able to shut the window for five years. There was only a cold tap in the basin, and while the kettle was boiling, I washed the cups under this, dried them on the towel that we used for our hands, and went upstairs with my fingers blue.

While I was trying to warm them at the fire, which was as sulky as a waiting-room grate, Mr Pellet came in.

'Got nothing to do?' he asked me. 'Didn't you go to Sessions this morning? There's no reason why you shouldn't write up some of the smaller cases now. By the way,' he said to Victor, 'that possession case came up this morning, didn't it? Woman with the foul mouth. Leave it alone. Major Back, friend of mine who made the application, asked me to keep off it. Says there's been too much talk about it already.'

'Oh, but,' I said, 'it was the best case of the lot. It would make a wonderful story, and anyway the Messenger will run it.'

'Blast them,' said Mr Pellet. 'We won't. A friend's a friend. I want you to come up to my office and go through that school concert report. It's time you learned how to do the damn things properly.'

He passed by the kettle, which lifted its lid at him. 'What's this?' he asked. 'Tea again? I don't know. Women. There never was all this tea drinking before you came to the office.'

I spent the rest of the afternoon correcting proofs with

Victor. He read out the original copy, while I made mysterious signs in the margins of the galleys, indicating where the type was wrong. I had never been shown how to correct proofs properly. They had all been doing it for so long that they could not imagine anyone not knowing, so I had to pick it up as I went along, inventing symbols where necessary. The comps were getting to know what I meant.

Victor read very badly, with no inflections, running one sentence into the next and making it duller than it was already. After columns and columns of sits. vac. and wanted and second-hand car advertisements, we were both nearly asleep and ready to go home. Harold came in with 'just the one more roll dears,' and we sat down again, reviling him as he tripped out of the room. He always walked on his toes, as if the floor was hot. Joe said he was in the first stages of locomotor ataxy.

' "On Tuesday last week," ' gabbled Vic, ' "the St Mary's group of Boy Scouts held their annual sale of work and exhibition of" – what's this? – "handcarts." ' He never could read people's handwriting, often not even his own.

'Handicrafts.' I was thinking about going back to Mrs Goff's. 'Vic,' I said, 'are you sure it was number five Bury Road where the murder was?'

'What murder? "The stalls were well stocked with all manner of useful and ornamental articles. The organizing committee consisted of Mrs Morris, Mrs Bagley – Budget – Rickey" – what the hell?'

'The bread-knife murder. What was the house like?'

'Oh that. I don't know. Tall thin house with – ah, I've got it! Rigley. Mrs Rigley. Got that? "Mrs Rigley, Mr Stott, Mr T. F. Mannering. A. Buffer" – no, hold it – "a buffet tea was provided by" – hm – hm – God! Why can't people learn to write?'

'It was number five though?'

'Might have been. I forget. It was ages ago. Why are you all steamed up about it, anyway? Shut up, and let's finish.'

'I've just taken a room there. I *told* you.'

' "... by Troop Leader – caps there – Dwight and Patrol Leader – caps ditto – Perks, ably assisted by –" Oh yes, so you have – "by T. E. Smart and F. Tonks." Might have been fifteen. No, I shouldn't think it was number five.'

'But Ronnie said he knew it was.'

'Ronnie never knows anything. He wouldn't be on the *Messenger* if he did. "The sale realized the grand total of seven pounds three shillings." Done, thank the Lord!' He jabbed the sheets of copy on to the spike where we filed them, and went home.

Not reassured, I walked slowly down Bury Road towards my new home, which rose up out of the dusk behind its high garden wall with what seemed to me a secret in its lighted eyes. The top floor was dark, since there was no one in Mr Z's room. I half expected to see a spectral face loom at one of the windows.

I went up the steps under the arcade, looking out for bloodstains. Mrs Goff had not given me a key, and I waited for a long time before the bell was answered. When it was, the opening door took me by surprise, for it was Mr Goff, and he was not tall enough to show through the glass behind the grille. He greeted me cheerily, but suddenly hiccoughed and dashed out past me, as one of the airedales hurtled between his legs into the garden.

When I was going upstairs the door of the room below mine opened and a watery-looking girl with limp hair and no make-up came out, carrying a kettle. She smiled with just a twitch of her mouth and began an embarrassed retreat as if the kettle were an indecency. She was probably going up to the bathroom, and I was glad of someone to go up to that top floor with me, so I introduced myself and we went up together.

She was Mrs Hawkins. She was so shy that it was almost an affectation. You had to drag conversation out of her, but she was company, and I asked her if she would like to see my room, because the light switch was not by the door, and I did not want to go into the dark alone. I was getting very silly. I thought I should probably have to go to sleep with the light on, and there would be trouble with Mrs Goff, and I should find myself homeless once more.

When I switched on the light, Mrs Hawkins stood in the doorway and looked round without comment. 'Quite nice, isn't it?' I said, hoping that she would persuade me of its charms. It still smelled a little fishy. I opened the window and saw her light shining from below. 'I suppose yours is about the same size.'

'Well, a little bigger, but of course, it takes up more space with the two of us.' She looked embarrassed at the mention of being in the same room as her husband.

I asked her what he did. She looked at the empty kettle in her hand and then towards the bathroom, as if longing to get away.

'He's a fitter at the White Star Garage,' she whispered, and started to back out.

I remembered that I had not asked Mrs Goff what time supper was. I did not want to miss it, as I had missed breakfast, but I did not like to go down to the kitchen to ask. I felt it would sound greedy, and they might not call it supper. It might be high tea.

I asked Mrs Hawkins, but of course she fed herself and the fitter, so she did not know.

'You could ask Mrs Ling,' she ventured, 'on the first floor front.'

'Go and knock at her door? Would she mind?'

'Oh no.' Again the twitch of a smile. 'She's lovely. If it wasn't for her, I don't know what I'd do.'

Did the fitter beat her then?

'She's ever so nice,' whispered Mrs Hawkins, and finally got herself away to the bathroom.

I took off my coat and went downstairs to call on lovely Mrs Ling.

I knocked on the door of the first floor front, but the wireless was playing a rumba that sounded like gravel being shaken in a canvas bag, and no one heard me. When the music grew more stealthy, I knocked again, and a muffled shout told me to come in.

The first thing I saw, and it nearly sent me straight out again, was a neat round bottom in a pair of white cotton trunks. It was lying on a table opposite the door, and from it two well-muscled legs rose into the air, ending in ankle socks and tennis shoes, on the soles of which a parasol was being juggled and spun and bounced in time to the rumba music. For a minute I watched fascinated, as the strong, fleshy legs rippled their dance in the air, and the *dégagé* feet tossed and caught and twirled the parasol like a ball on top of a fountain. The hips were raised on a bolster, so that the body was invisible, except for a pair of hands clutching the sides of the table.

In an armchair in front of the gas fire, which, like mine, fluttered yellow behind broken asbestos, a man sat reading with his back to me. I could see only his newspaper and the patent leather top of his head. The music stopped. I moved my foot with a squeak on the linoleum, and although the legs did not stop dancing, the prone head on the table screwed round to squint at me over a naked shoulder.

'Hi, there!' it said. The parasol came to rest on one foot. The other foot came up to steady it, and then with the tiniest movement of the knees, the parasol was tossed across the room to the man in the chair, who put up one hand to catch it without looking up from his paper. The legs swept down over the edge of the table to the floor, and with a little bounce and a skip, the juggler was on her feet, smiling at me with long, uneven teeth.

She was a not very young girl with a firm, squat athlete's

body clad only in the white trunks and a rather grubby brassière. The top part of her bright chestnut hair was set in curling pins, and the rest swung loose on her shoulders. She had a long, genial face, full lipped, broad under the eyes, tracked with much movement of expression, and glistening now with cold cream.

'Hullo!' she cried, as if I were the one person in the world she wanted to see. 'Excuse the jinks. Got to keep the old hinges from seizing up,' she shouted, for the wireless was now playing one of those jolly thumping tunes beloved of English dance bands.

'Turn that bloody noise off!' The man in the chair did so. 'How do you like the act?' she asked me.

'It's wonderful,' I said. 'I can't think how you –'

'Oh gosh,' she said, shaking her hair about round her short neck. 'You ain't seen nothing. That's just routine stuff. We open next week in the Empire panto – Mother blinking Goose, if you can believe it. You'll see then what we can do. Double uppers, tip-tops, over and unders, and with the balls and the rings, of course – all the works – don't we dear?'

The man looked round the back of the chair and grinned. He was a Japanese, wearing the inevitable Westernizing horn-rimmed spectacles.

'Your husband juggles too?' I asked, for she had said we.

'Oh, no, but he catches and throws for me. Matters a lot – the timing. And of course he does flip-flaps and fancy stuff on the way on and off. It's a double act, you know,' she said defensively, as if used to having this disputed.

'You're the new one upstairs, aren't you?' she asked. 'Mrs G. told me all about you, and what she didn't know, I guess she made up. Press, isn't it?' She leaned forward anxiously, and relaxed with her open, toothy smile when I nodded. 'Oh, smashing,' she said. 'We've never got to know the Press before, that's to say, not what you might call intimately, have we, dear? Do you cover the shows?'

'Some of them,' I lied, although Murray jealously guarded all the tickets and I had not been allowed the smell of a theatre yet. I was going to tell Mr Pellet soon that I needed the experience. I was sure that I could write better reviews than Murray, who wrote long sycophantic essays, calling everyone Mr and Mesdames So-and-So, like *The Times* when it tries to disassociate itself from the vulgar world of the cinema.

'Oh, look,' said the girl, who looked sometimes a girl, and sometimes quite old, 'you must come and meet my old man. I'm Maimie Ling. I expect you only know my stage name. Mimi del Robbio and partner. My name before I was married was Robb. del Robbio. Artistic, you see.'

I told her my name, and she introduced her husband. When he stood up, I saw that he was shorter than she and looked much younger.

'He's a Jap,' she said with pride, as Mr Ling grinned and bobbed a bow. 'But naturalized American. You can't get your tongue round his real name, so I always call him Tick. Tick Ling – get it?' She dug me in the ribs and gave a little scream of laughter. 'And doesn't he too? My dear, these Japs. He's naughty as a hat-stand.'

She was much given to these inapt similes – lively adjectives coupled to inanimate household objects. She put on a torn cotton kimono, told me that she was thrilled as a bedstead that I had come, and offered me a drink.

I accepted a toothglass of beer from a crate under the bed. 'God bless,' said Tick, and drank at his like a bird, licking the froth neatly off his flat upper lip. He was a trim, pleasing little man, more like a polite brother to Maimie than a husband. I could not imagine him doing anything so virile as tickling her. He did not speak much, for she did most of the talking, and when he did, his voice was a clipped, lighter version of a New Yorker's.

I sat on Mimi del Robbio's practice table and she sat on the

507

bed and cut her scarlet toenails and told me scandalous things about people in the house, and why Alice's husband had left her, and that I must lock up anything valuable, because Mrs Goff had a skeleton key to all the rooms and went through your drawers when you were out.

'Now, honey,' said Tick. 'You shouldn't talk that way. I still think you'd used those shillings for the meter.'

'O.K. then, it was the old man who took them. There – you see he won't have that. He and the old gent are as thick as sofa cushions. Mr G.'s getting to be his contact man, like. Tick's in the jewellery business on the side. Get you anything you want, Tick can.'

'Only the best stuff,' Tick said, moving his hands at me with a salesman's gesture. 'Strictly on the up and up. Why pay fancy prices in shops? What do you want – art, pearls, diamonté, slave bangles? What you want, I get. You've only to ask, remember.' I promised to remember.

A terrible noise sounded from downstairs, like the Fall of the House of Ussher. It was Mrs Goff beating the supper gong.

'Cripes!' Maimie slipped off the bed, picked up the eiderdown and shook her toenail cuttings out of the window. 'Better get buzzing. Doesn't pay to be late, because the old cow puts all the food out willy-nilly and them that aren't there gets theirs even colder than when she puts it on the table. No don't go dear. You've seen me in my scanties, anyway. Have a little quickie while Madame del Robbio slips into a hostess gown.'

I drank more beer, while Tick put on a tie and combed his unreal-looking hair carefully, with a geometrical centre parting. Maimie pulled on a pair of stockings, which she rolled below the knees, stepped into a bright green woollen dress, wiped off the cold cream with a few slick, professional movements, and slapped on some make-up. She took the pins out of her hair, combed the top part into a high swoop, flipped the rest out with her hand and a shake of her head, and we went down to the kitchen.

'Ah and aha!' said Mrs Goff. She had her social manner on for the evening meal. 'So you have introduced yourselves already. So well and good.' We seated ourselves at the table, which had pickle jars, sauce bottles, mustard pots, vinegar, sugar and a large bottle of soda mints placed at strategic intervals to cover the stains on the tablecloth. Little Barry was with us, sitting on three cushions and banging the table with a spoon, until his mother took it away from him and banged his own hand with it.

While Mrs Goff went out to the scullery, a furtive young man in a tight suit sidled into the room making an embarrassed face, nodded to the Lings, and sat down next to me. I smiled politely, and after one desperate sideways glance, he shifted a little away as if I wore a knife at my belt.

'Ah! Mr Casubon you don't know,' said Mrs Goff, coming back with a big cracked soup tureen which she put in front of her place at the head of the table. She introduced us, and the young man whispered how did I do, his grey, hungry face registering distress. He looked as if he had just suffered some tragedy which was still colouring all his actions and his attitude to the world. Maimie had merely told me that he was a crackpot. She had also said loosely that he was an abortionist, because he lived in a basement, which was where all abortionists lived, and Tick had clicked his gold-filled teeth at her and told her not to talk that way.

Mrs Goff served out the soup. It was interesting to see who got the biggest helpings. 'Come along, dear!' she called, and Mr Goff took his face and dripping arms out of the sink, towelled himself vigorously on a dishcloth, and came to join us, greeting 'the ladies' jauntily.

While we ate brown Windsor soup, which I have fortunately never discovered how to make, but which seems to be a tribal art with people like Mrs Goff, she told us some more about Cecil Salmon. The subject was evidently not exhausted yet. I had brought her home a proof of the wedding report I had written, because I thought it would be better to have objections now than after the paper was printed. It was passed round the table, collecting soup and butter stains, and to my surprise, was voted to be a fine piece of writing. Mrs Goff's bosom rose, but she did not push the corsets down. They stayed there, gratified, while she read the report out again for her husband, who apparently could read very little better than he could write.

I gathered that the Goffs had never had anything about them in the paper before, except that time when Dad took a highly commended at the dog show. Alice's wedding had been a hush-hush affair. 'At short notice, you know,' said Mrs Goff, making a funny mouth and nodding at little Barry, who was having soup poured into him from a teaspoon. Neither she nor Alice seemed at all abashed at this, because it was obviously all the fault of 'that Hubert'.

Mrs Goff was pleased because either Ricky or I had got Cecil's middle initial wrong. 'That'll take him down a peg, with his Cicil Watkins Salmon.' I felt that my entry into the household was favourable.

This emboldened me to ask, while Mrs Goff was measuring out the slices of meat loaf, and there was much passing round of potatoes and beetroot, whether I might have a small table in my room on which to construct further journalistic gems. Maimie looked at me, winked with the whole of one side of her face, and shook her head. Alice removed soup from little Barry's chin with a vicious swipe and made a slight hissing sound through her thin, cyclamen-coloured lips. Mr Goff, who was a slow eater, and always a course behind, imbibed brown Windsor like a gurgling drain. Mrs Goff either did not, or pretended not to, hear.

'Mr Casubon, I'll trouble your kindness to fetch the gravy,' she said, and the young man stumbled to his feet and went

510

out to the scullery, catching his toe on a piece of torn lino-leum. He could be heard crashing about in there, before he returned with a jug with a broken spout, which made another stain on the tablecloth as he put it down. He pulled out his chair with a grating noise, trod on one of the airedales, which yelped and went to Mr Goff, who fed it with bread, and sat down awkwardly, jogging my elbow as I was drinking water.

'So I thought,' I ventured on, when I had recovered, and we were all served and eating rather suspiciously, for it was that kind of meat roll, 'if I might just perhaps have that little bamboo table which seems not to be in use on the first floor landing –'

Mrs Goff gave me her drooping-eyelid look, a loaded fork half-way to her mouth. 'Your room,' she said, 'is let furnished, and that means it is furnished. It wants for no more.'

Everyone was silent, surprised that I had dared. 'I'm sorry,' I said, 'I only thought –'

'If we all said what we *thought*,' said Mrs Goff, 'the world would be a very funny place. I'll trouble you for the pickled beetroot, Alice.'

Dear Maimie came to my aid, as I felt she always would against people like Mrs Goff. 'But you know, Mrs G.,' she said, in her easy, generous tone of someone who does not expect snubs and seldom sees when they are given, 'there's such a heck of a lot of stuff standing about unused in this house, it does seem a pity –'

'It will all come to its use in good time, no doubt, my dear,' said Mrs Goff. Surprisingly, Maimie was one of the people to whom she gave big helpings.

I tried to curry my way back into favour. 'That tin chest there,' I said. 'There is someone naval in your family then?' Since it was marked Lieutenant-Commander, she would surely be proud to talk about him.

Alice gave what passed for a laugh with her. It came down

her nose, which was long, but cut back sharply at the end, with wide red nostrils. 'Some people,' she said.

'She wasn't to <u>know</u>,' said Mr Goff. 'One of my best bargains, but she wasn't here when I brought it home in triumph like the spoils of war.' He seldom spoke directly to me.

'Mr Goff is a great one for the sales,' his wife told me. 'There's hardly a Monday goes by but what he doesn't come home with some nice piece or other.'

'But he'll never sell,' said Tick. 'I tell him that's his trouble. If he'd only let me help him catch the markets at the right time –'

'He has his reasons,' said Mrs Goff, who sometimes treated her husband to a tempest of abuse, but would allow no one else to criticize him. 'There's untold riches in this house. Alice and Marjorie will be thankful when we are dead and gone.'

'I'll sell the lot for junk and be glad to get rid of it,' muttered Alice, but no one heeded, for little Barry chose to tip his plate of food into his lap and was hustled out with routine revilings and gravy running down his bare legs.

After supper, Mrs Goff suddenly felt mellow, even towards me, and announced that there would be tea for all. I gathered that it was the usual custom for the lodgers to make it on the gas rings in their own rooms. I would have to ask her to do something about mine, which stood on the floor detached, with a broken pipe leading to nowhere.

I had something else to ask her first. I dared not do it without her consent, after what she had said about the bamboo table. I despised myself for toadying to her, since I was paying – and had paid in advance too – but it was a question of anything for a quiet life.

'I was wondering,' I said, when she had poured out magnanimously and we were all stirring and sipping appreciatively, as if her tea were a special nectar, which it was not, 'I was wondering if you'd mind if I moved my bed over a little, against the wall. It's rather awkward having it so near the gas fire.'

Mrs Goff, who was just going to pour tea into saucers for the dogs, put the teapot down with a thump and stared at me, her cigarette hanging straight down and dropping ash on to her front.

'Mind?' she said, with an umbrage out of proportion to my request. 'And why should I not mind? You come into my house, and the very first day think you can turn everything upside down to suit your own whims and fancies. If you wanted an unfurnished room, you should have taken it. With a furnished, where the furniture is it stays, as I should have expected anyone to know.'

She glared at me. I felt myself blushing with anger, and hoped it did not look like shame. Mr Casubon, whose general distress about life embraced other people's troubles as well as his own, looked as if he would have blushed, too, if he had enough blood. He finished his tea with an unfortunate sucking sound, scraped back his chair, and mumbled that he must go and work.

Mrs Goff took no notice of him, even when he fell over the dog again. She was still looking at me, and she muttered something to her husband about 'knew we should have trouble taking on the Press', which I suppose I was meant to hear. I was afraid that I was going to supersede Cecil Salmon as a conversational issue.

Maimie got me out of the room. The Goffs sat on, a dour family party among the debris of supper. They looked as if they would stay there a long time discussing me, and never get round to the washing-up.

'You are a dope,' Maimie said, as we went upstairs. 'Why fly against the old bag? She's perfectly O.K. as long as she thinks she's got it all her own way, but she'll devil you now like she did poor Mr Zenobia, and these aren't bad rooms really, as they go. My dear, you should see some of the

513

places we've been in, eh Tick? I could show you some, even in this town. Last time we played the Empire here, I got typhoid from the water, honest.'

'Now, Maim,' said Tick. 'Now, honey. You know that was only a little colic. Never mind, kid,' he told me, patting my arm. 'Come and have a drink.'

We went back into the litter of their room, which smelled of stale scent and American cigarettes. Maimie threw the bolster off the table and moved it in front of the fire, and Tick told my fortune with cards. They said that I should be rich and famous.

'He'll tell them again for you tomorrow and they'll say something different,' Maimie said. 'He knows all the tricks, Tick does.'

She took off her dress, and I thought that I ought to go, but I was not anxious to get upstairs to my bogey.

'No, don't go, darling,' Maimie said. 'The night is young and there's four more bottles. I'll go and ask the Jacksons in. Do 'em good, poor mutts.'

She put on the kimono and went out on to the landing. Mrs Goff was there, and I wondered if she had been listening to what we said about her. I heard her voice running on, and Maimie's cackle of a laugh. Presently, her heavy tread went downstairs, her hand squeaking along the banister, and Maimie returned with Mr Jackson, who looked worried. He said his wife would not come, as she did not feel quite the thing.

'*That* sort of thing?' asked Maimie inquisitively.

Mr Jackson said 'Oh *no*,' and licked his forefinger, and drew it nervously along his moustache. He was a slight man with short stiff hair and dangling hands. He looked as indeterminate as his wife.

'Oh well, dear, it happens to the best of us, you know,' said Maimie cheerfully. 'I thought I was caught that way myself once, but it was a false alarm, thank God, and me with my living to earn. However,' she giggled, 'there's always Mr Casubon in the basement.'

'Maim – please,' said Tick.

Mr Jackson looked at her over his tumbler, which seemed too big for his meagre face. Her kimono was coming apart in front, and he lowered his eyes quickly and coughed into his beer.

'You want Tick to read the cards for you?' Maimie asked him. 'Oh no, perhaps better not, after last time. Well, come on, what shall we do? You're not very jolly any of you.' She roamed about the room, fiddling with her hair, picking up underclothes with a mind to put them away and then dropping them where they were, turning the wireless on and off. She never sat still for long.

I did not want any more beer, and I would have to go soon. I voiced the thought that was foremost in my mind.

'Murder!' Maimie swung round from the mirror. 'But, darling, no! Tell us *all* about it!' When she was excited, her voice had a husky catch, which was probably too many cigarettes, but was attractive. She leaped on to one of the beds and cuddled the brass knob eagerly, showing the whole of a muscular leg. Mr Jackson, who was listening to me, stared at it without seeing it. Tick leaned forward with his face unruffled but his ears sticking farther out than ever.

I told them what I knew and what I feared, and they believed every word of it.

'I knew there was something about this house,' Maimie breathed, awed by the thought of herself psychic. 'Didn't I say so, Tick, when we came? I wonder you didn't see it in the cards.'

'There's one thing I must ask,' said Mr Jackson, 'that you don't mention it before my wife. It would upset her dreadfully.' We nodded. Mrs Jackson should not be upset. He looked pretty upset himself, and I wondered if he would now give up shaving in the bathroom at that ungodly hour.

Maimie insisted on coming up to see my bedroom. Tick was coming as well, to smell out murder with his oriental sixth sense, but when we were on the landing, Mrs Goff hooted at him from below.

'Mr Ling! Could you spare a moment? Alice has blown the fuse again with her iron.'

'Tick's the only one who can fix it,' said Maimie, so we went up alone.

She manufactured a shudder as we stood outside my door. She was behaving like a child trying to frighten itself for the sake of a thrill. Hand in hand, we tiptoed across the dark room to turn on the light. I found the switch but nothing happened when I clicked it down. Maimie gave a little scream.

'Of course –' I said. 'The fuse.'

'But ours was on. And the radio.'

'Different circuit perhaps.'

'Could be. This house is mad enough for anything.'

'Let's light the fire.'

We found that we were both whispering, but when the gas had stopped roaring and settled down to its fitful flames, the room looked more friendly, and we talked normally again.

'All nonsense, of course,' Maimie said. 'I expect your friend did get the number wrong. I do hope so, dear. I wouldn't like to think of you as good as alone in the room with a corpse. They never rest, you know, when there's been violence done. And what about us below? Blood dripping through the ceiling and that. Oh no, it would be on to the Jacksons.' She giggled. 'That wouldn't half upset the little woman.'

She went about in the half light, peering at my photographs and my make-up and asking me why I had so many books. 'I see what you mean about the bed though. It is daft to have it there so near the fire. Let's move it over.'

'But Mrs Goff –'

'Oh, b— her. It's your room, isn't it? I don't suppose she ever comes up to clean it, and if she does, she can bloody well

516

move the bed back if she doesn't like it. Come on. You take the bottom end. I'm stronger than you. Last year, when we were doing the coast towns, I used to lift Tick on my feet, but he didn't like it really. He thought it was unwomanly. So we – oopsadaisy!'

We lifted the bed over to the wall. As we put it down, the lights came on, and Maimie gave one loud scream and stood staring at the floor with her mouth open.

Where the bed had been was a large, irregular, dark brown stain matting the pile of the green carpet. No wonder Mrs Goff had not wanted me to move the bed.

'She *knew* !' breathed Maimie, and we fled downstairs.

I spent that night with her in her bed. She snored and Tick clicked in his nose and the church clock told me all the hours I did not sleep.

## Chapter Five

'WHAT'S the matter with you?' Victor asked me the next morning. 'You look as if you'd seen a ghost.'

'I have,' I said. 'Or as good as.' I told him about the stain on the carpet.

'Looks as if Ronnie was right for once after all,' he said. 'And yes, you know, now I come to give my mind to it again, it was number five Bury Road. Dead sure. I say, you have got yourself in pretty, haven't you?'

He was suitably impressed. He looked at me with a new respect. So did Mike. We were supposed to be checking corrected proofs and filling in last-minute football and darts results ready to go to press that evening, but we did not do much work. We made our morning tea half an hour earlier than usual and discussed the bread-knife murder. Vic and Joe told me what they remembered, or thought they remembered, and Murray, who was trying to write his notice of last night's performance of *A Damsel in Distress* by the Co-Op. Drama Circle, put his lean head in his hands, shuffled his feet, refused tea, and eventually removed himself pointedly to a small table by the window, where his papers kept dropping on to the floor.

Mr Pellet stumped through on his way to the comp room with the purposeful executive air he wore on Wednesdays, and asked how was it going.

Fine, we told him, and Vic took his feet off the table and said, 'Be on the rollers early tonight, sir.' He always called Mr Pellet Sir when he was telling him a lie. When the editor had gone, refusing tea with an impatient grunt, Vic put his feet up again and we went on hashing over the murder. Downingham was not a great spot for homicides, and this one, which had reached nation-wide interest, had made a breeze in the doldrums of the *Post* office, which had been remembered longer than most news stories.

Mike went down to the basement to look it up in the files, but some heavy bales of art paper for printing Christmas cards for the District Council had been put down there in front of the old copies of that year, so we never knew whether Joe was right about the wedding finger being cut off.

Everyone agreed that I could not stay on at number five. It was my nerves, we said. That was where it would get me. I felt despairing about starting the hunt for rooms again. I thought of going up to Mr Pellet then and there and turning in my job. I would go back to London and live with my family until Fleet Street realized my worth, but Vic said they would never do that in a million years, and Mike offered uncertainly to take me home until I found somewhere else to live.

'I don't say Mum will like it – but in a crisis. She always rises to a crisis, Mum does. Sylvia did promise to come round after supper tonight, so we might be using the sitting-room till late –'

'Oi, oi,' said Vic, as Mike's face went moony.

'But you won't mind that, perhaps.'

I said I would go to the cinema.

Harold came in from the comp room in his black alpaca overall and asked what the blazes we were doing with those proofs. He'd ought to have two page formes screwed down by now, but screwed or not screwed, he was going out to his dinner on the dot, and see how the old man liked it.

I went back early to number five at lunchtime, not to Mrs Goff's fishcakes (she always told us in the morning what was for lunch, whether or not as a deterrent, I don't know), but to pack up my things and tell her that I was going. I would have to write off the fortnight's rent. She would never give it me back, even if I dared to ask her.

Maimie was just getting up. They had finished rehearsing for her pantomime, and she had nothing to do all day but eat sweets and read magazines and do her exercises on the table. She finished dressing and came up to my room with me to help me pack. The bed had been moved back to its original position.

'There, you see! Talk about a guilty conscience! I wouldn't say no to it being the old girl herself who done the deed.' She lifted the counterpane and peeped under the bed at the stain to make her flesh creep.

I told her that it could not have been Mrs Goff who murdered the crippled woman, because the family had not been there five years ago, and then I told her the things that Vic and Joe had remembered about the murder. It did not seem possible, standing there in that ordinary, ugly room, with a pale winter sun giving substance to the dust on the chest of drawers, to imagine that it had seen such horrors. However, there was the stain, and there, when I went into the bathroom to get my sponge, was the unwholesome atmosphere, which was partly the meaningless door, and partly the bow-legged claws of the bath and the eternal gurgle in the wastepipe.

Maimie and I packed slowly. She had to examine all my clothes and try some of them on and pry into all my possessions. She was the most stubbornly inquisitive person I had ever met, but somehow one did not mind, for it was an open, not a sneaking curiosity. If she had wanted to read one of your letters, she would have opened it while you were watching, and said, 'May I, dear?' when she was already half-way through it.

'I'll miss you,' she said, trying on my only hat. 'It's been a short, sweet friendship, but I like you. You're about the only human being around this joint.'

I felt warmed. 'I'll miss you too,' I said. I would. Mike's home did not promise much welcome, and I did not expect to make a friendship so quickly when I found other rooms. People in rooms tend to creep about and keep themselves to themselves, and look at you like guests in a hotel dining-room when you come in on the first day of your holiday.

We had nearly finished packing, and were planning what I should nerve myself to say to Mrs Goff, when there was a knock on the door.

'It's her!' said Maimie, with instinctive guilt, and we faced the door together.

A plump girl with a stiff new coat and a badly-set perm came in and stood looking as surprised as we were. 'Excuse *me*,' she said. 'I didn't think – mother didn't think you were in. Dinner's on the table.'

I told her that I was just leaving. She said, 'Oh, fancy,' and her eye travelled to the mantelpiece, checking over the mugs and the photograph of Tyrone Power.

This was Marjorie Salmon, *née* Goff, back from her three days' honeymoon to fetch the rest of her things. She was not like the rest of the family. She would be large one day, like her mother, but rounded, not spread out sideways like a trodden bun. Her eyes had not her father's pebbly look, and she was milder, more gentle-voiced than her sister Alice. She seemed a little shy of Maimie, who greeted her like an old friend, and asked her rather coarsely how she liked married life.

She took her pink dress out of the cupboard, and turned it round distrustfully as if she thought I might have worn it, which God forbid. I fetched her mackintosh from the bathroom.

'It's a pity you're going,' she said, looking round the room. 'This is a nice little room, really. I should have thought you'd have liked it. I was always very happy here, I'm sure.' Her eyes lifted in their sockets and she gave the trace of a sigh, an implication of life with Salmon which her mother would have loved.

'Well, I don't know how you could,' said Maimie, 'with the hand of death on it, and the atmosphere enough to freeze the strings off rhubarb. Even to be up here like this in the day-time gives me the staggers, let alone spend a night in it.'

'What's the joke?' asked Marjorie. 'You're a great one for jokes, I know.'

'No joke,' said Maimie grimly, and we told her what we knew. It seemed inconceivable that she did not know about the murder. Surely she had seen the stain? 'Didn't you ever move the bed?' I asked.

'Move it? Well, I put it where it is now. At least, mother and me did.'

'Then you knew?'

'About the stain? Well, I ought to, seeing I made it myself. I wasn't going to tell mother about the hair tint, but of course, when I spilled the bottle, I had to and – well, you know how mother is. She did create that time. It didn't work, anyway, the hair tint. Fancy you thinking –' she giggled, sucking in her lower lip. 'That old murder! That was down the end of the street, where the music school is.'

'Why didn't it work?' asked Maimie, recovering enough to switch to her usual interest in someone else's appearance. 'What make was it?'

Marjorie told her. 'It was soft of me really to try it –'

'Nonsense, kid. I use it myself. Finest thing out. Didn't it do you? I expect you didn't mix it strong enough. I'll show you how to do it. It would suit you, a bit of copper would.'

'I don't think Cecil –'

'Oh, shucks. He'd be thrilled as a bedstead. Come on, let's go and have a bite before the dogs get it all, and I'll do it for you after.' She linked her arm in Marjorie's and they started downstairs. I opened my case, took out a few things to make the room look homey, glanced round it with a brightening pleasure, and went downstairs to fishcakes.

When I told them about it in the office, they were not particularly excited. Their interest of the morning had worn off. Victor and Joe had had too much to drink at lunchtime, and were embarking sourly on the afternoon pile of work. It did not look as if the paper would ever get to press, but then it never did, until one actually saw the formes of type going down in the lift to the machine room.

Mike said it was a good thing he had not asked his mother yet as there would have been no sense upsetting her for nothing.

Murray, who was poring over the first page proof of the paper, which had just been run off, looked up from the long columns of property advertisements and Council notices, which were the Post's idea of an arresting front page, and said, 'I could have told you all along it wasn't number five.'

'Why didn't you?'

'You never asked me.'

'Well, really –' I got up to go over and quarrel with him, but he said, 'Let's have a little quiet, please. Who do you think you are, upsetting the office like this on press day?' He hunched his shoulders over the wide shelf where the page proofs were spread out for him to fuss over for hours, and for Mr Pellet to skim through, picking up the mistakes that Murray had missed.

Mike and Sylvia had a satisfactory session in the sitting-room that evening, knowing that I would not be wanting the sofa. He was very happy the next day and could not stop whistling, which caused protests to be hurled against the wall by the comps, who always had a hangover after press day, and did not like the look of another week's work. Mike had washed his hair and it stood up in a fluffy brown crest. He wore a clean white shirt and his cricket-club tie, and looked like an illustration of the honest prefect in a boy's magazine. He told Vic that Sylvia was a girl in a million.

'Don't kid yourself,' said Vic. 'Just because she lets you. There's millions of 'em do. The odd thing, I always think, is when they don't.' He scratched his hair with the end of his pen.

Mike and I were going to the Licensed Victuallers' ball that evening. The office had been sent two tickets, and Mike had wanted them both, so that he could take Sylvia, but Mr Pellet had said that I must go, for the experience.

I did not know what to wear. I had no evening dress in Downingham. Maimie offered to lend me one, but it was too short, and I did not think even the Licensed Victuallers could have stood that colour on me. I supposed that as I was The Press it would not matter what I looked like. I would go in a suit and look professional and importantly aloof from the frivolous throng.

I met Mike in the Green Man, which was just round the corner from the Downingham Arms Hotel, where the dance was being held. He was wearing a dark suit and a light matri-monial tie, and his hair was slicked down, which did not suit him so well as when it was standing up and fluffy.

We fortified ourselves a little at the public bar. Mike did not usually drink very much, but the Licensed Victuallers' routs apparently lived up to their name, and he looked forward with misgiving to an evening of having to accept drinks from everyone who wanted to get their names in next week's paper.

We did not hurry to the dance. In fact, we stayed in the Green Man until we were thrown out, because Mike got talking about Sylvia. When we went into the ballroom, I thought that we were still too early, for although the dance was supposed to have started two hours ago, the long narrow room with the flag-hung picture of Edward VII was almost empty. A small band in royal blue dinner jackets was playing to itself in a bemused strict tempo. A blue-and-gold shield in front of each man's knees announced that they were Don Donald's Commodores. I had seen them often before, but I missed the maestro himself, a vast, moon-faced man with a tight collar who usually kept the party going with industrious hilarity. A few dejected women were sitting round the walls. An old man in a braided waistcoat thumped out the time with his foot. Two women in thick lace hissed confidences under the gallery, and three very young girls in unsuitable summery dresses were being very gay and giggly to show they did not mind.

Where were the Victuallers? Mike led me across the floor, which seemed endlessly empty, and we crossed a passage into another room, where gaiety burst upon us. There were chairs and tables here, and a long bar across one end, and the Licensed Victuallers and their wives were all hard at work victualling. They appeared to have been at it ever since the dance started. They were very smart, mostly in white ties and tails, the women in low-cut dresses, wearing jewels and silver fox furs, with more silver in them than seemed natural to any fox. I had not seen such a resplendent gathering since I came to Downingham. I felt very drab, and brought out my notebook to show why I was drab.

The crowd round the bar was so thick that Mike had difficulty in getting through it to buy me a drink. Several men greeted him, and one of them slapped him on the back and asked him what he was taking. I saw him look uncertainly at me, and then he was swallowed up by the crowd and I saw him no more for some time.

'Hullo!' an orange-nailed hand clutched my arm, pinching the flesh. It was Nancy from the *Messenger*, bunchy in a green taffeta dance dress with dangling ear-rings that looked as if she had taken them off a chandelier. She shook them against her neck and kept fluttering her hands about as she talked. If she had had a fan, she would have flirted her eyes at me over it.

'Here on business?' I asked.

'Of course. A woman's work is never done, I always tell Len. Lennie! Come here, dear. Look, here's the girl from the *Post* I was telling you about.' I wondered what she had told him. He looked me over unenthusiastically, and did not seem to remember that we had already met in the Plough.

Nancy twisted her arm through Len's and leaned heavily against him. She had had too much to drink. She was holding a glass of gin and every time she sipped at it, she shivered and snuggled closer.

'Put your arm round Nancy,' she said. 'Nancy's cold.' She did not notice when I moved away from them to the other side of the room. I fended off a man who could only walk backwards, and stood watching the crowd for a while, longing for something to eat or drink, and hoping that I was getting the experience that Mr Pellet had wished for me.

A balding man in an evening suit that must have been made for him some years before he got his middle-aged spread bore down on me from the bar with a whisky in either hand.

'The Press, isn't it?' he said. 'Oh – the *Post*. I thought so. I think I've seen you with the boys in the Lion. That's my brother-in-law's place. Allow me to introduce myself. I'm

M.C. of this do. Anything you want to know – be only too happy to tell you.'

I did not know whether Mike or I was supposed to be taking notes. I could not see Mike anywhere, so I thought I had better take something down, in case he let me write the story. I flipped open my notebook, with a casual air I was cultivating, and licked my pencil.

'There you are, for Christ's sake.' A minute woman with hair like thin straw and a blue satin dress that would have been revealing if her bosom had been in the right place, came up under the M.C.'s arm and took one of the whiskies from him. 'I've been waiting for my drink,' she complained.

Her collar bones, sternum, and top ribs were as visible as a chicken's that has been carved and left for soup. Her face was painted in primary colours, and her hoarse voice scarified her larynx on the way out.

'You naughty Dadda,' she said to the bald man. 'Who's the girl friend?' Her husband introduced us.

'I call him Dadda,' she told me, 'because we haven't got any kiddies, so he has to be Dadda to me.'

He beamed on her, and then introduced me to some of the right people. I wrote down as many names as I could hear. They all seemed fairly well victualled up, and none of them noticed that I had not got a drink. I needed one. I was finding it difficult to keep a foothold in the merry backchat that ebbed and flowed round me as the Licensed Victuallers milled about, toasted each other, slapped each other on the back, complimented the ladies and brayed at anything that could possibly pass for a joke. I could hear the band still throbbing away across the passage, but no one seemed to have come here to dance. Perhaps they couldn't by this time. A waiter passed by with a plate of ham sandwiches and my soul went with them.

At last I saw Mike. He swam through the crowd towards me with his tie a little crooked and his face pale and desperate.

He seized my arm and dragged me to the wall behind a potted fern.

'Poppy,' he gasped. 'It's terrible. What do you think?' I did not think anything by now.

'Syl's here. She told me she was going to the pictures with her mother, but she's here with that George Deakin. You know. Oh, yes you do. Everyone knows George Deakin, but I didn't think Syl did.'

'Go and knock him down,' I suggested.

'Oh don't.' He pushed back his glasses. 'How could I? They haven't seen me yet, and Syl mustn't. I didn't tell her I was coming, see, because I knew she wouldn't like me coming with you instead of her, even in the line of work. She wouldn't see that.'

'Well, as she's come with someone else,' I said, 'it doesn't matter. Do her good. I'll pretend to be awfully chummy with you if you like. Let's go and dance cheek to cheek.'

He drew away from me in horror. 'You don't understand,' he said, 'it would spoil everything, just when we were getting on so well last night. I must go, that's all there is for it. I must go before she sees me.'

I thought he was the silliest thing ever, and told him so, but his methods of conducting a difficult love affair were not mine. He left me, begging me to get all the names that mattered and to write the story, and disappeared, with his hair rebelling against the macassar, through the gents' cloakroom.

I went to find the M.C. He was sitting at a table eating sandwiches with two hands and talking to Don Donald, who did not look like conducting the band that night. They did not offer me a seat, so I stood up and made the M.C. spell out for me the names of all the officials and as many of the guests as he could think of. Mr Pellet had drummed well into me that the only thing that mattered in reporting a local function was to get as many names into it as possible, and to get the names right. 'You think I fuss,' he said, 'but I tell you, girl, a wrong initial here, or a Mrs there when it should be Miss can cost you readers.'

While I was writing the M.C.'s wife came up, holding a cigarette in one of her claws. 'Dadda dear,' she waved it at him. 'Set me on fire, for Christ's sake.'

He laughed and gave her the eye of alcoholic lechery. 'I'll set you on fire later on, all right, all right,' he crowed.

'Isn't he dreadful?' She sat on his knee, took a light from his cigarette, and blew clouds of smoke round his glistening head.

I turned away. A very small man surprisingly came up and asked me to dance. I did not want to, because I was in the wrong clothes, there was hardly anyone on the dance floor, he was half my height, and I wanted to go home. He told me that he was running a concert and gymnastic display at the Youth Centre next week, and wanted me to ask Mr Pellet to send someone along and give them a good write up, as they needed money.

He had not wanted to dance with me at all. It was just the Power of The Press.

The Power of The Press took itself home after that, jaded. Mrs Goff let me in, wearing a brown woollen shawl and felt slippers and grumbling because I was late. She threatened to come upstairs with me, but I told her that I must get straight down to work.

'Work?' she said. 'At this hour? I don't like it. I don't like it at all. There's the light, you know. We shall have to think about a separate charge if there's going to be all this turning night into day.'

I had to write up the dance that night, because I would be in court all day on Friday. Maimie and Tick were out, so there was no chance of getting any tea. I found a bottle of beer under the bed and two stale sponge fingers on the washstand in their room, and took them upstairs with me. My room seemed quite different now that I knew that its history had not been blotched by blood. I did not mind groping across it to find the switch, and when I had turned on the light and lit the fire and drawn the short curtains, it began to feel to me quite like the friendly little refuge it had been to Marjorie.

I took off my shoes and sat on the floor by the fire with the bottle of beer and the toothmug out of the bathroom. Really that had been a horrid dance. It was wonderful to be home. A horrid dance.

'Last Thursday evening', I wrote, 'saw the joyful occasion of the annual ball of the Downingham and District Licensed Victuallers' Association at the Downingham Arms Hotel. It was a memorable evening of gaiety and good cheer, at which a splendid time was had by all.

'To the melodious strains of Don Donald's Commodores, led by the popular Mr Donald himself, some hundred smartly dressed ladies and their partners danced the night away and kept up the revels until the town was long asleep.'

The door opened and Maimie came in. 'I saw your light under the door,' she said. 'Have a good time?'

'So-so,' I said, stricken, as one is sometimes, with that odd unwillingness to admit that one has not enjoyed oneself. 'I took your sponge cakes, and some beer. I hope you didn't mind.'

'That's good, dear. I'd left the cakes out for the dogs. What are you doing – *writing*?' she asked in wonder. 'Let's see.'

She bent down to look over my shoulder. 'Organizing secretary,' I wrote, 'was Mr William (Bill) Parkhurst of the Crown. Master of Ceremonies was that well-known figure Mr Gilbert Wagstaffe of the Flowers Hotel, who spared no effort to see that everything went with a swing and that all enjoyed themselves to the hilt.'

'That's beautiful,' said Maimie. 'I've always thought I'd like to write myself. I think that's lovely.'

So did I, all things considered. I only hoped that Mr Pellet would think so too.

## Chapter Six

WHEN the Press ticket for the first performance of *Mother Goose* at the Empire came into the office, Mr Pellet put Murray's initials down against it in the diary. I wanted very much to see Maimie's act, and she had convinced herself that I was the star reporter on the *Post*, and would be going along to write her up as grand as glory. However, it was no use altering Murray's initials to mine, for no one would believe it.

I asked Murray if he would give Maimie a good write-up. He blew his long nose and said that the integrity of a dramatic critic must never be attacked and that he disliked acrobatics anyway, so I wished I had not mentioned it.

I prepared Maimie for the worst. She was anxious to get good notices, as she had no other engagement after the panto-mime, and she would not understand that I was only the sweepings of the office floor and could not do as I liked. She seemed to think that I was letting her down. She was prac-tising on the table at the time, and her head, screwed round to look over her shoulder, carried on an acrimonious conver-sation, while her legs danced and bounced the parasol with smooth unconcern, as if they belonged to someone else. I asked her if she could get me a ticket for the first perform-ance, and she said no, and kicked the parasol at my head.

I was in for a dull time that week. There was a catch in Downingham's breath, before it let itself go in the gust of Christmas festivities. I was only down for a school prize-giving, a round of the shops to report on Christmas buying and the price of turkeys, a lecture on 'Bird Species and Be-haviour in the Outer Islands', and a demonstration of gas stoves. I could see myself spending most of the week in the office reading proofs and rewriting pick-ups about village dances and bazaars. A night out at the Empire would have brightened things up.

Murray was late in on Monday morning, which was unusual, for he was generally there before any of us, to do his big weekly tidy. He had lately taken to blacking round the grate of our narrow arched fireplace. Heaven knows why, but if he expected me to do it, he would just have to be disappointed.

A pile of wedding reports had come through the post. Vic, Mike, and I each took one with a sigh and settled down with our coats on to turn the information on the forms, which was always either too much or too little, into paragraphs of prose. When Joe came in, Victor pointed silently to the pile of forms, but Joe turned his back and stood hunched over the fire, which was burning extravagantly for once since Murray had not lit it, rubbing his hands and blowing his nose with a sad, hollow sound.

'Where's the head boy?' he asked. 'He owes me seven and six.'

'That's why he's not in, I suppose,' Vic said. 'Here, Joe, remember that girl who used to work at Filbert's? Here she is – bridesmaid to old Goldie's daughter. Not *bad*. Look, they've sent a picture.'

He propped the photograph up against 'Revised Guide to the Law of Libel, 1908'. Joe would not come over. He stood by the fire, snuffling and grumbling in his chest and knocking the fire irons with his foot. His overcoat, which was a long green raglan like a tent, wanted cleaning and darning. Both his socks had holes in the heels, and his shoe laces had been broken and knotted so many times that they would not reach to the end holes and were tied half-way down the shoe. His landlady was not good to him. She did not remind him to send shirts to the laundry, so that when he had worn all he had, he had to start on the dirty ones again.

Mr Pellet shouted down the stairs for Murray, and Joe

winced as Vic shouted back: 'Not in yet!' Our manners towards the editor were casual, but he liked it that way. Once, when I held a door open for him, he pushed me through it quite roughly and said he wasn't in his dotage yet, blast you, girl.

He came down presently to look for Murray and to ask Joe to go and see the Town Clerk about a rubbish dump that had come up at the last Council meeting. Joe kicked the fender, put his head on the mantelpiece, and muttered that he had a lot of work to get through and would go when he could.

'I've drafted out the story,' said Mr Pellet. 'It just wants some details filling in. Here.' He handed Joe some half sheets of copy paper each covered with a few lines of his overgrown handwriting. He was very wasteful with paper. We always used the paper torn in half, because that was supposed to be economical, but it defeated its own object, because there were twice as many margins.

'I could have done this,' said Joe. 'You're always trying to do my work for me. I wonder you won't let me be the editor and you be the hack. What's this?' He looked at the paper despondently. ' "Daneshill and Brocket Refuse." Refuse what?'

'Not refuse anything. Refuse. Garbage. Muck. Can't you read?'

'I can, but our readers can't. Ambiguous headline. No good.' He took a stump of pencil out of his pocket, licked it, and started crossing out on the mantelpiece.

'All right,' said Mr Pellet. 'Write the bloody thing yourself.'

A stout woman with heavy cheeks and a bold manner pushed through the swing door. 'Morning, Mr Pellet,' she said commandingly, as if he were the grocer. 'Bitter out.'

'I hadn't noticed. Anything wrong?' he asked, for the woman was Murray's wife, and she never came to the office

532

except for the annual tea party. Last year, they told me, she had refused to sit down, because she thought the chairs were dusty, although Murray had spent all day cleaning the place up.

'He's got flu,' she said, with some exasperation. 'Wanted to get out of his bed and come out this morning, if you please, but I don't want to have to nurse a pneumonia case, thank you very much.'

'Aspirin and hot whisky,' said Joe. 'You give him that.'

'Thank you,' said Murray's wife. 'When you've had three children and a husband who's silly about his health, you'll know how to deal with influenza.'

'Poor old Murray,' said Joe, wiping his nose on his sleeve.

'Caught cold from you, I shouldn't wonder,' said the woman, 'by the look of it.' She nodded to Mr Pellet and went out. The swing door rocked gustily after her.

'Nuisance,' said the editor. He looked at the diary. 'Joe, you'll have to go to Quarter Sessions tomorrow, and I'll do the Conservative dinner. Victor, you come up with me, and we'll settle up the letters. I want you to write one about the Sunday trains. It's time we stirred up that old subject again. And there's Burton's week-end speech. I've got the script of that. Let's see, what else was Murray down for? That Empire show tonight. Who wants to go to that?'

'Oh, please,' I said quickly, 'can I?'

'No, girl,' said Mr Pellet. 'The Empire panto is one of the few things people want to read about. You can't do it yet.'

I begged him to let me try. I even promised to copy almost word for word what Murray had written about it last year, but he said, why should I, when Joe or Victor or Mike were longing to go?

They displayed no enthusiasm. 'Let her,' said Vic. 'It can be her Christmas present.'

'She'll make a hash of it, like she did that dancing school show.'

'Well, I'm sorry,' I said. 'I couldn't help it if I didn't know which was Sir Alfred's daughter. I've said I was sorry.'

'On a newspaper, it's too late to be sorry,' snapped Mr Pellet, suddenly not genial any more, and cowing me. 'I've told you that hundreds of times. I never knew a girl be so sorry so often, and do the same damn fool thing so many times over. Joe, you can go to this brannigan tonight. The ticket's in my desk, and for Christ's sake give it a bit of Yuletide spirit. This paper's getting like the *Undertakers' Gazette*.' He went to the door. 'Come *on*,' he said to Victor, jerking his grizzly bear head. 'I told you to come upstairs.'

'Right away, sir!' Vic jumped smartly to his feet. 'Looks as if the widow didn't come up to scratch again this week-end,' he said as he followed the editor out.

'What widow?' I asked.

'Red-haired and squishy,' said Mike. 'There isn't one. Vic made her up.'

'Pity there isn't,' I said. 'She might make him less uncouth.'

'He's all right,' said Joe. 'He's only trying to make a journalist of you. You'll be grateful to him in twenty years' time when you're chief reporter on the *Downingham Post* and allowed to write a précis of the sub-postmaster's speech at the sorters' benefit, and sub it yourself. Tell you what, you can come to the show with me tonight if you like and we'll write it up together afterwards in the Plough. I'll get Abrahams to keep me another ticket.' He reached for the telephone.

'Save it,' he said, as I began to thank him. 'You've never seen panto at the Empire.'

It was all I could do to get him there at all. The show began at half-past six, and at twenty-five past he was dragging me into the Feathers to give us courage. By the time I had got him out of there and across the road to the Empire, the foyer was empty, except for the manager in a greenish dinner jacket refurbished with new silk lapels for the season. This was Joe's friend Mr Abrahams, so we had to go into his office for another drink, and by the time we found our seats, the panto-mime was well under way.

We pushed past dozens of knees and laps, whose owners said : 'Some people,' and 'It's not good enough.' Others added to the commotion by shushing. We sorted out a small child who was standing up and would not move, tripped over a rolled-up coat and a suitcase, and Joe kicked a woman's hat two rows forward under the seats.

The long-faced comedian who was on the stage dressed as a schoolboy and doing some kind of business with a blackboard was able to brighten up his act by calling attention to us. He wrote on the blackboard : 'SO GLAD YOU'VE COME,' and got an easy laugh. Joe did not see this. He was having a coughing fit, and soon afterwards he was taken with a suc-cession of volcanic sneezes. It was worse than taking a small child to the theatre.

We had missed the opening scene of the Village Market-place (Song : *All on a Summer's Day*). When the scenery had been changed, the comedian with the blackboard removed his ambiguous presence from in front of the drop curtain, which represented a Scottish glen, and we were now in Mother Goose's kitchen, and here was Mother Goose herself in the person of a thin but padded man with a lascivious mouth and bolting eyes, wearing the voluminous oft-lifted skirts, striped football jersey, and red topknot which showed he was the Dame. I had last seen him singing dirty songs in a London night club, and now here he was to bring joy to the hearts of the kiddies, and the best one could hope for the little dears was that they would not understand his jokes.

He sang one of his night club songs, with a few topical and local alterations, and then did a dance with twelve of Jack-son's Juveniles, who were dressed as tots, but looked as if they could understand him and a lot of other things besides.

At last the goose came on, with spindling legs in wrinkled tights and a vast feathered body, with movable jaw and a winking eye. It appeared to be under-rehearsed, for it managed the body awkwardly and knocked over one of Jackson's Juveniles who came to stroke it. The tot picked itself up, clutching a large handful of feathers. The goose was moulting all over the stage. By the end of the run, it would look as if it were plucked for the table.

With a skip and a jump and a merry laugh, here came the heroine, none other than Mother Goose's daughter, bursting out of the top of her simple cotton frock. She had fat bare legs, high heels, and a lot of black hair which she surely should have washed before the first night. However, she had taken a lot of trouble to arrange it in ridges and sausage curls, with long iron hair grips clearly visible from where we sat.

The Prince, when she arrived striding on even higher heels, was equally buxom. A front to front embrace between the two was going to be quite a sight. She had better legs than the other girl, or perhaps it was the silk tights, but when she turned round, there was a hole the size of a halfpenny in the seam behind one thigh.

She was struck all of a heap by the heroine, and curried favour by stroking the goose and calling it the dee-ar oh-erld crea-tewer. She was probably wont to say Creacher, and had been taught to be careful. Before the young folk could get together, the village lads and lasses, who had been standing round smiling when they remembered, but looking a bit slumped in the background, leaped forward into a Scottish dance, with shrill cries.

This quaint Scottish motif appeared all through the panto-mime, which, according to the programme, was set in a vil-lage of Merrie England on the road to York. That was so we could get Dick Turpin in later on (Song: *My Bold Black Bess*). In the Grand Finale, Mother Goose herself appeared in the full dress tartan of the Royal Stuarts, dirk, claymore, and a' and a'.

In the first interval, Joe wanted to go out to the bar, but no one else was getting up in our row. I could not face those knees and the coat and suitcase again. The woman's hat had not been found yet, and the small boy's family were settling down to a good meal out of paper bags, so I persuaded him to sit still. He dozed. Joe always nodded off when nothing was doing, and often when something was. He called it cat naps and said that all great men did it to nourish their vitality. Once, with me, he had slept right through a Council meeting, and fallen off his chair while the Borough Engineer was paying a moving tribute to the memory of Councillor Dutt, so sadly passed on.

'Aren't you going to take any notes?' I asked.

He laughed and put the programme in his pocket. 'This is all I need. I could write the notice without seeing the show.'

'But you must write something good about Maimie – my friend. She's wonderful.'

'She'd better be.'

I took the programme out of his pocket. There she was: 'Speciality Act in Act II by Mimi del Robbio and Partner.' I wondered if she and Tick were still pursuing the quarrel that had started that morning about making toast, and was still going when I went back at lunchtime. Maimie would not speak to Tick, and would hardly eat any stew. When Mrs Goff asked if there was anything wrong with it, Tick said: 'First night nerves.'

'Nerves my foot,' said Maimie, glowering at him. 'When you've played as many first nights as I have in hick towns like this –'

'Well!' said Mrs Goff, who was always telling us that she had lived in better places than Downingham, but would not have it belittled by Maimie. 'You don't disdain to come here and take our money, I notice.'

'Now, Letitia,' said Mr Goff, putting a whole boiled potato into his mouth. 'You mustn't be sharp with the young lady. We artists, you know, we have our temperament.'

'Mr Goff was quite a figure in amateur dramatics,' Mrs Goff explained to me, helping herself to the last bit of meat in the stew. 'Before his operation. After that, he took up dogs.'

Mr Goff's operation was often mentioned, but never specified, so that one imagined something quite indecorous.

'Yes, indeed,' he said. 'Remember my duet in *Maid of Mystery*? Now dawns the day' – he burst out, with his mouth wide open. He had not quite finished the potato – 'when all the flowers shall bloom!' His top note was like a factory siren, and one of the dogs howled and slunk to the door.

Mrs Goff smiled on him and lifted a ladleful of carrots and gravy to ask if anyone wanted seconds. Maimie got up.

'No sweet?' asked Mrs Goff.

'No sweet.'

Tick rose politely, but she pushed him back into his chair. 'Where are you going?' he asked.

'Never you mind.'

'Oh, don't think I care. I only thought –'

'Don't strain yourself.'

'Ha, ha. Funny, aren't you?'

'Oh, shut up.'

When they quarrelled, they were like children, with futile repartee, and sometimes slaps and pinches.

They were on at the beginning of the second act, for no reason at all in the middle of Mother Goose's kitchen, before the brokers' men came to smash it up. The kitchen table was placed endways to the audience, with a red velvet cushion on it. One of the village lasses, now disguised as a toy soldier and still panting from the dance in which they all fell over in a line, brought on the parasols and rings and rubber balls, and the band began a drum roll.

The crescendo grew like thunder, and then – crash ! went the cymbals, and Tick leaped on to the stage wearing tight bolero trousers flared below the knee and a white silk shirt with billowing sleeves. A red cummerbund clipped his neat waist. He looked like something that bounds with a troupe into the circus ring, looking very small from where you sit high up in the tent. He executed a few backsprings and cart-wheels quite featly, but without over-doing it, and finished up by the pile of props, with his hand outstretched to bring on Maimie.

She skipped in, bowed, flashed her teeth, and tossed her head with strenuous joy. I began to clap, praying that the audience would respond, and not maroon her high and dry with her *éclat*. There was a dribble of applause. In Downingham, you wait to see what people can do before you commit yourself.

Maimie was wearing a silk blouse like Tick's, with a short white skirt and ruffled panties. The panties were very important, for when she was on the table they were the only part of her that could be seen. I felt proud to think that I had put the elastic in them last night. She wore suntan make-up on legs and arms as well as face, and her hair, piled high on top and swinging round her shoulders, was a dazzling advertisement for the tint with which Marjorie Salmon, *née* Goff, had stained my bedroom carpet.

The band stopped doing rolls and chords, had a small hiatus while it turned its music, and then was off on an unassuming background version of the Destiny Waltz. Maimie lay on the table, settled the cushion, raised her legs smoothly and flicked a finger at Tick, who threw a parasol deftly to her feet from a much greater distance than in the bedroom.

The act went on for about a quarter of an hour, and although it was skilful enough, it was rather a solemn affair. You could not have done it yourself, but then, would you want to? One never saw Maimie's face, only the panties and the legs, endlessly treading and dancing on the air, while the parasols and the rings and the rubber balls, getting bigger and bigger, were thrown to her, juggled and returned to Tick, who received them with a jump and a little cry. Half-way through, the band speeded up the tempo with the Donkey Serenade – that was when the rings were whirling round Maimie's ankles – but otherwise the act went smoothly on with a mesmeric, almost soporific effect.

Then suddenly, when you were thinking that you would almost rather Maimie dropped something than went on like this for ever and ever, the band crashed into a chord, Maimie leaped to the ground in a graceful arc, sprang into the air and poised, receiving the applause open-armed and joyful, as if she were running to meet a lover.

She got quite a good reception. I clapped until my hands stung, and kept nudging Joe. He was sitting like a real dramatic critic, who will not give away tomorrow's notices by either clapping or booing. Tick did a few defiant acrobatics on his own, like a child in the corner of a drawing-room where an infant prodigy has been reciting, and then Maimie ran off the stage with her hair like fire in the wind, he bowling after in a series of somersaults. When she returned to take her call, she looked towards the wings, but he did not follow her. Perhaps the manager would not let him. I understood now why Maimie carried on a losing battle to get the salary due to a double act.

Having seen Mimi del Robbio and Partner, I took no more interest in the pantomime. Joe and I climbed out for a drink in the interval, and in the bar upstairs, he met a man called Captain Warwick, who looked like a newspaper picture of a bogus military man, taken outside the Old Bailey. Long after the curtain had gone up, I still could not get Joe away, so I went down myself to stand at the back, in time to applaud Maimie and Tick as they came down the palace steps in the grand finale.

Maimie said that the worst thing about pantomime was having to wait about in your costume and make-up in order to come on at the end and sing 'Land of Hope and Glory'. In variety, you could go home as soon as your act was over, and have your shoes off and something frying by half-past nine, as like as not, but panto could not be wound up without the whole crowd of muggers on stage.

After the show, I collected Joe and took him round to see Maimie and Tick. He had been drinking all through the last act with the bogus captain, and when we went down the cat alley to the stage door, he decided to become a stagedoor Johnny. He curled his atrocious felt hat up at the sides, threw the green raglan coat over his shoulders like a cape and gave saucy looks at chorus girls when we passed them in the passages. I was afraid he was going to pinch a Jackson's Juvenile with hard rouged cheeks and Dutch-cut hair, so I hurried him on through the rabbit warren.

We found Maimie in a tiny room like a cupboard, littered with other people's costumes and abandoned ends of make-up and old good luck telegrams. Joe and I had to stand pressed against the wall in order to get in there at all. He was still in his masher role. He had kissed her hand on being introduced, and when she offered us some beer from a suitcase under the make-up shelf, I half expected him to try and drink it from her shoe.

We were all going out to supper together, but Maimie and Tick, still in dressing-gowns, were in no hurry to get away. There was a certain amount of first night coming and going in and out of dressing-rooms, and laughter and excited chatter in the passages. Several people came in for beer, and Joe had to stand outside. Presently we lost him, and he was found later in the dressing-room of some of the chorus who had discovered that he was The Press and were trying to force their names on him.

The demon king, in red tights, a grubby vest, one false

eyebrow off and the other on looked in to say the show would run for ever. Mother Goose's daughter, surprisingly small and squat in a tight grey suit, with the sausage curls and hair grips wrapped up in a turban scarf, came in to say had they ever known such a flop, and this was the lousiest town since Barnstaple. The Dame, still with his make-up on, was even more terrifying close to than he had been on the stage. His nose was like ill-shapen wax, and the paint and powder were clogged with the sweat of his coarse-pored skin. His revolting mouth, the top lip painted in points up to his nostrils, was like a carnivorous sea anemone. His hoarse voice filled the cupboard with asinine remarks. He was even less funny off stage than on. Maimie took off her dressing-gown while he was there and began to change her clothes, for he was not at all interested in her. It was Tick he was after.

Joe came back while she was greasing her face, and drank whisky until she and Tick were ready. When we went out of the theatre, he put his arm round Maimie's waist and said she was a lovely little butterfly, too good for all this.

'Going to give me a good notice?' she asked.

'Of course,' said Joe thickly, tripping over the kerb. 'Write it yourself if you like. We'll do it at supper.' But in the Dover restaurant, which was one of the places where people went for celebrations, heaven knows why, Joe suddenly put his head down on the table among the lobster shells and slept.

'Before the trifle too,' said Maimie. 'What a shame.' We finished our supper, but the waitress did not like us much, because the Dover restaurant was not the kind of place where people slept, so we woke Joe and dragged him outside.

There was just time to go to the Plough. He was able to drink a double whisky, but his sadness was on him now, and he could hardly keep awake. He told me that he had not slept for three nights, and although Joe was just a joke, and we always laughed at him for being a disreputable old man, I could believe this, for he did now look really ill. His dry cough sucked at his stomach, and although he was by no means drunk by his standards, his dead fingers could hardly hold his glass.

Maimie was growing fond of him. She was one of those rare finds in life who took to the unlikely people that one liked oneself. She wanted to take him to the hospital, because she said that he was looking just the way her mother started with her kidneys, but Joe, with chattering teeth, said God forbid, because they would say in Casualty that he was drunk. Maimie, who was full of homely medical lore, put her hand on the back of his neck and said he had a fever. She sent Tick out to find a taxi, and insisted on taking Joe all the way home. She would have gone up to his room as well and probably helped him into bed had not Joe's landlady slid out of a downstairs room like a figure on the Stockholm clock and barred the stairs.

Joe crawled on up, dragging himself by the banisters.

'He's not well,' Maimie told the landlady. 'Will you get the doctor to him tomorrow?'

'No doctor can cure what's wrong with *him*,' said the landlady with a thin smile, folding her arms.

'That's libel,' said Mamie. 'How dare you?'

'It's not,' said the woman. 'You don't know what I meant.'

'I do,' said Maimie, 'and you'd better be careful and look after that poor old man properly, or you'll find yourself in court for wilful neglect.' Maimie's knowledge of the law was about as homely as her knowledge of medicine.

When he reached the top of the stairs, Joe turned and stood crouched forward like a beetle in his green coat, as if he were going to throw himself down again. He called to me that he would not be in tomorrow, and I would have to write the notice, and say that he had done it.

When we were outside the front door, I remembered that he had got the programme, so we had to ring the bell. The landlady had secured the door, and she opened it on the chain and put half her face to the crack. She refused to let us in. She said that we were turning her house into a Babel, making such a noise at this time of night, and Maimie said that she could have her up for unlawfully refusing entry. Tick, who did not like scenes and loud voices as Maimie did, held out two half crowns. 'For your trouble,' he said, with his quick, nodding smile.

I thought the landlady would be offended, but surprisingly, she took the money, unchained the door with far more noise than we had yet made, and let Tick go upstairs.

When we got home, Mrs Goff was in the hall with her monstrous cat on her bosom. She did not ask how the performance had gone, so Maimie told her.

'You left your gas fire on,' she said. 'It's been burning all evening.'

'I meant to,' said Maimie. 'That room's as cold as an outside privy to come home to. Anyway, we've got the meter.'

Mrs Goff murmured something about wear and tear on the fire, and dropped ash on to the ginger cat, which had a broad empty face and derogatory eyes like hers. She was cross about something, but we did not know what. It might not be anything to do with us, because when somebody annoyed her, she took it out of everyone else.

Maimie offered to get her free tickets for the pantomime any night she liked. That was the least that Mrs Goff expected, and she was not mollified.

'We'll have to see,' she said. 'It's not everyone can spare the time, you know, to go jaunting off to the theatre like some.' She looked at me.

'It's my work,' I said grandly, and went upstairs, while she was saying that she did not approve of working at night and never had.

I lingered on the landing, and when I heard her shut the kitchen door, I went into the Lings' room. The fire had been turned off, and Maimie, putting money into the meter, swore

544

that the lock had been tampered with and Mrs Goff trying to get at the shillings. Tick said: 'Now, Maim,' and we made tea and settled down to write the review of *Mother Goose*.

Next morning I took it in to Mr Pellet and said that Joe was not coming in today, but had written it last night and given it to me to copy out. I hung round while Mr Pellet glanced through it, hoping that he would say: 'There! That's the way to write a review. You can learn a lot from Old Joe.'

Maimie and Tick and I had taken endless trouble over it. We had sat up half the night rewriting it, but the editor got out his soft black pencil before he had read the first two sentences.

'Poor old Joe's going off,' he said. 'He can do good stuff, but he doesn't bother any more. This is all wrong for a paper like this. People don't want to know what we think of a show. They want to know who's in it, who played the triangle, and whether it was raining. Take a lesson from this. How not to do it. Oh, no, no.' The pencil moved. 'Terrible. What the devil's Joe been up to? Was he tight?' I saw the pencil striking through the paragraph which sang Maimie's praises. I thought her remark about Unequalled on any stage would not get by, but I did not expect him to kill the whole thing.

When the paper came out, her name was simply down among the 'many diverting and varied acts'. I could have shot Mr Pellet. Maimie could never understand that he was not completely under my thumb. She said she would never work in an office where she could not do what she liked with the boss, and I felt that I had failed her.

We soon found out why Mrs Goff was cross. When I got up one morning, the bathroom door was locked. This was unusual, for I knew everyone's bathroom habits by now, and timed my getting up to miss them. It was too late to be Mr Hawkins or Mrs Goff or Alice. Mr Goff, like a Paris concierge, never came upstairs, and Casubon only took a bath once a fortnight. No one knew where he washed at other times, but he looked quite clean. His greyness was constitutional.

It was too early to be Maimie or Tick, so it must be Mrs Hawkins. I tapped on the door and called: 'How long will you be, Margaret?' It was Christian names by now, and the fitter was William. Just one great big happy family at Five, Bury Road.

There was no answer from the bathroom, and the taps were turned on to drown my voice. Margaret would never do that. Though timorous, she was the kindest soul and obsessed by a desire not to hurt anyone. She was always the one who said: 'You're *not*!' when Maimie teased me about getting fat on Mrs Goff's carbohydrates. She had once been out all afternoon trying to get some brains for William, who, when he came home, was queasy and could not fancy them, but being as kind as she, had eaten them and been sick afterwards in the bathroom.

I left my door open, so as to see who came out. It was a tall, middle-aged lady, making a face to herself, with her hair in a net worn low on the forehead and a woollen dressing-gown clutched desperately round her angular bones. She saw me and scuttled for her life into the front room.

I had given up going down for breakfast. It was too early for me, and I didn't like Mrs Goff's porridge. I had seen it being made without cleaning out the saucepan from the day before, but if you refused porridge, there were looks given, and sometimes things said.

I had coffee and rolls in a snack bar on the way to the office, so I did not see the new lodger until lunchtime. As I came up the road in the rain, I met Mr Goff being pulled home by the airedales.

'Out in this weather?' I said. 'I thought you had a cold.'

'I have.' He remembered it and sniffed. 'Got fed up with being indoors, though. Between you and me, the wife's a bit upset.'

'I thought she hadn't seemed her usual cheerful self just lately.' I quickened my stride to keep up with the airedales.

'It's Vera. Miss Martlett, you know.' I looked blank. 'Of course,' he said, 'you wouldn't have seen her. She came last night while you were out. She's in the top front – and there !' He would have thrown out his arms despairingly if they had not been held down by straining dog leads. 'There's a likely let gone for goodness knows how long, for she can't or won't pay the full rent. Besides the aggravation of her.'

We paused at the high wooden door in the wall and had the usual difficulty in lifting and opening it.

'She suffers, you see,' he told me, 'with her nerves. And when a woman suffers with her nerves, everyone else suffers too.' Mr Goff knew a thing or two about life.

As we went up the leaky arcade, he told me briefly that Vera Martlett was the sister-in-law of Mrs Goff's brother, with whom she normally lived. The brother and his wife had gone away, and Vera had been foisted on to the Goffs, since there was nowhere else for her to go.

'Though an institution would be the proper thing,' he said.

When I met Vera, she did not seem to qualify for that. She was timid and awkward, as if she were sixteen instead of something nearer sixty, but she seemed in possession of all her faculties, and packed away a good lunch, saying briskly: 'Yes, yes,' and 'That's right,' to remarks which were not addressed to her. She had a nervous condition of the epiglottis, which made her clear her throat tensely when there was nothing to clear.

When I apologized for having disturbed her in the bathroom, she blushed, or rather, at her age, flushed, and said : 'I didn't answer because I thought it was *a man.*'

She did not bother me much upstairs, apart from spending hours in the bathroom, scrubbing herself madly as if trying to purge the original sin of mankind. I hoped she would not stay too long, for when Mrs Goff was not about, I had taken to working in that empty front room, since it had a table, and a much better light than mine.

I had to work on Christmas Day, so Mr Pellet let me go home for a long week-end before it, and I came back to Downingham with a second-hand typewriter, which I had bought with the money people gave me instead of presents. Since I was working on a local newspaper, they thought I must be badly in need of it. I was.

I took the typewriter to the office, and did not let Murray use it, to pay him back for not letting me use Mr Pellet's machine. His wife had chased him back to the office too soon after his flu, and he was feeling low and looking more than usually unloved. When he had to do a long article on the spirit of Christmas in Downingham, inevitably dragging in Tiny Tim, I took pity on him and asked him if he would like to use my typewriter.

'No, thank you,' he said stiffly. 'I can use the editor's if I want to.' He was like that. He was a difficult person to help.

Joe had gone to hospital with acute bronchitis, and Murray's doctor had overridden his wife and said he must not do any evening work yet, so Vic and Mike and I were busier than usual. I was sorry about Joe, but I was glad that it gave me the chance to do more on the paper. I was sent out alone quite often, and even allowed to cover Petty Sessions by myself, since there was no one else to send. This gave me great apprehension, for court reports were one of the major features of our newspaper, and allotted ample space, some of which the Women's Institutes would have liked. Didactic presidents were always ringing us up and complaining that they had been squeezed out. I took my Petty Sessions very seriously, sat alert even during the succession of Riding Without Lights cases, and sat up late at night anxiously composing my report. It was rather like being a hospital nurse. One day, you are not trusted to take temperatures, and the next you are suddenly left in charge of a ward full of dying men, because there is no one else.

With more to do in the daytime, I often had to write my stories up at night, and I could have done that in the front room, where every evening at nine o'clock Vera locked herself in against Men. There was nowhere to type in mine, except standing up at the chest of drawers, or with the machine on your knees in bed, where there was no light.

Vera was Mrs Goff's new subject. She had abandoned the topic of the gas-meter man, who had forced an entry with a penknife one day when everyone was out, and she talked about Vera all the time when she was not there, and sometimes when she was. She kept inventing people who would have liked to take her room, and tried to forget to serve her at meals, but we thwarted her by passing on our plates.

If poor Vera had never suffered with her nerves before, Mrs Goff would drive her to it now. Short of actually pushing her out of the front door and slamming it, she did all she could to get rid of the wretched woman. She even found a distant cousin in an isolated farmhouse who might take her, but when she mentioned this at supper Vera cried and choked on a rissole and said she would not go. She had stayed there once before, and they had all gone to the cinema and left her alone with not a house for miles, and she had heard footsteps round the house, and heavy breathing.

'Cattle,' said Mrs Goff. Vera hiccoughed and tried to put a forkful of rissole in among her tears. She was always ravenous.

In the end it was I who, quite inadvertently, got rid of her. One night after supper, when there had been a scene about Vera knocking over a glass of water, we went upstairs together and I asked her to come to my room for a cup of tea. She looked trapped, as if I were forcing her to a pipe of opium, but she did not know how to refuse. She would not sit on the bed, so she perched on the only chair and drank tea with so many fingers crooked that I was afraid she would drop the cup.

We talked of this and that, but conversation did not flow because Vera had on her party manners and would only agree with everything I said without vouchsafing anything of her own. Eventually, because I could think of nothing to say, and she did not look like being able to find the way out for some time, I told her about the murder scare.

Her face worked. She clutched the sides of the chair and looked as frightened as if I had said there was a man under the bed. Before I could reach the reassuring anticlimax of the story, she had risen to her feet, still clutching the chair like a life-preserver, dropped it half-way to the door and fled to her own room. I followed her, but she had locked herself in. I knocked on the door and tried to explain that if only she would listen to the end of the story, she would feel quite happy.

She would not answer. I could hear her banging about in there – she always knocked into the furniture when she moved about a room – and then I heard the strident window thrown up. Was she going to throw herself out, or let herself down on sheets?

'Miss Martlett!' I banged with the flat of my hand. 'Please open the door. I want to talk to you!'

'What's the Dutch concert for?' Maimie came up the stairs. 'Tick has a headache and is trying to lay down.'

'Vera's gone berserk.'

'Oh yes,' she said, 'we had one of those, but it died.'

I explained to her, and we both kept knocking on the door together. All that happened was that Alice came up to the bathroom with little Barry, who always went to bed too late, and said that we were a crying shame, teasing someone who was not quite, and why couldn't we leave the poor soul alone. She'd never done us any harm.

Vera's room was silent all night. We went down to the

550

garden, but there was no body. No body scrubbing itself in the bathroom next morning either, and when I looked out of my room, there was Vera's door open, her drawers tilting out, and herself gone, with all her hair slides and stockinette skirts and modesty fronts.

When I told Mrs Goff what had happened, she was quite pleased with me. She would never have thought it of me, but she supposed it came from all this making things up for the papers. I was quite pleased with myself too, when I had got over feeling sorry about Vera, surrounded by breathing cows in a lonely farmhouse, for I could now take my typewriter into the front room and work in comparative comfort. Vera seemed to have loaded the meter with money and forgotten to use the fire, for I went on burning it for hours without having to put any shillings in. I had all the tea and coffee I wanted, for I was basking in Mrs Goff's good favour, and she gave me jugs of milk.

It did not last. I was tapping away up there like mad one night, when the back of my neck froze and my spine contracted. I turned round. Mrs Goff had come in unheard and was standing nodding her head at me, as if waiting to see to just what excesses I would go.

I apologized. I explained about the light and the table.

'If you want the use of two rooms,' she said, 'then you must pay for the two. I have my living to earn the hard way, unlike some.'

'But I don't *use* the room. I only come in here occasionally.'

'Occasionally is too often. And the machine. I've never had anything like that in my house before, even when those Australians were here. Mr Goff and I were on the first floor putting away his new mirrors, and I said to Mr Goff : "Whatever is that noise?" I said. "Like a thousand crickets in the wainscot, and they're a thing we've never had here, whatever else we may have had." '

I scratched my head.

'In any case,' she went on, 'this room's let. A gentleman came after it today, so that will put an end to your carrying on.'

Let to a gentleman? I was not pleased at that. Apart from using the front room, I liked to have the top floor to myself. I could wander in and out of the bathroom in a towel, and it gave me the illusion of having a flat. I was planning to get Vic and Mike along to have a small party up there. A gentleman in the front room banging on the wall for silence and wanting to know why beer bottles were cooling in the bath would spoil everything.

I would scare him off, as I had scared off Vera, only more convincingly. The murder story should be true, and I might even make a dark brown stain under the bed in his room. I would get Maimie to lend me the hair tint.

## Chapter Seven

ALTHOUGH Mrs Goff had stopped giving me milk after she found me in the front room, my stock went up a little when she heard that I was working on Christmas Day. When Mr Goff had been with the bus company, he had always been taken ill if they asked him to work at Christmas. I was held to be something of a martyr and treated to the mystified respect given to someone who elects to flog himself with a knotted cord. I did not say that I was not doing it from choice, but only because Victor and Mike said that they had had enough of spending their holiday trudging round the hospitals, so let Poppy do it.

There were five hospitals in the town, counting the maternity home and the Northgate Asylum. I had to go round them all and report on the festivities, and as they were spread out all over the town, with the asylum a mile outside, I asked Mr Casubon if I could borrow his bicycle. I had not made much progress with him yet. He was always agreeable for a 'Good morning' in the hall or a few seasonable remarks at meals, but he made some excuse to escape if you tried to go farther than that. He was still something of a man of mystery, and even Mrs Goff did not know exactly what his work was. She thought it was something to do with politics, which Maimie interpreted as either fascism or the I.R.A., and certainly the young men and women in mackintoshes who crept down the back stairs to visit him did not look as dedicated as if they were involved in a plot to overthrow the government.

When they left, he always came up the stairs with them and saw them to the front gate, guarding them off the premises. They would stand a long time talking under the lamp-post outside, as if they could not say all that they must inside. I watched them from Maimie's window, and they never laughed. They stood looking at their feet, never arm in arm or touching each other, like people exchanging good-bye banter. One talked at a time, earnestly, his white face pointed at the others, who listened until it was time for someone else to hold forth.

Casubon was holding one of these nocturnal conclaves when I tackled him about the bicycle. I had been to a dance with Vic. This time I had worn a long dress and mixed business with pleasure, and the only difference between being there as a reporter and as a reveller was that Vic knew me too well as an equal to bother to see me home. I walked along through the cat-haunted streets, and when I turned into Bury Road there was a little knot of conspirators under the lamp. They must have been there for quite some time, for Mrs Goff's rule was no visitors after ten-thirty, and she had her methods for getting rid of them if they were not gone by then.

The I.R.A. stopped talking as I approached, and watched me, waiting for me to pass by before they spoke again. Mr Casubon did not recognize me in my long dress and Maimie's pony-skin jacket, and when I slowed down and he saw who it was and greeted me, his friends, without waiting to be introduced, melted silently away down the street as if I were the Black and Tans.

Casubon did not call after them. He turned to lift the gate for me. 'Been on the spree?' he asked, screwing up his eyes commiseratingly.

'If you can call it that. Part of the job.'

'It must be very exciting – your job,' he ventured, pleating his forehead. People often thought that. I had thought so too, before I came to Downingham.

'Not half as exciting as yours, I'm sure,' I fished, trying to make him open up.

'Oh, well.' He looked down at the steps as we climbed them. 'It is pretty important, of course.'

Mrs Goff had shut the door while he was outside, and he had not got his key. While I was looking for mine, I said, 'You won't be working on Christmas day, I suppose, so I wonder –'

'Our work never stops,' he said darkly. What on earth was it? I did not dare ask him.

'You mean you'll be going to the office?'

'Oh, not that. I mean, it's not just a job. It's a way of life.'

Was it religion, then? That would account for the hats of some of his female friends. In the darkness of the porch, before I opened the door, I ventured to invade the privacy of his life by asking him if I could borrow his bicycle to do my self-conducted tour of the hospitals.

To my surprise, he said at once, 'Oh yes!' leaning towards me and looking much less distressed. 'I'd be delighted. Any time you like.' He seemed genuinely pleased at being asked for help. Perhaps he was really longing to be friendly, although he ran away. I must tell Maimie. She could culti-vate him.

On Christmas morning, I went down the back stairs and knocked on his door in the dark passage. He could not use the door in the little area outside, ostensibly because it was blocked by dustbins, but really, I think, because Mrs Goff did not want anyone coming or going in the basement without her knowledge.

'Happy Christmas,' I said when he cautiously opened the door.

'Oh – er – the same to you.' He glanced into the room be-hind as if he had a mistress spread out on the bed in there. 'Look – er – you go back and I'll bring the cycle up for you.' Evidently he did not like my going down there among the bombs and printing presses.

When he staggered upstairs with the bicycle, I saw that he had cleaned it up for me and tried to scrape the rust off the handlebars. He took it out to the street, settled it by the kerb, gave its saddle a proud little pat, and stood by to see that I got safely off. I performed the undignified feat of mounting a man's bicycle in a skirt, and as I pedalled away I looked back to see him standing smiling after his bicycle, as if it were his horse going into the show-ring.

At the first hospital, the matron was sticky and told me more about the places I could not go into than the ones I could. At the second, she was charming, and took me all round the hospital herself and told me what to write. At the third, the patients were having their Christmas dinner. A doctor was on each ward, carving up a turkey and ham, which the nurses carried round with paper napkins over the battered tin trays. I looked into all the wards and made a few notes about bows in the women's hair, and the dear old men in red bed-jackets, and the dear little kiddies with their Christmas tree and paper hats, almost as happy as they would have been at home.

Joe was in the medical ward, and I went in to see him. He had no red bed-jacket, but was wearing an old brown cardigan and a scarf. There was a system in that ward of opening alternate windows to avoid draughts, but Joe's bed seemed to be placed in the direct current from any window that was open, and, judging by the costumes of the other patients, so were most of theirs. Joe looked very shrunken. He was holding a hard brussels sprout on the end of a fork and tapping it with his knife. I was telling him the story of Mr Pellet and the lady editor of the *Messenger*, when a small, jerky sister in much-laundered navy blue fussed up like a toy engine and said that if I was The Press, Matron had deputed her to show me round.

'I've been round, thank you,' I said. 'I think I've got all I want.'

'Matron said to take you round, so you had better come with me. If you want to talk to any of the patients –' She looked at Joe, who put the sprout into his mouth guiltily.

'I'm afraid I haven't time. This is a friend of mine, you see. If you wouldn't mind me staying a moment?'

She stayed too, so I had to promise Joe that I would come and tell him the rest of the story next visitors' day, and depart with the toy train on a second tour of the hospital.

When I got to the maternity home, pedalling Casubon's bicycle through a slight sleet, it was not feeding time for the patients but for the babies, so I could not go into any of the wards. I noted down Christmas ribbons tied on the empty cots in the baby-room, and the rest would have to come from last year's files.

My last call was at the Northgate Asylum, a mile or so outside the town. I was cold when I reached the gates, and quite frozen by the time I had pushed my bicycle all round the drives and coal yards and cowsheds and laundries, looking for the way in.

Detached from the world by its high grey wall, the asylum

556

was like a self-sufficient little town. It was reputed even to have its own gasworks, which somehow set the seal of horror on the place for those who had not been there. Seen from the road, the buildings looked grim enough, spires and pinnacles and crazy turrets in which one could imagine lunatics immured, chained and slavering. Seen close to, however, the buildings looked more reassuring. There were window-boxes and bright curtains, a wireless playing somewhere, and the sound of a piano thinly tinkling. The main entrance, when at last I found it, had a glassed-in porch full of potted plants, like the Grand Hotel at any seaside town. I half expected to see an elderly couple come tottering out in scarves and mufflers to lean against the wind along the promenade, but all that came out was a pair of jolly-looking fat nurses, with caps on the back of their heads, and arms folded inside red capes.

Behind the glass porch it was warmer, and my hands and feet began to come to as I talked to the porter and waited while he telephoned to distant regions. He had a friend with him in the office and they were grumbling about having to stay on duty on Christmas Day.

'It isn't as if I didn't do it last year,' the porter kept saying. 'It isn't as if I didn't do it last year. I mean, fair's fair, and I'm ready to do my trick the same as anyone, but they take advantage. I don't know. This place is enough to drive you balmy.' He did not mean this for a joke.

A nurse came through a high, heavy door, locked it behind her, spoke to me and took me through the door, locking it behind us again. We went down tiled corridors and through several more doors, each of which had to be unlocked and locked again, until at last the sound of music brought us to a large hall like a gymnasium, full of men and women dancing, or standing and sitting round the walls looking on. There were more women dancing than men, so several of them were dancing together. Some of them were quite old, in faded, waistless dresses. They took the dancing very seriously, hold-

557

ing each other far apart and moving with slow, high steps like horses working in a ploughed field.

A young boy with a Mongol brow and small, surprised eyes was fooling about among the dancers, throwing his arms and legs about and uttering occasional yelps, as if he were at the Caledonian Ball. When he saw me he roared with laughter, stood on his hands and threw himself flat on his back on the floor. No one paid any attention to him. He was a natural hazard and they danced round him.

'He's showing off because of you,' the nurse told me. 'He always does that with strangers.'

He was the only one among the patients who looked as if he should be in an asylum. Most of the men and women who were dancing looked quite normal, although when the music stopped they wandered away a little vaguely, abandoning their partners, lost until there was something else to do. Behind me, a tall, stooping man with an exaggeratedly cultured voice was carrying on an intricate conversation about something that was 'purely a question of applying the laws of dynamics, old chap'.

'No, no,' he said after a pause. 'That's mathematically absurd. You must see that.' He sniffed, with mouth drawn down and nostrils pinched. The only difference between him and a dryly arguing professor was that the man with whom he was arguing was not there.

I stayed to see the staff concert. I had read and imagined a lot about the horrors of asylums, but Sister Taylor singing *Bless this House* in a different key to the piano, wildly thumping to try and bring her into line, was the only horror I encountered at the Northgate.

Afterwards, there was old-fashioned dancing. I stood with the assistant matron and watched the patients dancing the barn dance and the Valeta and the Boston two-step. They seemed to enjoy these more than the ballroom dancing, and executed the various movements with concentration and grave skill. One woman, however, with basin-cut grey hair and a parakeet-coloured dress too short for her square figure, was very hysterical about the barn dance. She kept trying to order the other dancers about, and then going the wrong way herself and getting lost in the middle of the set, throwing it into chaos, and prancing about with her knees very high and her elbows stuck out. At the end of the dance, she panted: 'Lovely, lovely!' clapped her hands, grabbed a man who was walking away for a rest, and swung him abandonedly into the Valeta.

I knew that there were many insane women in this hall, but she was the only one who looked it.

'Er – that lady in the bright dress,' I asked the assistant matron. 'She seems – poor thing – I mean, I suppose she's one of the worst cases –?'

'She,' said the assistant matron, 'has been sent from the occupational therapy centre to teach the patients old-fashioned dancing.'

She turned away, so that I could not see whether she was smiling. In case she was not, I found a nurse and got myself let out of all the locked doors to where my bicycle waited in the cold beyond the potted plants.

Boxing Day found me still working. Someone had to go and write up the Boxing Day meet in the market square, and Victor had said: 'You're always talking about horses. You can jolly well go.'

I hoped it would freeze, but when I woke next morning the sleet had turned to rain, so hey for boot and saddle, a fine hunting morning, with the rain soaking down as if it would never leave off until it had us all in arks. Casubon was obliging again, so I hacked my mettlesome bicycle through the veiled streets to the market place, which was a dismal, steaming pit of horses with their tails tucked in against the rain, riders ditto, with white mackintoshes over habits, and spectators with their collars up.

Quite a crowd of townspeople had come to stare and try to stroke the hounds. They viewed the scene without envy, glad that they had not got to do it themselves, but glad that some-one should uphold the old tradition, which they had been vaguely led to believe had made England what it was. Hunting, the rich man's sport, curiously inspired no anarchy. Out of the field, the hunting classes had had their day. They could not get servants, their homes were being sold for schools and institutions, no one called them Sir any more, and there were the *oddest* looking people nowadays in the Berkeley. But having achieved the bloodless revolution, the working man allowed them this small, picturesque pleasure, and rather liked to read in his paper in wartime that Major the Hon. Justin Ogilvy had gone into action blowing a hunting horn.

The other people on foot were the indefatigables, who had come in porkpie hats and indestructible clothes to dash about in cars to strategic points, and then wade over a ploughed field to stand in a gateway, waving to their mounted friends as they charged through and splashed them with mud, and telling the Master, who knew better, which way the fox had gone. They had brought friends who were staying with them over Christmas, because 'Everyone always goes to the Boxing Day meet.' No question of who wanted to and who did not, the friends had accepted the fate of their shoes and come partly to counteract last night's port, and partly because there was no fire lit in the drawing-room before lunch.

I wanted to speak to the Master, to get the Personal Touch, which was still my Mecca, whatever the others might say, or Mr Pellet's pencil might do. I found him struggling out of a small car, in a long camelhair coat, stamping about with his legs spread to get the feel of his boots.

I introduced myself and he said 'Morning' and started to walk away to where a rat-faced groom was trying to keep more than two legs of his horse on the ground at the same time.

I followed the Master. 'Excuse me, sir, er –' What on earth could I ask him? He stopped, surprised to find me still there. 'Er – do you expect a good hunt today?'

'Can't tell. Scent's tricky.' He walked on.

'Have you had a good season so far?'

'So-so.'

'How many couples have you out today?'

'Well, count for yourself,' he grunted, but then took pity on me and paused. 'Nineteen and a half. Bitch pack.' He walked on. I followed him like an insect, tickling him with questions, and he kept brushing me off with impatient answers. He reached his horse, exchanged sour nods with the groom, and put a foot in the stirrup, while the animal went round in mad circles on the slippery cobbles. When he was up, and his weight pressed the saddle on to its cold back, it became even madder, so I left him to his Goddams and went in search of further copy.

I was handicapped in Downingham by not having lived there long enough to know all the notables. Vic and Murray and Mr Pellet knew everyone, and knew how to spell their names and what letters came after. All these people in top hats and bowlers looked alike to me, except that some of the men looked more stupid than others, and some of the women were weathered and terrifying, with hair already at odds with the wind, and some were quite pleasing, with bright make-up and neat hair.

I found one of my constable friends from the magistrates' court and he pointed out to me the Joint Master, a moneyed type, who had been unwillingly co-opted to keep the hunt going. His vast white breeches squatted insecurely on a chestnut cob with a behind like a great round orange, which rolled its eye backwards at him as if it feared he would fall off.

My policeman also showed me Lady Peppering, who had the lean, cold-eyed face of a greyhound and legs that looked as if they had been sewn into her breeches and then moulded

561

on to her beautiful horse. I knew all about her. She was as much liked by men as she was disliked by women, and looking at some of them here today I wondered whether perhaps it was not the women's own fault.

When the hunt moved off, hooves clopping hollow on the wet tarmac, I asked a groom where they were going first. He told me Gibbet Wood. Of course he was wrong, but Mr Pellet, who uncannily knew everything, knew where they had gone, and altered my copy without comment.

When I got back from the meet, Casubon, who appeared to be spending Christmas in the basement, popped up the stairs to ask me how the bicycle had been, like a groom inquiring how the favourite hunter has performed.

'Of course, I don't approve of blood sports,' he said, as he carried the dripping bicycle through the hall, for fear of Mrs Goff's linoleum. 'I read a very interesting pamphlet on the subject. I'll lend it you if you like.' Pamphlets were the only things he read. He did not have time for books, but there was always a leaflet or two sticking out of his pockets, and he was often to be seen reading one as he tacked down the street. He had a slight weakness in his legs, more of a wobble than a limp. That was partly why he bicycled to work, to strengthen them.

Such few opinions as he expressed came from pamphlets. Whatever their subject, he took them for gospel truth, his argument being that if it was not true it would not be worth making a pamphlet of it. I found this out later, when I got to know him better, but at the moment I did not know that he was an inveterate pamphlet-sharer, so I accepted the tract on blood sports which, indeed, I found most convincing.

I condensed it next day into a Letter to the Editor, which I sent to Mr Pellet in the hope that he might print it. I signed it *Misericordia*. If it started a correspondence, I would write again under the pseudonym of *ex*-M.F.H. to say that the fox enjoyed being hunted, if no one else did so first.

Mr Pellet shouted down his belfry stairs for me. He had my letter on his desk. 'Think I don't know your typing by now, girl?' he asked. 'You always get a faint "8" under the apostrophe.'

'I'm sorry, I thought it –'

'Why be sorry? It's a good letter, though I suspect you cribbed it. We'll print it, and write the answers ourselves if the hunting mob are too illiterate. Ay, you're no sich a bad lass.' He looked on me with wondering approval. Scots mixed with Yorkshire meant mellowness indeed.

'Just for that, you can do the letters this week.' He handed me a bunch of unopened envelopes. 'Look through these, take at least one answer about last week's playground thing, and if there isn't one, write your own drip about kiddies playing in the streets. Cut your own a little. You can head it "This Cruelty Must Stop!" and then make up with road safety and housing – the usual thing.'

'Must be the widow,' Vic said, when I told them downstairs. 'She's always at her best, Christmas.'

'Of course,' said Murray, with his back to me, 'I usually do the letters, but naturally I shall be only too glad to have them taken off my hands. I'll help you, though.'

'Oh, no thanks. I'd like to try by myself. I'm going to make this a really super column for once – Oh, I'm sorry. I didn't mean that.'

To cover my confusion, I took the cups downstairs, filled the kettle and washed and dried the cups with extra care while the kettle boiled, hoping that Murray would have got over being offended by the time I came back.

When I did, he had gone out, so I had wasted my time over the cups. While we drank tea, laced with a little rum which Victor had saved from his home festivities, I read the letters. Some had no sense at all and went straight into the waste-paper basket, which had not been emptied since halfway through Advent. Others made too much sense but went the

563

same way, since we never printed any criticism of the paper. Most of them were about politics or local council affairs and were terribly dull, but there was one from a woman who had got it into her head that Mr Pellet was Aunt Mabel and wrote to ask him how to get rid of a fine growth of hair on her upper lip.

'You see,' I said, when I had read it out. 'We *ought* to have a woman's column. Hundreds of them would write in like this, and they'd all buy the paper.'

'They do already. Shut up,' said Mike. 'If I've got to do Joe's confounded Kiddie's Korner, I must have peace.' Sylvia had spent Christmas Day with him and Boxing Day with someone else. He was a little rattled.

'Some of them read the *Messenger*,' I said, 'and they've only got Nancy's silly little thing about how to crochet hats and knit toy bunnies. They'd all come to us. It would shoot up the turnover like mad, and we could have new lino on the stairs. Joe will break his neck one day.'

'Might even give you a rise for thinking of it,' said Victor.

'They might. It's a good idea. I'm going to try it out in the letter column. Who wants to read all this about road safety and housing? The daily papers don't have letters about road safety and housing. They have letters from ordinary people, about ordinary things that matter, like – like divorce, and who's got the oldest cat, and whether men respect the girl who says No –'

'And hair on the upper lip,' said Vic.

'Yes, hair on the upper lip. Woman's angle stuff. That's what people want. I'm going to put some woman's angle into the letters this week, instead of road safety and housing.'

'Never get past Pelly.'

'We'll see. He may come round to it when he sees it in writing. After all, he liked my letter about blood sports.'

'All right,' Vic said, pouring rum into his teacup, 'we'll see.'

I composed the letters carefully, with the help of Maimie and Margaret Jackson. Nothing about moustaches or the girl who says No. The editor would have to be broken in gently, with more serious matters. I asked Maimie and Margaret what they would like to see discussed in a newspaper. Maimie said hair-styles, and Margaret said the cost of living. We kept the cost of living and invented a weekly budget for a mythical Mrs Salter, trying to keep house with two children on the wages of a railway linesman. I liked Mrs Salter. I worked over her so long that I almost believed in her. I admired her gallant effort to give up cigarettes so that her children could have new shoes to go to the school camp, and I felt that Mr S. should either cut down on beer or go less often to the pictures.

Maimie, who always said that she and Tick would never have a child until she was too rheumatic to juggle, suggested a letter saying that people ought to have big families. Margaret blushed. Even an indirect reference to the intimacies of marriage embarrassed her. I wondered how she and William had ever got through their first night.

'We'll put in a stinger about landladies like Ma Goff who won't take children,' Maimie said. 'She reads the *Post*.'

'She won't after that.'

'And why not one for Alice about children not being house-trained at the age of three. Don't tell me it's the dogs.'

Margaret was still looking uncomfortable. She was paler than ever these days and a little of her negative quality had been supplanted by an active depression. I thought it was because she went out so little. She did her shopping, and for the rest of the day she cleaned her room and waited for William to come home. One afternoon when I was free I asked her to come to the cinema with me, but she would not be persuaded. I think it was because she could not afford it, but when I hinted that I would pay, she refused even more vehemently. She was a sad little person with only half a life, and William was incomplete too, because he had no joy or energy. Thank goodness they had each other. Even so, they had not much, but without each other they might be the quietly agonized kind who are found in the river, or in a gas-filled room, the surprisingly brave yet logical act of someone who sees no reason for living.

I liked my letters. If I had been an impartial reader, I should have paused in my idle turning of the pages and thought, Ah, good! The old *Post* is waking up at last. Page five was set early in the week, so I delivered the copy in good time to Mr Pellet. I put it on his desk before he came in, so that he could digest the innovation calmly and alone before he started shouting.

He came in at ten o'clock, and started shouting at half past.

'There you are,' said Vic. 'He likes it. What are you waiting for?'

'You go,' I said, 'and tell him I'm out,' but Mr Pellet was already coming down in search of me, his brows weighing down on his bright blue eyes.

I trailed up behind him, feeling as I had not felt since the headmistress summoned me for going out shopping during the individual study period.

Road safety and housing. Of course, it came up again. He had told me to put in road safety and housing, and I had put in tripe from silly women. 'But I suppose you wrote them.'

'Oh *no*. They're genuine. Readers really are interested in these things.'

'I'll see the letters later.' I would have to make Maimie and Margaret write them. He would recognize my writing, even disguised.

'When we want something new on the paper,' he said, 'I'll tell you. Otherwise, you'll do the job you're hired for.'

Then he suddenly became quite nice. He sat down and looked out of the window, so that I could not see whether his eyebrows had gone back into place again. 'Everyone who comes here', he said, 'starts off by thinking this is a lousy old rag and they must have been sent from Heaven to bring it up to date. Victor, Mike, even Murray – they all started like that. It didn't last, when they had rumbled what the job was. Do you know why people read this paper? Because they've been reading it for umpteen years, and it's still more or less the same as the first copy they ever read. It's safe. They know where they are. In Downingham, they've been eating meat pie and chips on Saturday nights since the world began, and if they were suddenly asked to eat their joint on Saturday and the pie on Sunday they'd think the bottom had dropped out of life. So they would if the *Post* started printing strip cartoons or life stories of sex murders. When they open the *Post*, they like to know what they're going to get. God knows there are shocks enough in this world already.'

'But you let me print my letter about blood sports. Isn't that a shock in a hunting county?'

'Lord, girl, we've been printing that letter at intervals for years,' he said. 'It's one of the old favourites.'

'Shall I do the letters again, then?' I asked, feeling crushed.

'Have you time? Harold wants the copy now. What have you got on?'

'Only to go and see a woman whose husband died in the coal shed.'

'The postman. That's page five too. Better get on with it. I'll do the letters, and you get on out and see the corpse.'

Which was truer than he knew. The postman's widow lived in a row of brown brick houses with bow windows, green paint, and a bit of stained glass in the front door. The road ran downhill so that the terrace of houses and privet-topped walls was built at the angle of a funicular railway. Some of the houses had numbers. Some had only names, and I walked right down the street and back up the hill again before I found 'Marengo'.

'I saw you go by,' said the postman's widow, as she opened the door. 'I thought you might be coming here. I saw you taking notes at the concert where my little grandchild sang.'

'I hope you don't mind me coming at a time like this?' It was a job I hated. I thought how furious I should be if someone came to make copy out of my bereavement, but most people were surprisingly agreeable.

The postman's widow was even pleased. 'Bless you, no,' she said. 'When mother went, in the big frost three years ago, I had ever such a nice young man from the papers come to see me. We had quite a chat.'

She sat me down and gave me a cup of cocoa with too much sugar in it and told me about the last hours of the postman. It seemed disrespectful to take notes. I felt I should have been sitting listening with nods and clucks, but the postman had been on this round for so long that he was a well-known figure, and Murray had told me to get a story, so out came the loose-leaved notebook.

'He should have retired two years ago,' his widow told me, 'when the doctor said it was his heart, but he wouldn't. They thought very highly of him at the post office, you see, but I didn't like it. Pant! I've seen him come home up this road sometimes and have to stop at the gate to draw his breath, though if I was at the window he'd always pretend he was tying his shoe. And then two nights ago, the fire was low, and he'd gone out the back to get me a scuttleful of coal. When he didn't come in, I thought perhaps he'd called over to his friend next door and gone out the side gate to go down the road with him. I never thought. But when I went later to get the coal myself, there he was, poor soul, laying forward on the heap, and I said to myself, "He's gone." Black, he was, from head to foot, but nurse has washed him and made him look really lovely. I expect you'd like to see him?'

'Oh no. No, thank you. That isn't necessary.'

She insisted, however, and I was taken up to a spotless bedroom. The widow drew back the curtains, and there on the high double bed was the postman, scrubbed and aloof, with his teeth prominently in, his hair plastered down, and his hands folded over the sheet. The nurse had not been able to remove the nicotine stains from his fingers, and although at first sight he had looked as reassuringly not there as all dead bodies, this small reminder of his living habits made me suddenly as afraid of him as if he had stirred and sat up.

'Doesn't he look beautiful?' the woman whispered, straightening a corner of the counterpane.

I took a step backwards, looking at his hands. He was laid out on one side of the wide bed, and the pillow on the other side was slightly creased with use. The thought came to me that the widow might be sleeping in the same bed as the corpse, and I left the room.

She came out after me, leaving the door ajar and taking a look back through it, as if a child had just been settled to sleep in there.

'I thought you'd like to see him,' she said, as we went downstairs. 'I wouldn't let them take him away. It's a great comfort to me to have him here and got up so lovely. I only hope someone will do the same for me when my time comes.'

When one outgrows the morbid visions of childhood, one does not think of oneself as a corpse, but she, already seeing herself laid out in that upstairs room, started me thinking about dying, and wondering what people would say and whether Mr Pellet would give me an obituary in the *Post* if I died while in his service.

Depressed but touched by my own tragedy, I went back to the office to write up the postman. Mike was still struggling with Joe's Kiddies' Korner. Joe had an intricate cross-reference system by which he could offer birthday wishes to members of the Korner Klub on the appropriate dates, but the files had got muddled and Mike was in despair. While I was trying to help him, Sylvia telephoned with what appeared to be a series of enigmatic remarks, for Mike's end of the conversation consisted chiefly of 'But what do you *mean*, Syl?'

He could not concentrate after that, so we left the birth-days and tried to think of a subject for the competition. The prizes for these were small, but it was surprising how many children entered. One imagined every week-end, the paint water spilled on the living-room table, the tongues between teeth, the hunched bodies, the flowers pressed under Pears' Cyclopedia, and every Thursday the tears, the bitter disappointment, the parents agreeing: 'Of course you ought to have won a prize dear. We ought to write to the paper.'

Joe knew the rule of all competitions: Never print the winning entry, so that no one can write in to claim that theirs was better than that.

Every subject we thought of had something against it. A model snowman, a poem about Christmas, a water-colour snow scene, had all been used recently by Joe. A story about 'What I got for Christmas' would be tedious for whoever had to read them, for we did Kiddies' Korner now as a syndicate, each tinkering with it when we had time. Victor wanted to have putting the last line to a limerick, but would not be serious about inventing four seemly first lines. We looked in the notebooks in which Joe kept his lists of subjects that could be used over and over again at decent intervals, but could not decipher his faint pencillings.

We thought we could have a Quiz – 'on your honour not to look up the answers, Klubbers!' – and let the little beasts cheat if they wanted. Harold came in for the copy while we were arguing about the capital of Brazil. We waved him away.

'Come back next month,' we told him. 'Not nearly ready.'

'Must have it by two,' he said. 'My deadline.'

'All right. What's the capital of Brazil, then?'

'And here's a little present for you,' he said, disregarding this and putting a fat roll of proofs into the broken-off tin suitcase lid that was our In Tray. 'Urgent.'

We ignored him. Mike was looking up dates of kings and queens of England in the encyclopedia, which went no further than the accession of Edward VII.

Victor could only think of racing questions. 'I'm fed up with this,' he said, going over to the coat hooks. 'Come on.'

'We'll never get done by two,' I said, 'and you know what Harold is. And all those proofs, and there'll be hundreds more this afternoon. They've been setting away in there like mad. I've got all the weddings to do, and some re-writes, and that man to see about the chicken killings. I'll have to stay in and miss lunch, I think.'

'Come off it,' said Victor. 'You're poison. When you've been here as long as I have –'

We went out to the Lion and played darts until a quarter to two, so I neither had my lunch nor did any extra work.

## Chapter Eight

AFTER the success of his bicycle, which he now kept pressing on me, even when I knew he wanted it, Casubon quite came out of his shell. He still did not speak at meals, because Mrs Goff paralysed his throat muscles. Sometimes, when she was having a carry-on, he could hardly swallow, but he would now exchange more than two words with me in the hall, and once I saw him walking down the road with Margaret, carrying her shopping bag. They were not speaking, but for two such shy people even to be walking together was good progress.

Casubon was also fired by the discovery that Maimie and Tick were not so terrifying as the label 'theatricals' had

571

stamped them in his mind. He came up to their room for tea, 'just for five minutes', and stayed for hours, because the basement seemed a lonely place after their room, which had the chaotic, casual welcome of a theatre dressing-room. Everywhere they lived would be like that, a room where no one ever knocked on the door.

One Sunday, he asked us all down to tea with him. He found that his tea tin was empty, so we had coffee made from dark brown syrup in a bottle. As with all Mrs Goff's rooms, the light in the basement hung in the wrong place, in the corner away from the gas fire, where no one would want to sit. On the table by the window, which was half below ground level, stood a rusted metal lamp with a green shade connected to the light by a long cord looped across the ceiling. It was a wonder Mrs Goff allowed this, for she was usually against anyone tampering with The Electric. The table was covered with papers and pamphlets, and a cracked leather suitcase and a music case bursting with more documents, for this was where Casubon worked.

He slept on a narrow divan bed by the wall, which was now covered by a green cloth, with flaccid cushions propped against the wall. Maimie and Tick and I sat there in a row, with aching backs and cricked necks, trying to foster the old illusion that a bed and a wall are a satisfactory substitute for a sofa.

There was a cane-seated bathroom chair by the table, with a newspaper over the broken canes, and by the fire, one of those sloping wooden chairs with square velvet cushions, which are called easy, and are very difficult to get comfortable in. The pile was rubbed off the velvet, and also off the rug of indefinite pattern which covered part of the floor boards.

Off the sitting-room, there was a little stone-floored cell, with a naked light and a gas ring and a shallow brown sink. This had once been the scullery, when the house was all one and the front room a kitchen. When Maimie and I were washing up the coffee cups, two of which had G.W.R. on them, we saw Casubon's moulting toothbrush and ragged sponge and a variety of medicines and digestive powders on a shelf over the sink. Two cloths hung on a nail, and we could not tell which was his towel and which was for drying up. In the cupboard, we found a heel of cheese growing mushrooms, and a lump of bread like stone. Mice had knocked off the top of the Bovril bottle, and eaten through a packet of soup powder. Maimie determined to find Casubon a wife.

His little underground home was depressing, but he did not seem to mind. He was too busy being eager about whatever it was he and his furtive friends were up to. One imagined him working down here under the green lamp night after night, with a cup of mouse-tainted Bovril growing cold at his elbow, then at last dousing his head under the cold tap at the sink, throwing off the green cover and falling asleep at once, with the blankets churned and his awkward young limbs sprawling over the edge of the narrow bed.

We still did not know what his work was. We might have asked him, but in the course of the rather leaden conversation, he had said something like, 'You understand, of course, that my work being what it is . . .' and we, sitting like a row of puppets on the bed, half hypnotized by the dullness of our visit, had nodded and said, 'Of course,' before we realized that we had lost our chance. We could never ask now.

After that evening, there was no holding Casubon. We were friends now, and he could come and go upstairs as he liked, and Maimie had elicited from him that his Christian name was Neil. Nothing would satisfy him but that he should give a party, not only for the conspirators, but for his fellow lodgers as well. The new gentleman in the top floor front was invited, but was gone before the party. I had not had to scare him away. Mrs Goff had done it for him, because he did not pay the rent. She had been enthusiastic about him at first, often mentioning his reputed connexions with some titled family of whom no one had ever heard, but now it was, 'There's a gentleman for you! You may all have been taken in, but I knew from the minute he set foot in this house that he would give trouble.'

Although my imaginings had been disproved, the top floor front did indeed seem to be haunted by a jinx. No one had ever stayed there long, and it was Mr Goff's favourite joke that when he wanted to get rid of me, he would ask me to move across into it. Then I would know. This jest called for loud laughter from me, a sudden hoot and cackle from Mr Goff, and wild barking from the airedales.

Because of Maimie's evening performance, Neil Casubon's party started late. I saw some of the Mafia arrive, and heard the Jacksons go downstairs, but I waited for Maimie and Tick, because I could not face going down to the basement alone. I thought they might be playing parlour games.

They were. When we went downstairs, we found William, with a handkerchief round his eyes, trying to stick the tail on to a paper donkey which was pinned on to the wardrobe. The small low room was full of people and empty of air. The gas fire roared, hesitated and roared again, and two of Casubon's friends were already sitting in the velvet chair, squashed in together, hip to hip. There was no funny business going on. Holding each other round the waist seemed to be the summit of their desires and, apart from them, the party was most refined.

We were introduced to half a dozen people who only had Christian names, and a girl called Bunch, who was cross about something, and sat by the table pretending to read a book. Margaret, in her best green, sat on the edge of a hard chair looking worried. Casubon looked even more worried. He had been tortured by the dilemma of whether or not to wait supper until we came. He had decided to wait. That was why the party was so refined, but now, with two girls coming in from the scullery with a loaded tray, Tick helping Casubon to open the beer, and Maimie finding a gramophone, which played 'What'll I do?', things livened up considerably.

There was not enough furniture for us all to sit down, so some of us sat on the floor, which lent the gay, Bohemian air. There were sausage rolls, hard-boiled eggs, potato salad, beetroot, and all the toothglasses in the house had been pressed into service for the beer. Bunch had brought the cutlery, but that was not what she was cross about, for she had volunteered herself to bring it.

'Good old Bunch,' said John, who wore his jacket open, with a white shirt loose over his long waist, and a wide, unpinned tie that trailed into the potato salad as he bent to offer it round. 'Good old Bunch, always turning up trumps in case of need.' But Bunch sat on at the table, reading moodily while she ate.

We ate off plates balanced in our laps, and the two in the easy chair shared one plate, and giggled when they both stabbed for the same bit of beetroot. Margaret hardly ate anything. Neil kept going to her with plates, but she always shook her head. She looked distressed, and kept glancing across the room into the shadows where William sat marooned on a stool, unable to get to her, because he had been put there and did not know how to change his place. He sank his moustache in the beer, and it came up rimed like a hedge at dawn.

Maimie sat on the floor next to Neil Casubon, and when it came to the jam tarts and fruit salad, again fetched by the girls, for the very young men had not the gumption to go and help them, she picked out the cherries she did not like and put them on to Neil's plate. When he had finished, she played 'This year, next year,' with his stones.

He called out excitedly, for he was not used to beer, 'Next year! I say, everybody, I'm going to be married next year!'

Bunch humped her shoulders and would not look round.

So that was why she was cross. She was busy being jealous with Casubon.

After supper, Tick went upstairs and fetched some more beer and half a bottle of whisky from the cornucopian store under Maimie's bed. He also brought down their portable wireless, and he and Maimie and another couple threw back the rug and danced, shifting on a few feet of floor. Neil went over and spoke to Bunch, but she shook her head and ran her propped hand through her hair, making it stick out at a funny angle. She wore no make-up and the collar of her blouse was not clean. I wanted to tell her that it was not much good being jealous with Neil, if she was not prepared to make a small effort herself. If only I had a woman's column in the *Post*, I could tell her so in print.

Later, when more people wanted to dance, and even the couple in the chair had prised themselves out and taken to the floor, moistly cheek to cheek, like two blancmanges meeting, the table was moved into a corner and Bunch had to get up. She went into the scullery to martyr herself over the washing-up. Neil went after her. I was dancing with John, and we got jammed near the door, so I heard Bunch say above the clatter of china, 'Well, who wouldn't be? Nothing but talk, talk, talk about her before she came, how wonderful she was, and then making a fool of yourself there on the floor for all to see. Anyway, she's not wonderful. She's thirty-five if she's a day. The –'

There was a gasp. Something breakable clattered into the sink and there came the sound of a wet smacking kiss. Well done, Casubon ! If you had read my woman's column, you could not have done better.

'Move along there,' said John, pushing against the couple in front. 'Let the dog see the rabbit.' He jiggled me round the room, compensating in upward movement for what he could not achieve lengthways.

Sausage rolls, kisses in the scullery, dancing in a ridiculous space – it was exactly like a hundred other parties in basements or top flats. I don't know what I had expected – secret signs, or whispering in corners – but certainly these were the most normal lot of revolutionaries I had ever met.

John and I were getting on rather well. He had taken off the wide tie, and we were sharing beer in a corner, because we could only find one glass. We watched the dancers. Maimie was teaching the rumba to a spotted youth in a state of high excitement. Tick was politely letting himself be steered by a girl twice his height. William had been forced to his feet by a frog-like girl called Betty, to whom Tick had been giving whisky, while Margaret sat on, tacitly left alone because she looked so unwilling. Casubon, who had come out of the kitchen with a trace of lipstick under his ear, dutifully asked her to dance, but she only gave him a frightened look, and Bunch pulled his jacket from behind and took him away. Every time William jogged slowly by, he bent and spoke to her, but she shook her head, and smiled until he had gone by.

John squeezed my arm absently and said he was glad that such a nice young lady as myself was a member of the Party. Communists then! I had feared as much when I saw the lean voracious girl who was steering Tick.

'What do you think I am?' I asked, finishing the beer. 'I wouldn't go within a mile of it.'

'But my dear,' he said with burning eyes, 'you're hiding something. You write for the Post, don't you? Well then, you always give us a good press. Say what you like about its being non-political, we know which way the wind blows.'

I was aghast. Communism in the Post? I knew Mr Pellet was a diehard Tory, and old Mrs Murchison, the owner, was reputed to wear blue garters and to fast, in weeds, on the anniversary of Disraeli's death. Had someone then been insinuating Red propaganda unnoticed, a party rally, disguised perhaps as a Women's Institute tea? Murray? Mike? Victor? You never knew these days, with the enemies of the old order

577

always at your door, and Central Europe a place where you could not go for a holiday without getting involved in a war.

Now was my chance to find out. 'Of course I'm with you really,' I whispered, taking hold of the arm that was squeezing mine, so that we stood there like two people about to give a bandy chair. 'All *sub-rosa*, but I'm glad you can spot the propaganda. I do some of it.'

'Then it was you who gave us that write-up last week about the dinner. Good, good. Have some more beer.'

He went across the room to get some. Dinner, dinner? I puzzled my brains. There had been no dinners last week, except the pensioners and the Young Conservatives. The Young . . .

I looked at Neil, dove-grey with semi-asphyxiation and beer. I looked at Bunch, with her uncalculated hair and face; at Betty, with her young skin patching through the places where the whisky had sweated off her cheap make-up; at Nigel, whose voice had only just broken and had gone back to adolescence now that he was singing with Maimie. I saw John, whose pleased, open face prophesied that he would early learn to wear a waistcoat and support a family, coming seriously towards me with an open bottle of beer in each hand dribbling a twin wake across the floor.

'The dinner at the Dover, you mean?' I asked casually. He nodded eagerly, trying to pour both bottles of beer into our one glass and flooding a pile of Casubon's pamphlets. 'No, I wasn't there. Our junior reporter covered that.' I de-ranked Murray.

'Never mind. Junior or not, it was all right. One day, they'll send the editor himself. We're going places. You'll see. They can't keep us down. All of us here –' He swept out an arm and knocked over the table lamp, which sputtered and went out. 'It's those like us who make the future. Your children will thank us.'

'I'm not going to have any children. Tick saw it in the

cards,' I put in, but he was carried away now, and talked on with his face straining forward and shining as I had seen it so often under the street lamp. He talked as if the Conservative party was an embryo and persecuted cause and he the crusader sent by providence to slash its way into history. He was wasted on the Tory party, but I suppose he and the others shut their eyes to its prosperous complacency, because there was no fun in being a Young Conservative if you could not have intrigues and flaming speeches and the hint of knives in dark alleyways.

Mrs Goff had been strangely quiet. Usually, if there were more than the right number of people in any of her rooms, she would hang about outside, or make some excuse to knock on the door, to see what was going on. Casubon, of course, had asked her about the party, and she had consented, subject to the usual curfew, with a possible half hour extension for good behaviour.

It was now after eleven, and Maimie and Tick were embarking on an acrobatic display in the middle of the room. Tick had his coat off, and Maimie whipped off her skirt and stood on his shoulders, bowed under the ceiling, with her blouse tucked into a pair of green trunks. A larger space was cleared, and Tick, who was incredibly strong for his size, whirled her about until her foot caught William in the teeth, and he retired to the scullery.

He came back, mumbling through a handkerchief, 'It's really time we went.' Margaret was still sitting transfixed on her chair, and Maimie, hanging wrong side up down Tick's back, called out, 'Don't break up the party!'

Neil gave William some beer, and he rinsed his bleeding tooth in that, still unable to get across the room to Margaret, because Maimie was whizzing round again like a chair-o-plane.

She landed on her feet with a bounce, quite unruffled. Tick shook back his plaited hair and spat neatly on his hands.

'Oh, let me try! Do let me try!' shrilled Betty, darting forward. 'It looks such fun.'

Tick smiled and shook his head.

'I toud. I'se only a ickle one.' She pouted and pranced before him, taking his hands and trying to put her foot up on his thigh.

'No dear,' said Maimie, pinning up her hair. 'You've got the wrong sort of knickers on.' But too late. Tick suddenly grasped Betty's wrists and swung her screaming into the air, where she teetered, more frog-like than ever, upside down on his shoulders, kicking the ceiling. Maimie was right about her knickers.

The door opened, and Mrs Goff stepped in, cigarette, drooping eyelids, and bosom charged with air. We were all in an instant silent, like children caught out by the dreaded nanny. Betty could not see her and went on screaming.

Tick lowered her to the ground in a heap. Sitting up, she saw Mrs Goff, and kept her mouth open on the unuttered scream.

'So!' Mrs Goff let half the air out of her bosom and kept the rest in reserve. 'So this is how you repay my latitude. It'll be out for you, Mr Casubon, whether you've a roof to put over your head or no.'

'Oh, come on, Mrs Goff,' said Maimie, going to her. 'It isn't his fault. We're just having a good time. No harm in that. Come and have some beer.'

'Mrs Ling!' She shook off Maimie's hand. 'I never thought to hear you bandy words with me like that. No harm, indeed, with young women naked to the waist in my basement! I'll give you No harm, with my decent place turned into a bawdy house for rabble. I'm calling the police, that's what I'm doing.' She turned towards the door.

Casubon cowered. John, tousled and excited, and looking like a boy who has just kicked the winning goal for the school, rushed forward and shut the door.

'Come on, Mrs G.,' he said, standing against it. 'Be a sport. All good clean fun. Take back them words, and I'll let you out.'

I thought she was going to hit him. She lifted her hand, and he jerked his arm up. We instinctively pressed forward, as if a fight was brewing, when suddenly there was a little cry behind us and a shout from William. We turned to see Margaret lying flat on the floor in a dead faint, with her arms to her sides and her toes turned up.

William carried her upstairs, and the party broke up, with shocked whisperings and guilty good nights. Casubon was left amidst the wreckage, not knowing whether he had a roof over his head or not.

Mrs Goff, having achieved more than she hoped for, went to her ground floor room, where her voice could be heard all through the house, waking up Mr Goff to tell him about it. Presently he got up and went into the garden in his pyjamas, with the airedales on a double leash, as if he thought there might be remnants of the party hiding in the bushes.

When we had brought Margaret round and made her comfortable, Maimie and I went out of the Jacksons' room. Mrs Goff was waiting for us on the landing. She stood as if she were nailed to the floor.

'Well, now you know,' she said. 'Now you know.'

'I suppose you think she was drunk,' said Maimie truculently, 'but let me tell you –'

'Drunk?' Mrs Goff's eyebrows shot up like gables. 'Oh dear me no. If that were all, I'd say no more.'

'You *would*,' muttered Maimie.

'I've suspected for quite a time what was wrong with that young lady,' said Mrs Goff, watching us carefully. 'You must all be blind, or else you've never seen a pregnant woman before.'

We gasped and looked at each other. 'God,' said Maimie. 'Poor kid.'

William came out of his room on tiptoe. 'She's asleep,' he whispered. 'Could you please –' His voice trailed away before Mrs Goff's expression.

'I suppose she hasn't told *you* either,' she exulted, feeling the oats of her triumph. Her voice rose.

'Told me what?'

'That she's going to have a baby.' The words dropped on to him like darts.

His face fell. 'Oh no,' he said helplessly.

It was so miserably wrong, all of us receiving such news like this, but Mrs Goff had announced it as a calamity, and calamity it seemed. We ought to have been pleased, and deflated her, but we just stood round in silence, while she watched us, gloating. Then William snapped himself out of her spell, mumbled something, and turned back into his room, looking less like a prospective father than a man condemned to the electric chair.

Mrs Goff said that they must go. There could be no argument about it. No children, she had said when the room was let, so with young madam four months gone, they had better set about finding somewhere else, for she was not going to have them leaving it too late, and then coming to her with a new-born baby and trying to impose on her charity.

Presently she announced that they must go in a month's time. The room was let to someone else from that date, and she would get the magistrates in if necessary to see fair play on her own property.

Margaret was too ill to go out looking for rooms. She was supposed to stay in bed, but she got up once when we were all out, and went searching desperately round the town. She was brought back in a taxi by a policeman who had found her in the street half fainting against some railings.

Casubon's dismissal had blown over in the excitement about Margaret. Mrs Goff could only run one subject at a time, and at the moment she had the Jacksons, so he stayed on in the basement, although the conspirators never came there again. They used to meet in teashops. I saw them once in an A.B.C., eating filling buns and making little puddles with their umbrellas and looking as dejected as if the Conservative Party had lost every seat in the House.

Anxious to help, Neil kept creeping upstairs with little gifts for Margaret: a pamphlet, an orange, or a bag of toffees. One day he came home in a state of ecstasy and announced that a girl at the office knew of a furnished room. We were all very excited, until it turned out that he had forgotten to ask the rent, and it was much more than the Jacksons could afford.

William spent all his lunchtimes and some of his working hours looking for a room within their means. Soon, this cost him his job at the garage. He could not find another. He spent his days waiting in queues at house agencies and the labour exchange, and trekking all over the town and sometimes out into the country on Casubon's bicycle, in pursuit of jobs or homes, but they were always either hopeless or gone by the time he got there.

Margaret was desperate, for now, with William out of work and nothing saved, they could not afford the baby, besides having nowhere to live with it.

'William pretends he's terribly pleased about the child,' she told me, 'but I know he doesn't want it really. He just says that to make me feel better. It will be even more of a burden to him than I am already. His mother was right. We should never have got married.' Margaret had no parents. William had a mother, who had not come to his wedding and had not seen him since.

We tried to help. At last, Tick found him a job with a friend of his who had a dubious workshop for renovating second-hand motor cycles. He only lasted there three days, because the police came round looking for a stolen motor cycle, and Tick's friend said he did not trust William.

One day when he came back to give Margaret her lunch, she had gone out. He was after a job at the bus depot, so he could not wait until she came back. Coming out of the kitchen after the midday meal with the Goffs, I heard someone fumbling at the front door. Margaret came in, looking weary and plain. She took off her hat and tried to shake out her hair, but it clung together in hanks. It could have been pretty hair, but she did not wash it often enough, and did not know how to set it. She could have been quite a pretty girl, but although no doubt William sometimes told her she was, she had long ago decided that it was not worth trying.

'Any luck?' I asked her.

'What?' She looked half stupefied, like someone wandering about after an accident.

'With the rooms.'

'Oh, the rooms. No, no luck.' She started to climb the stairs.

I followed her. 'You shouldn't have gone out.'

She turned, and looked at me with eyes that unaccountably seemed frightened. They were expressionless but widened, like a cat cornered by a dog. 'I had to,' she said, and went on into her room.

A few evenings later, before William came home, she went out again. I went down when I heard the front door, thinking that it was Margaret. It was William, but standing upright, not with that long thin stoop he had recently acquired.

His face was alight. He had found a room. A poky room, but cheap, and the landlady seemed kind. He could not wait to tell Margaret.

'How is she?' he asked, as he ran up the stairs.

'All right, I think. She's gone out, as a matter of fact.'

'Oh.' He stopped. 'Where is she?'

'I don't know.'

'Didn't she say where she was going? Oh dear, I do wish she'd come back.'

He kept coming up to my room and saying this at intervals while I was trying to write up an inquest on a lorry driver. He went to the garden gate and stared up and down the road, but she did not come back. My repertoire of reassurances was getting exhausted. He talked of going to the police.

I was worried about her too, because she had seemed so distracted these last few days. I kept imagining all the things that could have happened to her, and found with a shock that I was already concerned about not having a black hat for the funeral.

It seemed quite callous to go down to supper, but I was hungry. On the way upstairs again, I knocked on the Jacksons' door. William put his head out.

'She's back,' he said. 'She's laying down. She feels a bit queer.'

I could not get to sleep that night. When I did, I dreamed for the first time for weeks about the bathroom door. I was in the bath, with no water in it and my clothes on. The door was opening slowly, and as it opened, a feeling came in. Not a wind, or a change in temperature, or the suffocation that comes in dreams. It was not even an atmosphere, like tension, or malevolence emanating from someone else. It was a feeling of despairing sadness, and although it came in at the door, it was somehow part of me, and coming from me. I wanted to cry, but a river of tears would not relieve that feeling I had of utter hopelessness, that everything was lost.

The pounding on my door shocked me awake. It was Maimie in green pyjamas, her face white under cold cream.

I sat up in a fright. 'What's up? What's the matter?'

'It's Margaret. She's bleeding like a dustbin. Been there ages before that fool husband got me up. Tick's gone for a doctor.'

The doctor came in ten minutes, but it seemed like hours, while Maimie and I worked in a panic with towels and anything we could lay hands on, not knowing what to do and doing all the wrong things. William sat in a corner with his head in his hands, crying. We could not even get him to fetch water for us. Casubon, scenting trouble, had come upstairs in a flurry of distress and was hopping about on the landing, holding a blanket and a cushion, wanting to help. We sent him for water, and he panted up and down tripping over stair rods.

When the doctor came, he turned William out. He told us what to do, and we tried to help. 'Those damn Czechs,' the doctor said. 'I'll get them locked up for this.'

The ambulance arrived soon after the doctor. While they were carrying Margaret out of the front door, Mrs Goff came out of her room in a hair-net and a black quilted dressing-gown.

'What's going on?' she demanded.

'Margaret's having a miscarriage,' Maimie said.

'In my house?'

'Yes, in your house, and you know why, you horrible old woman. Because you wouldn't let her have the baby here.'

Mrs Goff made her face blank to the abuse. 'An abortion?' She gave the word its full ugliness. 'It's too much. No, it's too much. She needn't think she's going to stay on here by such tricks. There'll be things said when that young madam gets back.'

But Margaret never did come back from the hospital. She died from loss of blood within a few hours.


Naturally, we all hated Mrs Goff more than ever after that. We only spoke to her when absolutely necessary, but she did not mind. She had no remorse, but even a certain air of triumph about her.

Mr Goff did look a little uncomfortable. He kept opening his mouth to say something, and thinking better of it. He went out before supper and bought some bottles of stout to make William feel better, but William had already packed up and disappeared, and we all refused the stout because we had put Mr Goff into Coventry too.

Alice was affronted by the whole thing. She did not discuss it. Such subjects were not in the range of her vocabulary, which was limited to suspicion of the tradesmen and abuse of Barry. She went about looking thinner and flatter than ever, with her nose and mouth and chin drawn down to her arid chest, as if the tendons of her neck were too short. Maimie, whose vulgarity even tragedy could not dim, said it was a pity someone had not introduced Alice to the Czechs before little Barry was born. That was the day after he had crawled into their room and set fire to the eiderdown with a box of matches.

The run of *Mother Goose* ended at last. It was now nearly Easter, but pantomime at the Empire often went on as long after Christmas as that. It took a little time for the people of Downingham to decide whether it was worth going to see.

Maimie and Tick had the chance of an engagement in the north, and were going up to Sheffield to try and settle it. We did not want to lose each other, but I minded more than she did. It is always worse for the one who is left behind, especially when they are left at Five, Bury Road.

Maimie and I made the usual promises to meet again often and go on being friends, really believing that we should. I saw her once long afterwards, coming out of the Haymarket subway at Piccadilly. We had dinner together, and met two friends of hers from a band, who took us to dance. The friends became tedious, and we left them and went home in the all-night bus along Oxford Street. I got off at Notting Hill Gate and Maimie went on to Shepherd's Bush and I have never seen her since.

We had a farewell party before they left for Sheffield. We asked Casubon to come too, and he got drunk on gin and cider in the Feathers, and kept shouting slogans at people in the street on the way home. He finally collapsed in the market square, limp on the steps of the war memorial. We took him home in a taxi, and since Tick, who never drank too much, had elected to do so that night, Maimie and I put Neil to bed. When he was snoring on the divan, I looked round the room to see if there was a picture of Bunch, for he would not tell us how the affair was going.

There was no picture of Bunch, but the suitcase on the table was open, and lying on top of some papers in it was a snapshot of Margaret, taken in one of the water meadows by the river. She was wearing a short cotton dress and her hair was blowing about and she looked quite pretty.

## Chapter Nine

MRS GOFF had lied about the Jacksons' room. It was not let at all. No one came there, but two girls took the front room, which had been Maimie and Tick's. One of the girls worked in a bookshop. The other was in the costing office of the bicycle factory. When you asked her what a costing office was, she never could explain it satisfactorily.

I don't believe she knew herself, or wanted to know. She had been engaged to type and file from nine till five, and type and file she did, and never talked about her work at home.

The other girl talked about her work at the bookshop all the time. There was a certain Mr Jaggers, for whom she was privileged to make cocoa, and we heard a lot about what Mr Jaggers had said and done and what he was going to do. There were also customers who had been ever so funny, but what they had been funny about was usually lost in a maze of side tracks before the end of the story.

The names of the girls were Connie and Win, and they never seemed to do anything but go to the cinema, and wash and iron their collars and cuffs. The bathroom was always hung with the drying accessories of their black working frocks, and there was much calling up and down the stairs for more soapflakes and: 'Shall I risk the green sailor, Win, or do you think it'll run?'

'Soak it in salt and water first, dear.' They were passionate readers of women's magazines and did all that they were told therein. They made little round crochet hats with gloves to match, and Connie had embarked on an embroidered beach bag, months before their holiday was due.

They set each other's hair in a new way every week, trying to discover what shape their faces were, to match them to the magazine charts. They steamed their faces over the bathroom basin and wore hand cream and gloves at night, and when Win was going to the works dance she lay down for half an hour with her feet higher than her head and slices of cucumber on her eyelids. It did not make any difference.

The front room on my floor was taken by a one-armed commissionaire from the Majestic cinema. He played his wireless too loudly, so I told him about the bread-knife murder. He told me he was psychic and would love to be haunted, and played his wireless louder than ever, for he said that ghosts liked music. Connie and Win did his darning for him and washed his socks and took him cups of malted milk, and altogether the atmosphere at Bury Road was cosy.

They tried to draw Casubon into the family circle, but he had gone back into his shell again. A woman writer, who paid the income tax on her novels by writing about Love in one of their magazines, had told them that the way to get a man was to encourage him to talk about himself, so at meals they were always asking poor Neil about his work. Mrs Goff would lay down her knife and fork and say, 'Yes, let's *hear* about that,' as if she were grilling a suspect. Neil would stammer and choke and bolt his pudding so that he could get away. I'm sure he had indigestion all the time Connie and Win were there. In the magazines, the stories were nearly always about misogynist men who had to be tamed to romance, so the girls pursued Neil by every means except the obvious one of natural sex attraction. When I went to the basement to return some pamphlets, I found that he had taken to locking his door, and he had given up his fortnightly bath for fear of meeting Connie or Win descending the stairs in a turbaned towel after trying out a new scientific miracle shampoo.

Connie and Win did not read the *Downingham Post*. When I asked them why not, they stared at me and giggled. They always answered questions like that: first a stare then a giggle, never the other way round. All you had to do was wait until they had finished and then put the question again, in simpler form if necessary.

Why didn't they read the *Post*? Why should they? There was nothing in it they liked, except some of the court cases, and they got enough of those, really, with the Sunday papers.

This encouraged me to tackle Mr Pellet once again on the subject of woman's angle. There must be thousands of girls like Win and Connie in Downingham, who would read our paper if only we would tell them how to get rid of blackheads and how to make a film star bolero for five shillings. I chose a bad moment, for an amateur contralto had just rung up to complain about a misprint in her name last week. Mr Pellet said that he was not so interested in getting new readers as in keeping the old ones, and that if I raised the subject any more he would fire me. I believe he would have, too. He had fired Vic last week, but Vic was still there, and talking about asking for a rise to make up for the insult.

Mr Pellet turned off the gas under the kettle and said that

if I was so keen on women's angles I could go straight off to the corset show at Harper's. I did not laugh at his joke. Murray did.

The corset show was upstairs in Downingham's largest store. Nancy was there, and I sat next to her on a high little chair. Most of the spectators looked as if they badly needed new corsets, but they tried to convey the impression of having just wandered in there to take the weight off their feet.

The show was compèred by a commanding woman, armoured from armpits to thighs in uplift and diaphragm support and hip control. She walked stiffly about, introducing the models in ringing tones, and Nancy took copious notes with Len's screw pencil. She was one of those women who love to use men's things. Len had given her his second-best cigarette case, and sometimes she wore his shirts or pullovers.

I suppose she was taking notes to show off the pencil, for I did not see how any paper, let alone the *Messenger*, could print the esoteric details about brassières which we were given. I did not think Mr Pellet would print anything about the show. He had only sent me there because he was cross about the contralto on the telephone. After we had suffered the embarrassment of seeing a fat woman, who must have needed the money badly, appearing without corsets and with, I left.

'Then don't go ringing me up this afternoon asking me for details you missed,' said Nancy as I got up, 'for I'm sure I'm sick of writing half your copy for you.'

I found Joe in the Lion. He was back at work now, trembly and grumbling, and needing to leave the office even earlier before lunch than he used to.

He told me that Mr Pellet wanted me back in the office right away to do the film notes for this week, since Mike – lucky Mike – had gone off on the first good story that had come

591

our way for weeks. A patient from the Northgate Asylum had escaped from the activity method room and was now stuck in the top of a chimney, unable to move up or down.

I had my lunch and did not hurry back to the office, for I had a quicker way of doing the films than Mike. He would spend all afternoon poring over the handouts from the cinemas and old back numbers of film magazines, for the films that came to Downingham had seen the West End long, long ago. Many of the second features and Sunday films were westerns and custard-pie comedies that had never seen the West End at all, but we dealt with them gravely and gave them the same three lines allotted to the major epics.

I never wasted time looking up all the things that other people had written. The adjectives were not suitable for us, anyway. I used simply to take my list of films next door to the comps. Even if they had not seen the films, they had always heard or read about them. There was nothing they did not know. Maurice, the apprentice comp, who pulled the proofs, was like the memory man who knows the winner of every race since nineteen hundred. He could not be stumped.

'*Red Riders*,' he would say. 'Let's see. That was a remake of an old Tom Mix, wasn't it? Yes, that's right. Smashing picture. You saw a real scalping. The dame was Betty la Roche – only her second picture. She was still married to Leo Engel then. What you got next, dear? *Hearts in Paradise*. Ah, I seen that Monday. Lovely job. Coral Canning. What they call a star veekle for her. Listen, she's a knockout. She's got shape –'

'What's it about, Morrie? Downingham wants facts, not opinions,' I quoted Mr Pellet.

'Well she meets him in the park, see. Hugo Dilkes, he plays the millionaire, only he's pretending to be someone else, because he's sated with riches, see?'

'That's right,' Ernie stopped his machine and called across. 'It's all set in New York. There's a couple of super numbers. The floor goes round. All glass, it is.'

Ricky also stopped his Linotype and joined in. All work was shelved while we talked films. Harold came in from the reporters' room, glanced at my list, and sat down to light a pipe the better to tackle the subject. Between them, they wrote the column for me.

Mr Pellet came in while we were finishing off with Laurel and Hardy. 'Got a proof of the Snug-phit annual general meeting, Harold? I want to check something.'

Harold got up. Ernie and Ricky started their machines. Maurice stood upright and passed his roller busily across the ink table.

'There you are, girl,' said Mr Pellet. 'I wondered where you'd got to.'

'I just came in to see whether there were any proofs ready for us to read,' I said smugly.

'You're supposed to be doing the films,' said Mr Pellet, who knew that we were more likely to throw proofs back in Harold's face than go seeking them from him.

'I've done those long ago. Just waiting to copy them out when Vic's finished with my typewriter.'

'All right, you can go and do the B.D. and M.s then. Vic's got all the stuff.'

The Birth, Death and Marriage announcements were simple. You had to make a column of the details that people had sent, only altering the spelling and punctuation where necessary. Mr Pellet said that you should never alter anything in these personal announcements, but one could not let Downingham read on Thursday that Mable Emma Salter, aged 83, had passed piecefully away, sadly missed by husband, family and friends.

Above all, he said that you should never alter anything in the In Memoriam notices. This was difficult, for many of them

593

contained home-made poems that only needed a little juggling to make them scan.

Many of them were old favourites, made up once by someone and used again and again by other people.

> *Mother dear,*
> *We like to think you're near.*
> *We miss you every day,*
> *Since you went away.*
>
> *Pain and silence long you bore.*
> *Now you're at rest for evermore.*
> *A shining example you left behind,*
> *Loving and cheerful and wise and kind.*

This week there was a new one, 'from Jimmy to Mum':

> *She was beautiful and kind*
> *As a country day.*
> *I can't get her out of my mind.*

I did not like doing the In Memoriam column. It always made me cry.

To attend the Assizes, held three times a year in the county town twenty miles away, was one of the best jobs on the paper. The cases were those sent on from magistrates' courts, and there were always a few quite startling ones and often one important enough to bring reporters down from London. Everybody wanted to go to Assizes. Apart from the court, it meant a day out, with lunch at the paper's expense. Mr Pellet usually sent Murray. If something more important kept him in Downingham, Mike and Victor would argue with Mr Pellet about whose turn it was to go, and Mr Pellet would send Joe, who did not want to go, because the press bench in the county court gave him back-ache and the long bus journey made him sick.

594

I wanted to go, but short of everybody else in the office being asphyxiated by our leaking gas ring I would never have the chance. Mr Pellet, however, in one of his unpredictable bursts of goodwill, which fizzled out in a moment if you tried to take advantage of them, suddenly told me, in the middle of cursing me for coming in to the office too late and leaving it too early, that I could go with Murray to the next Assizes.

'Can I write up some of the cases?' I asked.

'You might try. Murray can decide which.'

Murray decided none of them. He was horrid to me all day, because he liked to go on his own and put on a big Fellow Journalist act with the reporters he knew and introduce himself as Assistant Editor, *Post*, to visiting newspaper men.

We met at the bus stop, in the rain. There seems to be a lot of rain in this story, but that was the way it was in Downingham that year. Murray said I was late, but as we had to wait five minutes for the bus, I could not see that it mattered.

There were two empty seats together on the bus. I sat there, thinking that it would look too rude if I deliberately went and sat with a stranger. Murray felt the same, and joined me unwillingly. Etiquette satisfied, we both opened newspapers and did not say a word to each other all the way to the county town.

Assizes day brought too much traffic to the jumbled old town with its narrow streets and its famous town hall, whose corner stuck right out into the main street, causing, like Scylla, its quota of accidents every year.

Murray took me into the building and then went off to the gents, leaving me stranded in the stone passage among the crowd of policemen and men with brief-cases and young barristers already robed. Everybody except me looked busy and important. I got out my notebook and tried to look like a special correspondent.

I was glad to be greeted by a detective-constable from Downingham who had come to give evidence.

'Never been to Assizes before?' he said. 'Never seen the trumpeters? Come on, you must see the judge arrive.' I abandoned Murray and went with him into the street. Police had cleared the roads round the town hall. A small crowd of idlers and some women with shopping baskets had stopped on the pavement to watch, but most people, blasé from many Assizes, were walking on, pushing past the sight-seers impatiently.

The judge arrived in a black saloon car, driven at walking pace, with two police cars escorting him behind. They skirted the town hall and drew up at the side entrance, where the two trumpeters waited, dressed in black jockey caps and rather dusty scarlet tunics with tarnished silver epaulettes and froggings, that looked as if they had come out of a child's dressing-up box.

The judge, in wig and robes, climbed out of the car in a rheumaticky way, and the trumpeters sounded a clarion call of three uninspired notes as he went up the steps and through the narrow door. I thought he should have entered with pomp through the main doors, but there were no steps there, and tradition decrees that an Assize judge must always go up steps. Prison slang for being committed to Assizes is 'going up the steps'.

The Assize court is full of tradition. One of them is that reporters must only enter the press benches from one end. I, of course, slipping in just in time before the judge made his entry, tried to go in at the wrong end. A policeman hauled me away and sent me round to the right end, and when I reached Murray and sat down next to him, he pretended not to know me.

'Rise, please!' shouted someone, just as I had sat down. We all stood up as the little procession filed on to the Bench. The judge looked like a monkey and kept blinking his eyes, as if he had been asleep in the car and was sorry to have been woken up. The High Sheriff was there in army uniform with medals, the chaplain in cassock and cravat, and two women who were somebody's wife and daughter came along in their best hats to see the fun. The judge's marshal unrolled a parchment scroll and in a flat voice which would make anything dull, read out the Commission of Assize, which was dull anyway. It was full of Know Ye, and All offences and injuries whatsoever within our said County, and was the most traditional thing we had had yet.

When we were all sitting down again, the two trumpeters, who were soldiers of the county regiment, came in without their jockey caps, climbed half-way up the public benches and sat down at ease on the steps. One of them put on a pair of tin spectacles.

Sex crimes of varying squalor took up most of the morning. They were startling at first. Until you go to Assizes, you don't believe that things like that really happen, but they do, and after two hours or so of them the only interesting thing is that the mild appearance of the defendants never tallies with the description of the passionate bestialities of which they stand accused.

Bigamists are the most baffling. They seldom look capable of getting one woman to marry them, let alone two, and the women for whom they break the law and usually go to prison are invariably dowdy, with fawn coats, untidy hair, and noses that speak of faulty digestions.

There was one important case at the Assizes that day, a kidnapping, which had already made headlines in the daily papers. A few London reporters had come down for it. One of them was sitting next to me and was making sure that everyone knew he was from Fleet Street and was more used to lounging among his peers at the Old Bailey than among people like me on the narrow yellow benches of the town hall court. All morning he had been yawning and fidgeting and giving little snorts of contempt, but when the kidnapper came into the box he ceased his slumming act and became the ace journalist, taking lightning notes with much jabbing of pencil and noisy flipping over of pages.

The defending counsel, a young and eager barrister who had been bravely but hopelessly trying all morning to defend the sex criminals with the time-honoured excuse that everything went black and an impulse came over them, now treated the judge to an impassioned harangue on the subject of the kidnapper's impulses. His Learned Friend, the prosecuting counsel, also young, with a wig made for someone with a smaller head, tied the accused in knots with an offensive cross-examination on the lines of: 'And do you really mean to tell his Lordship that, on the night of April 4th, you, etc. ... etc. ...'

When the accused stuck hoarsely to his guns, prosecuting counsel would say: 'Very good. Very well,' with the grim triumph of a Nanny defied by a small boy, but knowing that she will tell father when he comes home.

His triumph was justified, for the judge gave the kidnapper a very stiff prison sentence. Without a word, the kidnapper fell straight over backwards, out like a light into the arms of a policeman, who dragged him below to the dungeons with his heels going thump, thump on the stairs.

Sensation in court. Discreet sensation, but an outbreak of shocked murmurs and exclamations, sharply hushed by the clerk. The press bench was agog. There had not been a bit of excitement like this at Assizes since two years ago when a bigamist tried to jump out of the dock and make a dash for it. The London reporter shut his notebook, clapped on his hat, and began to push through the narrow space past our knees.

'Can't you wait a moment?' muttered Murray, who was writing. 'The judge will be rising in a minute.'

'Got to phone my story,' said the reporter with great superiority. He pushed on, dropped to the floor with a thud, and shouldered his way out through the policemen as if he were charged with a crucial dispatch from the Front.

Murray took me to lunch in the upstairs dining-room of the Blue Boar. He did not want to take me with him, but as I did not know anywhere else to eat in the town, I followed him, and when he sat down in a corner with two of his friends from other local papers, there I was.

The Blue Boar was doing a roaring trade, and trying to do it with the one defeated waitress who coped with the sprinkling of commercial lunchers on ordinary days. Murray and his friends talked of things I knew nothing about, and at last we were served – not with the dishes we had ordered, but time was getting on, so we ate them.

When I had picked all the currants out of my bread-and-butter pudding, I left the rest and went out to do some quick shopping. I was not quick enough, and I heard the last trump sounding while I was still in Boots. I ran back to the town hall, but the judge was already in court by the time I stumbled into the press bench, and he stopped speaking and gave me a fractious look which caused Murray not to know me again.

There had been some hundred and fifty people in that courtroom since ten-thirty in the morning, and tradition said that windows were never opened. The trumpeter with the tin spectacles, who with his mate had to stay until the end to pipe the judge over the side, dozed off. I slept nearly the whole afternoon, and the only thing I remember about it is the jury that tried one of the cases. After they had delivered their verdict, the foreman, a stout and serious householder, remained standing, clearing his throat and saying that the jury wished to make one more statement.

'Yes, yes?' said the judge, blinking at him.

'Well, your Lordship, we wish to lodge a complaint about the jury benches – that they are such that the heat of the body causes the clothing to stick to the paint of them.'

Everyone woke up. Everyone laughed, and the trumpeter with the tin spectacles sat up with a jerk and had the joke explained to him by his chum. Because the judge snickered, the public laughed with sycophantic immoderacy, like a B.B.C. studio audience. The foreman of the jury looked baffled, but then he laughed too, and the twelve good men and true filed out, popular figures of comic relief.

When the new jury was installed, a police sergeant came in and begged the judge's permission to disturb them, as one of the comedy team had left an overcoat behind.

'And the seat of his trousers,' said the young barrister with the perching wig, and got his laugh, to the bewilderment of a distressed mother who was in the witness box, telling the story of her daughter who was pregnant at the age of fourteen. Oh, it's hilarious fun, Assizes is.

The cases dragged on, and Murray began to worry about missing our bus. I thought we had plenty of time, and when the judge at last adjourned the court until tomorrow, and the trumpeters blew him down the steps and went away to put their uniforms back into the acting box, I dragged Murray into a café for a cup of tea. The waitress was slow, but I thought I would die before we got back to Downingham if I did not have a cup of tea, so we waited. There was not as much time as I thought, and when we reached the bus stop we saw the cream-coloured behind of the bus disappearing round a corner.

Murray was so cross that he would not come back for another cup of tea at leisure while we waited for the next bus. He stood on the pavement for an hour. I found him there when I came out of the café, propped against the bus-stop post with his collar turned up and his hands sagging his pockets. He was not knowing me again. I propped myself against the other side of the post and we waited in silence until the bus came. It was crowded. We had to stand most of the way home, swaying and bumping against one another without a word, while the bus rocked through the winding country roads back to Downingham.

We did not get back to Downingham until nearly eight o'clock. I should be too late for supper. I felt too tired to go and eat somewhere, so I went home to make tea and eat biscuits and chocolate in my room.

A small van stood outside Number Five. Mr Goff was watching a man unload from it an octagonal table with long, straight legs and a yellow top inlaid with black scroll-work. When it was on the pavement, the man dived back into the van and brought out a plaster statue the size of a six-months baby, which he put on the table. It appeared to be a nymph of some kind. It looked coy, like Nausicaa surprised bathing. Its hair fell over its shoulders in a decent way, and it clutched at lumpy draperies that for ever threatened to fall off. Mr Goff had been to a sale again.

On tiptoe with excitement, he hovered round the nymph, putting out a finger to her like a cat playing with a bit of fluff, and snatching back his hand as if she had stung him.

'Sorry I can't take 'em up for you, pal,' said the man with the van, 'but *she's* waiting.'

'Thanks, Charlie boy,' said Mr Goff. 'Thanks for obliging.' He made a pass with his cuffs, flexed his little arms, and braced his knees to lift Nausicaa. She was hollow and light as cardboard, and she came up so suddenly that he nearly fell over backwards. He grinned at me over the top of her coy head and staggered into the house with her, his legs wambling across each other like a stage-drunk. I pushed one of the dogs away from the legs of the octagonal table, picked it up, and followed him indoors.

When we were in the hall, Mrs Goff looked over the banisters and called down to us in the fluting, churchy voice which she used for strangers. She must have a prospective lodger up there. Sure enough, when she came downstairs, she was followed by a small dark girl with a melting smile and cheekbones so high that they pushed up her lower lids, giving her eyes a slightly oriental curve. Her black hair hung in a long, heavy bob like a tassel. She came down the stairs gracefully, just tapping the banister, her feet pointing down and outwards on every step.

I apologized for missing supper. To my surprise, Mrs Goff came quite close to me – she usually stood far off when she talked to you – and said: 'Never mind, dear. I'll get you a snack.'

Dear? A snack? I could only suppose that the girl had not yet made up her mind about the room. With a glance at her, Mrs Goff then asked me if I would like to have the octagonal table up in my room *for my writing*. She made it sound as if I were a best-seller come here to finish an important book.

Mr Goff was still carrying the nymph about, like a mother with her firstborn, unable to find anywhere to put it among the litter of his previous trophies in the hall and kitchen passage. I hoped Mrs Goff would not offer it to me as well.

I took the table upstairs before she could change her mind. It was not ideal for working on. It was too high, unless you sat on a pillow. The legs were in the wrong places, and the octagonal sides sloped away from you, so that papers fell off. The scrolls were irritating and distracted your eye, leading it along the whorls and curlicues trying to find an end. However, it was a table.

Either the 'Dear' or the snack or the gift of the table did the trick. Two days later there was a strange spongebag in the bathroom.

# Chapter Ten

THE dark girl's name was Myra Nelson. She was eighteen and a ballet dancer, working with a small but talented company, who were finishing their season with two weeks at the Empire, and then staying on in Downingham, where they had taken a studio, to train and rehearse new ballets until they found quarters in London.

Few people outside the ballet world had heard of them, but they were a promising young company, who were going to be important one day. Their principal, a famous Italian dancer, now middle-aged, but with a figure like a girl, set a standard so high, both of dancing and behaviour, that the girls had to work like niggers and live more or less like nuns. They accepted this, for to get into Signora's company was considered a great chance. Two of her pupils had already gone on to dance principal roles at Sadler's Wells.

'That's where I mean to go,' Myra told me, 'if only Signora keeps me. She's always throwing people out who aren't good enough, or who won't do as she says. She must keep me. She's the best teacher there's ever been since Preobrajenska, Signora is. She's incredible. She's never tired and she never believes you are. Even at her age, she can still do everything herself. She could dance Swan Lake if she had to. She was one of the best Odettes there's ever been, you know, except Pavlova. Signora saw her. Signora says –'

Signora this, Signora that. We heard more about Signora even than about Connie's Mr Jaggers. Signora was both the goddess and the terror of Myra's life. If she had praised her, the girl came home glowing and wanted to love everybody in the house, even little Barry. If she had scolded her and told her, as she told all the company at intervals, that she would never be a dancer, Myra came home washed out, with her hair limp, and shut herself away in her room to mope.

With every smallest decision that cropped up, even a change of lipstick, it was: 'I'll have to ask Signora.' She had to be told everything, and if you did not tell her, she found out. She dominated Myra completely and worked her much too hard. Often I had to drag her out of bed in the morning, to get her off to class on time.

'Why do you let her treat you like this?' I asked her, when she came home one day in tears, because Signora did not like her new coat and said that she must change it. 'She's a monster, and she doesn't pay you all that much.'

'Oh, it isn't the money.' Myra's soft face looked shocked. 'We ought to be paying her, really, for what she teaches us. We can't expect to have a life of our own. If you're a dancer, Signora says, you must give up everything else.'

'Yes,' said Win, who was with us in my room, darning the commissionaire's socks, 'give it up to her. Jolly nice for her, but I think you're ever so silly to stand for it.'

'I must. Everyone does. She's like that with everyone, and if they don't like it, they have to go. Patty Grigg had a terrible time with her last year because she didn't like the boy Patty was going out with. She said she mustn't see him, and Patty only just met him once on the corner near our hotel to say good-bye, but Signora saw her, and that was the end of Patty. She's in musical comedy now, poor darling.'

'If she's like that,' I said, 'I can't understand why she lets you live here on your own. Why don't you want to be with the others, anyway?'

'Oh well, you see.' Myra dropped her eyes. She could never keep anything from you if she was looking at you. 'That's a secret, really. But I told Signora that Mrs Goff was a relation of mine.'

Win and I gasped.

'Oh, she's not, of course, thank goodness, but although

604

Signora doesn't like it very much, she let me come here in the end, because they're overcrowded where they are. I have to tell her though exactly what I'm eating, and what time I get in if I go out at night.'

'Well pooh,' said Win, getting off my bed and shaking threads off her skirt. 'You could tell her anything.'

'I couldn't. She'd soon find out if I was lying. Signora knows everything.'

'She doesn't know why you want to live here though,' I said, 'nor do we. God knows why anyone should. Come on, what's this secret?'

'I daren't tell you. It might get round to her. Oh, not that I don't trust you, of course,' she said hurriedly, afraid of being unkind, 'but you know how things get round, and that would be the end of me with Signora. Perhaps one day I'll tell you. I hate having secrets. It seems so mean. Shall I tell you? But you'd have to cross your heart and hope to die.' She licked her finger and drew it across her throat. Her gestures, though always graceful, were as childish as much of her conversation. Signora's Simon-Legree-cum-kindergarten treatment seemed to have arrested her development in everything except dancing.

Win and I licked our fingers and crossed our throats. 'Come on then,' I said. 'Shall I lock the door?'

Win giggled. Myra got up and went to the window, with that curious duck-like ballet dancer's walk.

'Shall I?' She looked out of the window, then suddenly turned round excitedly, and stood with her hands behind her on the sill and her eyes shining. She opened her mouth on a deep breath, and at that moment Connie blundered in from the bathroom with her head wrapped up in a towel and asked who was going to dry her. Myra shut her mouth on her secret and went downstairs to darn her tights.

Mr Pellet would not let me have the press tickets for the first night of the ballet. He sent Victor, and I had to buy my own. The theatre was barely full, for there had never been proper ballet in Downingham before, and the whole thing was viewed with great suspicion.

In the interval after *Sylphides*, a man said to his wife, 'Well, the tunes are pretty enough, I'll give you that, but it's that man with the bow round his neck I can't stomach. Can't we go now?'

'You'll like the next one, dear. It's all about skating –'

'Well, we'll see, we'll see,' he grumbled. 'I must say these seats are damned hard.'

Signora's little company gave a more beautiful performance than anything Downingham was likely to see for many years to come. I thought Myra was wonderful. It is always surprising to see someone you know doing something difficult. The rest of the *corps de ballet* were probably just as good, but then I had not seen them staggering to the bathroom in the early morning with their eyes half shut, or sprawling on the bedroom floor in a petticoat, stirring cocoa over the gas ring.

I went home exalted into a dream of a lovelier life, but when I started rhapsodizing to Myra, she said: 'Oh, it wasn't. It was terrible tonight. Didn't you see Mervyn come in half a bar late? And in *Sylphides*, Sally made a face at someone in the wings, when she was going upstage with her back to the audience, and Signora saw and gave her a terrible blowing up. So, of course, she was in a furious temper in *Patineurs*, and she and Prue, who do one of the variations, were having a row all the time. You should have heard the language.'

It could not have been worse than the language in the office next day, when Vic was trying to write his report on *Lez Sylpheedes* and *Patinewers*. He had hated it, and did not know why anyone should want to see ballet, much less read about it in the *Post*.

'Well, I don't know,' said Mike. 'I'm afraid I rather like ballet. I'm sorry. I can't help it,' he said, as if apologizing for an offensive infirmity.

At lunchtime, I took Victor home and smuggled him up-stairs, and when Myra came home from rehearsal, we got her to help him with the ballet notice.

We sat in her room, and Victor, who always said what was in his mind, asked her why she wanted a double room. 'I'll know where to come, shan't I?' he said, with a heavy and rather unsuccessful leer. That was one of his approaches to women – daring remarks of a hobnailed unsubtlety that were supposed to shock them into submission.

'Shut up, Victor,' I said. 'She's married.' I winked at Myra, but she did not wink back. She sat on that dreadful little tapestry stool that Mr Goff had bought from the sale at the old rectory, and stared at the wall, tapping her teeth with a pencil and wondering how many superlatives she could per-suade the Post to give Signora.

'This is bloody good,' Mr Pellet said, coming into our office with the ballet notice. 'I didn't know you knew all this about ballet, Victor.'

Vic studied his nails. 'Oh, I'm pretty versatile in my way, you know, sir.'

The editor looked at me. 'Did *she* write it?'

'If I had,' I said, 'you wouldn't say it was bloody good.'

'True. But did you?'

'Of course not. Why should I?'

'You did that filth about the pantomime, and I know these boys. They'll always get someone else to do their work if they can.'

Joe swore that he had not told him about *Mother Goose*. How did Mr Pellet know? He knew everything. He ought to meet Signora. They would make a lovely pair.

Signora, however, was married. Or had been. She had married a Milanese masher called Alessandro long, long ago when she was a foolish girl and thought that a ballet dancer could find room for love.

Alessandro soon tired of being a ballet husband. He took Signora round the neck one night and said, 'You must choose between me and *la danza.*' Signora chose *la danza,* and Alessandro went straight off to live with a woman of wealth and high social standing, who had nothing to do all day but lie on a couch and polish her nails until he came home.

This explained why Signora was so adamant in her rule that none of the girls in her company should marry. She did not have to bother about the men. The question never arose.

Most of the girls were very pretty, and quite often one or other of them came to Signora in fear and trembling to say that she had fallen in love, and could she *possibly* get married, please, Signora, or at least, as a great favour, announce her engagement?

Signora would then thump the girl in the small of the back to correct her posture, and say that she would not waste her time training someone whose mind was half on other things, and she would quote Alessandro's remark about choosing between the man and the ballet. The girl nearly always chose the ballet, and there were many wretched young men in England who might have been held on suspicion if Signora had ever been found with a bullet through the narrow blue-black head.

The girls did not seem to think of getting married without telling Signora. I suppose they knew that she would find out before long, and meanwhile the strain of wondering when would be too much.

It was getting to be too much for Myra. She had to tell someone. I had gone home for the week-end and Win was in hospital having her appendix out so she told Connie, who stayed awake on Sunday night to tell me as soon as I got back.

Myra's light was on when I came out of Connie's room, so I went in to her. She would know that Connie would be sure to tell me, for Connie told everything. News leaked out of her like a tap without a washer, and Mr Jaggers would have retired behind the Novels Reduced to Clear counter in some dismay if he knew that we had heard exactly what happened to him that time he had food poisoning.

Myra was sitting up in bed in a shawl with a blue ribbon round her hair, reading one of Connie's magazines.

'It's awful,' she said. 'I can't go to sleep, and we're rehearsing *Aurora's Wedding* tomorrow. I'm doing the *pas de trois*. Did I tell you?'

'Yes, you told me. You didn't tell me what this other bed was for though.' I sat down on it, remembering the night when Margaret had lain there and we could not stop her life ebbing away.

'Connie told you? I thought she would. Well, you'd have to know soon, anyway, because he's coming home. That's why I took this room. He's been out East, and he'll get leave when he comes back next month, and how I shall ever face Signora, I just don't know.'

'You mean you're going to tell her?'

'Heavens no. She'd kill me. To have got married at all is bad enough. I never would have done it, only it was Andrew's last week, and – well, you know – we had to be together. But a soldier! She hates the Army, or anything like that which has nothing to do with any of the arts. And Andrew hates the ballet, and if Signora found out and was mean to me, he'd go and beat her up, you know. He really would. He's terribly violent.'

'But you can't keep it dark for ever.' It seemed a pretty poor lookout for Andrew if he was to be kept behind a baize door like a shameful secret. If he was so violent, he probably would not stand for it.

'While I'm with Signora we must. I must finish my training with her, and then when I'm good enough to go on to a bigger company, it won't matter everyone knowing. But Signora mustn't know now. She'd throw me out and that would finish me.'

We discussed the matter at great length. Myra told me all about the romance, from the moment when she had first met Andrew in a station waiting-room to the moment when, at another station, she had kissed him good-bye on the troop train, and gone behind a pile of empty ice-cream cans to weep while she took off his ring, which she had not been able to wear since. She could not even wear it tied to her shoulder-straps, because Signora was in and out of their dressing-rooms all the time.

She would not be able to wear it when Andrew came home, in case they met Signora in the street. She would hardly dare to go out with Andrew. They would have to stay in their room most of the time, and would he like the room? And Mrs Goff would have to know, and she might tell someone, and altogether married life was going to be very difficult.

'It's awful,' she kept on saying. 'Oh dear, I don't know what I shall do. It's awful.'

I did not think it was awful at all. I thought it was wonderful to have a romantic secret in those blatant days when everyone knew everything about everyone else's life. It was difficult, from the uninspired behaviour of most young married couples, to believe that they were in love, but with Myra and Andrew you could, because she had dared all for his sake.

It was like the princess secretly married to the shoemaker. One day, when I had learned how to write short stories, I would write a story about them, and I tried to memorize how she looked pattering across the floor in a torn nightgown to find his photograph for me, and sitting on the tapestry stool in tears, with her knees fallen apart in that jointless, almost ungainly way of a dancer at rest.

The season of fêtes was now upon us, and not a Saturday went by without some desperate village junketing to raise money for the memorial hall or the church roof. Usually, we got pick-ups on these from local correspondents, but if the village had managed to persuade any kind of a celebrity to open their fête, a reporter had to go along to get a first-hand story.

This was a job for the junior reporter, so it was always the job for me. There is nothing I don't know now about village fêtes. I have seen them in blazing sunshine when the ice cream had to be poured into the cornets, and the pig that was being bowled for collapsed from heat stroke. I have seen them in pouring rain, when the Rose Queen ran for shelter with a mackintosh over her head, and the tea tent came down like a wet sack on the vicar and most of his parish. I have seen them in a high wind, with boy scouts hanging on to the guy ropes, and I was privileged to be present on one occasion when the sausage rolls had gone off and people were laid out right and left with cramps. The St John Ambulance Brigade were beside themselves from excitement, for Steeple Bracken had not seen so many bodies lying about since a minor skirmish was fought there during the Wars of the Roses.

There were not many celebrities in our district, and the poor things, who started the season by thinking Noblesse Oblige, and one must do one's bit for the parish, soon became so overworked that they had not one free Saturday all summer.

In the old days, the lady of the manor used to open the local fête, but now the landed ladies had either sold up and gone away, or were living in small cottages in a far humbler way than most of the farmers. You could not expect people to get excited about seeing Mrs Heseltine-Raeburn on the platform in a floppy hat and long gloves saved from the good years, when they could see her any day at the village shop in corduroy trousers with her head tied up in a scarf, or lining up behind the fish van, which called once a week, for a bit of haddock, which might have been for her cat and might have been for her husband.

So a new class of fête openers had sprung up. They were the people of whom no one could say, 'She was one of the Shropshire Bletchleys, you know,' or 'Of course, he only inherited the Baronetcy through a cousin.' The new local celebrities were upstarts. People from town, who had made enough money to escape from it, invaders from a more sophisticated world, whose habits sometimes baffled the country people, but whose cottages and 'farms' (one pet cow, some pretty bantams, and a few self-conscious Muscovy ducks) were pointed out to visitors with as much pride as the ruins of the abbey where the nun had been walled up.

Authors, minor actresses, radio stars, and anyone who had ever had anything to do with films – these were the people who now opened fêtes. This was not Kent or Sussex, so we had not many of them, and those we had were bandied round from village to village, and must have got as sick of seeing me approach with my notebook as I was of having to interview them.

There was one wretched radio comedian, whose popularity depended on his pretence of personal friendship with his vast public. His voice over the air was intimate and confiding, and welcome as one of the family in millions of homes. When, therefore, he was asked locally to meet the people, he could not admit to being the lazy hermit he really was, but had to drag himself from his garden to register *bonhomie* among the children's fancy dress and comic dog shows.

I saw him at many fêtes, and he nearly always made the same jokes, but it did not matter. Nobody listens to an opening speech. They just want to stand round the platform and wonder if the rain will keep off, and think, well, he's quite old really. Not a bit like his pictures.

After his speech, the comedian, whose wife never came to back him up, would have to go round the stalls buying jam and bottled fruit, and jovially trying his hand at the skittle alley and the hoop-la stall, with face turned towards Hooky, the photographer we shared with the *Messenger*. Sometimes he would be given a consolation prize. I came up to him once when he had just been given some shaving soap, and then, his job done, his name having drawn the public, been abandoned in the middle of the field in the charming manner of amateur reception committees.

'You again?' he asked me morosely, looking at the shaving soap. 'What shall we write about this week? We can't very well put in about the vicar talking for so long they had to start the band to stop him.'

'It'll be the usual,' I said. 'I might as well have a block made of it to save the comps having to set it every time.'

He wrinkled his loose-skinned face. His professional humour was partly based on the idea that a man who is perpetually baffled by life is always funny. 'Do you have to go to all these shows?' he asked. 'Even more than I do?'

'Quite a lot,' I said. 'But then it's my job. It's not yours. I wonder you do it.'

'If you're an entertainer,' he said sadly, 'and get your money from the public, they expect you to be a public convenience.'

'Out of hours?'

'There is no out of hours. A factory worker knocks off when the whistle blows, but nobody blows a whistle for me.' He signed an autograph book for a child, who looked at his signature suspiciously before she walked away, as if afraid he might be somebody else.

'Isn't it worth it, though,' I asked, 'to be famous and successful?'

'They say so. But the point is, that if you let them, people would stop you doing the very thing for which you *were* famous. If I went to all the do's I'm asked to, I wouldn't have any time left for my own work. Look at authors who get caught up in lecture tours. They never have time to write another word and so after a bit the public forgets them, and then nobody wants them to lecture any more, and then what have they got? I tell you. People will destroy you. Like sucker fishes. Those things that feed on whales. Last week I had a letter from a sucker fish in Cumberland – hundreds of miles away – wanting me to open the vicarage garden party. "I'm sorry we can't offer to pay your fare, or any fee, my dear sir, as funds are low, but if you would honour us with your presence, you can be assured of a warm welcome." No thank you, madam, I've had a guess.' He bowed away a lady with a large fruit cake and a pencil and a notebook.

'I wrote back to say I was sorry but I couldn't support a wife and children on warm welcomes. Do you think that was too stiff?' He looked at me anxiously, fearful of having lost the ears even of one vicar in Cumberland.

'I say,' he said, 'none of this is for the *Puddlefoot Clarion*, of course. Officially, I just love to spend my Saturday afternoons this way.'

'Just one more, sir, if you'd oblige.' Hooky was suddenly with us in his curious tweed hat, throwing himself on one knee in the attitude in which he thought press photographs had to be taken.

The comedian tilted his hat and made his hangdog grin.

'Go away, Hooky,' I said. 'We don't want any pictures, except that one with the babies.'

'This isn't for the *Post*,' said Hooky, getting up. 'This is for the *Messenger*.'

'D'you have the same photographer for two papers?' asked the comedian. 'What happens if he gives you both the same pictures?'

'It doesn't matter,' I said. 'No one reads both papers.'

'I don't read either,' he said. 'Perhaps I should. Here, have some shaving cream.' He thrust it into my hands and loped off for the gate before two small boys and a jolly woman could reach him with grubby bits of paper for his autograph.

It was also now the season of horse shows. These were not popular among reporters because they went on for so long and there was such a list of names to get right. A lot of the children had tricky double-barrelled names, and their horses were worse.

I did not mind going to shows, except when it was cold and wet. When it was, I used to spend most of the time in the tea tent with the fat girl from the *Moreton Advertiser*, and horse shows for me are now for ever connected with the taste of Bakewell tarts and sweet tea made in a tin urn.

I took Connie and Win with me one Saturday. Win was back at work now after her operation, and I thought a bus ride and a day in the open air would do her good. Connie was very fond of horses. She stood by the ropes and called out, 'Isn't that sweet!' and went click-click as the children's ponies trotted by. She fell in love with a great Roman-nosed charger in the open jumping, because it had a noble face, and when it hit a jump she screamed, and Win and I were very ashamed of her.

We spent a lot of time in the tea tent. 'I'm silly about horses,' Connie said, as we waited in line by the urn. 'Well, all animals really. I wouldn't even tread on a beetle. There's a milk horse stops on the corner by our shop every morning, and I give him sugar, the dear. Mr Jaggers says he's sure I take his tea sugar for the horse, but I don't, of course. The tea things are kept locked up. Mrs Robb has the key.'

The open jumping went on and on. Horse after horse came into the ring and bounded agitatedly round. You were no longer pleased when you saw a clear round, because it just meant one more for the jump off. Connie was beginning to change her mind about horses, and Win was bored and irritable. She told me accusingly that the doctor had said she mustn't stand too much, so we sat her on the bumper of someone's car, and the car suddenly moved off backwards and jerked her on to the ground, and she said it hurt her scar. I

615

had to stay until the end to get all the gymkhana results, but Win and Connie would not go home by an earlier bus. Outside Downingham they were helpless, and afraid of trying to find their way anywhere alone.

They perked up a bit when a child fell off in the bending race. Connie screamed again, and a man standing next to her, who was the father of the child, said, 'For God's sake! It's people like you who cause these accidents. Come back, dear! Angela's all right,' he called to his wife, who was running out into the ring among the galloping ponies in a felt hat and Newmarket boots, shouting, 'It's all right, Angie! Mummie's coming!'

'I hope she gets killed,' said Connie.

The gymkhana dragged on, until we were in danger of missing the last bus. I went to the secretary's tent to get some names that I had missed. If you are a reporter, you can usually barge your way in anywhere, and people at small country functions are delighted to see you; but the two tweeded men with badges and the woman in the square grey flannel coat and skirt did not want me in the tent. There appeared to have been some muddle about the money. Someone had been given too big a prize, and there was not enough for someone else, and the grey flannel woman was telling the treasurer that he must make it up out of his own pocket. The treasurer was telling the grey flannel woman that he would see her damned before he did, and furthermore, that she could do his job next year. He had done it for five years, and he'd just about had enough of it.

'Doesn't look as if there'll be another year,' the other man said. 'An objection has been raised about the judging of the light horses, and all the hack people are saying they'll boycott the show. You still here?' He turned on me savagely. 'I told you to clear off. And if you print anything about the objection –'

I assured him that our readers did not live or die by the

news of doings in the hack world. 'But if I might just have a look at the list of winners, for the *Post* –'

'For the Lord's sake, don't bother us now,' said the square woman. 'We're busy.'

'All right,' I said, 'if you don't want the publicity. It helps for another year though. If you're going to have the show another year.'

'Who said we weren't? Of course we are,' said the man who had said they wouldn't.

I left them to their wrangling in the little tent, which smelled sourly of trodden grass, and took Connie and Win home. As the bus drove past the field, we saw the riders still at it, playing musical chairs in the fading light.

Signora's company were not dancing at the theatre any more. When we got back, Myra, in a creased skirt and one of the shocking torn old jerseys that she would wear, was helping Mrs Goff wash up the supper things. Mrs Goff had quite taken to Myra, who she said reminded her of herself at that age. Win had giggled the first time she said this, and Mrs Goff, who had not liked Connie and Win from the start, now searched out reasons to find fault with them, although, apart from their activities in the bathroom, they must have been two of the most harmless lodgers she had ever had.

'I must say,' she said, as we came into the scullery to see if there was a hope of getting any food, 'it is nice to be given a hand for a change. That Alice – I can't get her near the sink. It's all knit, knit, knit now, but I'm glad *somebody* is willing to help me.' She smiled at Myra. Like Axel Munthe's housekeeper, it was worse when she smiled than when she did not.

We had often offered to help her wash-up, but she always said Too many cooks spoil the broth. Tonight, because she was power-drunk with Myra's tractability, it was Many hands make light work, and we all had to seize a cloth and

617

set to. Perhaps she hoped to distract us from wanting something to eat.

However, Mrs Goff had news to impart, and she could not resist telling it with full ceremony, so she made tea and cut bread and butter, and we sat at the table, laid for breakfast with the usual complement of sauces and pickles, while she told us.

It was about the commissionaire. There had been a smash and grab raid at the shop next door to his cinema, and his sole remaining arm had been broken trying to jump on to the running-board of the bandits' car. Mrs Goff was surprised to hear that I did not know about it. 'Though I suppose newspaper people are always the last to know of any news.'

I tried to explain that I had been out in the country all day, but she was pleased with her joke, and kept repeating it.

'Like jackals they've been, round here all day,' she said. 'A pert young lady from the *Messenger* and a young man with spectacles from your paper. Very interested, he was, in all I had to tell him about poor Mr Davies.'

Bother Mike. Not content with being lucky enough to get the smash and grab, he couldn't even leave the personal end of it to me, although I lived on the spot. Fancy missing such an excitement. I *would* have to be stuck out at the horse show when something really thrilling happened in Downingham. I always missed the best things.

We were terribly proud of our Mr Davies, as we now called him. He was a hero. We wished now that we had known him better. He had been a shadowy figure in our lives, coming and going quietly, shutting himself in with his ghosts and his wireless and never joining the bedroom tea parties. Connie said that she had known all along that he was the kind of man who would do a brave thing like that, and Mrs Goff said, 'More foolish than brave, I should say, interfering in what was not his business. That's how he lost his other arm, I shouldn't wonder, for all he said it was the war.' She spoke like this because the commissionaire's heroism had cost her a lodger. He was expected to be in hospital a long time, and would probably give up his room.

'If he does,' said Myra, 'I know someone who'd like it. Someone in our company, actually, who's had a row with Signora about having to share a room, and would love to come here, if Signora allowed it.'

'A dancer?' said Mrs Goff, dropping a cigarette stub into the dregs of her tea. 'Another girl for ever holding on to the backs of chairs and swinging her legs about?'

'Well, it's a man actually,' said Myra blushing.

Mrs Goff caught on to the blush and immediately assumed that the man was Myra's boy friend. I went down to tell Casubon about the smash and grab, and when I was coming up the back stairs, I heard her in the kitchen talking to Mr Goff about No nonsense, and We'll have to keep our eye on that young lady.

When Mervyn came, however, with some odd-looking luggage and a black Spanish shawl to drape over his bed, it was plain that there was no cause for anxiety. I went in for supper before the others, and heard Alice telling her mother scornfully that she could have told her that all male dancers were like that.

'Like what?' asked Mrs Goff who, although she was libidinous about straightforward sex, was fairly innocent about its finer points.

'Well – like he is.' Alice made her disgusted face and knitted faster. 'You know. I wouldn't put my lips to the word, but you know.'

'And what does your mother know?' inquired Mr Goff, coming over from the sink with wet arms, eager to share the conversation of the family circle.

'Oh, you wouldn't understand,' said Alice, in the kicking-

619

around voice she always used on her father. 'I wasn't talking to you anyway.'

'What do I know?' asked Mrs Goff, bringing in the potatoes without a lid, long before anyone was ready for them.

'Well. That he doesn't like women. One could put it that way.'

'Oh, but he does. He has been ever so charming to me, and most polite. I wish all would follow his example.' The deliberate way in which she did not look at me made the remark as pointed as if she had. I sat down and began to eat bread.

'Don't be so simple, Ma,' said Alice, rolling up her knitting and jabbing the needle through it. 'I don't mean like that, you know I don't. I mean, he doesn't like women *in that way*.'

Mrs Goff's eyebrows went up. 'Oh, I see,' she said. 'You mean he's One of Those. Well, I don't know. They say it takes all sorts.' Her reactions were always unexpected. She was outraged about ridiculous little things, and then suddenly tolerant of something that should have shocked her.

'One of what?' asked Mr Goff, sitting down and tucking a napkin under his chin.

'Oh, be quiet,' snapped Alice. 'I told you, you wouldn't understand.' And he never did. He had one joke for each of us, and to the end of Mervyn's stay, he pegged away at the one he had thought up for him, calling him a Lady killer, and asking him : 'And how many hearts did you break last night, young man?'

Win and Connie did not understand about Mervyn either. Their magazines had never told them about anything like that. They were skittishly excited when Mervyn took the front top room. Although he was much too small for strapping girls like them, he was very good-looking, with soft brown eyes and a delicate pink mouth. He wore Indian sandals with curly points on the toes and coloured shirts and bow ties, and he talked with a slight faked American accent, which gave them the illusion of living in the same house with a film star.

When he behaved in a way they did not understand, like the time he found a spider in the bath and went screaming about the top two floors clad only in a towel, they simply giggled, 'Oh, isn't he funny? Oh, he's a scream, that Mervyn, honestly, isn't he?' They pursued him unsuccessfully all the time he was there, and Mervyn, who liked to be snug, enjoyed their attentions and the cosy chats in bedrooms, which were such a feature of our life at Bury Road. Sometimes the place seemed more like a nurses' home than a boarding house, with coffee brewing in an enamel jug on the gas ring and people in dressing-gowns curled up on each other's beds, talking endlessly about themselves, until Mrs Goff, like Night Sister, knocked on the door to inquire if we thought she was made of electricity.

Mervyn made friends with everybody, even little Barry, with whom he would romp rather sweetly on the kitchen floor. He took Alice to the pictures, he came to socials and amateur concerts with me, he helped Mrs Goff in the kitchen, and he went for walks with Mr Goff and the airedales, although he was nervous of the dogs, and squeaked if they came smelling round his legs. Mr Goff took to him so much that he gave him the plaster nymph for his room. Mervyn had to accept it. We put it on his table, and he walked round and round it wringing his hands in distress and crying that his life would never be the same again. Finally he put it on the chest of drawers, turned its face to the wall and draped it in the top half of his yellow silk pyjamas.

He was often down in the basement, playing racing demon or having soulful talks, for while Connie and Win were chasing Mervyn, Mervyn was chasing Casubon.

He and Myra were very thick. He was like a girl friend to her, only safer. She could confide in him without the complications that arise when women confide in other women. They talked ballet shop together all the time, and when Signora had upset her, she would weep on Mervyn's bosom, and he would hold her hand and pat her thin shoulder. If Connie or Win saw this, they would be jealous, and give him the routine tossing the head with indifference treatment, until he oozed into their room begging for cocoa, or for someone to cut the nails of his right hand.

He was in my room one morning having a splinter taken out of his finger, when Myra, who always watched for the postman, came in like a small tornado and flung herself on the bed, with the skin over her high cheekbones fairly bursting with the smile that was springing from her face.

'He's back, he's back!' She waved a letter and kicked her legs about. 'Oh, isn't it wonderful! He's back. He's in Yorkshire, and he's getting leave in a week's time!'

Mervyn was bowed over his tiny splinter. I made a face at Myra over his back.

'Oh, that's all right,' she said. 'He knows, but he'd die rather than tell Signora, wouldn't you, darling? Mervyn knows everything. He was one of the witnesses when we were married.'

'Yes,' said Mervyn sadly, 'and now I shall play cupid for your second honeymoon. Herbs under the pillow, and all that glorious pagan stuff. I shall sleep on the mat outside the door, like Charmian did for Cleopatra. When's he coming, the great lover?'

'Next week.' Myra rolled on to her stomach and began to read the letter again, pushing up her hair with her fingers.

'Oh dear. There'll be no more crosswords then. Never mind, I shall do them with Neil. He's really much better at them than you are.'

I asked Myra if she had told Mrs Goff yet. 'Oh, don't be sordid,' she said, with that smile still shining out of her face like the sun. 'I'll face that when I have to. She won't mind,' she convinced herself boldly. 'I say, imagine, you know, that

Andrew's actually in England. It doesn't seem possible, does it?'

We agreed that it hardly seemed possible.

'How much does it cost to ring up Yorkshire, I wonder? But then I don't know. They might not let him come to the telephone. He's only a corporal, you know. He was a sergeant, but they put him down for saying what he thought. They're horrid to him in the Army. I'll send him a telegram and tell him where to come to, and look,' she said to me, 'if he comes while I'm at class or anything, you will ring up at once, won't you, and tell Signora you're dying, or the house is on fire and my clothes burning, or something?'

'Wouldn't matter if they were,' I said. 'You'll have to give up those old jerseys when Andrew comes.'

'Oh, he won't mind. He doesn't care about things like that.'

'He will, dear,' said Mervyn, who had been reading Win and Connie's magazines, 'when you're going off a bit and can no longer rely on the fresh charm of youth.'

'He won't. He's not like that. D'you know, once he said – No, I shan't tell you, because Mervyn will only say something cynical. Mervyn's awfully cynical, did you know?'

'Mervyn will now say something very cynical indeed,' Mervyn said, snatching his finger away and slapping my hand as I probed too deep. 'Have you forgotten that next week you and I and the entire company are supposed to be going to Buxton for two nights to adorn the Hydro centenary of arts and music with our rendition of *Coppelia*?'

Myra had forgotten. She buried her face in the pillow, and then came up not smiling any more, but suddenly grown up and determined. 'I shan't go. I shall have my chest again. I can always say I've been to a doctor –'

'As if Signora didn't always insist on going to the doctor with us,' said Mervyn.

'I'll manage it somehow if it kills me. I'd die rather than go to Buxton. It'll be all right.' She sat up with her legs crossed.

'If you only want a thing badly enough, you know, you do get it. Oh, you do.'

'If you've quite finished messing about with my finger,' Mervyn told me, 'I would remind you that I have a class in exactly half an hour, and that it takes twenty minutes to get to the studio from this neck of the woods, and furthermore that I have had no breakfast. I would remind you of all that too, Mysie.'

'Oh class,' she said. 'Breakfast. What dull things you talk about.' She lay down to read the letter again, and then suddenly rolled over and jumped off the bed in one movement.

'Class! Why didn't you tell me what the time was? Gosh, I'll have to simply dash. I was late last week and Signora nearly murdered me!'

## Chapter Eleven

WHEN the fruit was ripe and onions growing to monster size, the Women's Institute held a produce show in Downingham. They said in the office that the Women's Institute was the only thing that made them glad to have a girl on the paper. Before I came, it was always Mike's job. The other papers all had girls to send, and when he went to the annual meeting of all the branches, he was the only man among hundreds of women with hats and cavernous handbags. When a delegate got up to speak, she would say: 'Ladies and – er – gentle*man*,' and all heads would turn to Mike and he would have to take off his glasses and start polishing them on his handkerchief.

The produce show was in the upstairs room of the town

hall. The Women's Institute craved publicity, and I was well received and shown round by Mrs Phelps, the organizer, who was all in a dither over some contretemps about the judges' lunch. She was a tall, waistless woman with treading shoes and a brown velvet hat and a lot of pepper and salt hair, coarse, like a horse's tail, that seemed to be bothering her as much as the judge's lunch.

The exhibits had been judged in the morning. Bottled fruit was tested for sealing, cakes cut open, and pickles and jams tasted with a long-handled spoon and much delicate smacking of lips. It was a wonder the judges wanted any lunch, because there were hundreds of pickle entries, and some of them were made of things like quinces and turnips and elderberries.

Each exhibit was labelled with its marks, and some had gold stars. Mrs Phelps offered to let me taste, but I was still tasting Mrs Goff's luncheon roll and thought that it would not mix. I took copious notes of prize-winners, and she told me many more things that I must put in the report: 'Because, you see, this is the *greatest* day of the year for us. The members all work so hard to keep up the *standard*.' She had a way of stretching her lips in a grin when she emphasized words, which made them come out as *greetest* and *steendard*. She was keyed up with enthusiasm, and clasped her hands ecstatically over the strawberry jam, which was the highest *steendard* so far of any other *yeear*. I had not the heart to tell her that she could only have one column, or less if the cricket news was big this week, so that none of what she was telling me about the triumph of the eggless sponges would ever reach the public eye.

When the doors were opened at two-thirty, a mob of women surged in and spread out like water tracking through sand, searching for their own exhibits. Mrs Phelps and I were at the bottling counter. I was taking down names, and she was fighting yet another round of the losing battle to get all her horse hair secured under the brown velvet hat.

'Where's my blackcurrants?' A small woman in black lunged up and down the table, searching among the bottles. 'Florrie, I don't see my blackcurrants anywhere. Come and look. Come all this way on the bus to see my currants, and then – Well!' She held up a jar. 'Look at that if you please! Only fifty out of a hundred, and there's Mrs Pryby got the gold star and her fruit not graded half as well as mine. Look at this, Florrie. Where's Gran? Gran, have you found your popovers? Look how they've marked my blackcurrants. It's not good enough, that's what it isn't. Let's go and see the cakes. If they've put me down on my simnel, there's going to be trouble for someone. It's not good enough.'

'I think you will find, Mrs Warren,' said Mrs Phelps, taking an extra large hairpin out of her bag and thrusting it under her hat, 'that where you lost marks was on the sealing.' She wiggled the bottle lid and it came off quite easily. 'There, you see. It's no good if it isn't sealed.'

'But it *was* sealed,' said Mrs Warren, 'when it left home. I know these judges. They'll fiddle and fiddle with the cap and take a knife to it as like as not to get their way. I've never had a batch of bottling yet that didn't all take. And look at this. Unsealed, and now the currants won't keep. I shall have to use them tonight for His tea, or lose them.' She put the bottle into her basket with baleful tenderness and walked off, like a mother leading away the child who didn't win the hundred yards race.

'Some of our *meembers*', said Mrs Phelps to me, 'are a little touchy, you know, about their exhibits. They work so hard at them, good souls, that one can *understeend . . .*'

We drifted away via the root vegetables and fancy biscuits to where a lady in a green smock was giving a talk on flower arrangement to a group of sceptical country women. She had some roses and leaves and a piece of wire-netting, which she bent to hold the flowers at different angles in a shallow glass bowl. She took about ten minutes to make each new arrangement. One could hardly imagine these women fiddling about at home with wire-netting and rhubarb leaves, with the washing still to do and the chickens to feed and Dad and Johnny coming back for their dinner at midday. Anyway, they could get much better results with a handful of marigolds or a row of geraniums on the window-sill.

Back in the office, Victor was on the telephone, making his bets for Saturday's racing. Joe had his shoes off and his feet up on a chair, and was rolling cigarettes and cramming them into the pocket of his buttonless waistcoat.

Mike was playing the gramophone, which was the latest addition to our office furniture. Mr Pellet did not mind it so much as he minded the tea kettle, and would even sometimes come down and ask us to play him 'that waltz thing, you know, that goes tum, tum, *tum*, te tum'. He would lean on the window-sill with his muscular behind stretching his tight trousers, and gaze dreamily out down into the street while we played him 'I'll see you again'. He was getting quite dulcet these days, and Victor said that the red-haired widow was always at her best in summer, in spite of the sun not agreeing with her skin.

Sylvia had given Mike a new record of 'Tiger Rag' for his birthday. She was a hot number and she liked hot tunes. He was playing it for the hundredth time, and young Maurice, who had been lured by its strains from the comp room, was tapping his feet and clicking his fingers and making breathy hotcha noises.

Murray had cottonwool in both ears and was pasting press cuttings into the morgue. He waited until I had sat down, put the paper into my typewriter, and started to grind out the epic of the Women's Institute in a rival rhythm to Tiger Rag before he asked me to go downstairs and look up something for him in the files.

I went down the ladder staircase to the basement, climbed over some bales and boxes and hunted about among the dusty copies of old newspapers. I was going home for the week-end, so I did not mind about Murray, or Mike's gramophone, or Joe's socks, or Vic's eternal 'Right . . . Right . . .' on the telephone.

Heavy feet came slowly down the steep stairs, dropping from step to step as if carrying a weight. It was Mr Pellet, bringing down some large old volumes. I stood up, and he started when he saw my head appear above the bales and packing cases.

'Oh – hullo, girl. I didn't know you were down here. Thought I'd turn out my office a bit,' he said quite apologetically. 'You can't move in there for junk. Give the place a bit of a tidy up.'

'Shall I help you?' Anything was better than writing up the produce show.

He seemed pleased. 'Well, thanks,' he said. 'It's always more pleasant to do those sort of jobs with someone else.'

Mike was right. He ought to get married. It must be a dreary life, trying to run the *Post* without anyone at home to grumble to about it. I wondered whether we could possibly mate him with Win or Connie. They were young for him, but Win would do anything to get out of the costing office. She had lately joined a pen friends club and was writing letters to lonely soldiers and frustrated men in Wales who were fond of music and cycling. She would jump at Mr Pellet. She would whisk round his flat with feather dusters and darn his socks and iron his shirts and cook macaroni dishes for him and grill up left-overs with bits of cheese. In the evening, she would work on a *gros point* fire-screen and say: 'Fancy' when he told her about the rising cost of newsprint. I saw it all.

Mr Pellet put down his books and waited while I found the paper that Murray wanted. 'Er – look girl,' he said, as we came to the foot of the ladder. 'You know the civic banquet tomorrow night? I've got to go. Big do, you know. General Berkeley's guest of honour, and they've got some cabinet minister speaking.'

'What fun,' I said politely.

'Not much. But better if you go with someone. Like to come? I can fix another invitation.'

I was staggered, but dismayed. As far as I was concerned, he was a bear, and I was still a bit nervous of him. To get this favour was cheering – but I did so want to go home for the week-end.

I hesitated. He started up the stairs and said without looking at me, 'Of course, if you don't want to come . . . I know these shows are not always. . . .'

'But of course I do.' I hurried after him, which was difficult on the steep stairs. 'It's terribly kind of you to ask me. It was just that I –' He had gone on ahead, going fast along the corridors. He had reached his office and shut the door before I panted in and said: 'Please, I would like to go. Very much. It would be lovely.'

'All right,' he said ungraciously. I stayed and helped him to tidy his office, and he did not mention the banquet again. When we had finished, and I was going out with two waste-paper baskets full of rubbish, he called me back.

'And by the way,' he said, as if we had not left the topic, 'I – er – well, you'd better not mention the banquet to that lot downstairs. Cause ill feeling. They'd like to have the chance to go.'

Strange. He knew as well as I did that none of the others would want to go to the civic dinner. They were only too thankful that he had to be there, so that none of them had to go and report it. He knew that. He was having an intrigue with me. Not much of a one, but still an intrigue. I was glad I had given up my week-end. I would go with him, and work on this promising start, to get him humanized for Win.

He called me back again. I stuck my head round the door, because I had a wastepaper basket under each arm. 'Evening dress, of course, girl,' he said. 'Your best. Meet me downstairs in the town hall at seven.'

My best evening dress! I had not got any evening dress. It was five o'clock and I had jobs that would keep me busy all day tomorrow. I would have to do the Women's Institute at home. I dumped the rubbish and dashed back into the reporters' room to get my typewriter. Victor was using it. He had thrown away the beginning of the produce show, and was pounding out the unsavoury story of a man committed to trial at the Assizes for bigamy with three women. I knocked Vic's hands aside, pulled his copy off the roller, told him: 'That ought to be polygamy', shut the typewriter, and ran with it out of the building to buy an evening dress for Mr Pellet's delight before the shops closed.

I spent more than I could afford on a dress for Mr Pellet, and only hoped that it would come in for something else. It was as pretty a one as you could get in Downingham, but he did not seem to notice it. I was groomed for stardom by Win and Connie, who were as excited about my night out as if they were going themselves. They made me take a foam bath and lie down with my feet on a pillow while Connie did my nails and Win tortured my eyebrows. They slapped my face with astringent and combed the back of my hair round their fingers, and finished me off with a touch of perfume at pulse points and daringly down the neck of my dress.

Mr Pellet did not notice any of this either. He greeted me without a smile at the town hall and told me I was late. In his dinner jacket, with his curly hair already springing out of its brushing, he looked more like a farmer than ever, dressed up for a gala Harvest Home.

He seemed abstracted. He did not enjoy himself at the banquet, and was probably sorry that he had brought me. I think I made him nervous, although I used the right knives and forks and did not try to smoke before The King. We had quite a lot of drink, because it was free, but it was difficult to find things to talk about. Obviously we could not talk about

630

the office, since the fact that he and I were sitting side by side in evening dress eating vinegary hors d'œuvres and *sauté* of chicken and ice-cream with unripe fruit salad was such a very unoffice situation. As he had never before talked to me about myself, and never talked to me about himself, he could not start now.

The speeches were interminable and full of laboured wit. Mr Pellet dozed off with his eyes open, but glazing. I stiffened my back, stiffened my jaw against yawns, and tried to look bright, hoping that people were impressed by the sight of the junior reporter out with the editor.

When it was over at last, and the sad waiters were left to clear up, Mr Pellet said with a bad grace that he would see me home. I did not want him to. He had had too much port and was morose, and although he did not seem to like me tonight, I had half a feeling that he might suddenly savage me in a bear hug under the glass arcade. When he was disgruntled, you never knew how he would vent it.

We walked together for a while, and when we reached the market square, we saw that the fair was still on. Lights, racketing dodg'ems, shouts, shots and blaring music, and dominating all, the roundabout, the flags round its crown spinning, the horses rising and falling, the riders floating by with a fixed smile of ecstasy to see their world go whirling by below them.

As we turned the corner into the square, the noise and lights hit us like the clash of a cymbal. We stood for a moment to watch, outsiders in evening dress, carriage folk watching the peasantry at play.

The stall nearest to us had a circling aeroplane and a glass case like the train indicator at King's Cross Underground, which flickered with changing names. Several people were standing round holding tickets and waiting for something to happen, while a man in a white scarf and a decayed golf jacket was shouting: 'Only two more; who'll try their luck?

Ev-ryone a chance to win! Just two more ladies or gents and then the game begins. No waiting! Who'll try their luck?'

The people round the stall looked restive. They had been lured to buy 'the last two tickets' and then found that there were two more to sell and two more after that before the game could start.

'Just two more! Come along, that lady and gentleman, be a couple of sports. Two more only – chance of a lifetime, the very last two!' he shouted at Mr Pellet and me. The crowd looked at us. The aeroplane whizzed round, the china and glass and trumpery glamour piled up in the middle of the stall sparkled with the allure of a gamble.

'Oh, come on,' I said to Mr Pellet. 'Let's have a go.'

He let himself be dragged up to the stall, where he stood glumly clutching his ticket, while the aeroplane spun faster and the light flashed madly up and down the indicator and at last slowly came to rest, hesitating, jumping on to one more name, and just reaching the next.

Mr Pellet had not the faintest idea what the game was about, and his surprise when he received a three-foot high pink rabbit was tremendous. He turned and walked away, holding the rabbit with the helpless dismay of a man given charge of a baby. Then, suddenly, the drink that was in him bubbled up out of its sluggishness and flooded him with the joyous passion of capture. He grinned at me for the first time that evening, his bright blue eyes electric.

A klaxon on the Rocket Ride ('Thrills! Speed! Laughter!') yelled just by our ears, and: 'Come on!' he shouted above it. 'This is bloody good fun!' He ran up the wooden steps and climbed into a car. I followed him, and had to pay our fares because he was too encumbered by the rabbit and by excitement to find the money when a man jumped on to the outside of our car and balanced there with a dirty palm thrust out while the rocket gathered speed.

Round and round and up and down it went, faster and

faster, until you knew that you would die if it did not stop. Hanging on to the rail with one hand, and trying to stop my precious dress billowing out of the side of the car with the other, I glanced at my editor. With the pink rabbit in his lap, he was leaning forward clutching the rail with stiff arms, his eyes fixed, his mouth half open, his head jerking back every time we took the steepest corner.

One would have given a month's pay if only it would stop. Just when you knew that it never would, the car jerked and slowed, your body slackened, your breath came back, the top of your brain returned to you from the stars, and you were suddenly at rest and wondering what all the fuss had been about.

'Let's have another go!' we both cried.

'And shut your mouth this time,' shouted Mr Pellet, as the rocket started again. 'Screaming like a bloody hyena!'

'Was I?' I did not know that I had screamed. The car whipped into the speed of the delirious torture, and I felt myself screaming again, although I could not hear it. Again I prayed for the rocket to stop, again I knew that it never would, again I was sorry when it did. We had another turn, and at last climbed out and staggered down the steps, more dizzy and drunk than all the port in the town hall could have made us.

Mr Pellet was beside himself. It is banal to say that he was like a little boy, for stocky, blue-eyed men are always likened to their childhood when they get excited, but I can think of no other way to describe him. In prodigal abandon, he changed two pound notes into silver, and we went on every single sideshow that moved, and tried our luck on all the ones that didn't. We bought treacle rock and toffee apples and Mr Pellet spilled half an ice-cream down the lack-lustre lapel of his dinner jacket. We saw the tattooed lady and the man with india-rubber skin and the smallest horse in the world, which was only a Shetland pony standing in a pit to make it look shorter. We played the slot machines until our pennies ran out, and at last we tottered out of our third ride on the ghost train to find the lights being dimmed all over the fairground, stubble-chinned men putting up shutters, and ourselves among the last of the crowd to wander away exhausted over the littered cobbles, clutching three glass butter dishes, the rabbit and a quantity of tiepins and beaded brooches.

Sober now, we walked back to Bury Road, surprised to remember who we really were. A junior reporter in a creased and dirtied evening dress and an editor in an old-fashioned dinner jacket, who never floated on the roundabouts of life.

We did not talk much. Our elation had gone, and there was nothing to say. When we were under the glass arcade, Mr Pellet did not give me a bear hug. He gave me the pink rabbit instead.

It sat on my window-sill with a ribbon round its neck, and made me feel like a girl of the nineteen-twenties with limp Spanish dolls and harlequins strewn on the zigzag divan cover of her emancipated bed-sitter.

Mervyn was wildly jealous of the rabbit. He offered to swop it for Nausicaa, but I would not part with it. It was all I had to remind me that Mr Pellet had ever cut loose. In the office, we neither of us ever mentioned our night out, and he treated me exactly as before, even a little more churlishly, as if he feared that I would take advantage of his midsummer madness.

The week after the civic dinner, Myra was so excited that we thought that she would have to tell Mrs Goff about Andrew soon to explain her high spirits. She went singing about the house in a sweet, flat voice, crouched on the floor and barked at the dogs until they nearly went demented, and could hardly sit still through a meal. She spring-cleaned her room and bought a picture for the wall, which Mrs Goff removed, tutting at the nail-hole, and hung from the picture rail, too high to give any pleasure.

She danced to the wireless with Mervyn on the first floor landing, and Connie and Win danced together, like two girls in a palais de danse. Mr Goff, who had been on the beer, came up and hopped some polka steps and asked whose birthday it was.

'Nobody's,' said Myra, 'but something much more wonderful.'

'Aha!' chuckled Mr Goff, producing his special joke for her. 'You've found that millionaire at last.'

'Even better than that,' hinted Myra, but she refused to tell Mrs Goff until the very last minute. Nor had she yet told Signora that she was not going to Buxton. She was a coward, that Myra. Even the thought of Andrew did not embolden her.

Two days before he was due, she knocked on the bathroom door while I was in the bath. I dripped across to unlock it, and she came in crying. She gave me a letter which turned to pulp while I held it in my wet hands to read it, and what with her tears and my dripping bathwater, the place was nearly awash.

The letter was from Andrew. It was short and furious. It began with just 'Myra', and did not end with love. It said that he was not coming to see her. His leave had been cancelled and he was confined to barracks because he had hit an officer. I wrapped myself in a towel. The bathroom door was open and Mervyn came in to see what the keening was about. He sat on the edge of the bath and read the letter.

'Well, you always said he was violent, Mysie, didn't you?' She was crouching on the linen basket still sobbing, and he took her hand and kissed it.

'He is,' she gasped, 'but why must he do it just now?'

'Man's a fool,' said Mervyn. 'Got no sense of timing.'

'Oh, he's not!' Myra stopped crying and looked up. Her narrow eyes had almost disappeared above the puffy cheeks. 'If he hit the beastly officer, it must have been the officer's fault. I hope Andrew hurt him. But oh . . .'

635

She slumped on the linen basket, staring at the blank door, seeing all her plans of joy vanishing down the pitiless corridor of disappointment.

'Oh, pardon me,' said Connie, opening the door. 'I didn't know it was engaged. I only wanted to rinse my stockings through.'

'Come right in,' said Mervyn. 'Bring all your friends.'

'Well, Win's gone out, as a matter of fact,' said Connie. 'Why? Are you having a party?'

'A wake,' I said. 'Andrew's leave has been cancelled.'

'Oh dear,' said Connie, noticing Myra's face and looking embarrassed. Then she quickly jollied up. 'Oh well,' she said brightly, 'they do say it's an ill wind that blows nobody any good. Now you won't have to worry about making excuses not to go to Buxton.'

Myra looked at her and began to cry again.

'Go away, Connie,' said Mervyn. 'Can't you see this bathroom's occupied?'

'If you'll allow me to get to the basin *please*.' Connie pushed past him and turned on the taps. We took Myra away to my room, and Alice, prowling up the stairs, asked me if I had a dressing-gown, and if so, whether I did not know what it was for.

## Chapter Twelve

MYRA went off to Buxton with Mervyn. Win had to do her packing for her, because she had gone limp with disappointment and could not give her mind to anything. She cheered up a little just before she left when she remembered that for two nights on the big stage at the Hydro, she was going to dance the *pas de trois* in *Aurora's Wedding*. In the morning, when they went off to meet Signora and the rest of the company at the station, she was talking ballet quite animatedly on the stairs with Mervyn.

'Maybe,' he said, 'but if you forget to put that silly little ruff round your neck again, Signora will never let you dance it in London.'

'Oh, she will. I'm going to dance so well tonight, she'll never give Felicity the part again. You never know, I might even get a chance to do the *Bluebird*, if Norma's really leaving. You'd dance it much better with me. She's too heavy for you.'

'I dance it very nicely already, thank you,' said Mervyn. 'I got a better press here than anyone.'

'Only because I wrote the notice for the *Post*. You wait. When you dance the *Bluebird* with me, you'll get a good press everywhere. I'll make you famous. I'm going to be famous. Oh darling Merv, I know I'm going to be good one day, I *must*.'

'You will dear,' he said in the hall. 'Hang on a minute. I must just pop down and say good-bye to Neil.'

If it came to a showdown, I wondered which would come first with Myra – the ballet or Andrew.

On the second night that they were away, Marjorie Salmon was at supper. She looked plump and pleased with herself and talked a lot about My flat and My kitchen and My new curtaining material.

'But it is nice to be back home,' she said, as Mrs Goff brought on the cracked soup tureen, which I suppose reminded her of her childhood. It had probably been cracked even then.

'You should come home more often, baby,' said her father, putting butter on her plate.

'Of course you should,' said her mother. 'It would save your reason. You look thoroughly washed out and overworked. I don't like it at all.'

'Oh, she doesn't Ma,' said Alice. 'She looks as fat as a pig.'

'I do *not*,' said Marjorie. 'Anyway, it's better than being skinny like you.'

'Well!' Alice put down her soup spoon and wiped little Barry's chin savagely. 'Of all the cheek. You rude little brat.'

'Just because you're older than me,' said Marjorie. 'I'm married now, don't forget. If Cecil heard you, he wouldn't stand for it.'

'Oh, he wouldn't?' Mrs Goff's bosom rose. 'And who is he, pray, to presume so on his family connexion? I'll give him not stand for it. Goes jaunting off like this into the blue and leaves his wife to run home to her family for comfort. And who knows when he'll come back, that's all I say. Who knows? I've had experience of sons-in-law, thank you.' She nodded at Alice.

'Oh, don't be silly, Ma,' said Marjorie. 'He's coming back tomorrow, I told you. It isn't his fault if he had to go up to the engineering exhibition.'

'That's what they all say.' Mrs Goff shook her head sorrowfully. 'Never mind, my chick. You've always got a good home here, when things go wrong.'

'Oh Ma,' said Marjorie. 'Don't carry on. What will everyone think?' She looked at Connie and Win and Neil and me, and we smiled brightly, to show her that we did not think. 'You know I've only come here for the night because I don't like being alone in the flat.'

I wondered where she was going to sleep. In the double bed with her mother and father? In the narrow bed with Alice? In Barry's camp bed and he on the old mattress in the scullery with the airedales?

I soon found out where. I sat up late, finishing some work on my inlaid octagonal table. Since it had come to Bury Road, it had somehow developed a crippled shortening of one of the legs, and had to be propped with a folded newspaper. The top had come right off one day when Mervyn and Myra were practising a lift in my room, and we had stuck it on again with nail varnish.

When I had finished, I hung out of the window to clear the twitter of petty sessions out of my head. It was a beautiful night, with a great yellow harvest moon standing over the corner of the hill by the breweries, so I put on a coat and took a walk up to the park before I went to bed.

When I got back to Bury Road, a soldier was standing under our lamp-post. He was biting his nails. While I was having my struggle with the gate, he took a step forward, hesitated, and then came up to me, clearing his throat. He was a solid, sunburnt soldier with a short nose, a boxer's jaw and a deep frown pleated between his sandy eyebrows.

'Oh, er –' he said. 'Excuse me.' He cleared his throat again, and I waited.

'Do you, by any chance – I mean, do you happen to live here?'

'Yes.'

'Who – oh, dash it, no. You'll think this very odd. I mean to say – are you one of the family?'

'I hope not,' I said. 'No, I'm only the lodger.'

'Thank goodness.' His frown grew shallower. 'I say, you're not by any chance the girl who works on a newspaper?'

'I am,' I said. 'But what's all this about?'

'Oh, that's all right then. She's told me about you. I say, what a colossal bit of luck you coming along. I've been hanging about here wondering how to get in to her.'

'Who?'

'Myra. My wife.'

'You're Andrew! But that's wonderful. Why didn't you ring the bell?'

'Well, you see – oh, never mind. Where is she? can you sneak me up to her room?' He leaned forward, quivering like a terrier.

'She's not here.'

639

He fell back on his heels, his jaw sullen. 'You mean she's moved. Why the hell didn't she tell me?'

'She's only gone away for two nights. She wouldn't have, but she thought you weren't coming when she got your letter about – you know. You said your leave had been stopped.'

'Oh, that worked itself out,' he said hastily. 'The point is, I'm here. And she isn't, blast her.'

We discussed what to do with him. He said he could not go to a hotel because he had no money. I offered to lend him some, but he refused. He seemed unnaturally anxious, even a little furtive, and I supposed that Myra had communicated to him her own worry about the Signora finding them out. I decided that the only thing to do was to take him up to Myra's room and let him sleep there, and get him away in the morning before Mrs Goff was up. I was not going to have the task of telling Mrs Goff who he was. Myra could do that when she came back tomorrow evening.

As we tiptoed up under the arcade, I saw that he had no luggage.

'I left in a hurry,' he said. 'Only just had time to catch the train. I'll buy a razor and things here.'

'I thought you said you had no money,' I said. A cat tore the night with a squall and we both jumped, and I forgot to notice that he did not answer.

I got him safely up the stairs and showed him the door of Myra's room. 'I'll come and fetch you at six,' I said, and started up the stairs.

Before I got to the top, there was a scream like a pig-killing from Myra's room, and Andrew shot out, hurtled down the stairs, and was out of the front door with a bang like a bomb blast.

Marjorie appeared at the door of Myra's room, pot-bellied in a satin nightdress, white and shaking and about to have hysteria all over the first person she met.

I left her to it. I locked myself in my room and refused to

come out even when Alice came banging at my door crying: 'Burglars! Burglars! We shall all be murdered in our beds!'

If the Goffs had the nerve to put Marjorie in Myra's room, they could cope with the consequences by themselves.

My chief worry was how to get hold of Andrew again. He would not dare come back, and I hoped that he would have the sense to find me at the newspaper office.

When I went off to work next morning, I was startled, as I passed under the arcade, to hear a low whistle from behind me on my right. It came from the direction of Casubon's window, but he was not given to whistling at girls in that clandestine way. The whistle came again. I turned and stepped between the pillars into the garden. Casubon's window was shut, but from behind the dustbins in the area, a head rose and then ducked quickly down again. It was Andrew.

I went down into the area and pretended to be putting something into one of the dustbins. Andrew crouched there looking up at me, his frown like chisel cuts.

I told him when Myra would be back. 'I'll tell her to meet you – let's see – in a pub somewhere?'

He shook his head.

'What about the war memorial? You'll find that easily. Or the Downingham Arms?'

'Too public.'

'Well, think of somewhere quickly. I can't stay here any longer, or someone will wonder what I'm doing.' Why was he being so hole-and-corner? No one had seen him last night except Marjorie, and she only in the dark. He must be as frightened of Signora as Myra was.

'The park,' he whispered. 'That's where I slept last night. I climbed over. Tore my blasted pants. What time do they shut it? Nine o'clock? It'll be nearly dark by then. There's a little summer-house. Tell her to meet me there at a quarter to.'

I shut the dustbin in which I had been poking about

pretending to look for something I had thrown away by mistake. 'Have you got any money for food?' I asked.

'That's all right.'

'Well look.' I gave him a shilling. 'Get yourself a shave for heaven's sake before Myra sees you.'

'Go and hold the gate open,' he said, 'and I'll skip.'

I opened the gate. He swung himself out of the area without using the steps, streaked past me, swerved like a polo pony and was gone round the corner of the street.

I went on to work, pleasantly elated by the adventure and the thought of telling Myra tonight. It is not always easy to see what other women see in the men they choose, but you could with Andrew. She would be silly if she did to him what Signora had done to Alessandro.

Myra was due back about eight o'clock. At five, when Joe and I, who had been reading proofs all afternoon, were thinking about going home, Mr Pellet came into the office with his hat on and his thick stick swinging.

'Sorry girl,' he said to me. 'I forgot to tell you. The Labour candidate is speaking tonight at Frierley. You'll have to go.'

'Can't someone else? I've got a date.'

'Got yourself a man at last?' asked Mike who, now that he was engaged to Sylvia, was always trying to settle me down.

'He'll keep,' said Mr Pellet. 'Reporters can't make dates. You'll have to go and hear this Red. Everyone else has got something already.'

'I can't get to Frierley. There aren't any buses.'

'You've got a bike.'

'It's raining.'

'It's stopped. What's the matter with you? You're getting as lazy as the others. So long, Joe.' He pushed the swing door open with his stick and went out.

I cursed him, and Mike said: 'Well, I wouldn't go, if you've really got a fancy date. You can get the notes of the speech from the committee rooms probably.'

'Don't worry,' I said. 'I wouldn't dream of going.' If Mr Pellet found out, I would say that my bicycle had had a puncture. I would say that I had been stranded for hours in a country lane, and that would make him feel bad. Or would it?

At home, I waited about with my door open so that I could hear the minute Myra came back. When I heard the front door, I ran down, pulled her up to my room and told her about Andrew. Although it was much too early, she insisted on running off at once to the park, in case he was there before time.

'What's eating her?' asked Mervyn, coming into my room as the front door slammed. 'Passed me on the stairs like a dose of salts. Where's she gone? She and I are going to go a bust and have supper at the Dover.'

I told him. 'Well, damn her,' he said. 'What about my supper?' He was very put out. I hoped he was not going to be like that all the time, if Andrew was going to stay here.

Later in the evening, Mrs Goff came up to my room and stood portentous in the doorway, nodding her head. I wondered what I had done, but for once it was not me.

'It's too much,' she said. 'This house is becoming a den of indecorum. First that horrible man last night – I don't suppose the police will ever catch him. They never catch anyone. Frightening my poor little Marjorie half out of her senses. I doubt if she'll ever get over it. And now tonight. Just now. That Myra Nelson. That innocent little minx. Oh yes, indeed, I'll give her innocent, never fear.'

'Why?' I asked. 'What's happened?'

'You pretend, no doubt, though so friendly with her, to know nothing about her goings on. You pretend, no doubt, not to know that she's just gone into her bedroom with a Man.'

'A man?' I echoed stupidly, trying to gain time to think what to tell her.

'A man. I was in the kitchen and I saw his legs through

643

the banisters. Don't tell me I don't know a man's legs when I see them.'

'It was Mervyn, of course.'

'Oh, it was Mervyn, of course,' she mocked me. 'You know as well as I do that Mervyn is in the basement playing whist with Connie and Mr Casubon.'

She would have to know some time, so I told her that Myra was married to Andrew. I had to, to stop her bursting in on them.

I braced myself for her wrath, but to my surprise her flat pulpy face lifted into one of her rare and hideous smiles.

'The dear little thing,' she said. 'Fancy her not telling me. I suppose it was because she was so happy here, and was afraid I might turn her out. And why shouldn't she have a husband, pray? Though, of course, she'll have to pay more if there's going to be the two of them, bless her heart.'

Myra came up to my room early the next morning.

'It's awful,' she said, sitting down on my feet.

'Don't keep saying it's awful about Andrew,' I said, waking myself up. 'He's lovely. There was nearly a bit of trouble last night, but it's sorted itself out.'

'It hasn't,' she said. 'It's awful. He's deserted. Run away from the camp because they stopped his leave. The police will be after him all over England. Now say that isn't awful.'

'It is, but it isn't the end of the world. He must go back and give himself up. Perhaps there'll be a sentimental colonel, who'll understand why he ran away.'

'He says he's never going back. He hates the Army.'

'They're bound to find him sooner or later. Then it will be much worse. You must make him go back.'

'You don't know what Andrew is. You can't make him do anything. He says he's going to stay here with me. I want him to, of course, but if he stays too long, Signora is bound to find out. It's awful.'

It was worse than awful. To be hiding from Signora and

644

the police at the same time seemed more than anyone could stand.

However, we worked something out. We called in Mervyn, and the idea of an intrigue tempted him out of his last night's sulks. We arranged that for the time being, Andrew would have to stay in Myra's room. We would tell Mrs Goff that he was not well, and if he wanted to go out, he would have to sneak out at night when everyone was in bed. If Mrs Goff would not send up any meals, we would all help to feed Andrew off gas rings. Mervyn insisted on telling Neil all about it. It did not matter, since he seldom spoke in public, but he did not tell Connie and Win the truth. One might as well have advertised it on the front page of the *Downingham Post*.

Apart from the fact that we all lived under a great nervous strain and jumped every time the door bell rang, and went out of our way to avoid policemen in the street, everything went fairly well. Mrs Goff did not object too violently to Andrew, although she said his manner was abrupt. She agreed to provide his meals, and as her idea of invalid food was plenty of starches to build up the strength, he did all right. We could not stop her going in there when we were all out. She made the excuse of doing his room, although she had never dusted any of our rooms, and it was no wonder his manner was abrupt, because he said that she fiddled about in there for ages telling him all the stored-up grievances of her life.

Connie and Win were in their element with an invalid in the house. They made jellies and blancmanges for him. He and Myra hated blancmanges, and once Myra threw a vanilla shape out of the window, because she did not know how to get rid of it without them seeing. In the morning, there it was, sitting on the path like a jellyfish, and Mervyn had to engage Mrs Goff in conversation in the front room, while Neil went out and buried it in the back garden with a spoon.

Andrew was restive, but behaved himself well. We all liked him, and he fitted in well to our family circle. We used to play vingt-et-un in his room at night, with Andrew in bed and Myra solemnly giving him his medicine of water tinted with gravy for Win and Connie's benefit.

How long we could have gone on like this, I don't know. Myra was getting thinner than ever with the worry of it. She hardly slept, because she was always listening for trouble. Her dancing suffered and she regularly came home in tears because of what Signora had said to her. It was all we could do to stop Andrew jumping out of bed and going out to knock her in the teeth in the pyjamas which we had clubbed together to buy for him.

One Sunday evening, the Goffs went out to the cinema. We were all in our own rooms for a change, except Mervyn, who was in the basement writing poetry with Neil. When I heard the front door bell, I thought that the Goffs had forgotten their key, and went downstairs to let them in, as I was stuck with what I was writing.

It was a man in a trilby hat and a mackintosh. When he stepped into the hall, I recognized him, for I had seen him many times giving evidence in court. Beyond him, I saw dark uniforms moving about in the garden.

A letter from Myra to Andrew had been found at the barracks. I prepared for a last stand.

Why the detective sergeant did not search the house at once, I did not know, but it seemed the correct order of things to question us all first. When he had finished with me, I took him down to the basement. While he was talking to Neil, Mervyn said that he would run up and fetch Connie and Win, and I knew that he had gone to warn Andrew. I could not think why the detective let him. Perhaps the films were right, and the police really were dumber than the crooks.

Mervyn had managed to explain briefly to Connie and

Win, and although pop-eyed with mystification, they repeated their piece staunchly.

'Right,' said the detective. 'Well, I'll just look through the house if I may.' He was very polite. When we went up the stairs, I saw why he was not hurrying. A policeman was posted at both the front and back doors. A constable that I knew quite well was in the hall. He would not return my smile.

'Come on, Martins,' the detective said to him. 'We'll just have a look round.'

We trailed after him as he went into all the rooms and looked methodically in cupboards and under beds. The airedales slept peacefully on their mattress, and he patted them, and laughed: 'Good house dogs, eh?' We did not laugh with him.

We followed him in a silent, hostile bunch. At last he came to Myra's room. She was in there alone, sitting on the tapestry stool pretending to sew, but she had not got any thread in her needle. Idiotically, she at first denied that she was married to Andrew. When the detective said kindly: 'Oh, come on, my dear,' and showed her the marriage certificate and her letter to Andrew, she went limp, but continued to protest that she had not seen him. She said it too often and too fast.

'He might have gone to Ireland,' she said wildly. 'His mother's there. Yes, that's where he must be. In fact, he wrote and told me he'd be going to see her. No, I don't know where she lives. Dublin. Yes, that's where. I don't know where he is.' She was the worst liar I ever saw.

The detective gave her a disappointed look, as if he were used to a better performance. 'Come on Martins,' he said. 'We'd better take a look on the top floor for this soldier.'

Andrew was not in Mervyn's room. He was not in my room. They found him in the bathroom in his pyjamas, kneeling in the bath, trying to open the door that led to nowhere.

# Chapter Thirteen

MR PELLET went away for his annual holiday to his sister at Angmering. He always left it until the autumn, because he did not want to go, but finally Mrs Murchison, the owner of the paper, appeared in the office, and when I took tea upstairs for her, I found her ordering Mr Pellet away.

Murray was the editor for a fortnight. 'Two weeks' hell,' said Joe. 'Dictator complex, that's what he gets. You wait. He'll probably take the opportunity to fire you.'

'I shan't accept it,' I said.

'You might have to,' said Joe, surprisingly ethical. 'He's the editor. He's *in loco Pelletis* and we've got to swallow it, or else.'

Murray sat up in Mr Pellet's office smoking cigarettes in a holder which he brought out every year for his editorial season. He affected a spotted bow tie and would not come with us to the Lion at lunchtime. We lost all our darts matches against the *Messenger* that fortnight, because whatever his limitations, Murray could play darts. He kept summoning us upstairs to impugn us for some slip that Mr Pellet would have put right himself without a word. He kept lists of things that had to be done, and ticked them off in red pencil, and if all current proofs were not read and rechecked by the end of the day, we had to stay on and finish them, instead of knowing happily that tomorrow was another day, as we did with Mr Pellet.

Murray would not come down for his tea. I had to take it up to him. He had to have the only saucer in the office, so I slopped it into that, instead of on to the stairs.

'Careless you are,' he said, tipping the saucer into the cup. 'Just a moment,' he called me back from the door. 'Magistrates' court tomorrow.'

'Yes, I'm down for it, I think.'

'I'll cover it. You can come with me and learn how.'

'But look here,' I said. 'I've been dozens of times on my own. I can do it.'

'You never get your cases set out as I would like to see them,' said Murray, taking a biscuit out of Mr Pellet's tin and biting it with his front teeth. 'You'll come with me tomorrow and learn how to do it properly. Mr Pellet may be soft with you because you are a girl –'

'I hadn't noticed it.'

'There are more things that I notice in this place than you think,' said Murray. Had he somehow, in his nasty way, found out about the fun fair?

We had another skirmish the next morning, when I announced that I was not going to Sessions with him. There was no children's court, and it was a waste of time for two of us to go when it was press day and there were so many other things to do.

'You'll do what I say!' Murray flared up, red in the forehead and white round the corners of his nose. 'I will not stand for all this laxness and answering back. If you can't behave yourself, you'll have to go.'

'There you are, Poppy. What did I say?' said Joe without looking up from his writing.

Murray ignored him. 'You can do what you like for the rest of the year,' he said, drawing down his upper lip, 'but while I'm editor, we'll have this place run like a proper newspaper office.'

'Then you should wear your hat,' said Vic, 'and have six telephones on your desk all ringing at once, instead of wasting time arguing with your juniors. Don't you know what time it is? You'll be late for Sessions.'

Murray looked at his watch and hurried out. I followed him more slowly. Murray had never been late for Sessions. I always was.

The magistrates were already on the Bench. Colonel Burrows wore his summer suit of creased gabardine with a regimental tie and the last rose of summer in his buttonhole. The large lady, who looked hot even in winter, wore much the same clothes and looked hotter. The old gentleman in the wing collar had had his holiday and was sun-burned on the top of his head. Mrs Chase wore a white straw hat with a kind of walkie-talkie aerial sticking up on one side of it. She wore a linen suit and white crochet gloves, and if she had had her holiday, she must have had a parasol up all the time over her alabaster face.

I pushed into the press bench over the knees of Nancy and Ronnie, and sat down next to Murray, who was making neat headings of the cases on the list on his half sheets of paper. The first case was not on the list. There was some dispute about hearing it. The clerk, standing in the well of the court with his chin on a level with the Bench, talked to the magistrates. Colonel Burrows leaned forward and cupped his ear. The little old man had no hope of hearing. Mrs Chase inclined her neck and looked sceptical and the large lady supported her bosom on the Bench and looked at the clerk as if she were Mussolini. I borrowed Ronnie's penknife and got on with the elaborate engraving of my name which I had started the week before. If Murray ever did succeed in firing me, I would at least leave my epitaph in the magistrates' court.

'Oh, I see – mph,' grunted the Colonel. 'Got to get the train with him. I see. Mph.' He nodded to the clerk, the clerk nodded to a police sergeant, and Nobby took a deep breath and called out, 'Andrew William Phillips!'

I sat up with a jerk. Andrew came in with his uniform creased and stepped smartly into the box. He looked once into the body of the court, saw me, and looked away.

He did not look at the magistrates, or at the detective who gave evidence. He stood at attention and kept his eyes in front of him all the time, as if he was afraid that if he looked at anyone, he might jump out of the box and take a swing at them.

The case only took a few minutes. It was simply a formality before sending him back to Yorkshire under military escort for his court martial.

The M.P. who had come in with Andrew touched his arm and he stepped down and walked out with his head up, looking as though he could fight the whole War Office. He looked worth ten of anyone else in that court, and I saw why Myra loved him.

I began to get up. If I dashed out, I might just have a chance to wish him good luck, even if I was not allowed to talk to him.

'Sit down,' said Murray, taking my arm and pinching it as he pushed me down. 'What do you think you're doing?'

Nancy leaned across and said to me, 'Sorry dear. I was talking to Ron and missed something. What was the name and address again of the wife?'

It was only then that I realized the consequences of Andrew's appearance in court. It would be in the local papers, and Signora would either see Myra's name herself, or be told about it by some sycophant who wanted to dance the *pas de trois* in *Aurora's Wedding*.

I pretended to look at my notebook, then I gave Nancy a false name and address. That would settle the *Messenger*, but there was still the danger of my own paper betraying Myra. Murray was already writing out his brief report from the notes he had made about Andrew.

'Please,' I said, 'Murray. Don't report that case.'

He stared at me as if I were a tropical fish, then looked back at his paper and went on writing.

'I'll explain afterwards,' I said. 'Please. It matters terribly and it's not as if –'

'Ssh!' He dug me in the ribs with his pointed elbow. 'Behave yourself.' The next case had arrived, and was standing in the box being asked if its name was Ann Maria Sedgwick. Murray drew a fancy line under his story about Andrew and began to take fresh notes in his pin-neat shorthand.

He shut me up every time I tried to speak to him during the morning. When we went out I tried again, but he hurried away through the crowd, jumped on a bus, and left me in distress on the pavement.

I went back to see Myra. We did not have any lunch. We sat in my room and she cried and cried. She cried for Andrew, but she cried about Murray too, and it was no use thinking that she would ever snap her fingers at Signora, and tell her that she was married and so what?

'She'll see it, she'll see it,' she moaned. 'And she'll know I'm married and she'll turn me out.'

'Suppose she does? There are other companies, plenty of other teachers.'

'Not like Signora. Anyway, I wouldn't have the heart. If she throws me out, I'll never dance again.'

'Well then,' I said, trying to jolly her up, 'you could settle down with Andrew and have lots of children.'

'If I can't dance, I'll die,' she said melodramatically. 'You must help me. You mustn't print that story.' Like Maimie, she could not understand that I had not supreme powers to do what I liked on the *Downingham Post*.

'If you don't help me,' she cried, 'I'll kill myself.' I knew she would not, but I had to help her.

Murray was out when I got back to the office. Half-way through the afternoon, Harold came in with a roll of proofs. Since this was press day, Murray had written up his court cases during the lunch hour, and among them was the little story of Andrew, giving Myra's name and address and even her stage name and the fact that she was a dancer. Murray, who was usually against too much human interest, had chosen to make quite a sob story out of this, playing up the romance of a husband risking punishment to see his wife, and heading it: 'THE SOLDIER AND THE DANCER,' so that everyone would be sure to read it. Just a small paragraph, it was; a mere two inches of print, but it was enough to ruin Myra's career.

Mike read out the story, and despondently I corrected the proof. 'Husband leaves wife, four children,' he went on. 'I say, that last case. You've got a girl who's a dancer up at your digs, haven't you? Wasn't her, was it? She must be quite a piece for him to do a silly thing like that.'

'Of course it wasn't her,' I snapped. 'Get on about the wife and four children. Get on for heaven's sake, or we'll never be done.'

All afternoon, I thought and thought about what I could do, and rehearsed different things to say to Murray. If only Mr Pellet were here, he might have understood. If I had known where he was, I might have rung him up. Only Murray knew his address in Angmering, and he would never give it to me.

I thought of cutting the story right out of the column, but Murray would notice it when he corrected the page proofs. I could not even alter Myra's name and address, because after what I had said in court, he was cunning enough to check that paragraph carefully, probably from his own copy.

Later in the afternoon, when all but the last two pages were made up and screwed tight in the formes, and Maurice was pulling page proofs for Murray to read when he came in, I went into the comp room to torture myself with the sight of Myra's fate in type. There it was, half-way down the middle column. Even with the letters the wrong way round, it seemed to leap direfully to the eye, like a notice on palace gates telling of the passing of a king. The very shape of it looked ominous. There it was, a little lump of type not much bigger than a matchbox, but by tomorrow it would have spread its back-to-front secret all over the town.

'What's the matter, ducks?' Harold tiptoed up behind me.

'Got nothing to do in there? because if not –' He held a roll of proofs.

'Plenty thanks. I was just checking something.' I heard Murray's feet going up the corkscrew stairs to the editor's office, and ran up to appeal to him once more before he got busy with something and would not listen.

He was not busy. He was rolling up his umbrella as carefully as if he were to walk with it in a bowler hat down Bond Street, but he still would not listen.

He was very cross. He had been to a buffet social. Having missed his lunch, he had taken a big tea there, and something on the buffet had not agreed with him. He asked me who I thought I was, and when I told him, and followed it up with what I thought *he* was, he threw me out of the office.

'You'll regret this!' I shouted from the bottom of the stairs. 'I'll tell Mr Pellet. He wouldn't have let that story go in. I'll pay you out for this. I'll get you fired. I'll –' Murray slammed his door.

'Calm yourself, Pop,' said Joe, leading me back into the reporters' room. 'We've all been saying that to him for years. Forget it, whatever it was. It'll all be the same a hundred years from now. Make the tea and forget it.'

I did not forget it. It was my turn to stay on with Murray and see the paper to bed, and after the others had gone, I sat on in the twilit office, not bothering to turn on the lights, trying to think of something to do.

I kept getting up and looking into the comp room. If only they would all go out for a drink, I might go in there, unscrew the forme of page five, and pick out the fatal paragraph. But even if whoever carried it to the lift did not notice the gap, Murray would never miss it when he checked through the specimen copy from the machine before they started printing the edition.

Should I risk it? I heard a lot of walking about in the comp room, and when I looked in again, they were all going out.

'Coming out for a beer?' asked Ernie. 'There's a bit of a hold-up downstairs.'

'No thanks.' When they had gone, I went like a thief to the metal table where the forme of page five had lain. It was not there. It was not waiting by the lift. It must have gone down to the press already. I went down to the basement. All the formes were leaning against the wall by the machine. I wondered why they had not been clamped into place. The pages were all complete and there seemed no reason why they should not start printing.

Murray was standing with his hands in his pockets, looking pinched and annoyed. He looked more annoyed when he saw me. The machine minder had his head and shoulders inside the works of the giant machine. His mate, in dungarees, was lying on his back in the well underneath, making noises like a garage. If I pressed the starter button now, they would both be killed and there would be no paper printed.

'Anything wrong?' I asked.

'Anything wrong. Anything wrong. Of course there's something wrong,' said Murray testily. 'Don't be a fool, girl.' His impersonation of Mr Pellet embraced even my soubriquet.

The machine minder withdrew his head and shoulders and faced us with oil in his eyebrows.

'Take a good two hours yet, Murray,' he said. 'Damn nuisance. We'd better send the boys off and get 'em back to start printing about ten. It'll mean overtime.'

Murray swore. 'I'm ill, dammit,' he said. He looked it. 'I want to go to bed. I'm damned if I'll sit up half the night with this damned paper.' He did not often swear, so when he did, he had no variety of words.

My brain jumped. 'I'll do it, Murray,' I said brightly. 'I'll check the copy. I've done it often with Mr Pellet. I'll be terribly careful. You go off to bed. You do look pretty bad. I'll take care of everything.' My whole plan was as neat as a geometry theorem worked out down to Q.E.D.

Murray turned on me. 'Of course you'll stay on,' he said ungraciously. 'I don't know about being *able* to do it, but you'll just *have* to do it. I'm off home. You be back here at ten sharp, and don't go home until you're sure everything's all right. And don't expect overtime either. You're not a printer.'

He thought he was punishing me, but he was playing right into my hands.

He went. 'Aren't you going out, then?' asked the machine minder's mate from his supine position.

'I think I'll hang on here,' I said. 'Might as well.'

'I thought you might go and fetch us in some sandwiches,' he said. 'There's some money in my jacket over there.'

'All right,' I said. He too was playing right into my hands. I went down the High Street to the Feathers and got them to make me some ham sandwiches. I bought cheese rolls and two pieces of treacle tart. It was quite a meal. I laid it all out in the reporters' room and I made tea and went downstairs and told the machine minder and his mate to go and feed themselves.

'Bring it down here,' they said.

'No, it's cleaner up there. And there's tea made and everything. You go on up.' I held my breath. Presently, they stopped working and went upstairs. I had got some of Harold's tools in my pocket. Feverishly, I searched along the row of formes by the wall for number five. With Harold's pliers, I loosened the screws. It was more difficult than I imagined, but it was easier than I expected to pick out the lines of type that made up the paragraph about Andrew. I put them in my pocket and screwed up the forme just in time before the two men came down the stairs wiping their mouths and picking bits of pastry out of their teeth.

When at last they had finished tinkering with the press, I watched them fit on the formes and clamp them down. They did not look at number five. Harold and Ernie had come back

656

with two bottles of beer and were waiting upstairs in case there was any resetting to do. There wouldn't be. Not on page five, anyway. The machine minder pressed the button, with a groan and a clank the rollers started turning, and in a moment, the first copies were jerking out at the end.

The mate threw the first few dozen away without looking at them. I picked one out of the next lot that were coming through. 'I'll check it down here,' I said. 'Can't be bothered to walk upstairs.' I did not want to risk Harold and Ernie seeing the paper. The machine minder lit a cigarette and went into a coma with his back against the wall. He was tired and was not going to bother to look at the paper. His mate started to go round the machine with an oil can.

I spread the paper on a table and looked through it with my back to them. I did not read page five. I turned it under quickly in case one of them came over.

The rest of the paper was all right. 'O.K.,' I said. 'Let her go.'

The button was pressed, the rollers turned, the papers jerked out in dozens, and the machine minder's mate began to lift them off and stack them in labelled bundles ready for the vans to collect them.


The *Downingham Post* was out on time next morning. It was in the shops. It was tucked through letter boxes. It was lying on front steps with the milk. It was being sold on street corners.

Every single copy had a two-inch space right in the middle of page five. It looked most odd.


'Well, there you are,' said Mrs Goff. 'Life has its changes, and we can't stand still and watch it. There's things have happened in this house that I could write a book about if I had the time. And now you tell me this, and there's Myra and Mervyn going away next week too, to London, so it's said. 'She made it sound very wicked. 'And well, I don't know, but I fancy that when all's said and done, you've been less trouble in your way than all the others.'

It was the first really nice thing she ever said to me. And the last, for I left her house at the end of the week.

When Mr Pellet came back, Murray told him who had tampered with the print and mutilated the *Downingham Post* for all the world to see. There was nothing for it. I went upstairs to hand in my notice and met him half-way coming down to give it me. It made quite a friendly transaction, and we agreed that women were a nuisance in an office, anyway.

We all had a tremendous party in the White Lion to celebrate my disgrace. Mr Pellet got a little drunk and said he did not know how they were ever going to get the paper out without me.

'We'll miss you,' he said, and they got a promising young lad of sixteen, fresh from school, to take my place on the *Downingham Post*.